P9-DVY-721

# *General Cartography*

McGRAW-HILL SERIES
IN GEOGRAPHY



*Bennett*—SOIL CONSERVATION

*Cressey*—ASIA'S LANDS AND PEOPLES

*Finch and Trewartha*—ELEMENTS OF GEOGRAPHY: Physical and Cultural

*Finch and Trewartha*—PHYSICAL ELEMENTS OF GEOGRAPHY
(A republication of Part I of the above)

*Freeman and Raup*—ESSENTIALS OF GEOGRAPHY

*Platt*—LATIN AMERICA

*Pounds*—EUROPE AND THE MEDITERRANEAN

*Raisz*—GENERAL CARTOGRAPHY

*Trewartha*—AN INTRODUCTION TO CLIMATE

*Whitbeck and Finch*—ECONOMIC GEOGRAPHY

*Whitbeck and Williams*—ECONOMIC GEOGRAPHY OF SOUTH AMERICA

# *GENERAL CARTOGRAPHY*

by ERWIN RAISZ

*Lecturer in Cartography*
*Institute of Geographical Exploration*
*Harvard University*

SECOND  EDITION



NEW YORK TORONTO LONDON
McGRAW-HILL BOOK COMPANY, INC.
1948

GENERAL CARTOGRAPHY



IX

51149

*To*

Marie Georgette Raisz
whose devotion and care
made this book possible

# *Preface to the Second Edition*

World-shaking events have taken place since the original "General Cartography" was published. The global war brought forth an interest in cartography unparalleled since the time of Columbus and Magellan. Soldiers were trained by the million in map reading, map making, and the use of airplane photographs. The public, confronted with geographical problems of all parts of the world, demanded maps, and maps were wanting. Our old types of maps and atlases failed to present the true nature, life, economics, and problems of the various parts of the world. In response to increased demands, a new school of cartography is developing with great promise for a renaissance of this art.

In view of these changes, this book has been thoroughly revised. As we now look more to the future than to the past, the section on the history of cartography has been shortened. Global problems brought new interest to map projections, which are discussed in more detail. The greatest changes, however, are in the second part of the book. The chapter on topographic and military maps has been enlarged, and an entirely new chapter has been added on the use of airplane photography in mapping. Airplane photoreading has also been treated in a separate chapter. A chapter on surveying methods has been added at the demand of geography students. With all these changes the book was enlarged by more than one third of its former length, and the number of illustrations is half again as many as before. The large double-column size helps the readability of the book.

The author received much assistance in the preparation of this edition. Part of the chapter on geographic names was written by Dr. Meredith F. Burrill; the rotation method for oblique projections is quoted from Richard E. Harrison; the chapter on airplane photography was read and corrected by Major Edward S. Wood, Jr.; much of the medieval history of maps is the work of Dr. Dana Durand. All the laborious work of inserting, proofreading, indexing, etc. was done by Mrs. Donald M. Smith. Various government agencies, too numerous to mention here, were most helpful in supplying data for the new chapters.

Although the book was originally designed for use as a college text, it also proved to be of interest to a large circle of readers among the general public. The main purpose of this book is not so much to train topographic draftsmen in the technicalities of their profession as to help toward the deeper understanding of the broader aspects of this complex art. The purpose is to train leaders rather than followers.

ERWIN RAISZ

CAMBRIDGE, MASS.
*May*, 1948

# *Preface to the First Edition*

Maps constitute an important part of the equipment of modern civilization. Several million dollars' worth of maps are published every year in this country alone and their production gives a livelihood to thousands of persons. Maps are in the hands of school children and college students, railway passengers, motorists, and aviators. They are necessary to the statesman and the general, the historian and the economist, the teacher, the engineer, the merchant, and the salesman. The production of maps is bound to grow with the growth of the population and its interest and activities; yet, when we look for literature on the science and art of map making, we find that surprisingly little has been written.

Especially is this true of the United States. Most of the American books, such as those of Reed, Finch, Stuart, Deetz, and Ridgway, are written from the point of view of the practical draftsman. There are a number of works on map projections; of special importance are the publications of the Coast and Geodetic Survey. We find also a few treatises on historical cartography. Finally, there are some excellent books for use in military schools. There is, however, no American book which collects the scattered material in a manner satisfactory to the student of geography in our colleges.

The cartographic literature of Great Britain is rather more copious. The works of Reed, Hinks, Winterbotham, Debenham, and some others are very good. Much has been written for students in military schools, to whom cartography is an important subject. Most of the books, however, include the subject of surveying, which, in the present writer's opinion, can be better treated in separate works.

More important is the cartographic literature of Germany. Several German universities offer excellent courses in cartography; and there are admirable textbooks by Zöppritz, Zondervan (Dutch), Geissler, and others. Max Eckert's "Die Kartenwissenschaft," in two large octavo volumes, is the most extensive treatise on the subject. The French, Spanish, Italian, Swedish, and Polish literature is important also, especially in the field of historical cartography.

Clearly, there is room for additions to the literature on map making in the English language, particularly as addressed to an American public.

The field of cartography is a wide one. Although it has definite contacts with such varied studies as history, mathematics, and art, it comprises within itself a well-rounded course, without trespassing upon other branches of geographical science and without taking in the special subject of surveying.

Every department of geography in our institutions of higher learning should include a distinct course in cartography, and there should be a literature on the subject adequate and appropriate to the needs of both teachers and students. To promote this aim is the chief purpose of the present work.

The author is indebted to Profs. Vernor C. Finch, George B. Cressey, and Derwent S. Whittlesey for encouragement and professional advice in the preparation of this book. He is also grateful to Dr. Hamilton Rice, Director of the Institute of Geographical Exploration, Harvard University, who gave a generous allowance of time and advice to the author. Norman S. Burdett, E. A. Ackerman, Mrs. Margaret Curtis, and Elmer Harp, Jr., read parts of the manuscript and made many valuable suggestions. Chapter 18, which deals with the important topographical surveys of the world, was checked by Ena Yonge of the American Geographical Society; titles and quotations were also checked with the help of the extensive card catalogue of the American Geographical Society. Clara Egli of the Library of Congress made many important corrections in Chap. 4, dealing with the history of American cartography. Mrs. Grace Smith, Dr. Mary Catherine Welborn, and Anne Moran helped not only with typing but also with the phrasing of the manuscript. Walter G. Webster inked in many of the author's sketches. The author wants to express his gratitude to publishers and periodicals that gave permission to use their illustrations; their names are included in the legends to the illustrations.

ERWIN RAISZ

CAMBRIDGE, MASS.
*November*, 1938

# Contents

## PART SIX. OFFICIAL AND PROFESSIONAL MAPS



## PART SEVEN. CARTOGRAPHIC SPECIALTIES



## PART EIGHT. SCIENCE MAPS



## *APPENDIX*

# *Introduction*

**The Earth's Pattern.** "Like an ant upon a rug," says P. E. James, "man may know very exactly the nature of the fabric near by, but the general design is beyond his range of vision. In order to reduce the larger patterns of the face of the earth to such proportions that they can be comprehended in a single view, the geographer makes use of a map." In these words he states the essential problem of cartography, or the making of maps.

Let us imagine that our ants have conceived a desire to know the general layout of the rug and that they have assigned some of their number the task of measuring the various patches exactly and have given some others the task of collecting these measurements and of drawing up the results so that they can be viewed as a whole. Examination of this drawing will reveal a pattern of which they were ignorant before, and no doubt some wise ants will propose various theories to account for the nature and final meaning of this pattern.

How much easier and simpler is the problem of these ants in regard to the rug than is ours in regard to the earth on which we live! A man is a million times smaller in comparison with the earth's surface than is an ant compared with the largest of rugs, and the richest oriental carpet has a pattern much less complex than that of the earth.

The process of revealing the earth's pattern has three phases: The surveyor measures the land, the cartographer collects the measurements and renders them on a map, and the geographer interprets the facts thus displayed. Closely related to this process is the work of the geologist, whose study of the rock structures provides information that is essential to an understanding of the surface pattern. This book deals primarily with the work of the cartographer—the maker of maps. The other phases, such as surveying and geography, have a rich literature of their own.

**Definition and Classification of Cartography.** The purpose of cartography is to collect and analyze data and measurements of the various patterns of the earth and to represent them graphically on such a reduced scale that the elements of this pattern can be made clearly visible. For revealing the earth's pattern, the chief instrument of the cartographer is a map; however, other tools, such as relief models, globes, bird's-eye views, cartograms, etc., are also legitimate subjects of a treatise on cartography.

A map is, in its primary conception, a conventionalized picture of the earth's pattern as seen from above, to which lettering is added for identification. The word "picture," however, is used here in a wider sense. A map represents what is *known* about the earth rather than what can be seen from any altitude. Some maps are abstracted and conventionalized to such a degree that the original notion of a picture is hardly recognizable. In many special maps only a single aspect of the pattern is retained, as is the case in a rainfall map. Moreover, maps commonly exhibit many features that are in themselves not visible, such as political frontiers, lettering, parallels, meridians, etc. Nor is a map necessarily restricted to the earth's surface, for we have maps of the sky, moon, etc., and also maps of subsurface geology. But in either case a large-scale horizontal pattern is shown reduced to smaller scale.

In studying a map and in producing it, the following items should be considered: (1) the scale; (2) the system of projection, *i.e.*, the framework of coordinates upon which the map is drawn; (3) the content of the map as expressed by symbols, for example, the symbols for roads, cities, mountains, and other features; (4) the lettering; (5) the title, border, and other elements of the make-up.

Maps may be classified with reference to their scale and to their content, as follows:

1. General maps
   *a.* Topographic maps drawn on a large scale, and presenting general information
   *b.* Chorographic maps, representing large regions, countries, or continents on a small scale (Atlas maps belong to this class.)
   *c.* World maps
2. Special maps
   *a.* Political maps
   *b.* City maps
   *c.* Communications maps, showing railway lines, automobile routes, etc.
   *d.* Scientific maps of various sorts
   *e.* Economic and statistical maps
   *f.* Maps used in art, illustration, and advertising
   *g.* Charts used for navigation and flying
   *h.* Cadastral maps, drawn on a large scale to show land ownership

*Cartography—Science and Art.* The cartographer is both a scientist and an artist. He must have a thorough knowledge of his subject and model, the Earth. In representing it in different ways he must omit more or less, according to the scale and purpose of his map. This means that he must have the ability to generalize intelligently and to make a correct selection of the essential features to be shown. These features are represented by lines, patterns, and colors, the effective use of which requires more than knowledge of the subject—it requires artistic judgment.

*A Course in Cartography.* What should be included in a college course in cartography, as distinguished from geography and the other sciences that provide the cartographer with his material? The purpose of such a course is to qualify the student to give a clear and correct graphic expression of his ideas. To do this well he must adhere to certain cartographic principles and traditions, which can best be learned by a historical approach. The cartographic art is, of course, progressive, but it is also very conservative. Changes in the familiar picturing of the Earth are made step by step and with caution.

The student should know the commonly used projections and be able to construct them. The mathematics of projection, however, will be of little practical value to him.

The course should enable him to select his symbols intelligently, with special regard to the modern methods of representing relief. Laboratory exercises should teach him good composition, handling of tools, lettering, and fine drawing. If he wishes his work to be published, he should know the methods by which maps are reproduced.

The preparation of the various special maps and of globes and models is the subject of more advanced study (usually in a second term).

What other courses should a prospective cartographer take? Collecting data, analyzing them, and more or less predigesting them requires a thorough knowledge of geography. Without this knowledge he will not be a cartographer but just a topographic draftsman. To represent the earth's pattern skillfully, a cartographer should have some basic courses in fine arts, or at least in engineering drawing. Some knowledge of both plane and spherical trigonometry helps in understanding map projections. As cartography and surveying are closely related, a course in both plane and geodetic surveying is also recommended. Courses in geology, geomorphology, climatology, and oceanogaphy will round out the cartographer's education. It is said that a cartographer is 50 per cent geographer, 30 per cent artist, 10 per cent mathematician, and 10 per cent everything else.

There is no limit to the demands upon a cartographer's knowledge. The author, in his practice, had to find out such diverse matters as the kind of sails the ships had in which Orellana descended the Amazon; the fact that the name Hamada el Hamra implies that its flat and rocky surface is red in color; and the elements and dimensions of an average airport.

ERWIN RAISZ

NOTE TO INSTRUCTORS. A set of laboratory exercises is suggested at the end of the book. In the beginning of the course, while the lectures are on the history of maps, the laboratory hours are best utilized in teaching lettering and the use of drawing instruments, to the study of which the first exercises are dedicated.

# BOOK ONE

# *General Cartography*

# CHAPTER 1: *Manuscript Maps*

The history of maps is older than history itself, if we think of history as beginning with written records. The making of maps antedates the art of writing. This can be inferred from the fact, attested by many travelers, that various primitive peoples who have by no means reached the stage of writing have developed the ability to draw maps. It is a common observation of explorers in all parts of the world that a native, when asked the way to a certain place, will take a stick and draw on the ground a sketch of the road, perhaps adding twigs or pebbles to mark locations. Invariably these will be true maps, *i.e.*, to scale as seen from above. Apparently map making is an inborn aptitude of mankind. Living as hunters and warriors, and having to move about a great deal, such peoples may often find a knowledge of directions and distances a life-or-death matter, and many of them have developed a certain system in making maps and charts.

**Islanders' Sea Charts.** Perhaps the most interesting of such primitive works are the charts made by the Marshall Islanders. These charts consist of shells attached to a framework made of the midribs of palm leaves.[1] Anthropologists were for a long time puzzled by these curious structures before they found them to be charts used in navigation. The straight network (see Fig. 1) represents the open sea; the curved lines show the wave front approaching islands; and the islands themselves are marked by shells.

[1] LYONS, H., The Sailing Charts of the Marshall Islanders, *Geog. Jour.*, Vol. 72, pp. 325–328, 1928.

The use of these charts ceased about the middle of the last century, when they were supplanted by European charts, and the present islanders know very little about them. These charts illustrate the point that the products of primitive peoples are not necessarily simple, for their manner of representation is much more complex than that of modern charts.

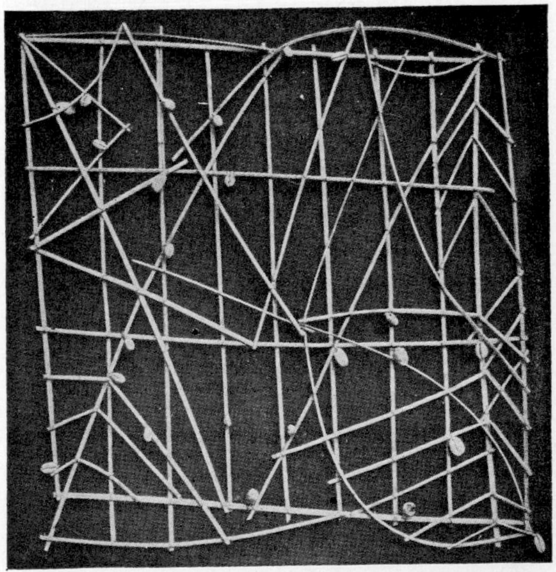

**Fig. 1** Chart of the Marshall Islanders. The islands are represented by shells; the framework is partly for support, partly to show the prevailing curvature of the wave fronts. (*Courtesy of Geog. Jour.*, 1928.)

**Eskimo Maps.** Much has been written about the map-making ability of the Eskimos. Figure 2 shows a map of the Belcher Islands, drawn with pencil by a

Hudson Bay Eskimo.[1] The work done by this unschooled man of nature, without any kind of surveying instruments, compares surprisingly well with our best hydrographic charts of the same region. This map is especially remarkable because the area that it represents comprises several thousand square miles. Similar maps covering even larger areas are described by Boas.[2]

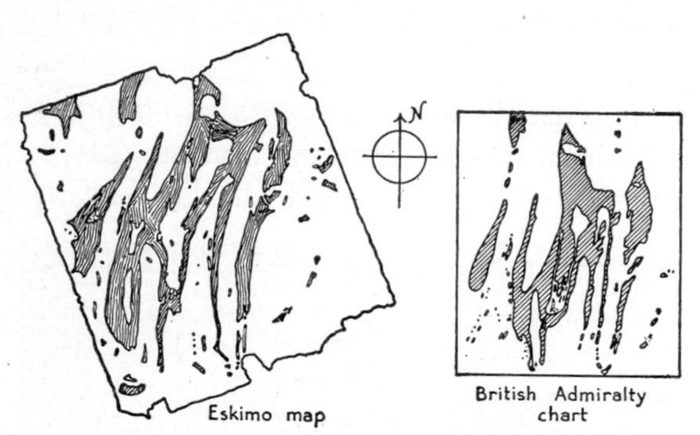


**Fig. 2** Eskimo map of the Belcher Islands in Hudson Bay. The length of the archipelago is over 100 miles. (*Modified from Geog. Rev.*, 1918.)

Many travelers have found the Eskimo maps superior to those of the same regions made by white men. As to this we may quote from a letter written by the noted Arctic explorer, Vilhjalmur Stefansson:

> . . . These Eskimo maps are likely to be good if you interpret them rightly. Here are some of the points:
>
> They are more likely to have the right number of curves in a river and the right shape of the curves than the proper distance scale. They are most likely to emphasize the things that are of importance to themselves; for instance, portages they have to cross are of more significance to them than mountains that stand to one side. . . .
>
> Primitive men are likely to confuse the time scale with the mileage scale—after a 10-day journey of say 6 hours each day, they are likely to dot these camps at equal intervals, although, because of better going, they may have made twice the average distance one day and half the average another.

**Indian and Aztec Maps.** The map-making skill of the American Indians is often praised, but in fact the Indian maps are crude affairs and do not equal those of the Eskimos.

The maps prepared by the Aztecs are interesting and are available in great numbers. Unlike the Eskimos, the Aztecs were more concerned with recording historic events than with details of topography. The marking of rivers, forests, fields, and temples is entirely naturalistic. Little figures on the villages represent their names. In general the maps are highly decorative.

It would carry us too far to record the map-making activities of the various Asiatic and African peoples. The student is referred to B. F. Adler's[3] "Maps of Primitive Peoples."

**Fig. 3** Aztec map showing the wanderings of a tribe. Roads are often decorated with footprints. Note the canoe and paddle.

We conclude this branch of the subject with the narrative of a traveler who arrived at the Ahaggar in the Sahara and asked the

[1] Flaherty, R. J., The Belcher Islands, *Geog. Rev.*, Vol. 5, p. 440, 1918.

[2] Boas, F., The Central Eskimo, *Bur. Ethnol., 6th Ann. Rept.*, 1884–1885, p. 6.

[3] Adler, B. F., "Maps of Primitive Peoples," St. Petersburg, p. 350, 1910. Abstracted by H. de Hutorowicz in the *Bull. Am. Geog. Soc.*, Vol. 43, pp. 669–679.

old Tuareg chief the way to Timbuktu. The old chief did not say a word. He covered part of the ground before him with gravel to represent the "reg," or great gravel flats of the Sahara. On this he piled small ridges of sand, representing the "sifs," or elongated sand dunes of the desert. The stony plateaus he indicated by flat stones. Soon a relief model of the region was rising before the traveler's eyes, perfect not only in direction and distance but also as to the nature of the country. No explanation was needed. Through the universal language of cartography the traveler learned his way better than by any number of words.

**Babylonian Maps.** The oldest known map, now on exhibition in the Semitic Museum of Harvard University, was discovered in excavating the ruined city of Ga Sur, about 200 miles north of Babylon. The excavators found there a baked clay tablet showing a river valley, which may be that of the Euphrates, with mountains indicated in fish-scale fashion on either side. The river flows through a three-lobed delta into a lake or sea. North, east, and west are indicated with inscribed circles, indicating that maps were aligned in the cardinal directions then as now. The tablet is so small that it can be held in the hollow of one's hand. Though broken, it is remarkably fresh-looking, and the clearness of the minute cuneiform characters would hardly suggest its venerable age of 4,500 years.

There are in the British Museum many similar tablets, showing in a primitive way estates, towns, or even the whole of Babylonia. Their importance to us is not in any cartographic merit but in the evidence they give of the great antiquity of the map-making art.

There is, however, a Babylonian contribution to cartography that is still preserved: the division of the circle into degrees. These ancient peoples used a numerical system based on twelve, as ours is based on ten, and this duodecimal system of theirs is directly responsible for our division of the circle into 360 degrees, of each degree into 60 minutes, and of each minute into 60 seconds.

The ancient Semitic culture culminated in the commercial activities of the Phoenicians of Tyre and Sidon and of that yet greater colony of Carthage. Phoenician ships carried on a trade reaching from the British Isles to the Red Sea; and there is little doubt that Hanno, a Carthaginian mariner, commissioned by an Egyptian Pharaoh, actually circumnavigated Africa about 600 B.C. That the Phoenicians, who drew much of their culture from Babylonia, developed maps to suit their needs seems highly probable. No Phoenician maps have survived, but it is probable that the chart made by Marinus of Tyre about A.D. 120, of which Ptolemy tells us, embodied the early Phoenician material. The influence of these early navigators upon Greek cartography was perhaps greater than we know.

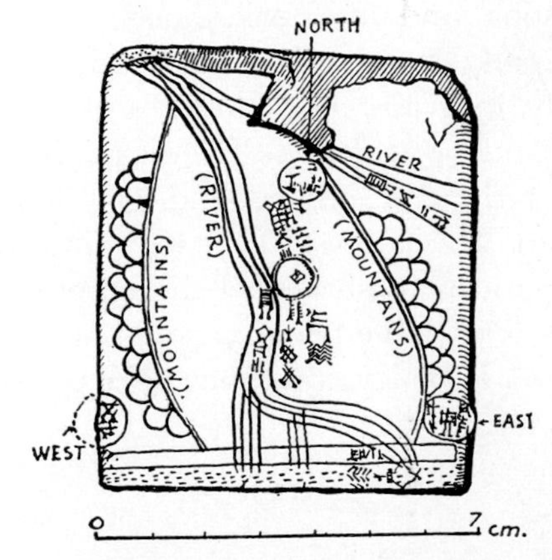


**Fig. 4** The world's oldest map is a small clay tablet preserved in the Semitic Museum of Harvard University.

The Babylonian conception of the universe figured a disk-shaped Earth floating in the ocean, with the vault of heaven arching above it, and the firmament over all. This notion was accepted by the Greeks and Romans, as well as by the Israelites, and through the Scriptures it was carried over to Christian Europe of the Middle Ages.

**Egyptian Land Surveys.** The surveying of land undoubtedly began in the great organized empire of the Nile Valley and delta. The enormous expenditures of the Pharaohs and the priesthood were met principally by taxes on the land, payable usually in grain. For purposes of taxation the land was carefully measured and registered, and the boundaries marked. Ramses II (1333–1300 B.C.) initiated a systematic land survey of the empire. The results must have been recorded, and there is reason to believe that they were put down on maps. Centuries later the Greek scientist, Eratosthenes, made use of early Egyptian measurements.

The few Egyptian maps that have survived, such as the rough map of a Nubian gold mine (now in the Turin Museum), are of minor interest from the point of view of cartographic history.

**Fig. 5** Ancient Chinese map showing China as the Middle Kingdom and all other countries as small outlying islands. 1. China. 2. The Mountain of Man's Origin. 3. The Land of Superior Men. 4. The Land of Women. 5. Land Where It Is Hard to Live. 6. Mountain of Fire Spirits (who control all fire). 7. Great Circumference Mountain. 8. All White Mountain. 9. Pusang (America?). 10. Land of White People. 11. India. (*After H. B. Hulbert, Am. Geog. Soc. Bull.*, 1904.)

**Early Chinese Maps.** In cartography, as in many other things, the Chinese developed as independently of the Western peoples as if they had been inhabitants of another planet. Cartography was flourishing in China when it was at its lowest ebb in Europe during the Middle Ages.

China had been mapped in detail before any Europeans visited that country. Since ancient times it has been one of the duties of each governor and prefect to prepare a complete geographic description of his lands and waters, usually accompanied by maps. There are old maps available in the archives of many cities. This rich material has been only superficially examined, and important discoveries are to be expected from future studies.

The earliest reference to a map in Chinese literature is from 227 B.C. Especially after the invention of paper (*ca.* A.D. 100) local maps were made in all parts of the empire.

A correlation of many local maps was carried out by Pei Hsiu, the real father of Chinese cartography, who lived from A.D. 224 to 273. It no longer exists, but the accompanying text has survived. In this Pei Hsiu lays down certain principles of cartography, as follows:

1. Rectilinear divisions, a network by which to state relative locations
2. Orientation, to show correctly the direction from one place to another
3. Accurate indication of distances
4. Indication of higher and lower altitudes

5. Attention to the right and left angles or bends of the roads

Evidently Chinese map making had even at this early period attained a certain scientific standard. In the use of the network Pei Hsiu was ahead of the cartographers of the West. His network, however, is not comparable to our drawing of meridians and parallels, for the Chinese conceived the earth as a flat surface with China in the middle.

In the period after Pei Hsiu, Chinese map makers gradually covered the entire territory from Persia to Japan. Noteworthy is the wooden map of Hsieh Chuang (A.D. 421–466) which could be taken apart province by province—the ancestor of the jigsaw-puzzle map. The most important map maker of this later period is Chia Tan (A.D. 730–805), who made a map about 30 feet square, covering more than the Asiatic continent. We may assume that the ideas of the Chinese were rather vague about the outlying regions; and it would be highly interesting to see their conception of the Western world. Unfortunately, this map did not survive either. There is, however, a stone tablet in existence from the twelfth century,[1] which is interpreted as a portion of the map of Chia Tan. This stone slab shows with fair accuracy the north-eastern bend of the Hwang Ho and the Chinese wall.

Under the succeeding dynasties the use of maps became more and more widespread,

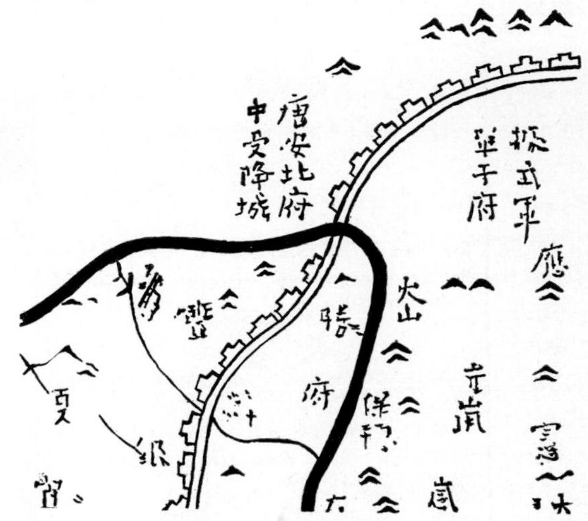

**Fig. 6** The oldest known Chinese map is a stone tablet engraved in A.D. 1137, probably based on Chia Tan's map of 801. The map shows the Great Wall crossing the Yellow River. (*After Hosie.*)

and when the Jesuit fathers came to China in the sixteenth century they found enough material to produce an excellent atlas of the empire. From this time on, the maps of China were influenced by Western cartography, but even the present maps of some remote parts of China are based more on material inherited from the past than on actual instrumental surveys.

## Greeks

The foundation of our present system of cartography was largely laid down by the ancient Greeks, who advanced it to a height not reached again until the sixteenth century. They recognized the spherical shape of the earth, with its poles, equator, and tropics; they developed our longitude-latitude system; they designed the first projections; and they calculated the size of the earth.

**Ionian Geographers.** Most of what we know of Greek cartography has been transmitted to us through the writings of Herodotus and Strabo. There we learn about the early Ionian geographers: Anaximander of Miletus (611?–547? B.C.), who made a map of the "whole circuit of the Earth, every sea and all rivers," and Hecataeus (*ca.* 500 B.C.) of the same city, who improved the map of his countryman

[1] SOOTHILL, W. E., The Two Oldest Maps of China Extant, *Geog. Jour.*, Vol. 69, pp. 532–555, 1927.

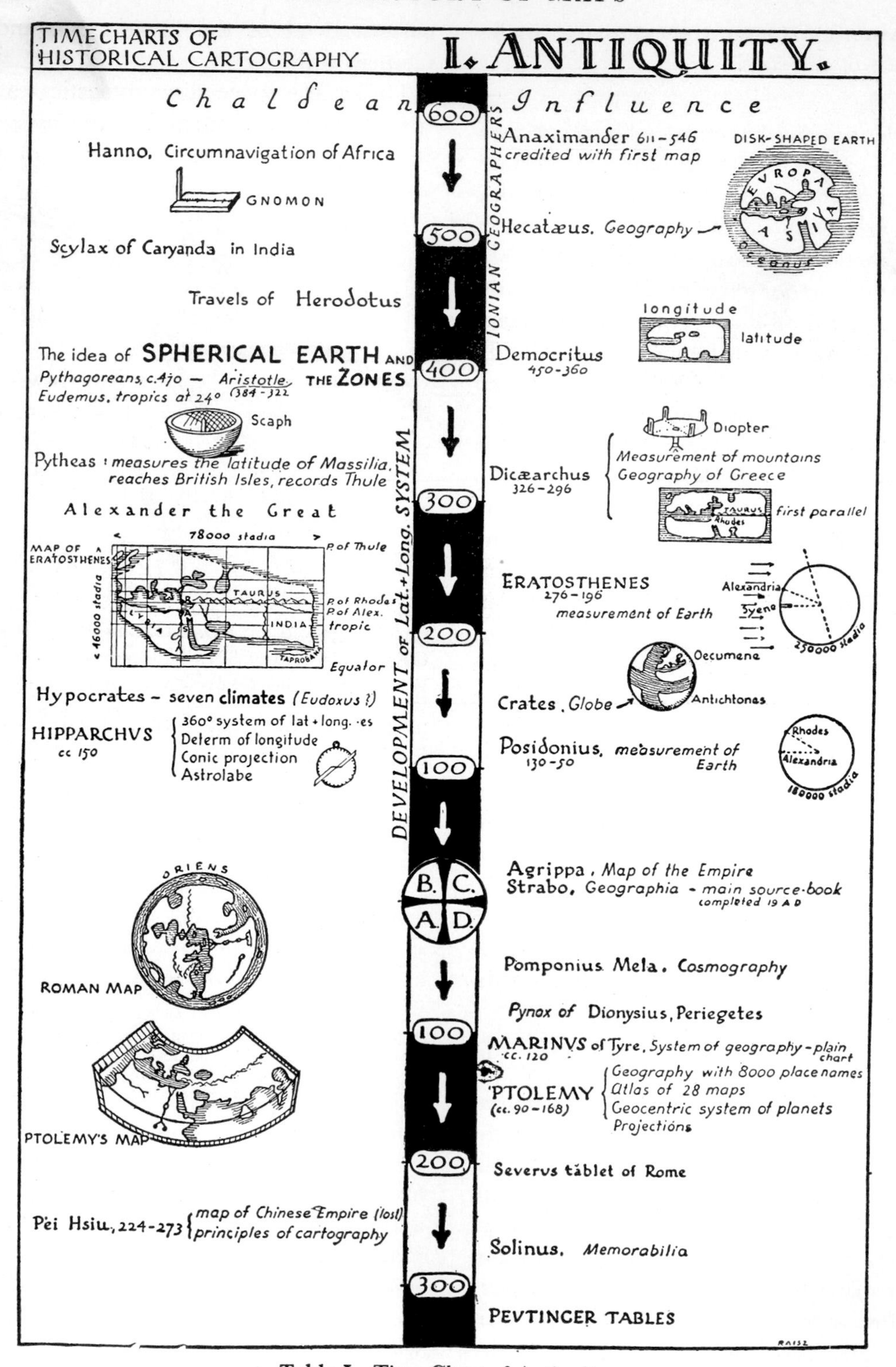


**Table I** Time Chart of Antiquity

and wrote a systematic description of the world, of which some scanty fragments and several quotations survive, so that we can reconstruct his map with some claim to accuracy. Hecataeus regarded the earth as a flat disk, around which the waters of the oceans flow.

The world known to the Greeks in the fifth century B.C. extended from the Indus River to the Atlantic Ocean, with more limited knowledge of the north and south. They had a vague idea about the Caspian Sea, in spite of their contacts with the Persian Empire. It would be highly interesting to find a contemporary map made in Persia; the well-organized empire of Cambyses and Darius probably produced good maps.

The geographers of the fifth and early fourth centuries B.C. taught that the oekumene—the habitable world—was more or less oblong in shape, twice as long from east to west as from north to south. Our terms "latitude" and "longitude" are survivals of this conception.

In the early fourth century B.C. a new idea was introduced—the spherical form of the earth. Who the originator of the idea was we do not know. The attribution to Pythagoras or to Parmenides is now discredited.[1] The idea itself was derived not so much from astronomical observations as from philosophical considerations. The sphere is the most perfect of all forms; hence, the earth, the masterwork of the gods, must be a sphere. Later observations, however, corroborated this idea so well that about 350 B.C. Aristotle was able to formulate the six arguments to prove that the earth was actually a sphere. The obliquity of the earth's axis was recognized and correctly measured. The conception of the equator, poles, and tropics was established, and the earth was divided into hot, temperate, and frigid zones as we know them today. It is a high tribute to the faith of the ancient Greeks in science that this theory of a spherical earth, so contrary to common sense, was accepted at so early a period.

[1] HEIDEL, W. A., "The Frame of the Ancient Greek Maps," American Geographical Society, New York, 1937. 141 pp.

Practical geographical knowledge was expanded by the bold seamen of Greece. Particularly interesting is the voyage of Pytheas of Massilia (Marseilles). So far as we know he was the first Greek to reach Britain. There he heard of a land 6 days north where the three fundamental elements, Water, Earth, and Air, lose their identity and merge into each other—a poetic description of the misty, icy coast of Norway. This land he called "Thule," and for 1,500 years it appears as the Island of Thule on almost every map of the world.

**Eratosthenes.** Eratosthenes of Cyrene (276–196 B.C.) was the head of the Library

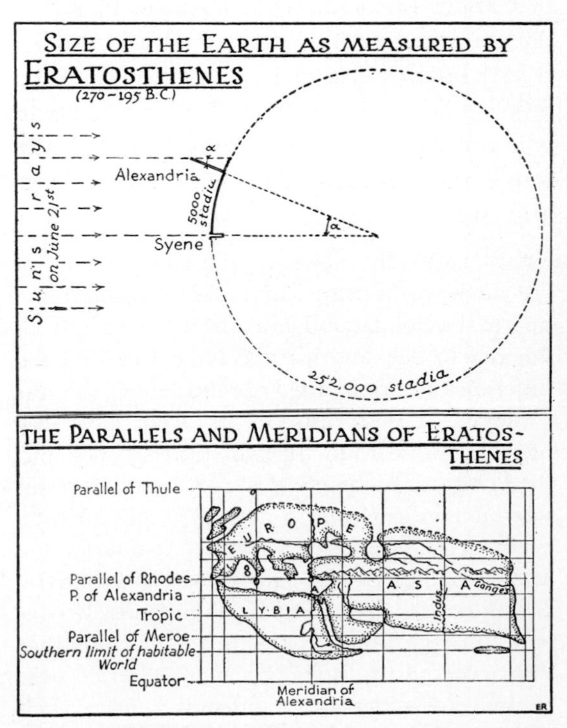


**Fig. 7** Eratosthenes calculated the Earth's size correctly within 14 per cent. The map of the oekumene is a reconstruction.

of Alexandria, the highest institution of learning of that time. He undertook to measure the earth. As the tradition goes, there was a well in Syene (Aswan), to the bottom of which the sun's rays penetrated only on June 20–22. This means that Syene is located on the Tropic of Cancer. As the distance of Syene from Alexandria was known from the early Egyptian land surveys to be 5,000 stadia, assuming that Alexandria is directly north of Syene, all that Eratosthenes had to do was to measure the angle of the noonday sun on June 21.

The inclination of the sun's rays to the vertical in Alexandria was found to be one-fiftieth of the circle (a little over 7°). Therefore a meridian of the earth must be 50 times 5,000, or 250,000, stadia—about 28,000 miles. The measurement is remarkably accurate (within 14 per cent), especially since neither is Syene on the Tropic of Cancer but somewhat north of it, nor is Alexandria on the same meridian with Syene but 3° west of it; nor is the distance 5,000 stadia but, rather, 4,530; the angle was not measured correctly either, but the four errors compensated each other remarkably well.

Unfortunately, however, the measurement of the earth was repeated by Posidonius about one hundred years later. He used the distance from Rhodes to Alexandria; and for calculating the difference in arc he used the altitude of the star Canopus. His measurements were probably more accurate than those of Eratosthenes, but his errors did not compensate, and his result was later interpreted to be 18,000 miles for the earth's circumference, a figure one-quarter too small. While 1° was equal to 700 stadia by Eratosthenes, according to Posidonius 1° was equal to 500 stadia. It was this later value that was accepted by Ptolemy and was carried over to the geographers of the fifteenth century. It is no wonder that Columbus mistook America for Asia, since he underestimated the size of the earth. The fact that we call our Indians by this name can be traced back to the measurement of Posidonius.

Eratosthenes also made a map of the habitable world, with seven parallels and seven meridians. This map has been lost, but it has been described in sufficient detail so that its restoration can be attempted. It gives all the rich geographic information gathered by Alexander the Great and his successors. Taprobana Island, a misplaced Ceylon, makes its debut here and has been given on maps for more than a millennium. The short-cutting of Africa and India in the south was the result of the misconception that the equatorial waters are too hot to be navigated.

Hipparchus, the astronomer, criticized the irregular network of Eratosthenes and proposed a parallel-meridian system of even intervals. On his pıoposed maps he divides the habitable world into 11 equal-spaced parallels, the location of which he describes in detail. For measurement of longitude he proposed to make simultaneous observations of the moon's eclipses. This was an ingenious method, indeed, but, practically, very little was done in that time.

The various measurements of the earth raised a curious problem. The known dimensions of the oekumene were too small to fit this immense sphere; it hardly covered a quadrant of it. Such an unbalanced world was contrary to the Greek sense of symmetry. Crates, on his globe, solved the problem by drawing three more balancing continents—an anticipation of the Americas and Australia. Here was born the conception of the Antipodes or the great southern continent, the Terra Australis. It took 1,700 years for this legendary continent to shrink to the size of Antarctica.

**Ptolemy.** The culmination of Greek cartography is associated with the name of Claudius Ptolemy of Alexandria, A.D. 90 to 168. We know very little of the man himself, but his work had a greater influence on cartography and on geography in general than that of any other single figure in history. Primarily an astronomer and mathematician, he showed relatively slight interest in the practical and human problems of geography. His famous "Geographia" has eight volumes. The first volume is devoted chiefly to theoretical principles, including a discussion of globe construction and the technique of map projection. Books II to VII contain a list of some 8,000 place names with latitudes and longitudes to determine their position. Very few of these 8,000 locations were based on scientific observation; the coordinates obviously have been taken from older maps or itineraries. The most important is the eighth volume, which contains his discussion of principles of cartography, mathematical geography, projections, and methods of astronomical observation. He also gives detailed instruction as to how a map of the world should be constructed. He describes two projections, both modifications of the conic projection. The text of Ptolemy's "Geographia" in most manuscripts was accompanied by a map of the world and 26 detailed maps. Whether Ptolemy himself prepared them is not known, but in their original form they date from classical times and constitute the first general atlas of the world. The Ptolemy map as we know it today certainly was augmented later, and according to Bagrow it represents Byzantine work of the eleventh century.

**Fig. 8** Reconstruction of the globe of Crates, showing the balancing continents.

Figure 9 shows the world map of Ptolemy. Degrees of latitude and longitude are marked by a scale on one side, and the system of "climata" on the other. Climata are parallels marking the increase in the length of the longest day from the equator (12 hours) to the Arctic Circle (24 hours). The known world for Ptolemy extended through 180° of longitude from a prime meridian (0°) through the legendary Fortunate Islands (Canary Islands?) to China (Serica, the "silk land"). The map is oriented to the north and shows the equator and the tropics, the latitude of the tropics being determined as 23°51′.

To us, accustomed to precise surveyed maps, Ptolemy's work may seem crude. Nevertheless, if we consider the limitations of travel in antiquity, we can only admire the genius of the Greek mind that it displays. In the eastern and southern sections its defects are naturally most conspicuous. Thus the Deccan Peninsula is shrunk almost out of existence, whereas Ceylon ("Taprobana") is enlarged far beyond its true proportions. Most peculiar is the form of Africa. As far south as the equator it is approximately correct, but below that line, instead of contracting to a point, it flares out in both directions. Toward the west the map breaks off abruptly; but toward the east, Africa is connected with Asia; and in this way the Indian Ocean is made into an enclosed basin. The grounds for this mistaken conception are unknown. In all probability it contributed to the long delay in attempting to reach Asia by circumnavigating Africa.

Ptolemy's most fundamental error, however, is his underestimate of the earth's size, an error that helped strengthen Columbus' belief that he would reach Asia by sailing toward the west. Accepting the figure of Posidonius (1° equals

500 stadia), and applying it to the distance measurements at his disposal, he concluded, as we have seen, that Europe and Asia extended over one-half the circuit of the globe. In reality they cover only about 130°. Similarly, he showed the length of the Mediterranean as 62°, whereas in reality it is only 42°. Although the Arab geographers and the marine chart makers of the thirteenth century had corrected this distortion, it continued to figure in European cartography until 1700.

Ptolemy marks the culmination of cartography in the ancient world. Henceforth there was a steady decline. Although the "Geographia" continued to be available in the Arabic world, it disappeared in western Europe and was not recovered until the fifteenth century. As a result, the Latin-Germanic culture of the Middle Ages was forced to depend for its geographic knowledge on an inferior source, the tradition of Roman cartography.

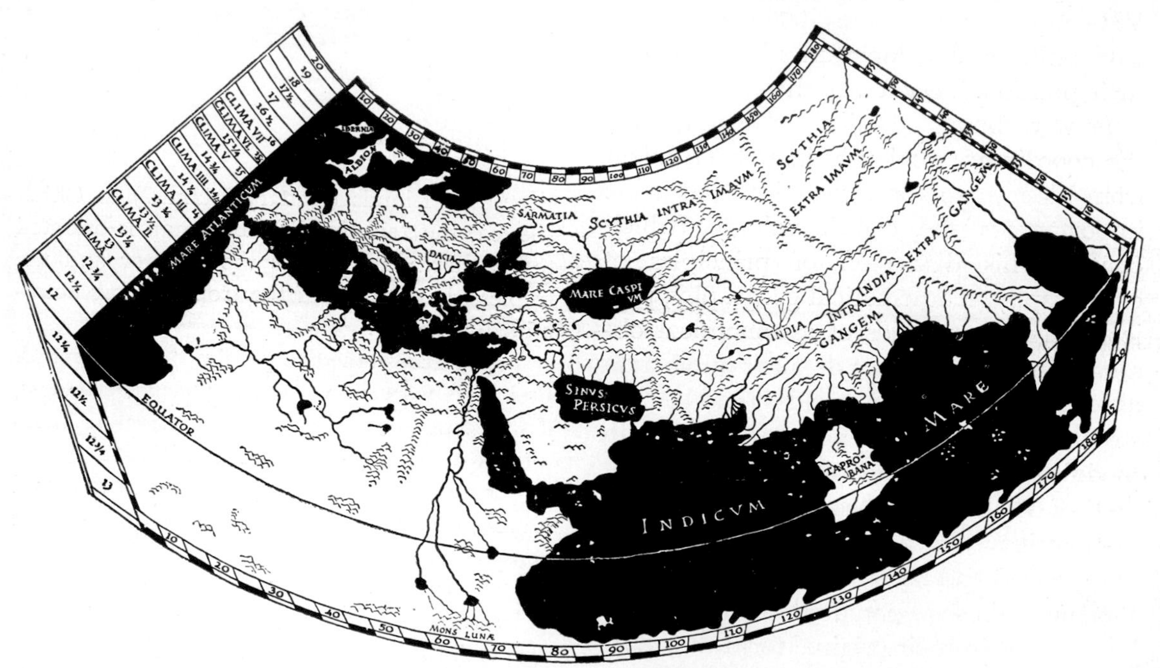


**Fig. 9** Ptolemy's map represents the summary of Greek geography. Note the conic projection and the system of climate (length of the longest day).

## Roman Cartography

The profound difference between the Roman and the Greek mind is illustrated with peculiar clarity in their maps. The Romans were indifferent to mathematical geography, with its system of latitudes and longitudes, its astronomical measurements, and its problem of projections. What they wanted was a practical map to be used for military and administrative purposes. Disregarding the elaborate projections of the Greeks, they reverted to the old disk map of the Ionian geographers as being better adapted to their purposes.

Within this round frame the Roman cartographers placed the "Orbis Terrarum," the circuit of the world. The three great continents were shown in more or less symmetrical arrangement, with Asia in the east at the top of the map (hence the term "orientation"). The emphasis upon Rome

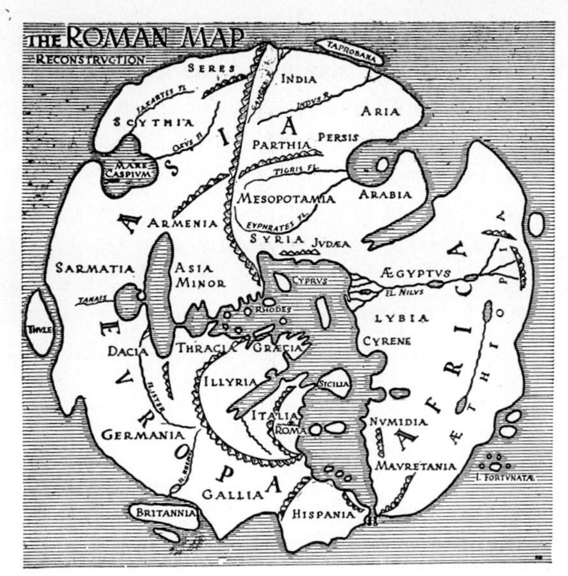


**Fig. 10** The Orbis Terrarum of the Romans. Note that almost the entire Earth is part of the Roman Empire. Compare this map with the ancient Chinese map, Fig. 5.

is reflected in the stubby form of Italy, which made it possible to show the Italian provinces on an enlarged scale. Moreover, about four-fifths of the area of the map was devoted to the Roman Empire alone. India, China ("Seres"), Scythia, and Sarmatia (Russia) are shrunk to small outlying regions on the periphery. It is amusing to reflect that the almost contemporary Chinese maps show China occupying most of the map and the rest of the world grouped around it as a cluster of unimportant islands (see Fig. 5).

Such was the Roman world map. At least so it has been reconstructed, for no original has survived. We may have some confidence in the reconstruction, however, for it is based upon data in the medieval world maps, which have been shown to be based on Roman originals. Moreover, we have a number of good textual descriptions by the great classical geographers, such as Strabo and Pomponius Mela, to aid in the reconstruction.

One example of Roman cartography actually has survived, the so-called "Peutinger Table" (Fig. 11). Although copied by a twelfth-century monk, it seems to be an exact duplicate of an original from the fourth century, probably the work of a certain Castorius. The Peutinger Table is not a map in the true sense of the word but a cartogram showing the imperial highways, drawn on an enormously elongated outline of the world (21 feet long but only 1 foot high). There is no pretense of showing the whole world or even its major parts in correct proportion. It is merely a graphic compendium of mileages

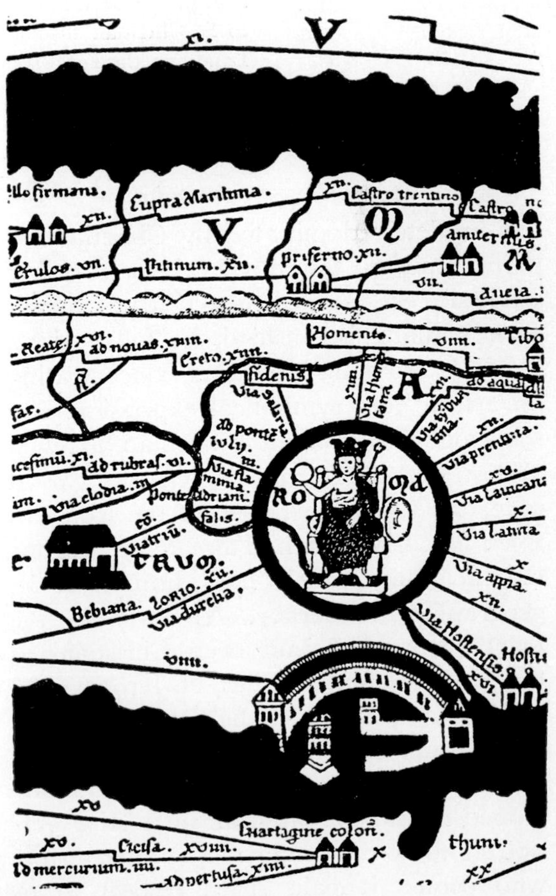

**Fig. 11** The Peutinger Table shows the roads of the world on a scroll 21 feet long and only 1 foot high. In the section above the lower black strip is the Mediterranean Sea, and the upper black strip is the Adriatic Sea. (*Modified from Konrad Miller, "Die Peutingersche Täfel," Stuttgart,* 1929.)

and military posts throughout the empire, drawn up on a convenient scroll. As such it is extremely rich in data. It gives the names of more than 5,000 places and has long served as one of the major sources of our knowledge of Roman geography.

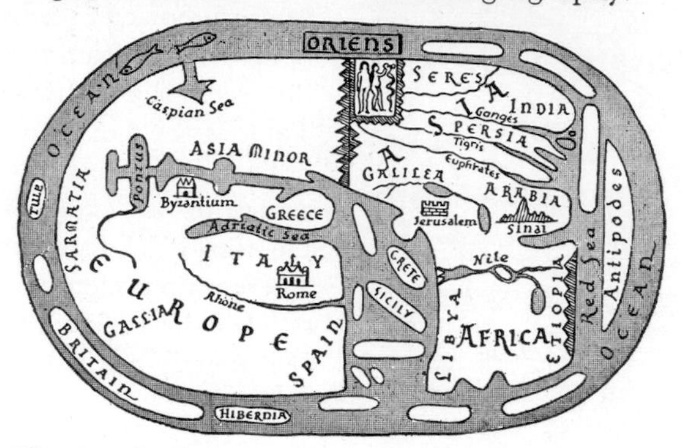


**Fig. 12** St. Beatus in 776 patterned the Roman map to fit Christian theology. Note the enormous Holy Land and the Paradise with its four rivers. The outlines of the lands were simplified for more regular and decorative aspect.

## The Middle Ages

Completely dominated by Christian supernaturalism, the medieval map maker made no serious attempt to show the world as it actually is. Instead, he followed an ideal pattern in his own mind, concentrating on artistic and symbolical expression. For the geographic content of his map he relied almost exclusively on the circular world map, the Orbis Terrarum of the Romans. Even this, however, had already undergone modifications, which had diminished its geographical accuracy. As early as the fourth century it had been Christianized by the great church father, St. Jerome, who made a map in which he exaggerated the Holy Land beyond all real proportions. In the eighth century a Spanish monk named Beatus prepared an interesting version of the old Roman map. Later scribes who copied it paid slight respect to its geographical contents. Even the oval shape of the map itself was frequently distorted, sometimes to a rectangle, sometimes to a circle.

The typical world map of the Middle Ages remained a disk, as it had been for the Romans. In its most extreme form it is known as the "T-in-O" (Orbis Terrarum), or the "wheel" map. In this schematization Asia was usually shown occupying the upper half of the O, with Europe and Africa more or less equally dividing the lower half.

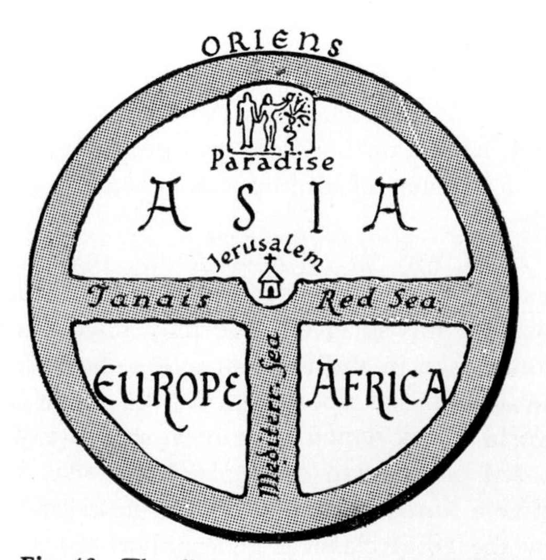


**Fig. 13** The divine perfection and simplicity of the T-in-O map (Orbis Terrarum) appealed to the medieval mind.

Jerusalem was generally placed in the center following the Biblical text: "This is Jerusalem: I have set her in the midst of the nations, and countries are round about her."[1] Nothing could have pleased the medieval mind more than the divine harmony displayed by this map. Not only did God create the world in perfect symmetry but he also made it in the form of the Latin monogram of its name.

There also existed during the Middle Ages another type of world map, based upon the conception of the earth as a sphere. Although this type has survived chiefly in the form of simplified cartograms (such as the so-called "Macrobius" maps), it is important because it kept alive not only the knowledge of the earth's sphericity but also the division into zones, which the Greeks had developed (see Table II).

Medieval maps were produced in fairly large numbers from the eighth to the middle of the fifteenth century. More than 600 maps have now been discovered. The vast majority of these are extremely simple, often showing little more than the mere T-in-O outline. A few examples that have come down to us contain an astonishing wealth of detail. The two finest specimens are the Hereford and Ebstorf maps, both prepared toward the end of the thirteenth century, the period when the Gothic style in architecture was at its peak.

**Hereford and Ebstorf Maps.** Perhaps the most impressive feature of these *mappae mundi* is their size. The Hereford map is more than 5 feet in diameter, and the Ebstorf map more than 13 feet. Each is conceived in terms of Christian symbolism. On the Hereford map the figure of Christ presides in majesty at the top of the disk, as at the Day of Judgment. The Garden of Paradise is placed in the east, and the entire map is richly adorned with Christian iconography, the Ark of Noah, the Tower of Babel, etc. The illustrations are not confined, however, to Biblical lore. The outlying sections of the earth, particularly a thin strip of land along the southern edge of Africa (which was incorrectly labeled "Europe" by the cartographer!), are peopled with satyrs, griffins, and other monstrosities such as the quaint figure of a man who is shading his single-eyed head with an enormous single foot held in the air. On the Ebstorf map the general symbolical concept is somewhat different. The world is depicted as the body of Christ, whose head, hands, and feet protrude beyond the circular frame of the map itself.

[1] Ezek. 5:5.

**Matthew Paris.** It is quite true that even in these elaborate monuments the medieval cartographers were doing little more than perpetuating the geographical knowledge of the Romans. Nevertheless, from the thirteenth century on small amounts of new information began to be shown. Indeed, the Hereford map surprises us by its extremely inaccurate representation of England. But an earlier cartographer, the English chronicler, Matthew Paris, had already drafted a map of Great Britain, in which the general outline and the location of individual towns are distinctly recognizable (see Table II). Besides ranking as one of the finest productions of the cartographer's art in the early Middle Ages, the Matthew Paris map also indicates the emergence of a new interest in the appearance of the world as it actually is. This interest, which had been dormant for nearly a thousand years, was still weak, but, as we shall see, it was to grow rapidly in intensity.

**Arabic Cartography.** During the period when Western cartography was little more than decorative illustration of theological texts, the Moslem world carried on the tradition of classical antiquity and, in some respects, even advanced beyond it. It is not surprising that the Arabs, who possessed a remarkable gift for astronomy, mathematics, and geometry, should also have been

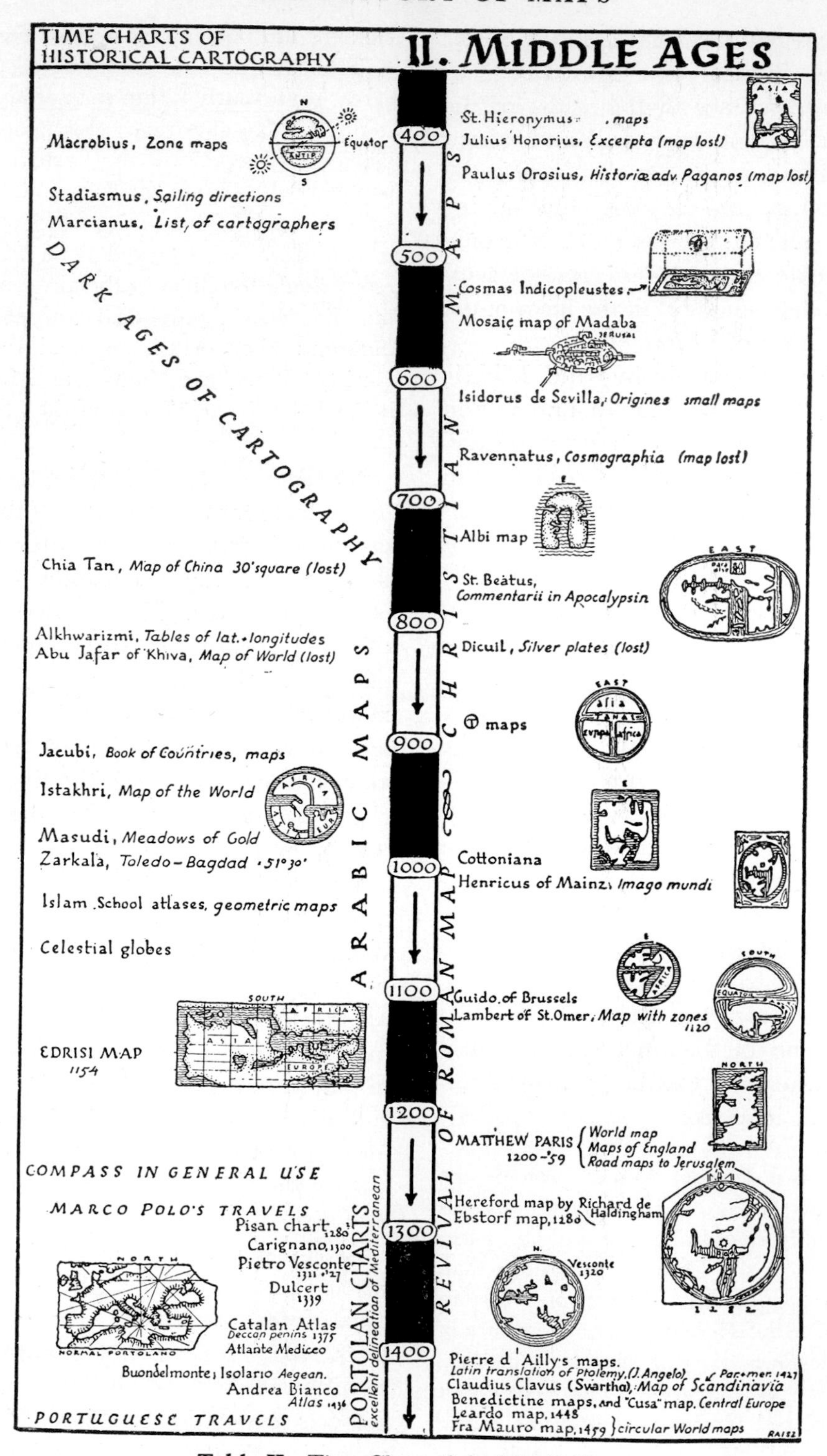


**Table II** Time Chart of the Middle Ages

skillful geographers and map makers. Even their religion, with its principle that every mosque must face toward Mecca, favored a knowledge of the location of places. They also had access to the text of Ptolemy's "Geographia," which had disappeared in the West.

The principal achievements of the Arabic geographer were directed along lines laid down by the Greeks. Improving on the method of the ancients, they recalculated the length of a degree and arrived at a very accurate result. They constructed celestial globes and studied the problem of projections. Maps were regularly used for geographical instruction in the schools. These maps have a tendency to force the outlines of land into geometrical patterns, distorting them sometimes beyond recognition.

**Edrisi Map.** The most important work of Arabic cartography was the world map of Edrisi, prepared in 1154 at the court of Roger II, the Norman king of Sicily. Through the enlightened patronage of King Roger, Edrisi was able to draw not only from Moslem but also from Christian sources. The map was based on a rough, rectangular projection. The Asiatic part of the map is very rich in information. It represents correctly the Caspian and Aral

**Fig. 14** These cartograms were used in medieval Arabic school maps.

seas, which were misrepresented in antiquity. In the shape of Africa we find the influence of Ptolemy, although Africa and China are not connected. The map is oriented with the south on top—a common feature of Islamic maps.

## Portolan Charts

At the same time that the ecclesiastical cartographers depicted an imaginary world, a new type of map emerged, surpassing in accuracy everything that had preceded it. This group of maps, the so-called "portolan charts," appears to have been created by the admirals and captains of the Genoese fleet during the second half of the thirteenth century. The oldest surviving specimen, the so-called "Pisan Chart," is still relatively imperfect, but by 1300 an accurate outline had been perfected and was copied almost without modification for the following three centuries. As late as 1620 it was still regarded as adequate for the purposes of practical navigation in the Mediterranean. The origin of the portolan charts is still a debated question. There can be little doubt, however, that they are based on a survey by compass, which instrument came into general use about this time.

Numerous specimens of portolan charts have survived, particularly from the sixteenth century. The great majority are made on a single sheepskin. They show approximately the same area: the Mediterranean and Black Seas with great accuracy, and the Atlantic Ocean to Ireland very poorly. They are oriented according to the magnetic needle, which at that period must have shown a declination of 10 or 11° west of the true north. The lettering is confined

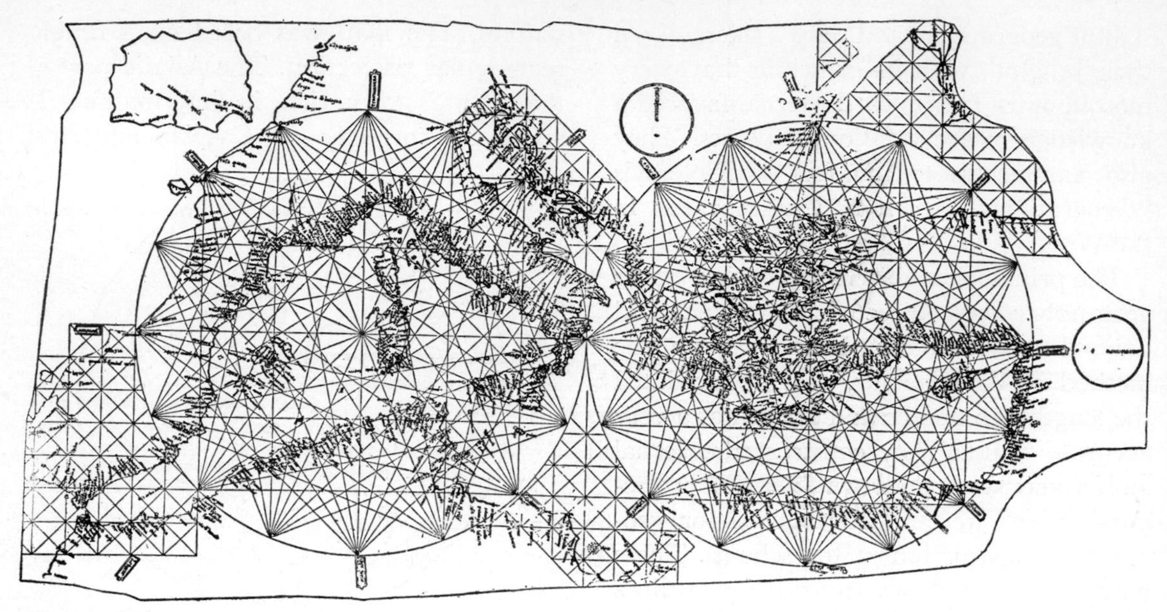

**Fig. 15** The portolan charts represent the high point of medieval cartography. Their accuracy is in great contrast with the fanciful maps of the "Middle Ages."

largely to harbors, capes, and other coastal features. The land surface is left blank or decorated with coats of arms, flags, and pictures of kings. Occasionally, however, rivers and a few inland cities are shown, usually with no greater accuracy than on the contemporary ecclesiastical maps. Perhaps the most striking feature of the portolan charts is the elaborate system of compass roses and rhumb lines (lines of compass directions) which crisscross their entire surface. Usually one or two central compasses are shown, each with 16 peripheral compasses with 32 lines of varying color radiating from each. They appear to have been drawn after the outline of the map was finished, and were probably intended to help the navigator in setting his course. Whether they were really of any practical assistance is by no means certain.

**Catalan Atlas.** The portolan tradition reached its height in the work of a family of Catalonian Jews who worked in Majorca at the end of the fourteenth century. Its greatest monument, the Catalan Atlas of 1375, differs from the ordinary portolans in that it has been expanded into a sort of world map. Following the text of Marco Polo, it depicts eastern Asia, the Deccan Peninsula, and the Indian Ocean far better than any of the earlier maps. Prepared originally as a gift for King Charles V of France, the Catalan Atlas is now cherished as one of the finest treasures of the Bibliothèque Nationale in Paris.

The fifteenth and sixteenth centuries are generally regarded as the period of decadence in the portolan tradition. Nevertheless, many beautiful specimens have survived, especially the work of the Sicilian school of Olives and Homem.

# CHAPTER 2: *The Renaissance of Maps*

Never in history did man's conception of the earth change more rapidly than around 1500. Compare the circular world maps that were still produced after the middle of the fifteenth century with the almost modern Ribero map (1529), and we see a different world. What brought about this change?

**Rediscovery of Ptolemy.** Three major events contributed to the renaissance of cartography. The first of these was the rediscovery of Ptolemy's "Geographia," which was translated into Latin about 1405. This event must be viewed as a product of the attempt made by Italian humanists to recover as much as possible of the Greek and Roman legacy. It is true, of course, that Ptolemy's "Geographia" had never been totally lost. It had been preserved by the Arabs, and through them part of its substance had been introduced in indirect form into the West during the Middle Ages. Nevertheless, the recovery of the complete work, especially the maps, gave a tremendous stimulus to the development of cartography. During the fifteenth century it was transcribed in numerous superb manuscripts, two of which are now preserved in American libraries (the Ebner Codex in the New York Public Library and the Wilton Codex of the Huntington Library in California). In the last quarter of the fifteenth century a number of printed editions, which contained maps engraved on either wood or copper, were issued. Copies of these are naturally much more numerous than the manuscripts and may be consulted in the libraries of many American cities.

**The Errors of Ptolemy's Map.** Such was the authority of this newly recovered classical work that armchair cartographers were ready to discard much of the sound information that had been added to the world map since antiquity. Ptolemy's elongated shape of the Mediterranean, which, as we have seen, rested on an underestimate of the length of a degree, threatened to oust the remarkably accurate outline of the portolan charts. Ptolemy's distortion was reproduced on the majority of sixteenth-century maps. Mercator reduced its length to 53°, and it was still further corrected by the great astronomer Kepler in 1630. It was not until the map of Delisle, published in 1700, that the Mediterranean appeared in its true length of 42°.

Among other Ptolemaic errors which influenced cartographers during the Renaissance we may cite the outline of a great river which flowed across the Sahara Desert. It must be pointed out, however, that Ptolemy's errors sometimes led to fortunate results. Thus, it has been shown that his underestimate of the earth's size was a decisive factor in convincing Columbus that Asia could readily be reached by sailing westward.

**Tabulae Modernae.** Finally, we must recognize that not all cartographers were content to be slavish copyists of the Ptolemaic models. From the first appearance of the Ptolemaic maps it was apparent to scholars that they stood in need of modernization. This was particularly true of place names, which had, of course, become completely changed during the centuries. Consequently, we find new maps, the so-called "Tabulae Modernae," included in many of the manuscripts as supplements to the regular Ptolemaic maps. The earliest of these was a map of Scandinavia, prepared by a Dane named Clavus, who had visited Rome in 1425. Although following Ptolemy

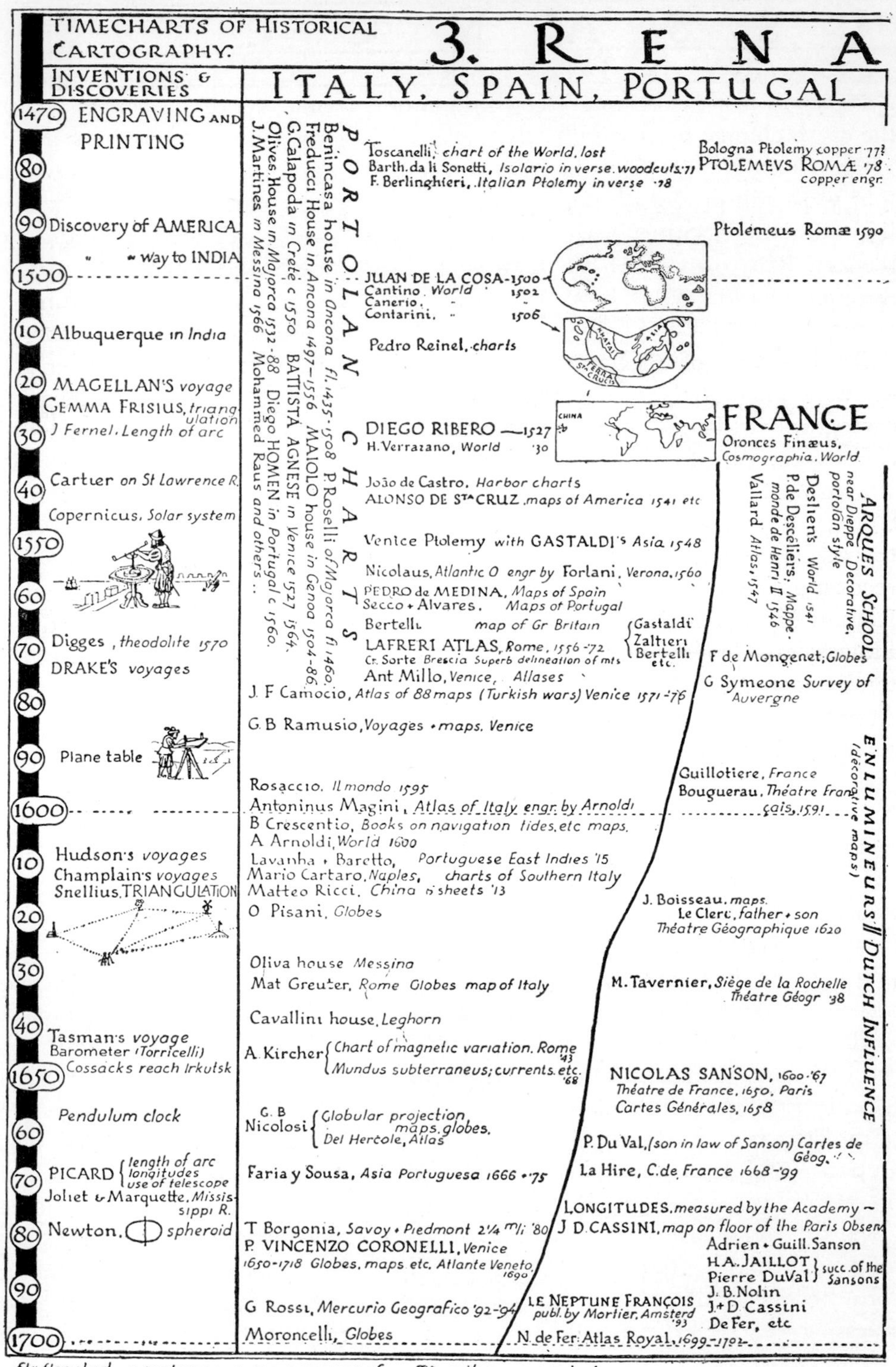


Table III Time Chart

of the Renaissance

as far as his coordinates extended, Clavus broke through the limits of the classical map to include Norway, Iceland, and even southern Greenland, which he had personally visited. It was the first extension of the cartographic horizon beyond the northern limits of the ancient world.

In the following generation (about 1425 to 1460), additional "Tabulae Modernae" were prepared, which showed Spain, France, Italy, and central Europe. These works were frequently reproduced in Ptolemy manuscripts, and also served as models for the earliest printed maps of the Renaissance. They may be said to stand at the very head of modern scientific cartography.

**Printing and Engraving.** The second event that stimulated the progress of cartography was the invention of printing and engraving. Hitherto all maps had to be drawn by hand, expensively and laboriously. In some places, as in Venice, there were map factories where large staffs of draftsmen were engaged in copying maps; even so, their expense necessarily limited their use to royal courts, naval officers, and to some of the universities. The average man had almost no contact whatsoever with maps. From the flaming descriptions of maps given by some of the medieval writers we may see that their production was regarded as little short of miraculous. With the introduction of printing and engraving, thousands of copies could be obtained from a single plate, and the price of the maps sank to a fraction of what it had been before.

The earliest maps were woodcuts, but very soon copper engravings took their place and remained in universal popularity for 300 years. In preparing maps of this type, lines and letterings were carved with a graver or burin into a polished copper plate in reverse, mirrorlike fashion. Ink was rubbed into the grooves; the plate was wiped clean and then pressed against a slightly dampened sheet of rag paper. Coloring was added by hand. Map engraving became a lucrative business, and the big establishments of Amsterdam and Venice employed hundreds of workmen.

**The Great Discoveries.** The third and perhaps most far-reaching event inductive to a renaissance of cartography was that of the great discoveries. The age of the great discoveries was itself made possible by a number of inventions. We have already noted the influence of the compass. Equally important was the development of a better type of sailing vessel, particularly the Flemish karak and the Portuguese caravel. These were three-masted, decked ships with the sails rigged in such fashion that the vessel could be managed even in adverse winds. Henceforth it was no longer necessary to hug the coasts as in the old galleys; it was also unnecessary to carry an enormous amount of provisions for the oarsmen, a circumstance which had usually made it difficult for the earlier galleys to go more than a week without landing. The caravels could be provisioned for months and were ready to sail anywhere in the seven seas. It is largely because of this fact that in the following centuries the known world more than doubled in size; and this, in turn, produced the most far-reaching effects on history.

The first of the important discoveries were those made by the Portuguese along the coast of western Africa. They were recorded piecemeal in contemporary maps of the portolan type. They also appear on the globe constructed by Martin Behaim of Nuremberg in 1492, the oldest terrestrial globe in existence. In the same year, Columbus actually reached some islands about 70° west of Spain. Seemingly this confirmed Ptolemy's conception of a small earth. In the following years, however, Pinson and Cabral found extensive lands located only

30 or 40° west of Spain, and south of the equator; and Sebastian Cabot discovered islands lying only 45° west of Spain in the latitude of England. None of these had been recorded on Behaim's globe.

**Juan de la Cosa.** The cartographers of that time did their best to reconcile the new discoveries with the Ptolemaic tradition. The four maps in Fig. 16 show strikingly the development of this attempt. Juan de la Cosa's map is the most famous of the time (1500). (Some authorities think the map is of later date.) Juan de la Cosa was probably not the owner and mate of the *Santa Maria*, the flagship of Columbus on his first voyage but a seaman recorded on the admiral's second voyage. His map records the landfall of Cabral in Brazil, Cabot's voyage to Canada, and Vasco da Gama's route to the Indies.

**Waldseemüller.** The first map that shows both North and South America clearly separated from Asia was prepared in 1507 by an Alsatian cartographer named Martin Waldseemüller. It is a stupendous work ($4\frac{1}{2}$ by 8 feet, printed on 12 sheets), very rich in detail, and executed in a fine German Renaissance style. Except for the new discoveries, the map is based mostly on Ptolemy. It is constructed, however, on a new and interesting projection, resembling that of Bonne. One of the most far-reaching effects of this map was that for the first time the name "America" appears on it. Impressed by the account of the Florentine traveler, Amerigo Vespucci, Waldseemüller placed the name "America" on the southern large island. In an accompanying pamphlet he writes: "I do not see why any one may object to name it Amerige—that is, Amerigo's land—from Americus, the discoverer, a man of sagacious mind . . . or America, since both Europe and Asia derived their names from women." The name "America" was not indeed accepted for some time; its final acceptance must be attributed to Apianus and to Mercator, who applied the name to the northern continent as well.

**Diego Ribero.** On Sept. 8, 1522, a badly worn ship arrived at Seville with 18 men on

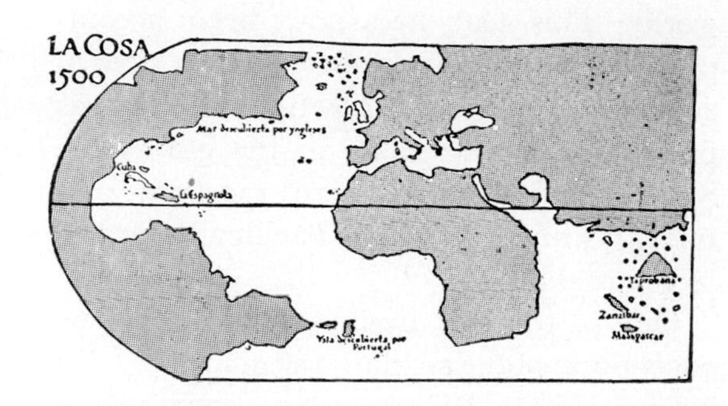


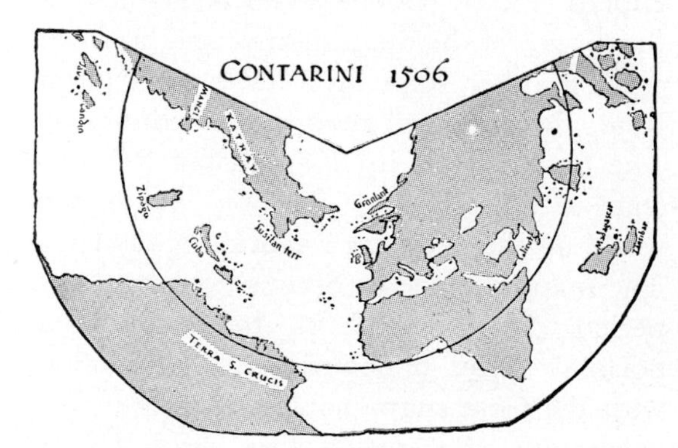


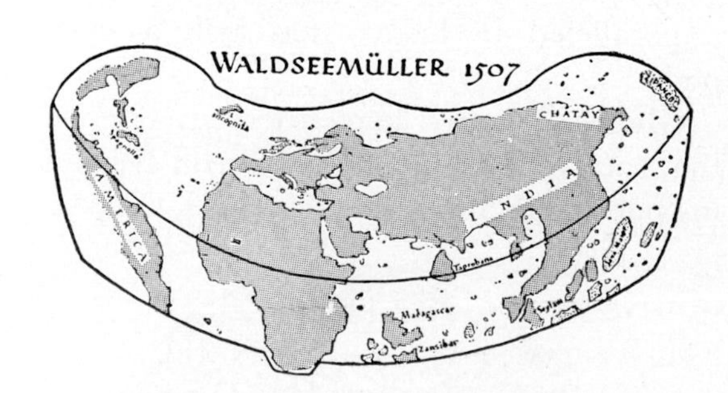


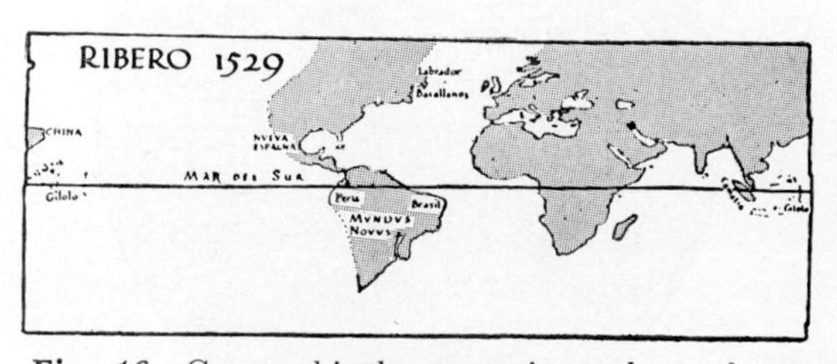


**Fig. 16** Geographical conceptions changed more rapidly in the first quarter of the sixteenth century than ever before or ever since.

board. Great was the astonishment of the people to learn that these were the sole survivors of the proud fleet which 3 years before had left under Admiral Magellan with the purpose of circumnavigating the world. This feat had now been accomplished, and with it the Ptolemaic system of geography was overthrown. America was put in its proper place on the globe; the Straits of Magellan were marked; and the vast immensity of the Pacific Ocean was recognized.

One of the first maps showing this new conception of the world is the chart of Diego Ribero (1529). Ribero was a Portuguese in the service of the Spanish king and, as royal cosmographer, kept up to date the Padrón Real, the standard map of the admiralty. The Padrón Real itself is lost, but Ribero's chart is a close copy. The outlines of the world on this map are remarkably modern. The map, like all the Spanish charts of the period, is executed in the traditional portolan style. A comparison of this map with the Cosa map shows a change in the geographic concepts of the world that is unparalleled in history for such a short period.

**Globes.** The first known terrestrial globe that survived was made by Martin Behaim in Nuremberg and finished in 1492, the year of the discovery of America. There is no trace of America on it; it shows entirely the geography of Ptolemy, with additions based on the Portuguese discoveries. Martin Behaim was for some time in the service of the Portuguese king and took part in voyages to West Africa. His globe is 20 inches in diameter and artistically delineated, with ample descriptions and notes. He fills the ocean south and east of Asia with a great number of islands, which reach well out into the region where America should be located. The globe is now in the Germanic Museum in Nuremberg.

The most famous globe maker of this period was Johannes Schöner of Nuremberg. Two of his globes from the years 1515 and 1520 show a South American strait even before Magellan's voyage. This, however, was little more than a happy guess. Moreover, on the southern side of the strait we find the enormous Terra Australis, that great imaginary southern continent which figured so prominently in all the maps of the sixteenth century. Globes at this time became popular. A favorite pose of contemporary portraits is a man solemnly measuring a globe with a drawing compass (see Fig. 19).

**The Italian School.** In the first half of the sixteenth century Italian map makers were very productive. The Italian Renaissance

**Fig. 17** The Behaim Globe of 1492. (*Courtesy of the Encyclopaedia Britannica.*)

reached its peak at that time, and Italian artists ranked first in all arts, and also in cartography. The earlier maps of the Italian school were mostly rendered in portolan style, with rhumb lines and compass roses. In the later maps and charts, however, regular projections were introduced. The most active among the Italian map makers was Battista Agnese of Venice. His beautifully drawn and colored manuscript maps can be seen in many museums of Europe. He was among the first to give the proper delineation of Lower California. The most important cartographic monument of this period is the Lafreri Atlas (Rome, 1556–1572). This atlas contains a miscellany of printed maps prepared by the best cartographers of the age, Gastaldi, Bertelli, Zaltieri, etc. Copies of the Lafreri Atlas are rare and highly prized.

Great advancement has been made in the realistic delineation of mountains. Superb are the maps of Crescencio Sorte of Brescia, in which the scenery of the Piemonte is drawn in bird's-eye-view manner.

**The Cosmographiae.** Among the most popular books of the Renaissance were the so-called "cosmographiae." These were textbooks of geography, astronomy, history, and natural sciences, described in regional order and illustrated with maps and figures. One of the earliest and most popular of these manuals was the "Cosmographia" of the older Apianus. Petrus Apianus (1495–1554)—his name was Latinized from Peter Bienewitz—was professor of mathematics in Ingolstadt, Bavaria, and one of the foremost cosmographers of his time. He invented the stereographic projection and is credited also with the so-called "Apianus projection." This projection, which consisted of horizontal parallels and arcuate meridians, has been revived in Germany in recent years. Apianus' "Cosmographia" appeared in 1524 and speedily became one of the most

**Fig. 18** Instruments for measuring land were used in the early Renaissance. (*From Apianus, "Cosmographia,"* 1524.)

popular textbooks in its field. At least 15 editions are known, and it was translated into five languages. Later editions were augmented by Gemma Frisius, a Dutch cosmographer who introduced the basic principles of triangulation.

More voluminous was the "Cosmographia" of Sebastian Münster. Published at Basel in 1544, Münster's compilation was the main source book of information for half a century. The maps, indeed, were rather primitive woodcuts, and the text abounded in fabulous stories; but its importance in disseminating knowledge was great.

## The Dutch School of Cartography

Situated amid three great powers of Europe—France, England, and Germany—and subject to Spain, the greatest sea power of that time, the small Netherlands became the market place of Europe. Through its thriving commercial cities passed the merchants and sailors of all nations, and the Dutch were able to get firsthand information from every part of the world. After the Netherlands gained their independence at the turn of the century, the Dutch themselves became an active sea-faring and colonizing nation. The central position of the Netherlands, the industry and artistic ability of the people, and their interest in distant lands made the Dutch first-class map makers. In no other period in the history of cartography can we find such prolific production of high-grade maps as in the *golden age of Dutch cartography*, which began in the middle of the sixteenth century and lasted over a hundred years.

**Mercator.** The father of Dutch cartography was Gerardus Mercator (1512–1594), as his name was Latinized from Gerhard Kremer. He studied in the University of Louvain, and one of his teachers was Gemma Frisius, the noted cosmographer. He became a maker of globes and instruments in Duisburg and in this connection began to make maps. Later he settled in Louvain, where he became the founder and head of one of the most important cartographic houses of that age.

The chief merit of Mercator was the liberation of cartography from the influence of Ptolemy. He compiled his material from all available sources; he examined critically the older maps and read the records of sailors and travelers; and he traveled widely himself. He became famous by his map of Europe of 1554, in which he reduced the length of the Mediterranean Sea to 53°, a correction of Ptolemy's map. At present Mercator is best known for the Mercator projection. This is a system of horizontal parallels and vertical meridians where the relation between the two is true on any part of the map. This is the only projection in which the lines of compass directions appear straight, and for this reason it is well adapted for navigation. Mercator designed this projection for his large chart of the world in 1569.

**Fig. 19** Mercator (*left*) and Hondius were among the greatest cartographers of the Renaissance. The cross-staff on top of the frame was used for measuring latitude at sea.

**Ortelius.** Mercator did not publish any great atlases in his lifetime, but he encouraged his friend, Abraham Ortelius, to prepare one, and the "Theatrum Orbis Terrarum" was published in 1570. This is regarded as the first modern atlas of the world, preceding in publication the equally famous Italian Lafreri Atlas. It has 53 plates engraved in copper, beautifully executed, and colored by hand. In the accompanying essay Ortelius listed 87 geographers and cartographers whom he had used as references in this work. It is characteristic of the rapidly increasing interest in the subject that the 1587 edition of the same atlas has 108 plates and lists 137 references.

**Mercator's Successors.** Mercator's own atlas was published in 1595, after his death, by his son, Rumold. His establishment was taken over by his son-in-law, Jodocus Hondius (1563–1611), a cartographer of renown himself. The great traditions of the house were carried on by his son, Henricus, and his son-in-law, Jan Janszoon (1596–1664). Janszoon's "Nieuwe Atlas" had

**Fig. 20** The Western Hemisphere from Ortelius' "Theatrum Orbis Terrarum." This much-reduced copy gives but little indication of the beauty of the colorful original. Note the large Terra Australis.

over 400 plates wonderfully engraved and colored.

His works were surpassed only by the rival establishment of the Blaeus in Amsterdam. The founder of the house, Willem Janszoon Blaeu (1571–1638), was a man of scientific standing and a friend and student of Tycho Brahe, the great Danish astronomer. He was given the title "Cartographer to the Republic" and was invested with the right to examine all records of seamen, to improve upon his maps. His "Atlas Novus" of 1634 grew to six large volumes. His work was carried on by his sons, Jan and Willem, and his grandson, Cornelius. Their "Atlas Major" grew into 12 large folio volumes and was translated into several languages. Their establishment was destroyed by fire in 1672, and those plates which could be salvaged were bought by De Wit, one of the later Dutch cartographers.

**Later Dutch Cartographers.** By the end of the seventeenth century dozens of establishments were publishing maps, atlases, and globes, mostly in Amsterdam, and all Europe was flooded with their products. Even at the present time, for a few dollars one can buy original imprints of old Dutch maps. Among the more prolific publishers we may mention the Allards (Carolus and Aberon), the Donckers (Justus and Cornelius), the Schencks (Pieter and Pieter, Jr.), the Valks (Gerald and Leonard), the Visshers (Nicholas and Nicholas, Jr.), and the later Janszoons (Nicholas and Carl). Hundreds of atlases of folio size were published, but few of them achieved the excellence and beauty of the Blaeu and Janszoon maps. The maps had to be cheaper to meet competition; quality gave place to quantity; and the supremacy held by Dutch maps soon passed to France. In the publishing of sea charts, however, the Dutch still retained their supremacy during the early eighteenth century. Later they were superseded by the English.

**General Characteristics of the Dutch Renaissance Maps.** The early Dutch maps represent the culmination of the art of cartographic rendering. The maps of later ages may be more accurate, but in the art of cartographic expression we still can learn from Janszoon and the Blaeus. Each sheet was a well-composed unit; land and sea, title, lettering, and decoration were harmoniously distributed. A more legible type of lettering was introduced by Mercator. Characteristic are the so-called "swash" lines, masterful strokes of the pen, which were often used to decorate otherwise empty surfaces. The title, scales, and descriptive material are usually collected into decorative frames called "cartouches," often adorned by animals and products of the country. These attempts are not always fortunate; the artist probably never left Holland, and his conceptions of tropical regions, as, for instance, African kings living in Dutch palaces, are often very naïve. Orientation to north was far from universal. If it fitted the page better, the map has been turned in any direction; and the north direction was shown by decorative compass roses.

The most objectionable feature of Dutch maps is in their indiscriminate use of information. To show large empty spaces did not help to sell the map, and commercially inclined artists were more than willing to fill the land with any kind of information or to extend the known detail into the unknown, a common practice in olden times.

"So geographers, in Afric maps
With savage pictures fill their gaps,
And o'er unhabitable downs,
Place elephants for want of towns."[1]

Mention should be made of the Dutch city maps. The great city atlas of Braun and Hoefnagel, "Civitates Orbis Terrarum," depicted cities with most masterful detail. Ortelius regarded this atlas as equal in merit to his own.

**The French Cartography of the Renaissance.** The waves of the Great Awakening reached France in the middle of the sixteenth century. In cartography, however, the French long retained some medieval features. The early French maps were rendered in the portolan tradition, but with more finesse, very much like mural paintings. The charts of the cartographers of the Dieppe school, somewhat in the style of mural paintings, are among the most beautiful maps ever made. Somewhat less decorative are the maps of the "enlumineurs" of the late sixteenth century (see Time Chart, Table III).

The further development of French cartography was strongly influenced by the work of the Sanson family. The founder of the house was Nicolas Sanson d'Abbeville (1600–1667), who, himself of Flemish origin, was under the influence of Dutch map makers. He was assisted and succeeded by his sons, Adrien and Guillaume; by his son-in-law, Pierre Duval; by his grandson, Gilles Robert de Vougondy; and by his great-grandson, Didier Robert de Vougondy, one of the most influential cartographic dynasties of all times. The Sansons were prolific producers of maps; they published several atlases, maps of the postal roads and the rivers of France, and many historical maps. Closely connected with the

[1] SWIFT, JONATHAN, "On Poetry, A Rhapsody."

Sansons was Alexis Hubert Jaillot. He bought the plates for his atlases from Guillaume Sanson and added much of his own work. Jaillot also edited the most important geographic work of this period, "Le Neptune François" (1693), in collaboration with Jean Dominique Cassini and many other noted cartographers of that time.

In general the maps of the Sanson house resembled the Dutch maps, but usually manifested a more scientific attitude. Decorations are far less frequent, and extensive notes of geographic information are common.

**The English School.** Notable cartographic work was done in England in the time of Queen Elizabeth. The English maps of this period are very similar to the Dutch in style, but greater detail and less sense of proportion make them seem more crowded.

The pioneer of English cartography is Christopher Saxton (1542–1608?). His chief contribution is an atlas of county maps of England, published in 1579. His work was authorized by Queen Elizabeth and is one of the first detailed surveys of the country. The nature of his survey we may learn from his passport: "All shieres . . . shall be assisting . . . to see him conducted into any towne, castle or hill to view the countrey, and he may be accompanied with II or III honest men such as do best know the countrey. . . . "

**Fig. 21** Sanson's map of America, which was conceived as the legendary lost Atlantis. Note that California is shown as an island, although on the earlier Ortelius map it was shown correctly. All five Great Lakes are shown. The map is in the sinusoidal projection.

An important English map is the chart of the world of 1599, which is occasionally found bound into Hackluyt's work and which is now very rare. It is probably the work of Edward Wright, a friend of Hackluyt and author of "Certain Errors in Navigation." The map is in Mercator projection; it shows the results of Drake's voyages and the discoveries along the Northwest and Northeast Passages. It is one of the best maps of its age. This is the map to which Shakespeare refers in "Twelfth Night": "He does smile his face in more lines than there are in the new map with the augmentation of the Indies. . . . "

Another interesting work is John Ogilvie's atlas of road strip maps. This idea, to show roads in the form of furls, was first used by Matthew Paris in the time of the Crusades and has often been employed since. Figure 22 is interesting because it shows how Ogilvie's survey was carried out. We see the figure of the surveyor on horseback, and his apprentice with a perambulator measuring distances.

At the end of the seventeenth century, English charts became widely used. Notable is Halley's magnetic chart of 1683, one of the first charts of this kind. Cartographic curiosities are the beautiful tapestry maps of Sheldon, naturally more decorative than informative.

**Other Nations.** The earliest "basic" maps of many countries were produced in the Renaissance, *e.g.*, those of Austria and Hungary by Lazius, around 1620, of Russia by Herbertstein, and of Scandia of Oleus Magnus, which is one of the most richly decorated maps of the period. The detailed map of Bavaria by Philip Apianus is notable because it is claimed to be based on triangulation.

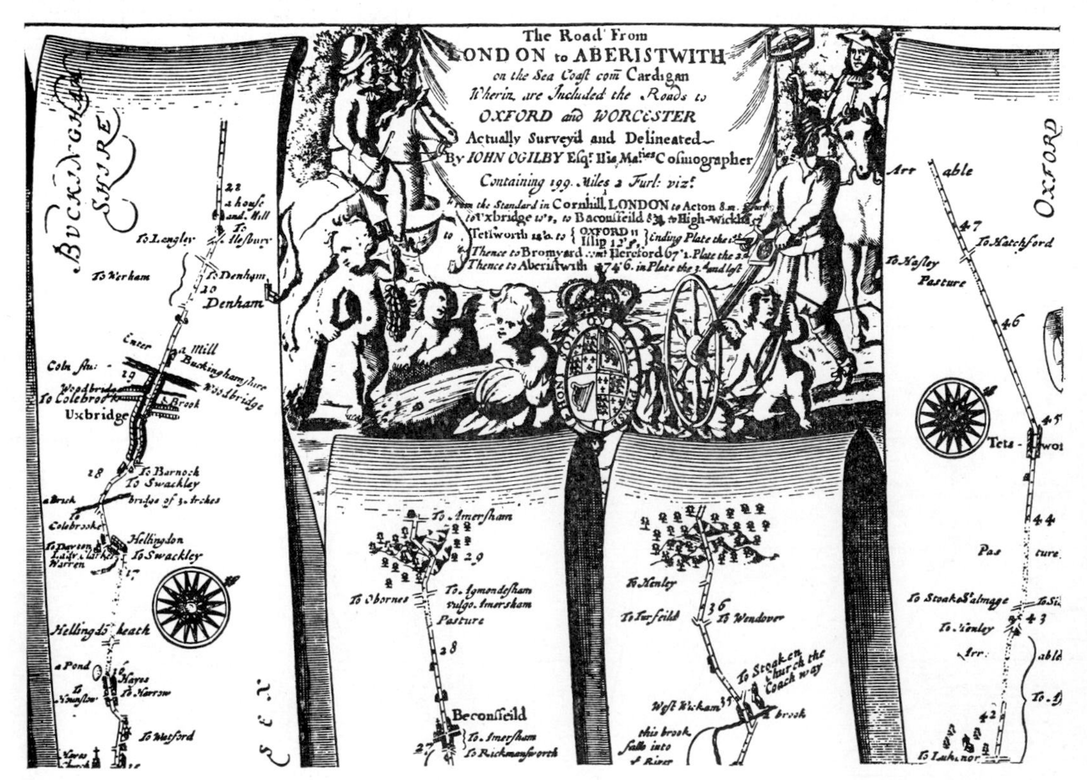


**Fig. 22** Furl-map showing roads from Ogilvie's "Britannia." Note the picture of the mounted surveyor with a compass-diopter in his hand and his assistant with a calibrated wheel measuring distances.

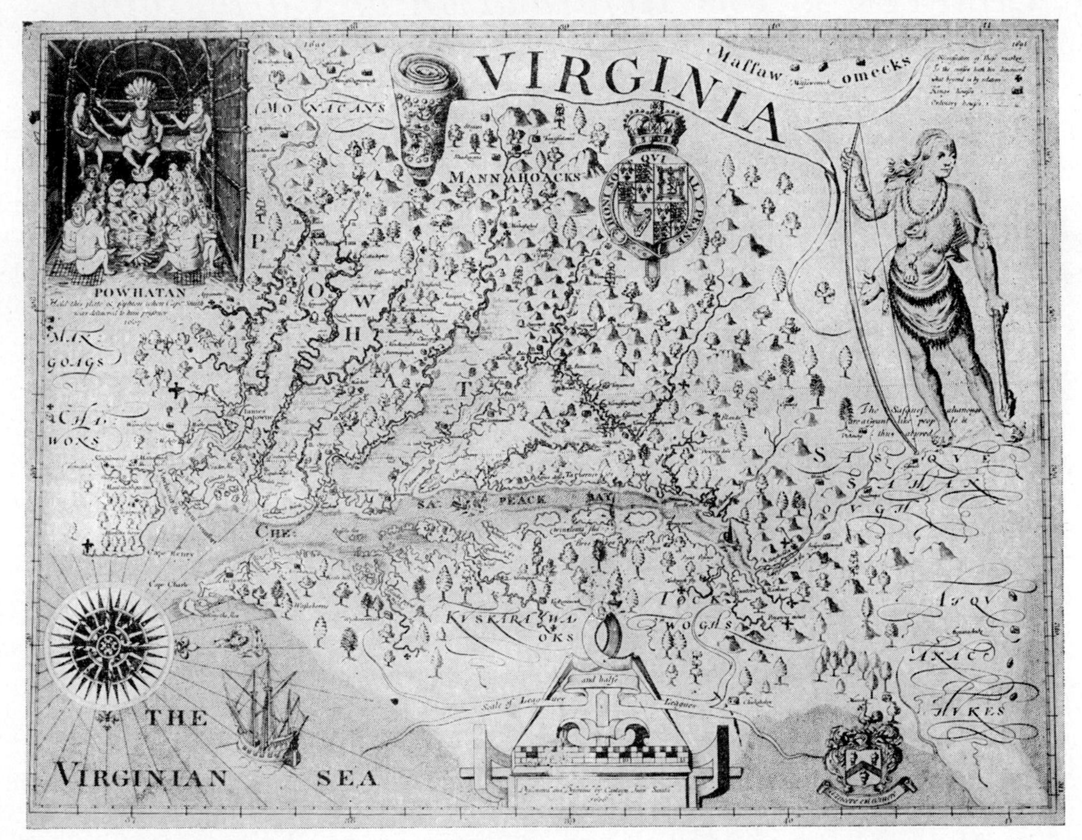


**Fig. 23** John Smith's map of Virginia, 1608, is based on a compass survey made from canoes. Note the small crosses marking the limits of the actual survey.

The greatest cartographer of the later Renaissance is P. Vincenzo Coronelli (1650–1718) of Venice, who especially excelled in globes. His 10- and 15-foot globes, prepared in Paris for Louis XIV, evoked much comment. He founded the first geographical society, the "Argonauts," in Venice.

Of particular interest to us are the "Virginia" and "New England" maps, based on the surveys of Capt. John Smith. The maps themselves were not drawn by the great colonizer. The Virginia map is based on compass sketches made from canoes, considering which it is remarkably accurate. The map has crosses to mark the limits of actual survey; beyond these everything is "by relation." This seems to be the first "relative reliability" map. The New England map has an accurate shore line, but most places are misnamed. Equally fundamental are the maps of Champlain, in which the great navigator delineated the St. Lawrence River and the intricate coast line of eastern Canada.

# CHAPTER 3: *The Reformation of Cartography*

The fundamental changes between the seventeenth-century Dutch school and the eighteenth-century French school of cartography can perhaps best be understood by comparison of two maps. Figure 24 shows Africa as delineated by Janszoon in 1628: Africa is divided into kingdoms with well-defined boundaries and is full of cities, rivers, and lakes, even in the Sahara Desert. Monsters, elephants, lions, or swash-lined lettering fill the space. At this time the actual knowledge of Africa's interior was practically nil.

How somber in comparison appears the Africa of d'Anville of 1747! Gone are the monsters, elephants, lions, and swash lines; a cartouche around the title is the only decoration. The map looks empty; the regions of which nothing is known are left blank; where information is doubtful, a note to that effect is given. The traditional large river of the Sahara Desert is still present, but a note states that it is by the authority of Ptolemy and Edrisi and that there is information available that the river flows east instead of west, as is actually the case of the Niger. Accuracy, clearness, and attention to detail mark the French map in

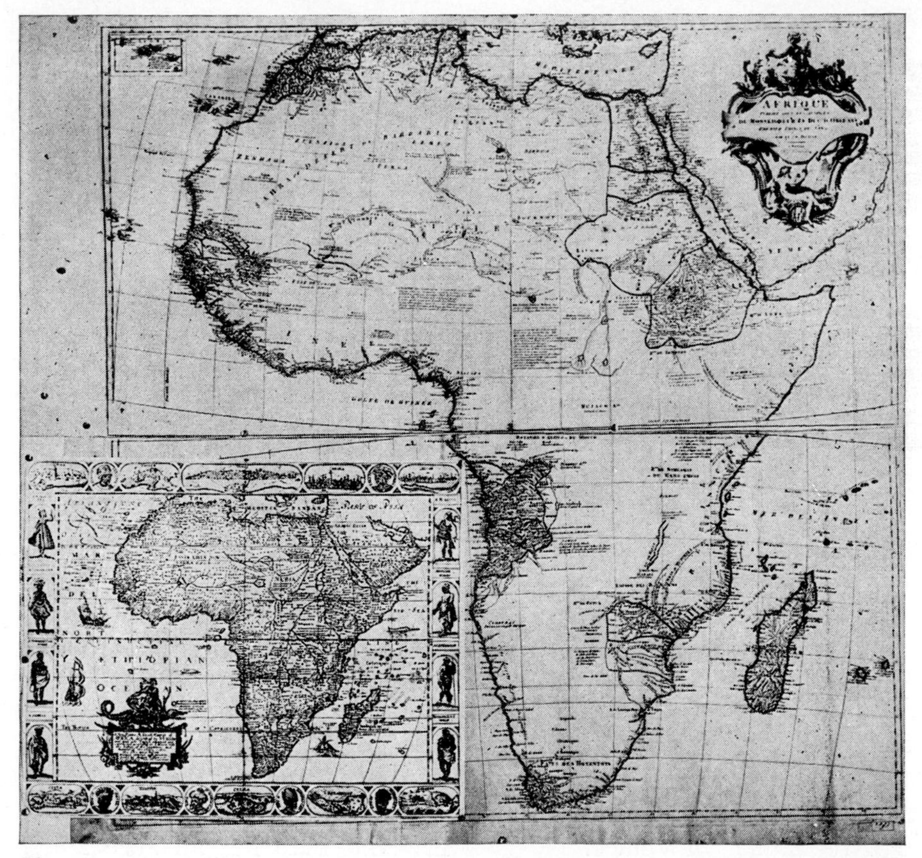

**Fig. 24** D'Anville's Africa illustrates the reformation of cartography. Its scientific accuracy and omission of all doubtful data is in contrast with the decorative map of Janszoon, which is shown in the lower left.

contrast to the older maps of the Dutch school.

The difference between the French and Dutch schools is chiefly the result of the more scientific attitude of the eighteenth century. This was the Age of Reason, and its spirit appears in maps, too. There is, however, a further difference. In Amsterdam, maps were made for profit, and, therefore, quick output and attractive rendering were important. Information was obtained where it was available most inexpensively—by copying other maps. Old plates were used, in spite of new discoveries, as long as the maps could be sold. To make expensive surveys or critical studies would not have been profitable. The French cartographers, in contrast, were scientists, often men of noble rank subsidized by the King and the Academy. Their motive was scientific reputation rather than monetary profit.

The new cartography was based on new instruments. At sea the old cross-staff and backstaff were replaced by the octant and the sextant. Longitude measurements were no longer a feat in higher astronomy. The

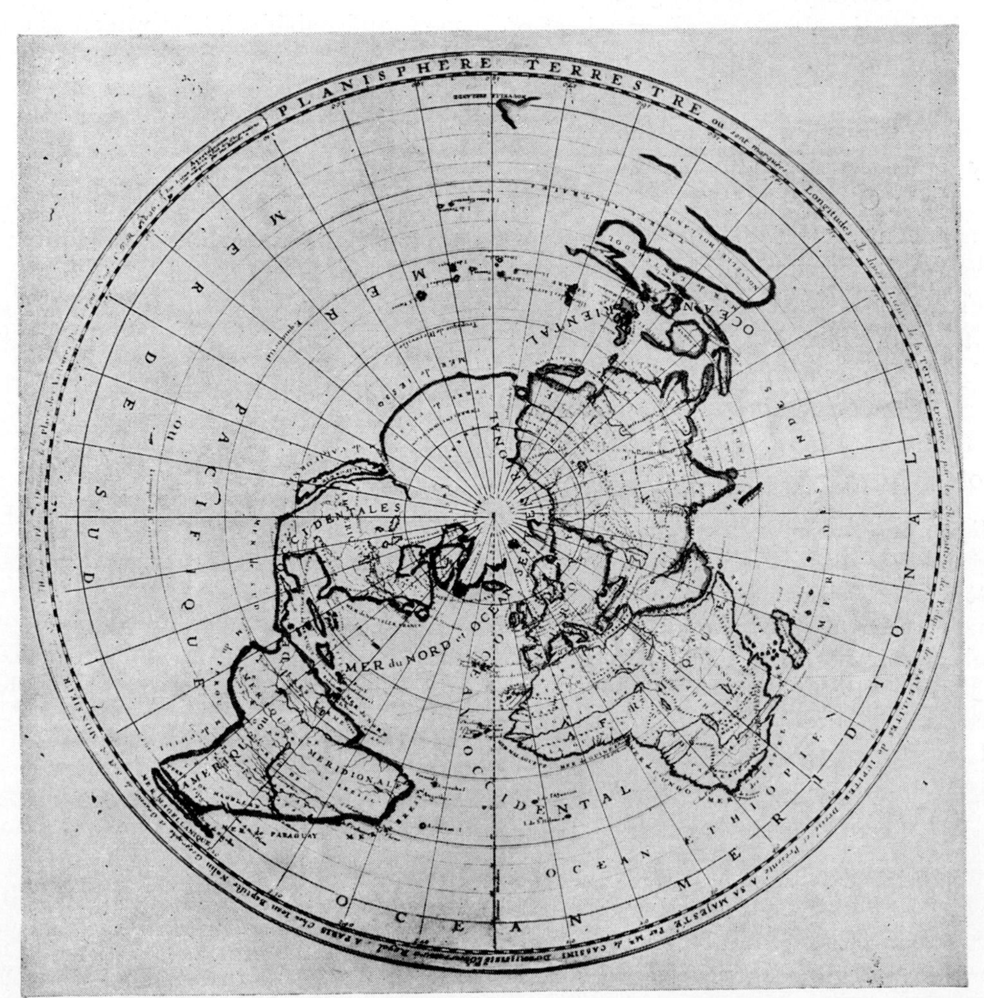


**Fig. 25** The reformation of cartography dates from this map of 1696. The original was laid out on the floor of the Paris Observatory and embodies the new longitude observations of the Academy under J. D. Cassini. (*After reproduction from W. L. Clements Library.*)

chronometer, invented by Harrison, enabled seamen to read their longitude as easily as their latitude. On land the system of triangulation was perfected by William Blaeu who actually triangulated a part of the Netherlands coast. For measuring angles the old diopter was still much in use, but at the end of the century it was replaced by the telescopic theodolite.

**Longitude Measurements of the Academy.** The reformation of cartography was introduced by the longitude measurements of the French Academy at the end of the seventeenth century. These longitudes were measured by simultaneous observations of the occultations of Jupiter's satellites at various places all over the world. The result was a new map of the world, which was laid out by Jean Dominique Cassini on the floor of the Paris Observatory in 1682—one of the fundamental maps of history. One of the curious results of these measurements was that France appeared to be much smaller than it was delineated by Sanson; it is said that Louis XIV remarked to Cassini that his measurements took away from France more than the King had added by all his wars of conquest.

**Delisle and His Successors.** The outstanding cartographer of the early eighteenth century was Guillaume Delisle. His chief merit was the elimination of many errors which had crept into cartography and which had been copied so often that they were accepted as truths. He reduced the size of the Mediterranean to its actual length, thus breaking completely with the Ptolemaic tradition. He also corrected the map of California. Lower California was shown correctly as a peninsula by Mercator and his contemporaries. Later, however, California was shown as an island on all the late seventeenth-century maps. Delisle reestablished its peninsular form in 1700, based on the overland voyage of Father Kino. His map of North America of 1700 was the best of its period.

We have already mentioned the work of Jean Baptiste Bourguignon d'Anville (1697–1782). His maps of the continents made the world realize how little it knew of the interiors of Asia, Africa, and the Americas. His remarkably rich atlas of China was based on the extensive surveys of the Jesuit missionaries.

The most important atlases of this period were made by Gilles and Didier Robert de Vougondy; their general atlas was used the world over; it is particularly noted for its "Préface Historique," in which the history of geography is recorded in 33 folio pages.

Mention should be made of the famous atlas of charts, "Hydrographie Française," the greatest collection of marine charts hitherto made and published. The work was organized by J. N. Bellin, who ranks equal to d'Anville and Delisle as a leader of this great period of cartography.

**English Cartography of the Eighteenth Century.** In the eighteenth century, England became the foremost maritime power of Europe. With the growth of the oversea dominions and the resulting trade and prosperity, maps and charts were more and more in demand, and London became a cartographic center surpassing Amsterdam and rivaling Paris. Indeed, many famous Amsterdam map makers established themselves in London, while others came from Paris.

The English maps did not differ in style and composition from the French maps; many of them were copied directly from Delisle or d'Anville with or without acknowledgment. Among the most prolific cartographers we may mention Hermann Moll, a Dutchman who came to London in 1688. Characteristic of his maps is the extensive use of descriptive notes with which he covers every available space, thus making his maps almost a textbook of geography.

The golden period of English cartography was the second half of the eighteenth century. We cannot discuss all the great map makers here; for them the student is referred to the time charts. This period has direct connection with American cartography, for the first important American maps were published in London.

**German Cartography in the Eighteenth Century.** In the eighteenth century, Germany was divided into several small states, among which Austria and Prussia struggled for supremacy. There was no strong central government to support military cartography, and the German maps of this period were either business undertakings or surveys supported by some of the more enlightened princes. The largest map-publishing house was founded by J. B. Homann in Nuremberg in 1692, and until 1824 he and his successors produced an incredible number of maps and atlases. Their chief rival was the equally prolific Säutter house in Augsburg. Characteristic of the German maps is an enormous amount of detail, to the point of overcrowding; they are full of insets, pictures, and notes, sometimes only distantly related to geography.

More important are the surveys of the individual principalities. They are too numerous to be listed here, and therefore the reader is referred to the time charts. The most important map of this period is the 1: 50,000 Kabinetskarte, which shows Brandenburg, Mecklenburg, Prussia, and the surrounding principalities in 270 sheets. This enormous work was carried out under Count F. W. von Schmettau (1767–1780). It was never published, but remained as manuscript in the secret archives of the Prussian kings. Collection of the various surveys of Germany into a single great work was accomplished in 1789 by J. G. A. Jaeger in his "Grand Atlas d'Allemagne."

**Italian and Spanish Cartography in the Eighteenth Century.** In the eighteenth century Italy also was divided into many small states, whose rulers were often great patrons of arts and sciences, and much outstanding cartographic work was accomplished under their patronage. As in their style of architecture, the baroque maps of Italy strove to be monumental. In the great libraries of Europe we often find maps of colossal size, in striking contrast to the fine and minute lettering and exquisite detail.

The most prominent cartographer of Italy was G. A. Rizzi-Zannoni (1734–1814), a native of Dalmatia. He traveled all over Europe and did notable cartographic work in Poland, Germany, England, and France before he settled at the court of Naples. His detailed maps are outstanding in vivid delineation of the geographic landscape. His two maps of the Bay of Naples are described by Sir George Fordham: " . . . The surface of the maps is marvelously minute in execution . . . the panoramic representation of the coast line is a lovely piece of work, and the borders and other ornamental features are superb."

In the same class belongs the monumental "South America" of La Cruz Caño y Olmedilla, on a nearly 1: 5,000,000 scale. A detailed map of this entire continent on such a large scale was not attempted until modern times. This is an important map from the historical point of view because it shows the distribution of the various Indian tribes, and also the sites of the Jesuit missions, many of which were ruined after the dissolution of the Order.

Other nations, too, did remarkable work during the eighteenth century, especially the Swiss, Russians, and the Scandinavians, but discussion of these would lead beyond the limits of this outline.

## National Surveys

The eighteenth century witnessed the rise of the great powers of Europe amidst almost constant large-scale warfare. The operations of the great armies could not be planned and coordinated without detailed and accurate maps, which the private cartographers were not able to furnish. It was as a result of this necessity that the great armies

TIMECHARTS OF HISTORICAL CARTOGRAPHY **4. MODERN**

| Year | EVENTS | ITALY-SPAIN LATIN AMERICA | FRANCE |
|---|---|---|---|
| | | | LONGITUDE MEASUREMENTS OF THE ACADEMY J. D. Cassini. La Hire, Nolin Claude Delisle. Pene, etc. |
| 1700 | | Sam. Fritz Amazon R. 1691-1707 | J. B. L. Franqueline maps of Amer. Neuv. France 1702 |
| 10 | | C. Feuillée Chile-Peru coast 07-12 | Guill. DELISLE 1675-1726 { reduction of Mediterr. to 42° / maps of Amer. 1700, '03, '18 / California as peninsula / Secant conic projection / Ferro meridian (Royal order since 1734) |
| 20 | | | Mr C***. Atlas Historique, 7 vol. |
| 30 | Octant, Hadley<br>Chronometer, J. Harrison | J. Petroschi Jesuit map of Paraguai '32<br>J. Escandon, surveys in Mexico | J. B B. D'ANVILLE 1697-1782 { Atl Général '27-'80 / Africa '47 Asia '51, S Am. '48 / clearing maps from false detail / History of geography |
| 40 | V. Bering, North Pacific '28-'48<br>La Condamine, measuring the arc in Peru '36-'45 - Earth as an ellipsoid | G Nolli, ROME 1:3000 (superb) | TRIANGULATION OF FRANCE '34-'44<br>C. F. CASSINI 1714-1784 Carte Géometrique de la France 1:86000<br>Ph BUACHE 1700-'73 succ. of Delisle { Contour lines. English Channel '37 / Géogr physique '53 |
| 50 | Tobias Mayer, longitudes by Tables of the Moon '53 | P M Vinchio in Casale maps, globes | J N Bellin '03-'72 { Atl Maritime '51 / Antilles '58, St. Domingue '68 |
| 60 | | A. Dury, Sardinia + Genoa (fantastic mountains) | R. J. Julien Atlas of France '51, '58, '68<br>Rigobert Bonne '27-'94 { Atlases - America 81 / Projection |
| 70 | J Bruce in Abyssinia<br>J. Cook in S. Pacific and Antarctic | LA CRUZ, Cano y Olmedilla South America 1:5000000 | Gilles Didier } ROBERT de Vaugondy { ATL UNIVERSELLE '57 on / Globes atlases<br>C. F Delamarche, 1740-1817 maps atlases<br>Jos. Roux, Charts, Harbor views |
| 80 | Ramsden, theodolite | G. A. RIZZI-ZANNONI, 1736-1814 (supreme engr) Medit Sea. Naples etc.<br>Ant Zatta, Venice Atl. Novissimo | G. L Le Rouge Atlas Amer. Septentrional 78<br>J. Lattré, maps atlases<br>N. Desmarest, Atlas Encyclopédique '87 or.<br>Dupain-Triel. Contour line map of France '91 |
| 90 | Metric system.<br>Mackenzie in Canada | TOMÁS LÓPEZ de Vargas, 1731-1802 survey of Spain, maps of America | |
| | | NAPOLEON'S | SURVEYS OF EUROPE — |
| 1800 | Humboldt in America<br>Mungo Park on the Niger | Spanish Admiralty, Atlas of Amer coast 1801. Langara Valdes etc. | ↳ Bacler d'Albe Italy 1:256000<br>Le Sage Atlas Historique 07 |
| 10 | Karl Ritter, Erdkunde; | A. v. Humboldt, Atlas de Nouvelle Espagne | C. de la France de l'État Major 1:80000 '17-'80<br>C. Malte-Brun, Geographies and atlases |
| 20 | LITHOGRAPHY used for maps | | A. H. Brué, maps atlases '16-'32<br>Pierre + Al. Emile LAPIE { N. America 1806 / Turkey 1:800000 / Greece |
| 30 | | J. B. Pentland, surveys in Bolivia<br>R. H. Schomburgk " - the Guianas | |
| 40 | Ross in Antarctica<br>WAX ENGRAVING.-S. E. Morse in New York | | FRANCE 1:100000 587 sh |
| 50 | D. Livingstone on the Zambezi | NEW GRANADA, A CODAZZI '49-'55<br>BOLIVIA, Castelnau | HISTORY OF MAPS { de Santarem ... mappemondes, 78 sh '42-'53 / J Lelewel, Géog du moyen âge '50-'57 / E. E. Jomard, Monum. de la géog. '42-'62 / L VIVIEN de St. Martin { Hist de géog. '73 / Atlas '27 on |
| 60 | HELIOGRAVURE<br>PHOTOZINCOGRAPHY | PORTUGAL, 1:100000 1856 on<br>MEXICO, G. Cubas, '58, '74, '86<br>ARGENTINE, M. de Moussy '65<br>PERU, PAZ SOLDAN '65 | A. H Dufour, maps atlases |
| 70 | Stanley on the Congo<br>Richthofen in China | NAPLES, 1:250000, 25 sheets '71-'74<br>ITALY, 1:100000, 277 sh. '73 on<br>SPAIN, 1:50000, 1080 sh. '75 on (Ibero) | |
| 80 | E. J. Reclus, La Géographie 19 v. '75-'94<br>Fr. Ratzel, Anthropogeogr | CUBA, Atlas, E. Prichard '75<br>PERU, 1:500000 under Raimondi, '31 on<br>ARGENTINE, Geogr. Inst. Atl. '86-'98 | Avezac du Castera-Macaya, medieval maps<br>F. Schrader, Atlas Univ '83 on (Vivien de St-Martin)<br>ALGIERS, 50000 since '86 |
| 90 | Fd. Suess: Das Antlitz d. Erde '83-1901<br>Nordenskiöld: Facsimile Atlas '89 - Periplus '97 | M. Fiorini, Sfere terrestri e celesti.. | P. Vidal de la Blache, Atlas Général '94 on. |
| 1900 | | ECUADOR, Th. Wolf '97<br>MEXICO, 1:100000, '97-1911 unfinished<br>CHILE-ARGENTINE, boundary | FRANCE 1:50000, colored, 846 sheets |
| | | CARTE GÉOLOGI | QUE INTERNATIONAL |
| 10 | PHOTOGRAMMETRY | CUBA U.S. ARMY 1 m/i '06-'08 | Carte Bathymetrique des Océans, Monaco since '05 |
| | WORLD WAR | INTERNATIONAL MAP | OF THE WORLD, 1:1000000 — |
| 20 | Echo sounding<br>AIRPLANE | Mexico, Atlas, '21<br>TOURING CLUB ATLAS Milan, '27 | INDOCHINE 1914 on<br>Service Géogr. de l'Armée, topographic maps of Africa, Madagascar, Levante, China and Indochina |
| 30 | PHOTOGRAPHY<br>Stereogrammetry | R. Almagià, Studies in cartography | Atlas des Colonies Fr. under G. Grandidier '34 |

Atl. = atlas. ms. = manuscript Am. or Amer = America N. = North sh. = sheets m/i = miles per inch

**Table IV** Time Chart

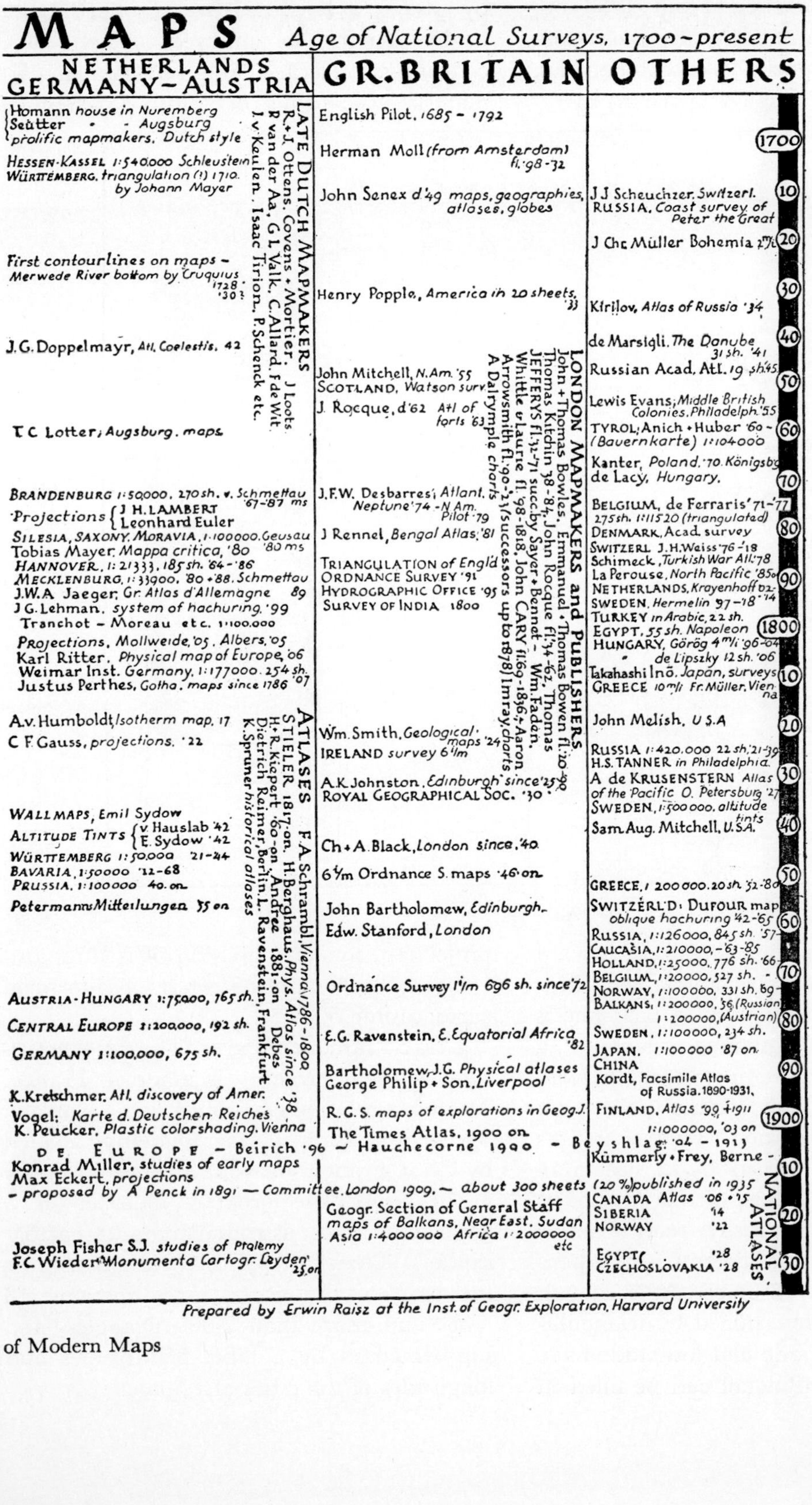

# MAPS Age of National Surveys, 1700 ~ present

## NETHERLANDS GERMANY – AUSTRIA

Homann house in Nuremberg
Seütter · · Augsburg
prolific mapmakers. Dutch style

HESSEN-KASSEL 1:540,000 Schleuslein
WÜRTTEMBERG, triangulation (?) 1710. by Johann Mayer

First contourlines on maps – Merwede River bottom by Cruquius 1728 '30

J.G. Doppelmayr, Atl. Coelestis. 42

T.C. Lotter; Augsburg. maps

BRANDENBURG 1:50,000. 270 sh. v. Schmettau '67–'87 ms
Projections { J.H. LAMBERT / Leonhard Euler
SILESIA, SAXONY, MORAVIA, 1:100000. Geusau '80 ms
Tobias Mayer. Mappa critica, '80
HANNOVER, 1:21333, 185 sh. '64–'86
MECKLENBURG, 1:33900. '80 + '88. Schmettau
J.W.A Jaeger. Gr. Atlas d'Allemagne 89
J.G. Lehman. system of hachuring. '99
Tranchot – Moreau etc. 1:100,000
Projections. Mollweide, '05. Albers, '05
Karl Ritter. Physical map of Europe, '06
Weimar Inst. Germany, 1:177000. 254 sh. '07
Justus Perthes, Gotha. maps since 1786

A.v. Humboldt, Isotherm map. 17
C.F. Gauss, projections. '22

WALL MAPS, Emil Sydow
ALTITUDE TINTS { v. Hauslab '42 / E. Sydow '42
WÜRTTEMBERG 1:50,000 '21–'24
BAVARIA, 1:50000 '12–68
PRUSSIA, 1:100000 40. on
Petermanns Mitteilungen '55 on

AUSTRIA-HUNGARY 1:75,000, 765 sh.
CENTRAL EUROPE 1:200,000, 192 sh.
GERMANY 1:100,000, 675 sh.

K. Kretschmer. Atl. discovery of Amer.
Vogel: Karte d. Deutschen Reiches
K. Peucker. Plastic colorshading. Vienna

LATE DUTCH MAPMAKERS
R.+J. Ottens. Covens + Mortier. J. Loots.
R. van der Aa, G. L. Valk, C. Allard, F. de Wit.
I. v. Keulen. Isaac Tirion. P. Schenck etc.

ATLASES F.A. Schrambl, Vienna 1786–1800
STIELER 1817-on. H. Berghaus. Phys. Atlas since '38
H.+R. Kiepert '60-on. Andree 1881-on Debes
Dietrich Reimer, Berlin. L. Ravenstein, Frankfurt
K. Spruner historical atlases

## GR. BRITAIN

English Pilot. 1685 – 1792

Herman Moll (from Amsterdam) fl. '98–'32

John Senex d.'49 maps, geographies, atlases, globes

Henry Popple, America in 20 sheets. '33

John Mitchell, N. Am. '55
SCOTLAND, Watson surv.
J. Rocque, d.'62 Atl of forts '63

J.F.W. Desbarres, Atlant. Neptune '74 – N. Am. Pilot '79
J. Rennel, Bengal Atlas, '81
TRIANGULATION of Engl'd
ORDNANCE SURVEY '91
HYDROGRAPHIC OFFICE '95
SURVEY OF INDIA 1800

Wm. Smith, Geological maps '24
IRELAND survey 6"/m
A.K. Johnston, Edinburgh since '25
ROYAL GEOGRAPHICAL SOC. '30

Ch + A. Black, London since '40
6"/m Ordnance S. maps '46 on
John Bartholomew, Edinburgh
Edw. Stanford, London

Ordnance Survey 1"/m 696 sh. since '72

E.G. Ravenstein, E. Equatorial Africa '82

Bartholomew, J.G. Physical atlases
George Philip + Son, Liverpool

R.G.S. maps of explorations in Geog. J.
The Times Atlas. 1900 on

LONDON MAPMAKERS and PUBLISHERS.
John + Thomas Bowles, Emmanuel + Thomas Bowen fl. '20–'90
Thomas Kitchin '38–'84, John Rocque fl. '34–'62, Thomas
JEFFERYS fl. '32–'71 succ. by Sayer + Bennet – Wm. Faden.
Whittle + Laurie fl. '98–1818, John CARY fl. '69–1846; Aaron
Arrowsmith fl. '90–'23 (successors up to 1878) Imray charts
A. Dalrymple charts

## OTHERS

J.J. Scheuchzer. Switzerl.
RUSSIA, Coast survey of Peter the Great
J. Chr. Müller Bohemia 1720
Kirilov, Atlas of Russia '34
de Marsigli. The Danube 31 sh. '41
Russian Acad. Atl. 19 sh. '45
Lewis Evans, Middle British Colonies. Philadelph. '55
TYROL, Anich + Huber '60 ~ (Bauernkarte) 1:104000
Kanter, Poland. '70. Königsbg
de Lacy, Hungary.
BELGIUM, de Ferraris' '71–'77 275 sh. 1:11520 (triangulated)
DENMARK, Acad. survey
SWITZERL. J.H. Weiss '76–'18
Schimeck, Turkish War Atl. '78
La Perouse, North Pacific '850
NETHERLANDS, Krayenhoff '02–'14
SWEDEN, Hermelin '97–'18
TURKEY in Arabic, 22 sh.
EGYPT, 55 sh. Napoleon
HUNGARY, Görög 4"/m '96–'04
· de Lipszky 12 sh. '06
Takahashi Inō. Japan, surveys
GREECE 10"/m Fr. Müller. Vienna
John Melish, U.S.A
RUSSIA 1:420,000 22 sh. '21–'39
H.S. TANNER in Philadelphia
A de KRUSENSTERN Atlas of the Pacific O. Petersburg '27
SWEDEN, 1:500000. altitude tints
Sam. Aug. Mitchell, U.S.A.
GREECE, 1:200000. 20 sh. '52–'80
SWITZERL'D: DUFOUR map oblique hachuring '42–'65
RUSSIA, 1:126000, 845 sh. '57–
CAUCASIA, 1:210000, –'63–'85
HOLLAND, 1:25000, 776 sh. '66
BELGIUM, 1:20000, 527 sh.
NORWAY, 1:100000, 331 sh. '69–
BALKANS, 1:200000, 36 (Russian) 1:200000 (Austrian)
SWEDEN, 1:100000, 234 sh.
JAPAN. 1:100000 '87 on
CHINA
Kordt, Facsimile Atlas of Russia. 1890–1931.
FINLAND, Atlas '99 + 1911
1:1000000, '03 on
Kümmerly + Frey, Berne

NATIONAL ATLASES
CANADA Atlas '06 + '15
SIBERIA '14
NORWAY '22
EGYPT '28
CZECHOSLOVAKIA '28

(Timeline: 1700, 10, 20, 30, 40, 50, 60, 70, 80, 90, 1800, 10, 20, 30, 40, 50, 60, 70, 80, 90, 1900, 10, 20, 30)

DE EUROPE – Beirich '96 – Hauchecorne 1900 – Beyshlag '04 – 1913
Konrad Miller, studies of early maps
Max Eckert, projections
– proposed by A. Penck in 1891 – Committee. London 1909. – about 300 sheets (20%) published in 1935

Geogr. Section of General Staff maps of Balkans, Near East, Sudan Asia 1:4000000 Africa 1:2000000 etc

Joseph Fisher S.J. studies of Ptolemy
F.C. Wieder Monumenta Cartogr. Leyden '25 on

Prepared by Erwin Raisz at the Inst. of Geogr. Exploration, Harvard University

of Modern Maps

organized their surveys. From 1750 on, country after country began detailed topographic surveys which, in most countries, are still under the auspices of the army.

by plane table. The cartographer's work begins where the surveyor left off. The collecting, selecting, and fine drawing of material, the fitting of it into a system of

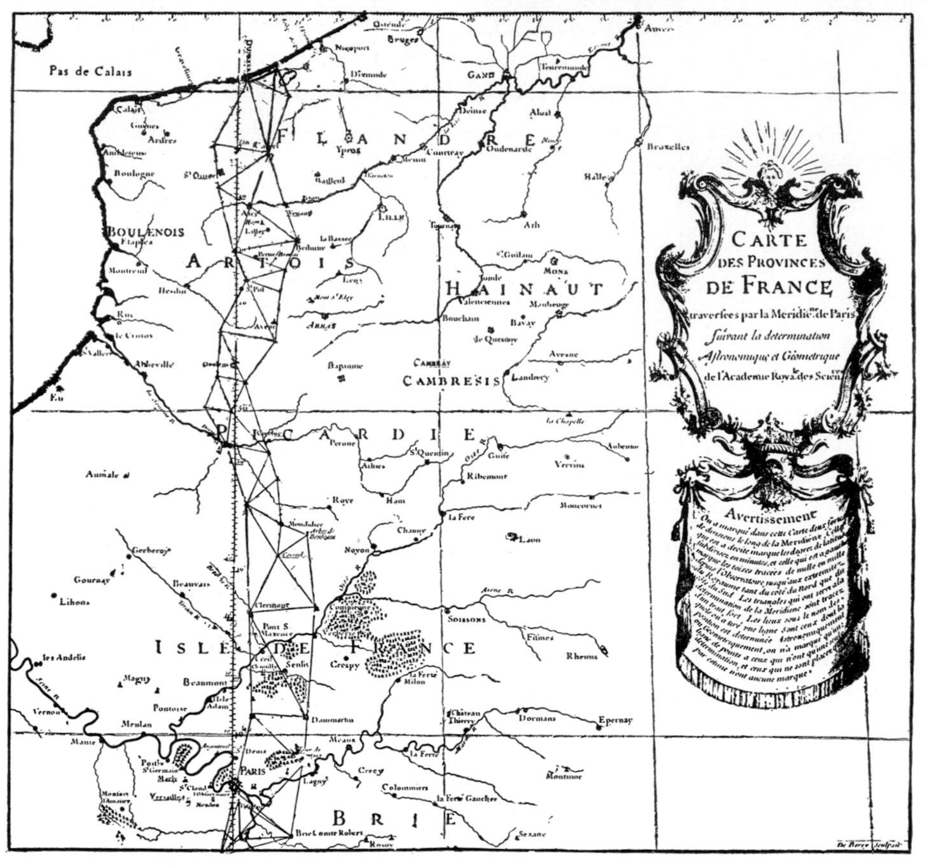


**Fig. 26** The first triangulation of France by Cassini, 1744.

A systematic survey consists of several steps. First, a number of points are astronomically determined. Then a base line is measured for triangulation. This is a straight line of 10 to 20 miles in length, from the two ends of which other points are obtained by intersection. Further points are similarly determined by a system of triangles. The advantage of this method is that angles can be easily read from a theodolite without the difficult and expensive measurement of distances. After enough points have been determined by triangulation, and their latitude and longitude have been calculated, the detail can be filled in projection, and the division of it into convenient sheets are the work of a central cartographic office.

**César François Cassini.** The first important national survey was made in France. The triangulation of France was organized by a commission of the Academy, headed by César François Cassini, Comte de Thury (1714–1784), the greatest member of a great family of astronomers and cartographers. The result of this triangulation is the map of France of 1744, showing 18 bases and more than 2,000 triangles, and supplemented by a table of latitudes and longitudes of the cities of France.

From a network of triangulation to a complete set of detailed topographic sheets is still a long step. It was in 1747 that Cassini accompanied Louis XV in his campaign to Flanders. Here Cassini laid before the King a new large-scale map of the region, which was based on triangulation and prepared by the army engineers. The King was so much impressed by this work that he declared that the whole of France should be similarly mapped, and Cassini was ordered to proceed with this work.

Difficulties, however, soon arose. In 1756, soon after the first sheets were published, Cassini was ordered to stop the work because of state bankruptcy. Cassini did not give up. By subscription and by the sacrifice of his personal fortune, he continued the work. The plan was a success, but Cassini did not live to see the series completed. The work was continued by his son, Jaques Dominique, and was finished during the French Revolution.

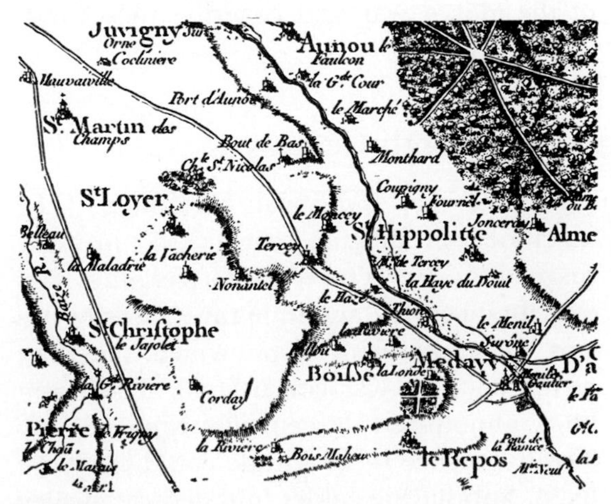


Fig. 27 Part of the "Carte Géometrique de la France," 1:86,400.

The "Carte Géometrique de la France" is composed of 182 sheets on the scale of 1:86,400. It shows remarkable detail but is deficient in showing mountains. A method of hachuring was adopted that is transitional between the pictorial representation of earlier times and exact systematic hachuring. The hachures usually show nothing other than troughlike valleys incised in flat uplands. This method was well adapted to the tableland of northern France but failed conspicuously in the Alps.

**Napoleon.** Like all great military leaders, Napoleon was an ardent supporter of surveys and mapping. During the Italian campaign he commissioned Bacler d'Albe to prepare a map of Italy in 1:256,000—one of the outstanding maps of the age. Napoleon started also a number of important surveys in Germany, Greece, and Egypt. His defeat prevented him from finishing his great project, a 1:100,000 map of Europe. Much of this work was already in manuscript when it fell into the hands of the Cossacks at Berezina.

**The Ordnance Survey.** The national survey of Great Britain was begun by the stimulus of France. Cassini pointed out that if the London and Paris observatories were to be connected by triangulation, not only could their exact position be determined but also the size of a degree could be more accurately measured. This was agreed to by England, and the triangulation was accomplished (1784–1787) by General Roy. In 1791 the Ordance Survey of Great Britain was instituted, and the first sheet in 1:63,360, or 1 inch to a mile, was published in 1801. It was several decades before the entire island was surveyed. In the middle of the century a new survey was begun on the scale of 6 inches to a mile, and maps of this very large scale proved to be useful for geologic and geographic work. Several editions of the Ordnance Survey sheet have been published since, and the latest, or sixth, edition is one of the best topographic maps of the present.

**Other National Surveys.** The Survey of Spain was organized under Tomas López de Vargas in the eighteenth century. The

Austrian 1:28,000 series was begun in 1806; from it the famous "Spezialkarte" (1:75,-000) was printed later, which was regarded as the most minutely detailed map of Europe. The surveys of the several German provinces were well under way in the first decades of the century. These were united into the 1:100,000 "Reichskarte" after the empire was unified.

The topographical survey of Switzerland was organized by Dufour in 1832. These maps have hachuring with brilliant oblique shadowing, well adapted to that mountainous country. The modern surveys of various countries are described in detail in Chap. 13.

**International Maps.** The nineteenth century created and satisfied the demand for national maps. The twentieth century created the desire for an international map of the world. Airplane, radio, cheap travel, and international commerce all carried problems across national boundaries, and consequently an international map of the world on a 1:1,000,000 scale was begun. The plan of this work was proposed by Prof. Albrecht Penck at the International Geographical Congress in Berne in 1891, but only the London Congress of 1909 worked out the specifications, which were supplemented in Paris in 1913. When completed, the map will consist of about 1,500 sheets, most of which cover 4° of latitude and 6° of longitude, in a modified conic projection. The plan was accepted with great enthusiasm, but the First World War and the subsequent impoverishment of Europe paralyzed the work, so that only about 400 sheets were published before the Second World War, those being principally of Europe, the Near East, India, and Africa. The Latin American sheets were completed by the American Geographical Society. Only four sheets of the United States were published in this series. The entire set was superseded by the 1:1,000,000 maps of the Army Map Service and the U.S. Coast and Geodetic Survey, prepared under the stress of the global war and covering most lands of the world.

## Private Cartography in the Nineteenth Century

The nineteenth century saw the expansion of Western civilization over all the world, so that at the end of the century, with the exception of Japan, China, and a few small states, all countries of the world were under the direct or indirect rule of Europeans or the descendants of Europeans. Colonization, which in previous centuries had confined itself to the seacoast, now penetrated into the interiors.

A map of the world of 1800 shows correct coast lines but great blank spaces in the interior of the continents. In 1900 there was hardly a spot on the Earth where the major features of topography were not known.

The nineteenth century was also the period of the industrial revolution. The machine age affected cartography in more than one way. A network of railways was exactly surveyed, and in many countries this was the framework upon which the map of the country was constructed. Telegraph lines announced Greenwich time in any locality; hence its longitude could easily be fixed. Submarine cables initiated the survey of the ocean bottoms, which was further advanced in the twentieth century by sonic depth sounding.

The development of lithography, wax engraving, photoengraving, and color printing profoundly affected cartography. Rich and colorful symbols replaced the black-and-white technique of older maps; and yet maps became cheaper and more abundant than ever before.

In the nineteenth and twentieth centuries great advances were made in science and education. Geological maps appeared in the beginning of the nineteenth century, and at present geological mapping keeps pace with topographical mapping—sometimes is even ahead of it. There are atlases of meteorology, oceanography, biology, ethnography, and so forth. School maps and atlases are now standard equipment in education, and their manufacture keeps many establishments busy.

The geography of the eighteenth century was largely descriptive—a collection of promiscuous facts. The establishment of geography as an exact science gave a profound impetus to cartography. Alexander von Humboldt emphasized scientific travel and critical examination of causes and results—interrelation of men and environment. He was followed, along pedagogic lines, by Karl Ritter, who outlined the trend of school geography for almost a century. Ferdinand von Richthofen, the great Asiatic explorer, emphasized the geomorphic landscape. All these ideas were expressed in new and better maps.

The study of historical cartography was begun in France by the monumental works of Santarem, Lelewel, and Jomard, who were followed by Nordenskjöld, Konrad Miller, Joseph Fisher, Wieder, and many others. At present books and atlases of historical cartography fill many shelves of our major libraries. Monumental works of the historical cartography of special regions were collected and edited by Teleki (Japan) and Wagner (Pacific Coast) and were officially collected by Italy, Chile, Guatemala, and many others (see Appendix 4, Bibliography).

The commercial and economic-statistical field proved to be especially stimulating for cartography; and cartograms, diagrams, and distribution maps are common in books, periodicals, and newspapers.

In the nineteenth century Germany became the most prolific producer of maps and atlases. These maps were characterized by a great amount of exact detail. Topographic relief was shown by a simplified system of hachuring, and the maps were printed in many colors. A list of German map-publishing houses is shown in the time charts. The outstanding one is the Geographical Institute of Justus Perthes in Gotha, founded in 1788, which, since 1817, has published 12 editions of the Stieler Atlas.

Other nations, too, published excellent atlases. The French atlases of Vidal de la Blache and of Vivien de St.-Martin excelled in finesse the German products; and the great English atlases of Philip, Bartholomew, Stanford, and Johnston were also widely used.

At the end of the century a new type of *national atlas* came into fashion. These are large volumes containing all available information about a single nation; climate, soil, economics, health, and social conditions are shown in maps, cartograms, and diagrams. These atlases form the most valuable basis for geographic study of the individual nations. Finland, Sweden, Scotland, France, and Czechoslovakia produced outstanding atlases of this sort. The "Grand Soviet Atlas" of 1937 is remarkable; in the United States, the successive issues of the "American Atlas of Agriculture" belong to this type.

*Airplane Photography.* At the beginning of the twentieth century cartography received a new stimulus from the introduction of airplane photography. Hitherto the land had to be surveyed by establishing a trigonometric network and filling in the detail by plane table. This method is both laborious and expensive; and in less accessible areas, such as forests and swamps, it is very difficult. By the use of the airplane camera, the detail can be filled in at a fraction of the cost and time, and with greater accuracy. Contour lines are drawn with the help of intricate machinery and the use of stereoscopic pairs of pictures.

All modern surveys, including that of the U.S. Geological Survey, use airplane photographs to a greater and greater extent. Airplane photographs are especially useful in less explored regions where data cannot be obtained otherwise. Several vertical airplane photographs are often combined into "mosaics" and are used directly, in place of maps. To show sufficient detail, an airplane photograph cannot be much smaller than 1:20,000, which is a much larger scale than our usual topographic sheets. If a map on a smaller scale is desired, it must be drawn by hand from the pictures. The present map conventions are not designed to record the rich detail with which airplane photographs provide us, and our entire system of cartography has to undergo a thorough change in the future. These developments are so recent and so much in flux that it is better to discuss them in a separate chapter.

# CHAPTER 4: *American Cartography*

The map of America has been gradually perfected since the time of Columbus. The early charts of the Spanish, Italian, Dutch, French, and English navigators, and the maps of the explorers and army officers, however important, are American in their subjects only. Their maps were engraved and published in Europe. The maps of Blaeu, John Smith, Champlain, and Delisle were mentioned previously. They are not discussed here, but the student is referred to the excellent works of Justin Winsor[1] or the much simplified discussion of Fite and Freeman[2] or Paullin and Wright.[3]

**Colonial Cartography.** It is somewhat surprising how few colonial maps made in America have survived. The walls of colonial mansions were likely to be decorated with maps, but these came from London or Paris. Map making in America was regarded primarily as a task of the army and navy; civil maps rarely went beyond delineations of estates, city plans, and a few state maps.

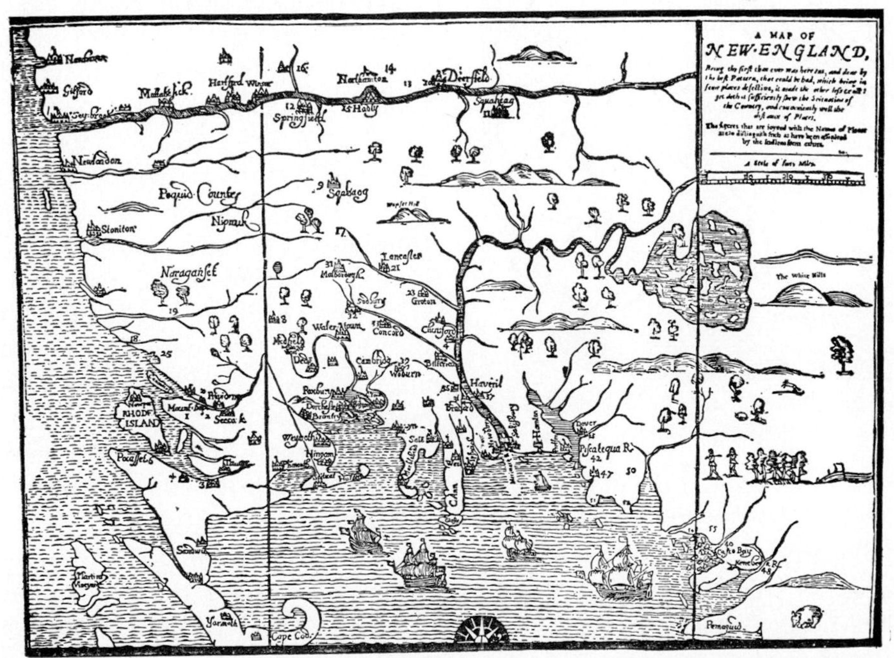


**Fig. 28** The first map drawn, engraved, printed, and published in the American Colonies. (*John Foster's woodcut, Boston,* 1677.)

The first map compiled, drawn, engraved, printed, and published in America seems to be one of New England made by John Foster, the first Boston printer, in 1677. It is a crude woodcut, drawn with charming simplicity, but even in its crudeness it must have represented, in its time, a brave attempt in the finer arts amidst the harsh life of the early colonists.

Among the first colonial maps the most famous is the Bonner-Price map of the city of Boston (1722), which, in its seven new

[1] Winsor, Justin, "Narrative and Critical History of America," 8 vols., Boston, 1884–1889.

[2] Fite, E. D., and A. Freeman, "The Book of Old Maps," Harvard University Press, Cambridge, 1926.

[3] Paullin, C. O., and T. K. Wright, "Atlas of the Historical Geography of the United States," 1932.

editions up to 1769, gives an unparalleled opportunity for studying the development of a colonial city.

**Fig. 29** Inset from Lewis Evans' map of the Middle British Colonies, Philadelphia, 1755.

*Lewis Evans.*[1] The highest development of colonial cartography was reached in the middle of the eighteenth century. The most important map of this period is the Evans map of "The Middle British Colonies 1755." Three great names are connected with this map. The author, Lewis Evans, compiled a map which is remarkable for its accuracy and wealth of information. In the accompanying "Analysis" he states his sources of compilation—maps, journals, and narratives of Indian traders. The map, he states, was prematurely issued because of the impending French war. Some of his statements in the "Analysis" involved him in a dispute with the governor of Pennsylvania, and Evans died in prison.

The map was cut in copper by James Turner, one of the greatest engravers of his time. In cartographic art the map is equal to the best works produced in Europe (see Fig. 29). Turner engraved several maps, and he is the author of a map of Nova Scotia, a supplement to the Evans map. The Evans map was printed by the press of Benjamin Franklin (this fact is not yet verified), whose contribution to cartography is a famous chart showing the Gulf Stream.

The influence of the Evans map was very great. Twenty-six subsequent editions, some of them piratical, were collected by the Library of Congress.

*John Mitchell.* Equal in importance to the Evans map is the contemporaneous map by John Mitchell of the "British and French Dominions in North America, 1755." This is a very large map with remarkable detail, and it was produced in London. This map was used by the Peace Conference of Paris in 1783, and on it were outlined the boundaries of the new republic. At least 18 editions were printed on the original scale prior to 1792 in England, France, Holland, and Italy.

*Army and Navy Surveys.* During the quarter century preceding the Revolution, intense surveying was done by the British army and navy.[2] Washington himself made many land surveys throughout his life. We should not imagine these army surveys to be very accurate. They had no framework of triangulation, and the instruments used were the chain, compass, plane table, and sometimes a diopter and a perambulator (odometer). A keen sense of distance and direction was the most important asset for these early surveyors in the densely wooded Appalachian Mountains. Most of these surveys remained in manuscript or were published

[1] GIPSON, LAWRENCE HENRY, "Lewis Evans," The Historical Society of Pennsylvania, Philadelphia, 1939. 246 pp.

[2] BROWN, RALPH H., The DeBrahm Charts of the Atlantic Ocean, 1772–1776, *Geog. Rev.*, Vol. 28, pp. 124–132, 1938.

in London, notably in Jeffery's atlases. These surveys laid the foundations of the future American maps, and many of the army surveyors later became leading figures in American cartography, as Thomas Hutchins, Simeon Dewitt, John Hill, and others.

*Pacific Coast.* At the time when outlines of the Atlantic Ocean were more or less correctly represented, the cartographer's imagination went wild in the delineation of the Pacific coast of North America. Even after the discovery of the Bering Strait in 1728 and of Alaska in 1741 the facts were misinterpreted to the extent shown in the Delisle-Buache map of 1752. Not until the end of the century, when the Spanish government made serious efforts to explore and settle California and the northwest coast, did this land receive its true outlines. The northern Pacific was the last of the world's habitable coast lines to be explored and occupied by the European nations.

**Emancipation of American Cartography.** With the establishment of the new republic began the slow emancipation of American cartography from European influence. Washington, himself a surveyor, and Jefferson, son of the author of the Fry-Jefferson map of Virginia, were both keenly interested in cartography. Thomas Jefferson's own map ("A Map of the Country between Albemarle Sound and Lake Erie, 1787"), although published in Europe, represents a major piece of American map compilation. Thomas Hutchins, the first and only "Geographer to the United States," organized the survey of the enormous tracts of public lands. He adopted the traditional 36-square mile township and section system, which still prevails over the greater part of the United States. The General Land Office became one of the most active mapping agencies of the government.

*State Surveys.* The most important mapping activities of this age were the organized state surveys. State after state appropriated a rather modest sum, ranging somewhere between $50,000 and $300,000, for the preparation of a state map, with scales varying from 2 to 8 miles per inch. None of these surveys was based on triangulation (up to 1830, Massachusetts), and the maps were based perhaps more on compilation than on instrumental surveys. These early state maps are listed in the Time Chart. The western states and territories were mapped by the General Land Office with remarkable speed, but less remarkable accuracy, under the pressure of the immediate demand for layouts and maps by the settlers.

The beginning of private cartography was very modest. John Fitch, the inventor of the steamboat, made a rough but significant map of the "Northwest United States," which he engraved himself. Abel Buell prepared a map of the United States (1789), which is said to be the first map of the United States drawn, engraved, printed, and published by its citizens. The first atlas made in the United States is a set of charts of the Atlantic coast, "The American Pilot," compiled and cut in copper by the noted engraver John Norman, and published in 1792.

*Atlases.* A few book publishers decided to add atlases to their line, the first being Matthew Carey in Philadelphia (1794). His atlas was republished almost every year, and from 1822 on, the work was continued by his son H. C. Carey (Carey & Lea). These early atlases were small in form and the plates for the maps of the foreign countries were imported or copied from European maps. More original were the state maps, which were chiefly the work of such excellent engravers and map compilators as Samuel Lewis, Benjamin Tanner, and Amos Doolittle. The clean-cut and very delicate lines and the selective use of decorative detail recall the charm and dignity of contemporary art and architecture.

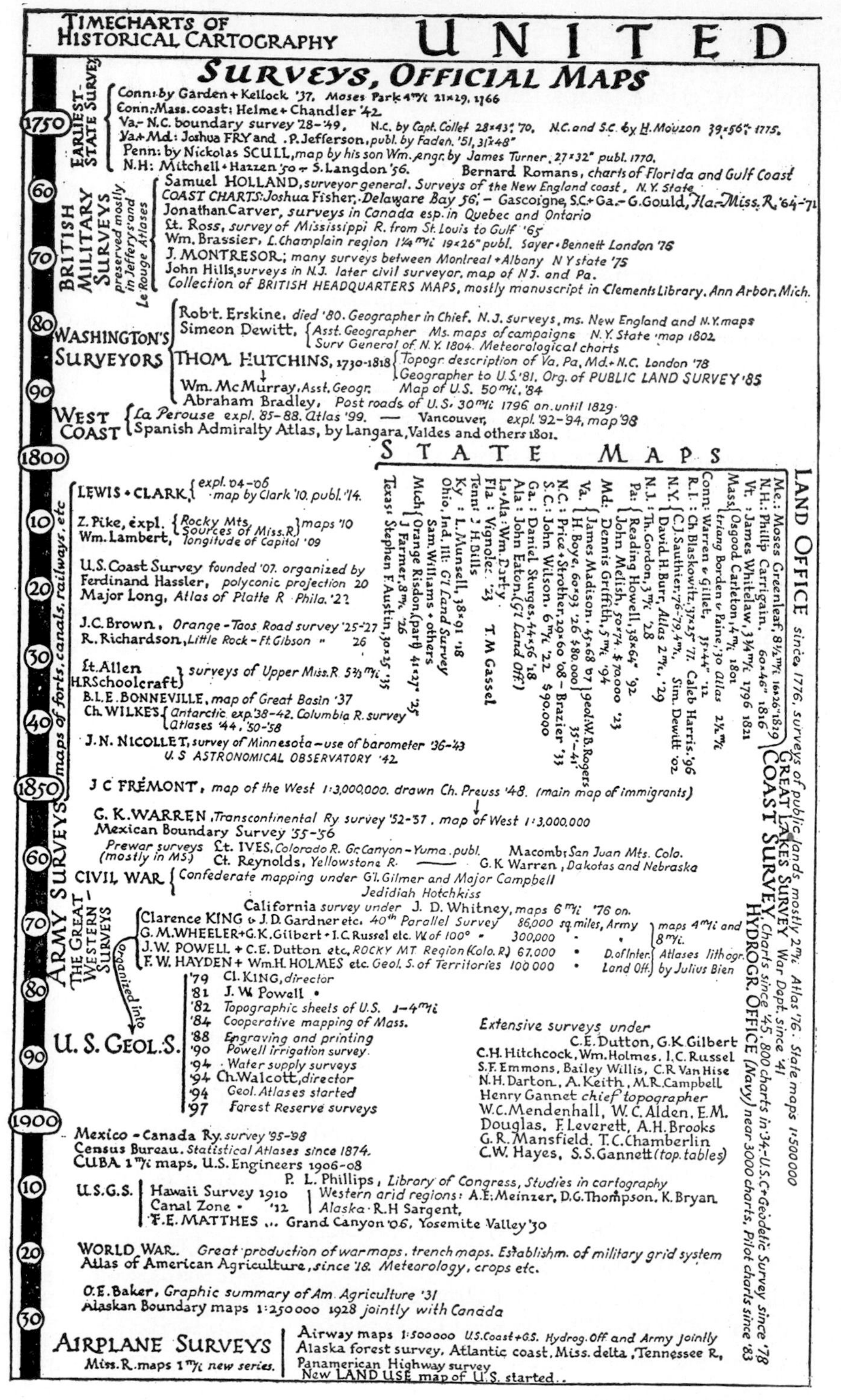


Table V Time Chart

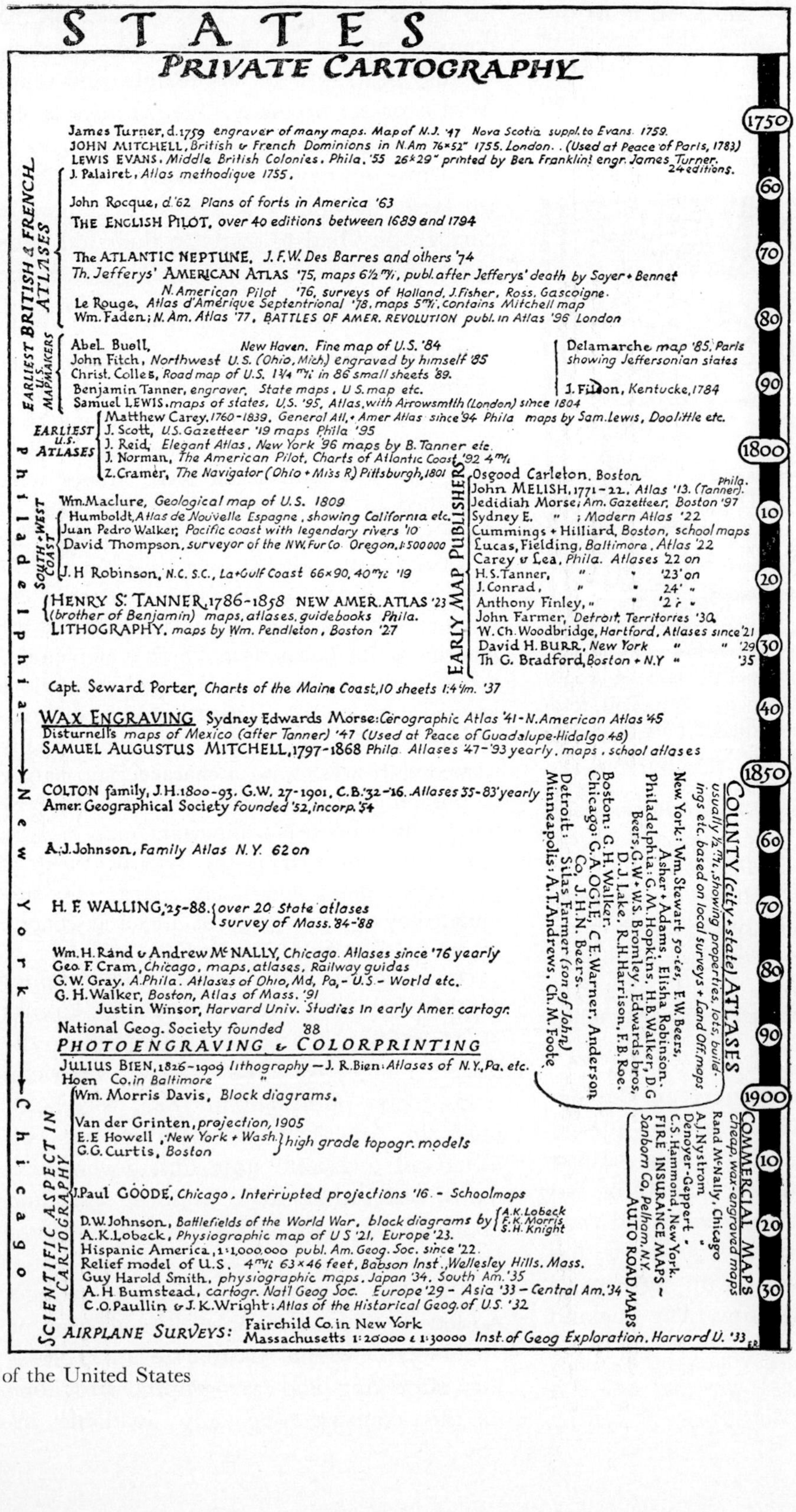

# STATES

## PRIVATE CARTOGRAPHY

1750

James Turner, d.1759 engraver of many maps. Map of N.J. '47 Nova Scotia suppl. to Evans 1759.
JOHN MITCHELL, British & French Dominions in N.Am 76×52" 1755. London. (Used at Peace of Paris, 1783)
LEWIS EVANS, Middle British Colonies. Phila. '55 26×29" printed by Ben. Franklin! engr. James Turner. 24 editions.

EARLIEST BRITISH & FRENCH ATLASES

J. Palairet, Atlas methodique 1755.

60

John Rocque, d.'62 Plans of forts in America '63
THE ENGLISH PILOT, over 40 editions between 1689 and 1794

70

The ATLANTIC NEPTUNE, J. F. W. Des Barres and others '74
Th. Jefferys' AMERICAN ATLAS '75, maps 6½ m/i, publ. after Jefferys' death by Sayer + Bennet
N. American Pilot '76, surveys of Holland, J. Fisher, Ross, Gascoigne.
Le Rouge, Atlas d'Amérique Septentrional '78, maps 5 m/i, contains Mitchell map
Wm. Faden; N. Am. Atlas '77, BATTLES OF AMER. REVOLUTION publ. in Atlas '96 London

80

EARLIEST U.S. MAPMAKERS

Abel Buell, New Haven. Fine map of U.S. '84
John Fitch, Northwest U.S. (Ohio, Mich.) engraved by himself '85
Christ. Colles, Road map of U.S. 1¼ m/i in 86 small sheets '89.
Benjamin Tanner, engraver, State maps, U.S. map etc.
Samuel LEWIS, maps of states, U.S. '95, Atlas, with Arrowsmith (London) since 1804

Delamarche map '85, Paris showing Jeffersonian states
J. Filson, Kentucke, 1784

90

EARLIEST U.S. ATLASES

Matthew Carey, 1760-1839, General Atl. + Amer Atlas since '94 Phila maps by Sam. Lewis, Doolittle etc.
J. Scott, U.S. Gazetteer '19 maps Phila '95
J. Reid, Elegant Atlas, New York '96 maps by B. Tanner etc.
J. Norman, The American Pilot, Charts of Atlantic Coast '92 4 m/i
Z. Cramer, The Navigator (Ohio + Miss R) Pittsburgh, 1801

1800

EARLY MAP PUBLISHERS

Osgood Carleton, Boston
John MELISH, 1771-22, Atlas '13. (Tanner) Phila.
Jedidiah Morse; Am. Gazetteer, Boston '97
Sydney E. " ; Modern Atlas '22
Cummings + Hilliard, Boston, school maps
Lucas, Fielding, Baltimore, Atlas '22
Carey & Lea, Phila. Atlases '22 on
H. S. Tanner, " " '23 on
J. Conrad, " " 24' "
Anthony Finley, " " '2? "
John Farmer, Detroit Territories '30
W. Ch. Woodbridge, Hartford, Atlases since '21
David H. BURR, New York " " '29
Th. G. Bradford, Boston + N.Y " '35

Wm. Maclure, Geological map of U.S. 1809

10

SOUTH + WEST COAST

Humboldt, Atlas de Nouvelle Espagne, showing California etc.
Juan Pedro Walker; Pacific coast with legendary rivers '10
David Thompson, surveyor of the NW. Fur Co. Oregon, 1:500000
J. H. Robinson, N.C. S.C., La+Gulf Coast 66×90, 40 m/i '19

20

HENRY S. TANNER, 1786-1858 NEW AMER. ATLAS '23
(brother of Benjamin) maps, atlases, guidebooks Phila.
LITHOGRAPHY, maps by Wm. Pendleton, Boston '27

30

Capt. Seward Porter, Charts of the Maine Coast, 10 sheets 1:4 m/i. '37

40

WAX ENGRAVING Sydney Edwards Morse: Cerographic Atlas '41 - N. American Atlas '45
Disturnell's maps of Mexico (after Tanner) '47 (Used at Peace of Guadalupe-Hidalgo 48)
SAMUEL AUGUSTUS MITCHELL, 1797-1868 Phila. Atlases '47-'93 yearly, maps, school atlases

1850

COLTON family, J.H. 1800-93, G.W. 27-1901, C.B. '32-'16. Atlases 35-83' yearly
Amer. Geographical Society founded '52, incorp. '54

60

A. J. Johnson, Family Atlas N.Y. 62 on

H. F. WALLING, '25-88. { over 20 State atlases
survey of Mass. '84-'88

70

COUNTY (city + state) ATLASES
usually ½ m/i, showing properties, lots, buildings etc. based on local surveys + Land Off. maps
New York: Wm. Stewart 50-ies, F. W. Beers,
Asher + Adams, Elisha Robinson.
Philadelphia: G. M. Hopkins, H. B. Walker, D. G. Beers, G. W. + W. S. Bromley, Edwards bros,
D. J. Lake, R. H. Harrison, F. B. Roe.
Boston: G. H. Walker
Chicago: G. A. OGLE, C. E. Warner, Anderson Co., J. H. N. Beers.
Detroit: Silas Farmer (son of John)
Minneapolis: A. T. Andrews, Ch. M. Foote

Wm. H. Rand & Andrew McNALLY, Chicago. Atlases since '76 yearly
Geo. F. Cram, Chicago, maps, atlases, Railway guides
G. W. Gray, A. Phila. Atlases of Ohio, Md, Pa, - U.S. - World etc.
G. H. Walker, Boston, Atlas of Mass. '91
Justin Winsor, Harvard Univ. Studies in early Amer. cartogr.

80

National Geog. Society founded '88

90

PHOTOENGRAVING & COLORPRINTING
JULIUS BIEN, 1826-1909 lithography - J. R. Bien: Atlases of N.Y., Pa. etc.
Hoen Co. in Baltimore "

1900

SCIENTIFIC ASPECT IN CARTOGRAPHY

Wm. Morris Davis, Block diagrams.
Van der Grinten, projection, 1905
E. E. Howell, New York + Wash. } high grade topogr. models
G. G. Curtis, Boston

10

J. Paul GOODE, Chicago, Interrupted projections '16. - Schoolmaps

COMMERCIAL MAPS
Cheap, wax-engraved maps
Rand McNally, Chicago
A. J. Nystrom
Denoyer-Geppert
C. S. Hammond, New York.
FIRE INSURANCE MAPS -
Sanborn Co, Pelham, N.Y.
AUTO ROAD MAPS

D. W. Johnson, Battlefields of the World War, block diagrams by { A. K. Lobeck, F. K. Morris, S. H. Knight
A. K. Lobeck, Physiographic map of U.S. '21, Europe '23.

20

Hispanic America, 1:1,000,000 publ. Am. Geog. Soc. since '22.
Relief model of U.S. 4 m/i 63×46 feet, Babson Inst., Wellesley Hills, Mass.
Guy Harold Smith, physiographic maps, Japan '34, South Am. '35
A. H. Bumstead, cartogr. Nat'l Geog Soc. Europe '29 - Asia '33 - Central Am. '34
C. O. Paullin & J. K. Wright: Atlas of the Historical Geog. of U.S. '32

30

AIRPLANE SURVEYS: Fairchild Co. in New York
Massachusetts 1:20000 & 1:30000 Inst. of Geog Exploration, Harvard U. '33

Philadelphia → New York → Chicago

of the United States

It soon became evident that these American atlases could compete with the European products, and the field was open for lucrative business. John Melish employed more than 30 map makers in his office in Philadelphia in 1810, among them the Tanner brothers.

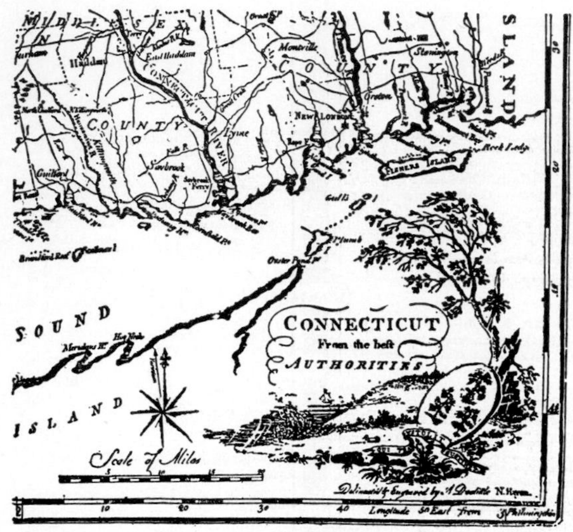


**Fig. 30** The American maps of the late eighteenth century excel in fine engraving. Fragment from Matthew Carey's "American Atlas," 1794. The map was engraved by A. Doolittle of New Haven.

Many geography books and school atlases were published at this time. Especially famous was the geography of Jedidiah Morse, a minister of Charlestown, Mass., which was accompanied by an atlas by Arrowsmith and Samuel Lewis. Boston remained for a long time the publishing center for school atlases. James Wilson of Vermont is credited with being America's first globe maker.[1]

**The Golden Age of American Cartography** (1820–1840). In the second quarter of the last century the young nation emancipated itself, not only politically, but spiritually also, from the Old World, and the westward expansion was in its full swing. Enterprising spirit ran high in all fields, and so in cartography. The demand for maps was great. The frontier of the country advanced year by year; roads, canals, and railroads were built, and maps were a prime necessity. The surveys of the General Land Office, of the states, and of the army and navy were hardly able to keep up with the rapid changes, and private cartography had to come to their aid. The maps and atlases of this period represent the best in the history of American cartography.

Philadelphia remained the cartographic center during this age, but New York, Boston, Baltimore, and Hartford were important producers of maps, too. During the 2 years from 1822 to 1824, not less than seven large atlases were published in the United States, and some of them were republished every few years. The maps and atlases of that time represent a great refinement in the art of copper and steel engraving. The lines are incredibly delicate, the lettering is tiny but perfect. There is no pictorial detail inside the map; pictures and decorations are concentrated into vignettes around the map or within the little cartouche. The title is usually framed with swash lines, a characteristic feature of this period. Mountains are represented by fine hachure lines. No important map or atlas was published without an extensive text of geographic data, and many maps were surrounded by quaint pictures of cities and scenery.

*H. S. Tanner*. The foremost cartographer of this age was Henry Schenck Tanner (1786–1858), brother of Benjamin, the famous engraver. His "New American Atlas," first published in 1823, is a landmark in American cartography. He collected all available state and government maps, reduced them to uniform scale and form, added much of his own wide experience, and produced a work that was equal to the best European atlases of his age. Added to this atlas are his geographic "Memoirs," which summarize all exploratory, surveying, and cartographic work done in this country—our only available in-

[1] KIMBALL, L. E., James Wilson of Vermont, America's First Globe Maker, *Proc. Am. Antiquarian Soc.*, Vol. 48, pp. 29–48, 1938.

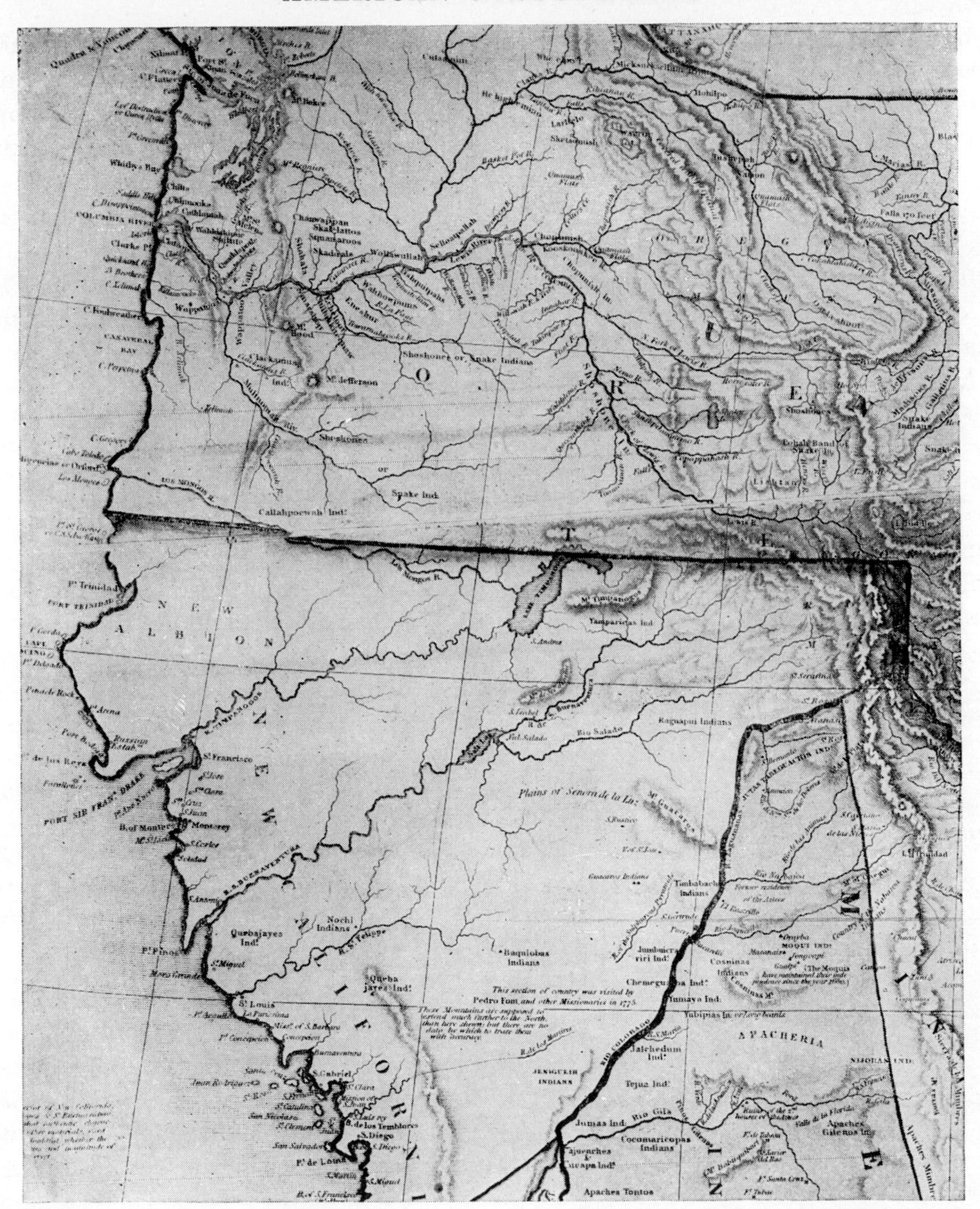


**Fig. 31** Legendary rivers of the West, from Henry S. Tanner's "New American Atlas," 1823. In the lower left is a note recording their doubtful validity.

formation of this sort. Henry was later joined by Benjamin, and the Tanner office in Philadelphia became one of the busiest producers of maps, atlases, and guidebooks.

*Explorations.* The most notable army explorations of this period were those of Allen, Schoolcraft, and later of Nicollet in the Upper Mississippi region. Bonneville from 1832 to 1835 mapped the Great Basin, the topography of which was remarkably misunderstood at that time. Juan Pedro Walker produced a map in 1810 in which he placed three enormous rivers arising from the Colorado Rockies and reaching the Pacific coast at various places in California. Lewis and Clark have shown in their map an overlengthened Willamette River (called Multonomah River) rising also in the present Colorado. These rivers were accepted by Tanner and put on his maps, with a remark, however, as to their doubtful validity. Other map makers copied these rivers, but the note as to their uncertainty was often left out, and the four legendary rivers of the West did not disappear from the maps until 1838.

**Lithography and Wax Engraving** (1804–1860). In the middle of the last century the invention of new methods of reproduction changed the entire aspect of cartography. Lithography was invented in 1798 in Germany, where it became the general method of map reproduction. In the United States it was first used for maps

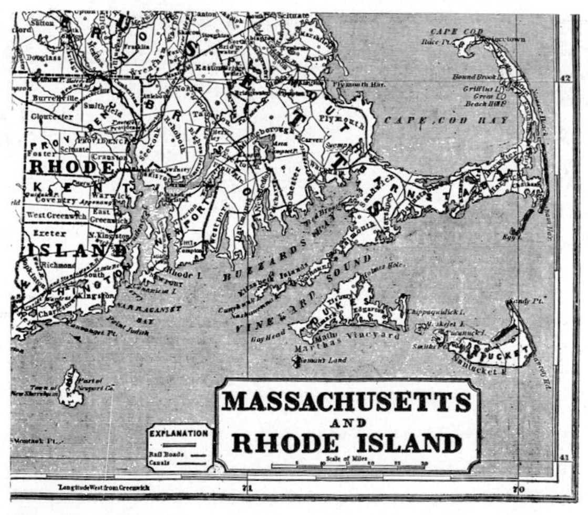


**Fig. 32** The first atlas reproduced by wax engraving already shows a tendency to overlettering and mechanical appearance. (*Part of S. E. Morse's "Cerographic Atlas,"* 1841.)

probably by William Pendleton in Boston in 1827. The principle of lithography is that the map is drawn reversed as in a mirror, with a greasy ink upon lithographic stone. The stone has the quality of taking either ink or water, and if the stone is rolled over with printing ink, the ink will adhere only to the lines. The advantage of this method is that it does away with the laborious engraving into copper and also that the map can be printed on ordinary cheap paper. The lines are delicate enough, but not so clean-cut as on the copper-engraved maps. Lithography became a popular method of reproducing maps in the middle of the century.

Wax engraving was invented by Sidney Edwards Morse, son of Jedidiah Morse and brother of Samuel Finley B. Morse, the painter and inventor. He worked out the system of wax engraving together with Henry H. Munson, and his first "Cerographic Atlas" was published in 1841. In wax engraving the map is engraved into a thin sheet of wax, which is spread over a polished plate. The wax with the grooves in it is then electroplated. After the removal of the wax the electroplate is strengthened and mounted. Printing is done directly from the electroplate, which will print from raised lines, as ordinary type does. The chief advantage, however, is that the lettering can be set up in type and pressed into the wax. Mechanical tints can also be easily applied by combing the wax surface. Wax engraving became the universal American method of map reproduction, and the overlettered and mechanical-looking maps still are characteristic of American commercial cartography. Morse's style imprinted itself so deeply that the map of Fig. 32 could be published today, 100 years later, without most people realizing its age.

The outstanding cartographer of this period was Samuel Augustus Mitchell (1797–1868) in Philadelphia. He was a disciple of the Tanners and took over the Tanner establishment in the middle of the century. The "Mitchell Atlas," published yearly from 1847 to 1893, was a characteristic product of American culture of the Victorian period.

The most prolific producer of maps at this time was the Colton family in New York. The "Colton Atlas" was published yearly from

1855 to 1883, with an excellent and extensive geographical text. Characteristic of the Colton maps is a very ornamental border consisting of interlacing vines. The Colton establishment printed, besides a variety of maps, gazetteers, and atlases of the United States, many South American maps, too, in competition with the cartographic establishments of Paris.

Among the governmental offices, the army was the most important producer of maps. The most important army survey was that of Fremont, whose excellent map of the new West (1848) was drawn by Charles Preuss, and appeared just in time for the California gold rush.

**County Atlases** (1860–1900). With the spreading of lithography, the most specially American cartographic products, the county atlases, began their development. They were probably first made by William Stewart in New York in the 1850's, and were imitated by most map makers of Philadelphia, New York, and later of Chicago, and in the 1870's and 1880's attained the significance of a national industry. They were still published at the beginning of the twentieth century, but at that time, with the growing industrialization and urbanization of the country, they lost their significance.

The typical county atlas remained very much the same during the half century of its history. It shows detailed township and property maps, generally 2 inches to the mile, based upon the Land Office surveys, and contains also much original material collected by the agents of the publishing company. Besides the maps there is extensive text material, profusely illustrated with pictures of farms and factories in the quaint style of old lithographs. They were generally sold by subscription, and of course every farmer was glad to part with $10 or $20 if he knew that a picture of his farm or of himself would win him county-wide distinction, even if this distinction would be shared with many others. Although these county atlases were made purely from a business point of view, they contain much original material and form a valuable aid in historical research. In the 1890's, when photoengraving came into fashion, the quaint lithographs were replaced by half-tone copies of photographs, and thus the artistic touch of the earlier drawings was lost. The largest publisher of county maps was G. A. Ogle in Chicago, who has more than 700 county atlases to his credit.

**Fig. 33** The county atlases of last century are typical American products. They are composed of maps, text, and quaint pictures in half-tone lithography.

The most important cartographer of this age was Henry F. Walling (1825–1888), professor of engineering in Lafayette College, who prepared over 20 state atlases with extensive texts. His maps and atlases have the distinction of thorough research, an enormous amount of detail, and perhaps a little more artistic appearance than the generally rather drab maps of this period.

**The Age of the Great Surveys** (1870–1900). In the middle of the nineteenth century the United States acquired enormous tracts of land west of the Rocky Mountains. To survey these territories, the U.S. Army sent out party after party. These did notable work in spite of the hardships and danger from Indian attacks. The early surveys of G. K. Warren, Lieutenant Ives, and Captain Reynolds were interrupted by the Civil War. The Civil War itself disclosed how inadequately the country was surveyed, and after the war was over, surveying activity was renewed with fresh vigor. The four great western surveys known as the King, Wheeler, Powell, and Hayden surveys covered hundreds of thousands of square miles, but it was soon found that these individual efforts resulted in so much duplication that a nationally organized survey was necessary. In 1878 there came into existence the U.S. Geological Survey, the chief mapping agency of the United States today.

From the cartographic point of view, the atlases of the early surveys are remarkable achievements. The field parties were accompanied by first-class artists, among them William H. Holmes, whose set of views of the Grand Canyon is a classic of topographic art. Most of these atlases were engraved by Julius Bien, New York. He represented relief by plastic shading, which was made possible by the perfection of half-tone lithography. Parallel with the exploratory surveys an extensive network of triangulation was started after the Civil War. The great transcontinental arc of triangles from the Atlantic to the Pacific was accomplished by the Coast Survey, henceforth called the U.S. Coast and Geodetic Survey.

It would be hard to name the foremost cartographers of the age of the great surveys. The production of maps became an extremely involved process, requiring the cooperation of so many men that the individual can hardly be distinguished.

**Modern Maps** (1900– ). The modern age in American cartography is characterized by a more scientific trend, and by the enormously widespread application of maps, not only in the scientific field, but also in the everyday life of people. This was made possible largely by the introduction of photoengraving. By this method the map is drawn on paper on an enlarged scale and photographic reduction will produce a fine-looking map. The importance of this is perhaps greater than it seems at first glance. Maps can now be made by geographers and not necessarily by highly skilled engravers. The resulting maps may be less perfect technically, but they will more informally express geographic ideas. Photoengraved maps can be printed together with text. Not only are all our textbooks generously endowed with maps but even newspapers use maps nowadays to illustrate daily events. The perfection of color printing enables cartographers to represent the most complex geographic concepts. Modern geological and soil maps, the maps used in economics, meteorology, and other sciences, often require a dozen successive printings and the use of mechanical tints.

The American Geographical Society was founded in 1852, and since that time it has produced maps of high excellence in its publications. Its outstanding piece of work is the 1:1,000,000 series of Hispanic America, a part of the "International Map of the World," the greatest cartographic undertaking of modern times. The National Geographic Society in Washington is also a prolific producer of maps, which reflect the genius of the late A. H. Bumstead, who had a special ability to give the greatest amount of information with the minimum of overcrowding.

There is a closer connection between geology and cartography in the United States than elsewhere, perhaps owing to the organization of the U.S. Geological Survey, where many cartographers received their training. A result of this connection is a specially American product, the physiographic, or landform, map. In this method, instead of emphasizing the altitude of the land, its geomorphologic aspect is delineated, giving on small-scale maps a better representation of the geographic landscape than the other methods. This method originated with W. M. Davis, and was further perfected by A. K. Lobeck, and is now recognized overseas.

Notable work has been done during this period in topographic models. E. E. Howell was a distinguished producer of numerous excellent models, always emphasizing the geological structure of the land. Equally excellent is the work of G. C. Curtis of Wiscasset, Maine, whose models of the Boston region and of the Kilauea in Hawaii are now the prize exhibits of the University Museum at Harvard. He started the huge relief model of the United States at the Babson Institute, Wellesley Hills, Mass., which shows the United States 63 by 46 feet in size on a scale of 4 miles to the inch.

How deeply cartography has entered the life of the great masses is shown by the present automobile road map. The making of these maps, given away freely by any filling station and printed in millions of copies, has assumed the scope of a national industry. They are much derided, yet the amount and exactness of their information and their practical delineation can best be appreciated by those who have used similar products in Europe, bought at an excessive price.

Airplane photography and the global war introduced a new epoch in American cartography, which will be discussed in a separate chapter.

# CHAPTER 5: *Scales, Parallels, and Meridians*

We defined a map as a conventionalized picture of the earth's surface pattern. Every picture is in a definite proportional relationship to the object represented. This proportion is its scale. An ordinary picture is usually not very much smaller or larger than its object, and thus the scale is obvious. A map, however, is many thousand or million times smaller than the corresponding part of the earth's surface; the relationship is beyond recognition, and therefore the scale must be stated on the map.

It is indeed most important for a cartographer to realize through actual experience the scale of maps, and modern airway travel makes this possible. To look down upon Cape Cod, for instance, from the height of 10,000 feet makes one realize the breath-taking reality of the little hook on the map. A cartographer should use every opportunity for air travel. Thus he will learn the real relationship between map and land, and his maps will be more than mere location diagrams. Indeed the greatest experience of some future cartographer will be to look down upon the whole earth from a rocketship a thousand miles up.

**Expression of Scale.** Scale is usually represented on maps in one of three different ways:

1. *Numerical scale,* called also "representative fraction," which gives the proportion between the length of a line on the map and the corresponding length on the earth's surface in the form of a fraction, as

$$\text{Scale } \frac{1}{250{,}000} \quad \text{or} \quad 1:250{,}000$$

2. *Inch-to-mile scale,* which indicates that an inch on the map corresponds to a certain number of miles on the land. Such scale is usually used on topographic sheets, as

Scale: 1 inch to 4 miles
(Not 1 inch = 4 miles)

3. *Graphic scale,* or rod scale, which records the mileage on a graduated line. This scale has the great advantage of remaining true after the map has been reproduced by photographic processes

Scale 0 500 Miles

Scale 0 1 2 3 4 5 Miles

On some maps we find an extension of the scale to the left divided into tenths, which enables us to measure distances more accurately. On small-scale maps the use of such extensions should be discouraged, for it gives the false impression that you can take any distance on the map and measure it exactly. We shall see, however, that no map can in every part or in every direction be true to scale. On *large-scale* maps (meaning large maps of a small area) this distortion of the scale is small, but on small-scale maps, such as those of countries and continents, the given scale may be quite wrong, especially in the corners of the map. The scale should always show a round number of miles. Subdivision of the scale rod is done by "proportionate dividing," as shown in Fig. 34.

We draw an auxiliary line $AC$ at an angle from $A$. We measure off on line $AC$ 10 known divisions, so that $A$-10 shall not be much longer or shorter than line $AB$. Then we draw line $B$-10; and parallels to this will divide line $AB$ evenly into 10 parts.

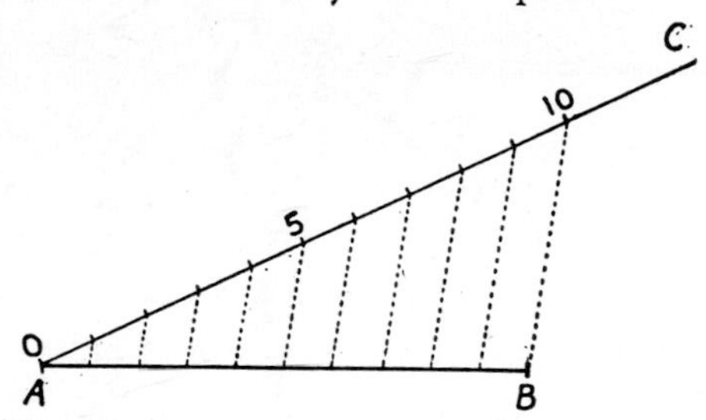


**Fig. 34** Line $AB$ is divided into 10 equal parts by proportionate parallels.

**Transformation of Scale Types.** A common problem in cartography occurs when one type of scale is given and must be transformed into another type. The solution of such a problem is always easy if we keep in mind that

$$\text{Scale} = \frac{\text{distance on map}}{\text{distance in nature}}$$

1 mile equals 63,360 inches

1. Given numerical scale, 1:250,000; find mile-to-inch scale and make a graphic scale.

*Solution:* Since an inch on the map corresponds to 250,000 inches in nature, and since 63,360 inches make 1 mile, 1 inch will correspond to 250,000:63,360, which equals 3.95 miles or, roughly, 4 miles. One mile on the map will be 1:3.95 = 0.254 inch, by which the graphic scale can be drawn.

2. Graphic scale is given:

Scale: 0 — 5 — 10 miles

*Solution:* One inch corresponds to 5.5 miles; this can be simply measured off with a ruler. The numerical scale will be

$$1:5.5 \times 63,360 \qquad \text{or} \qquad 1:348,480$$

3. Inch-to-mile scale is given, as, for example, 1 inch corresponds to 16 miles. Since 1 mile will be $\frac{1}{16}$ inch long, and 10 miles will be $\frac{5}{8}$ inch, the graphic scale can be easily drawn. The numerical scale will be

$$1:16 \times 63,360 \qquad \text{or} \qquad 1:1,013,760$$

In countries using the metric system, the most usual map scales are 1:50,000, 1:100,000, 1:200,000, etc. In the British Empire the scales 1:63,360, 1:126,720, 1:253,440, etc., are customary. In the United States a compromise between the British and the metric system has been adopted; the topographic sheets are on a scale of 1:62,500, 1:125,000, and 1:250,000. The use of the metric system simplifies most scale problems; on 1:100,000 maps 1 centimeter corresponds to 1 kilometer. It is desirable that both miles and kilometers should be indicated on graphic scales. One mile equals 1.6093 kilometers, and 1 kilometer equals 0.621 mile or, roughly, 5 miles equal 8 kilometers.

If a map has no scale, its scale can be found by considering that 1° of latitude equals on the average 69 miles. The measurements should be made in the center of the map or on a straight meridian, because on curved meridians the scale may be very different. For example, if we find that 1° of latitude is 2.3 inches long, the scale is

$$2.3:69 \times 63,360 \qquad \text{or} \qquad 1:1,900,800$$

A ready-made scale prepared by S. W. Boggs, geographer to the U.S. Department of State, is available for this purpose; by it both natural scale and inch-to-mile scale can be directly read.

**Changing the Scale of Maps.** One of the most common operations in cartography is to reduce or enlarge a map to change its scale. This is sometimes done photographically. For copying purposes a negative *photostat* will serve, and it can be obtained at low cost from special establishments. It must be kept in mind, however, that the photostatic process often distorts the map more in one direction than in another. Making a positive from the negative while reversing the grain of the photostat paper will help. Even so errors of 1 to 3 per cent are not uncommon, and for precise work film negatives are preferable.

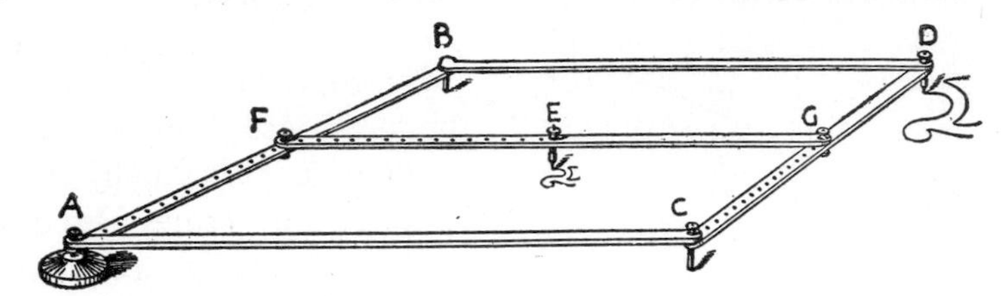


**Fig. 35a** Pantograph. (*Keuffel and Esser Company.*)

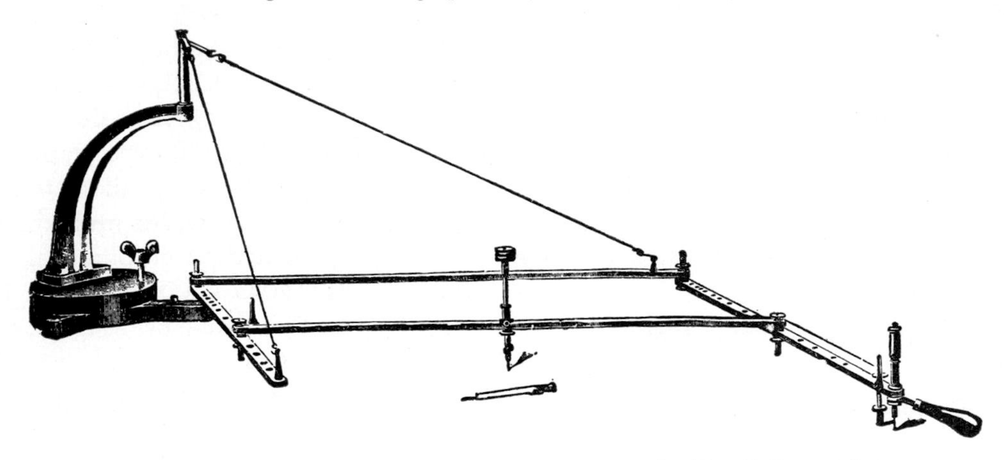

**Fig. 35b** Suspension pantograph for precise work. (*Coradi Company.*)

For changing the scale of simple maps, which must be done quickly, the *pantograph* is a useful instrument. It works on the principle of parallelograms; its parts and function are explained in Chap. 15. A *pantograph* is especially good for reduction; when used for enlargement, very exact handwork is necessary, because the slight irregular motions of the hand are also magnified.

If no photostats or pantographs are available, we may use the *square method.* On the map that is to be reduced or enlarged we draw a network of squares with lines about $\frac{1}{2}$ inch apart. This can also be done with celluloid overlay, having the lines scratched in. On the drawing paper we draw a similar graticule but with smaller or larger squares on the desired scale. All features are plotted by hand. This same method is used when we wish to transform a map from one projection to another, but in this case not squares but a network of parallels and meridians is used.

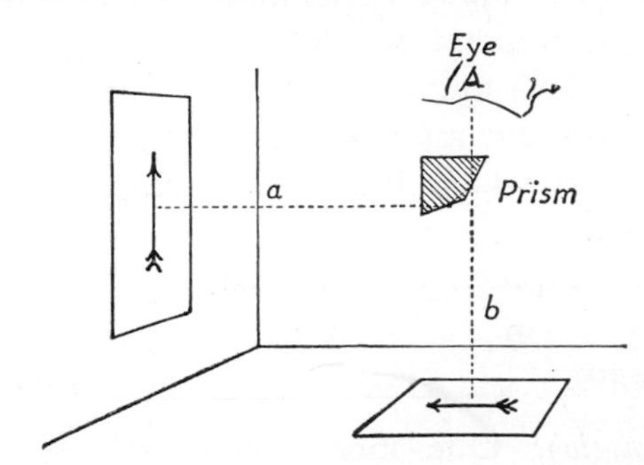


**Fig. 36** The principle of the camera lucida.

There are several modern instruments that, with *lenses*, *mirrors*, or *prisms*, reflect the image of the map directly on the drawing paper, and the scale can be changed by varying the distance between object and image. Such an instrument is very useful in cartographic establishments. The simplest instrument is the camera lucida, the principle of which can be understood from Fig. 36. The image produced by a camera lucida is likely to move if the eye is not kept exactly in the same position. This instrument can be used for rough magnification or for reduction of maps.

## Parallels and Meridians

The most fundamental principle of cartography is the establishment of a coordinate system on the earth to which each point can be related. The main reference directions are already given us; the conception of east, west, north, and south is one of the oldest of mankind. A network of evenly placed parallels and meridians was established by the ancient Greeks, and their system is still in use. How this coordinate system developed and how the words "latitude" and "longitude" came into use was traced in the first chapter.

**The Dimensions of the Earth.** We have already mentioned the measurements of the earth by Eratosthenes and later by Posidonius, and the consequences of these measurements. In the early Renaissance the size of the earth was underestimated, but, after Magellan's voyage disclosed the vastness of the Pacific Ocean, the figures for the size of the earth were gradually corrected. In France, by the use of the telescope, Picard arrived at a very close figure for the radius of the earth, 6,372 kilometers, which figure Newton used for the calculation of the force of gravity.

Up to this time the earth was regarded as a perfect sphere, but Newton, with his deep insight into the laws of nature, postulated that the form of the earth, as a resultant of two forces, gravitation and the centrifugal force of rotation, must be an ellipsoid, flattened at the poles. In 1743, the Peru-Bothnia expedition of the French Academy confirmed this assumption. Later some slight divergences from the true ellipsoid were found in the earth's shape, and the true dimensions of the "geoid" is a much-discussed question of higher geodesy. For practical cartographical purposes it is satisfactory to regard the earth as an ellipsoid, and on less exact maps only slight error is made if it is regarded as a sphere. It should be considered that on a large 30-inch globe the polar diameter would be only $\frac{1}{10}$ inch shorter than the equatorial diameter.

In recent years the dimensions of the earth have been determined with great accuracy, and the following figures are those of Hayford (1909):

Equatorial radius: 6,378.38 kilometers, or 3,963.34 miles

Polar radius: 6,356.90 kilometers, or 3,949.99 miles

Ellipticity: $\frac{a-b}{a} = \frac{1}{297}$

Equatorial circumference: 24,901.7 miles

Meridional circumference: 24,860 miles

Length of 1° longitude near the equator = 69 miles (Clarke spheroid)

Length of 1° latitude at equator = 68.7 miles

Length of 1° latitude at poles = 69.407 miles

Total area of earth (approx.): 196,950,000 square miles

Radius of the sphere of equal volume: 3,958.7 miles, 1° of latitude on which would be 69.2 miles

Radius of the sphere of equal area: 6371 meters, or 3956.4 miles

For conversion into or from the metric system, the following figures may serve for measurements in kilometers:

1 mile = 1.60934 kilometers
1 kilometer = 0.621 mile
1 meter = 39.37 inches = 3.2808 feet
1 foot = 0.3048 meter

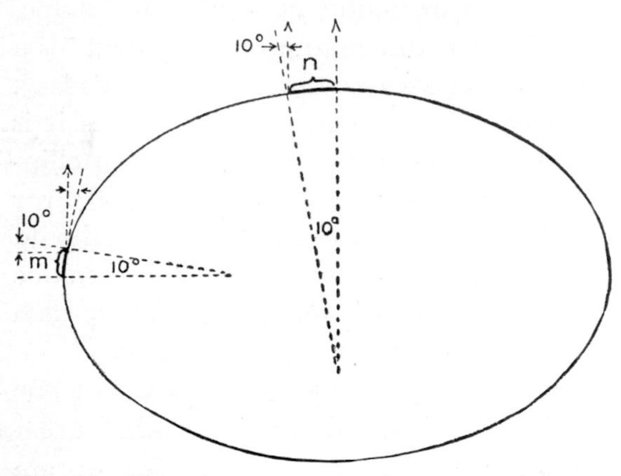


**Fig. 37** Near the equator it takes a shorter length of arc to effect 10° change in the altitude of the polar star than near the poles. This makes 1° of latitude shorter nearer the equator.

**The Parallel-meridian System.** The coordinate system of the earth is composed of two sets of coordinates with very different properties. The coordinate system is based on the rotation of the earth. The poles can be defined as points where the earth's axis of rotation pierces the earth's surface, but the surface in the case of the South Pole must be reduced to sea level. The equator is almost a perfect circle cut out from the earth's surface by a perpendicular plane which bisects the earth's axis.

**Parallels.** Between the equator and each of the poles are 90° parallels of latitude, which are small circles parallel to the equator. Each degree is subdivided into 60 minutes, and each minute into 60 seconds. The distance of arc between two parallels is roughly equal but not exactly so. Latitudes were determined by measuring the height of the polar star or of the sun over the horizon. If the earth were a perfect sphere, the distance between any two adjacent parallels would be equal. Because of the ellipsoid form of the earth, the curvature varies faster near the equator than at the poles, and with this the altitude of the stars also varies faster at low latitudes. To observe a change of 1° in the altitude of Polaris, we have to go a shorter distance near the equator than near the poles. The length of 1° of latitude is 68.7 miles near the equator and 69.4 miles near the poles. For still more exact measurements, considering the form of the Hayford spheroid,

$$1° \text{ lat.} = 69.0569 - 0.3494 \cos 2\varphi + 0.0007 \cos 4\varphi \text{ (in statute miles)}$$

where $\varphi$ means the latitude in degrees, minutes, and seconds.

**Meridians.** The other set of coordinates of the earth consists of 180 great circles radiating from the poles at equal angles and dividing the equator and the parallels into 360° of longitude. For cartographic purposes the equator and the parallels can be regarded as perfect circles, and arcs intercepted by the meridian planes can be regarded as being equal.

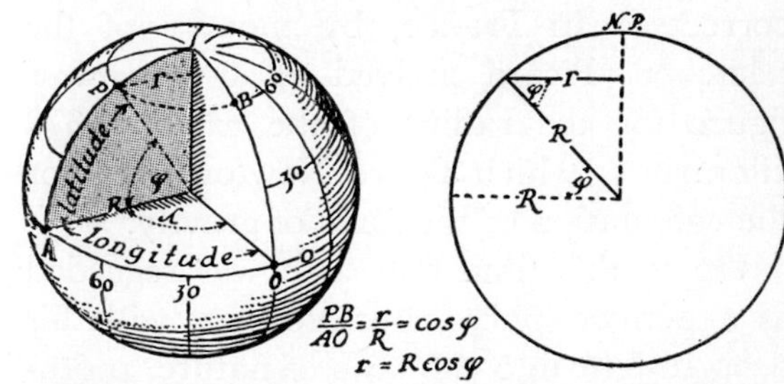


**Fig. 38** Longitude varies with the cosine of latitude. This is the fundamental rule of map construction.

The length of 1° of longitude will vary from 69.17 miles at the equator to zero at the poles. It is important to know the

**Table VI** Length of One Degree of Longitude at Different Latitudes

| *Latitude* | *Statute miles* | *Latitude* | *Statute miles* |
|---|---|---|---|
| 0° | 69.171 | 45 | 48.995 |
| 1 | 69.162 | 46 | 48.135 |
| 2 | 69.130 | 47 | 47.261 |
| 3 | 69.078 | 48 | 46.372 |
| 4 | 69.005 | 49 | 45.469 |
| 5 | 68.911 | 50 | 44.552 |
| 6 | 68.796 | 51 | 43.621 |
| 7 | 68.660 | 52 | 42.676 |
| 8 | 68.503 | 53 | 41.719 |
| 9 | 68.326 | 54 | 40.749 |
| 10 | 68.128 | 55 | 39.766 |
| 11 | 67.909 | 56 | 38.771 |
| 12 | 67.670 | 57 | 37.764 |
| 13 | 67.411 | 58 | 36.745 |
| 14 | 67.131 | 59 | 35.715 |
| 15 | 66.830 | 60 | 34.674 |
| 16 | 66.510 | 61 | 33.622 |
| 17 | 66.169 | 62 | 32.560 |
| 18 | 65.808 | 63 | 31.488 |
| 19 | 65.427 | 64 | 30.406 |
| 20 | 65.026 | 65 | 29.315 |
| 21 | 64.606 | 66 | 28.215 |
| 22 | 64.166 | 67 | 27.106 |
| 23 | 63.706 | 68 | 25.988 |
| 24 | 63.227 | 69 | 24.862 |
| 25 | 62.729 | 70 | 23.729 |
| 26 | 62.212 | 71 | 22.589 |
| 27 | 61.676 | 72 | 21.441 |
| 28 | 61.121 | 73 | 20.287 |
| 29 | 60.548 | 74 | 19.126 |
| 30 | 59.956 | 75 | 17.960 |
| 31 | 59.345 | 76 | 16.788 |
| 32 | 58.717 | 77 | 15.611 |
| 33 | 58.071 | 78 | 14.428 |
| 34 | 57.407 | 79 | 13.242 |
| 35 | 56.726 | 80 | 12.051 |
| 36 | 56.027 | 81 | 10.857 |
| 37 | 55.311 | 82 | 9.659 |
| 38 | 54.578 | 83 | 8.458 |
| 39 | 53.829 | 84 | 7.255 |
| 40 | 53.063 | 85 | 6.049 |
| 41 | 52.281 | 86 | 4.841 |
| 42 | 51.483 | 87 | 3.632 |
| 43 | 50.669 | 88 | 2.422 |
| 44 | 49.840 | 89 | 1.211 |
| 45 | 48.995 | 90 | 0.000 |

length of 1° of longitude on any parallel. If we regard the earth as a sphere, the radius of any parallel, $r = R \cos \varphi$, where $R$ is the radius of the earth and $\varphi$ is the latitude.

The radii of parallel circles have the same relationship to each other, as their circumferences or $\frac{1}{360}$ part of their circumferences, which is 1° of longitude.

$$1° \text{ long.} = 1° \text{ lat.} \cos \varphi$$

*Longitude varies with the cosine of latitude.* This is the most fundamental fact of the science of map projections, and should be thoroughly understood. In the case of latitude 60°, it is easy to see from Fig. 38 that 1° of longitude will be just half as long as at the equator.

The equator deviates slightly from an exact circle, and thus, for exact calculations, the Hayford spheroid of 1909 is used, in which

$$1° \text{ long. (in statute miles)} = 69.2316 \cos \varphi - 0.0584 \cos 3\varphi + 0.0001 \cos 5\varphi$$

Table VI gives the length of 1 minute of longitude at various latitudes. Table A · 4, Appendix 3, gives the value of cosines, and will serve better for simple constructions.

**Determination of Latitude and Longitude.** The location of each place can be

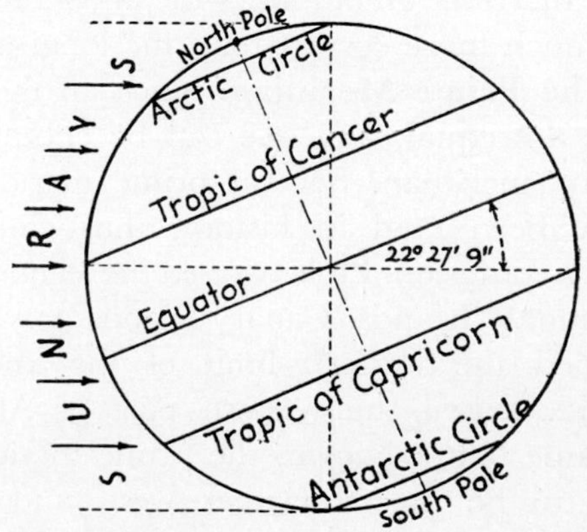


**Fig. 39** The tropics and the Arctic and Antarctic Circles divide the Earth in zones and are usually marked on maps.

fixed by determining its latitude from the equator and its longitude from a chosen prime meridian. The determination of latitude is usually done by observing the altitudes of stars or the sun. The polar star is not exactly at the celestial pole but about 1° off and the pole is determined by finding the mid-point between its upper and lower culminations. Longitudes are usually obtained by the determination of local time, from the position of stars or the sun. This time is compared with the time on the prime meridian, which can be carried along by a chronometer or obtained by radio. The difference between local time and Greenwich time will give the longitude, considering that 1 hour's difference equals 15° of longitude. The "equation of time," which is the difference between the observed solar time and the mean or clock time, also has to be added or subtracted. With modern methods and instruments, one set of observations of several stars will give latitude, local time, and longitude. The necessary figures are contained in the "American Ephemeris and Nautical Almanac," published yearly by the Naval Observatory in Washington. Before the chronometer was invented, the determination of longitude was extremely difficult, and therefore on old maps the latitudes will be much more correct than the longitudes.

**The Prime Meridian.** Since all meridians are equal, any one can be chosen as prime meridian. Several prime meridians have been used in history, thus causing much confusion. Ptolemy used the legendary Fortunate Islands (Canary Islands?), which formed the western limit of the known world. When the western part of Africa became better known, the prime meridian had to be placed farther west, and the Dutch and English cartographers of the seventeenth century used either the Azores or the Cape Verde Islands. The Spanish cartographers had a convenient prime meridian, the 1498 demarcation line of the Pope, which cut Brazil in half. The confusion was so great that the French king ordered all his cartographers to use Ferro, the westernmost island of the Canaries, for prime meridian; this was supposed to be just 20° west of the Paris Observatory, but in reality is 1 minute less. The Greenwich longitude of some common prime meridian is shown in Table A · 8, Appendix 3.

With the growth of national consciousness in the eighteenth century, each nation began to boost its own capital. London, Lisbon, Madrid, Paris and even Philadelphia and Washington were used for prime meridians. The British Admiralty reckoned longitudes from the Greenwich Observatory in London, and so great was the authority of this office that at present the Greenwich meridian is used by all nations. The Greenwich meridian has some disadvantages because it cuts Europe and Africa in two, and we usually reckon the eastern and western hemispheres from the longitude 20°W.; but on the opposite side of the earth, the location of the International Date Line along the 180th meridian is convenient.

It is customary to reckon latitudes north and south from the equator, and longitudes east and west from Greenwich, up to 180°. For example, the coordinates of the Harvard Observatory in Cambridge, Mass., read:

Lat. 42°22′48″ N
Long. 71°07′45″ W of Greenwich

which is a rather cumbersome method of expression. It is advocated that continuous numbering of the longitudes from 0 to 360° starting east from Greenwich, be used, and also that decimal values replace minutes and seconds. Since the change would mean a great deal of recalculation of tables and recalibration of instruments, and would require an international agreement, there is little hope that this change for the better will soon be accomplished. French maps often use grads instead of degrees. There are 400 grads in the circle. The U.S. Army uses *mils*, which divide the circle in 6,400 parts. This is an approximation of the angle distended by 1 foot at 1,000 foot distance, which would divide the circle into

$$2\pi 1{,}000 = 6{,}280 \text{ parts}$$

Two units of measurement are based upon the dimensions of the earth: (1) the nautical mile and (2) the meter, and with it the entire metric system.

**The Nautical Mile.** A nautical mile was originally 1 minute of latitude. As the length of a minute of latitude varied, so the length of a nautical mile was somewhat smaller at the equator than near the poles. To avoid the resulting confusion, the British Admiralty introduced the so-called "Admiralty mile," which is the mean value of 1 minute of latitude, 6,080 feet. The length of a standard nautical mile in the United States is about 2 inches longer.

1 nautical mile (U.S.) = 6,080.27 feet = 1,853.25 meters = 1.151594 statute miles

The nautical mile of Germany and France is 4 feet shorter—6,076 feet. The term "geographical mile" was originally used for 1 minute of longitude on the equator, corresponding to 1.1516 statute miles, but the term is also used interchangeably with nautical mile.

**The Metric System.** In the eighteenth century there was a great confusion of various units of length, such as miles, leagues, toises, etc.; so the revolutionary government of France introduced a new unit of length, 1/40,000,000 part of a meridian circle, and called it "meter." To establish the proper length, a new meridian measurement from the North Sea to the Mediterranean was completed in 1799. In 1801 the meter and its derivatives, the liter, the kilogram, and the square and cubic meters, were made compulsory in France. It took considerable time for other nations to follow suit. In 1875, 31 countries convened and adopted the metric system. At present the metric system is used by all civilized countries except the British Empire and the United States, and is legalized in both these countries.

More exact measurements of the arc have shown that the earth's meridian is actually slightly longer than it was found to be in 1799; so the meter is not the 1/40,000,000 part of the earth's circumference but, rather, the length of a platinum-iridium bar preserved in Paris under specific conditions. Copies of this bar are preserved by the signatory countries.

**Orientation.** We are so accustomed to having "north" at the top of the map that we hardly realize that it can just as well be otherwise. As we have seen, the Roman and medieval maps were "oriented," which means that they had east at the top. The Arabs, looking toward Mecca, liked to have south at the top of their maps. Early American maps were often oriented with west at the top. It seems to be the tendency among map makers of every country to put at the top of the map the direction toward which the national attention is turned.

North orientation came into use in the time of the Ptolemy revival, but became universal only centuries later. At present the idea that north is "above" is so deep in our consciousness that schoolteachers constantly have to guard against such expressions as "Canada is above the United States," or "Chicago lies nearly at the bottom of Lake Michigan." Such a name as "Lower California" is derived from its position on the map rather than from its relative elevation. There is no rule against orienting the map in any direction, provided that the cardinal directions are indicated either by parallels and meridians or by compass roses. Unusual orientation sometimes brings out hidden relationships.

**Hemispheres.** The earth can be halved an infinite number of ways, but certain hemispheres are of some particular interest. The most obvious division is the Northern and Southern Hemisphere, divided by the equator. We Americans are conscious of the Western Hemisphere, which in atlases is usually bound by the 20W and 160E meridians.

President Monroe's "this hemisphere," as used in the Monroe Doctrine, however, certainly did not include the Chukchi peninsula, half of Iceland, New Zealand, and the Cape Verde Islands. The term was then used somewhat loosely as a synonym for the Americas. "This hemisphere," meaning any hemisphere including the United States, would include all the earth except the antipodes of the United States in the Indian Ocean.[1]

More significant is the *land hemisphere*, the half of the earth containing most of the land. This is centered near Nantes, France, and contains 81 per cent of all lands, and if we do not regard the great icecaps as land the percentage rises to 90. Almost all people of the earth live in one half of the earth. The "people's hemisphere" is centered in the French-Italian Alps and contains 95 per cent of all mankind. Our earth is lopsided indeed.[2]

[1] BOGGS, S. W., "This Hemisphere," U.S. Department of State, 1945. 13 pp.

[2] RAISZ, ERWIN, Our Lopsided Earth, *Jour. Geog.*, Vol. 63, No. 3, pp. 81–91, March, 1944.

# CHAPTER 6: *Projections*[1]

The parallel and meridian system of the earth can be easily drawn upon a globe, but its application to a flat map needs consideration; for the surface of a globe cannot be flattened without some kind of distortion, such as stretching or tearing. If only a small part of the globe is represented on a map, say 100 square miles, this distortion will hardly exceed the stretching limits of the paper, but on maps of entire countries, of continents, or of the whole earth, we are confronted with a problem.

Various methods have been proposed to overcome this difficulty. The simplest of these is to envelop the globe with a cylinder, or cone, or to lay a tangent plane against it, and project a part of the grid system of the globe from its center or from some other convenient point upon the cylinder, cone, or plane. The cylinder, or cone, is then cut open and laid out flat, and we have a projection system that has been derived from an actual process of projecting.

Actually only a few projections have been designed by this method. Most others are modifications of true geometrical projections, often modified to such an extent that the original relationship can hardly be detected. For that reason the name "projection" is not a fortunate one. Other suggested terms, such as "graticule," "net," and "grid," are more correct, but the word "projection" is so well established that, although it is somewhat misleading, we shall continue its use.

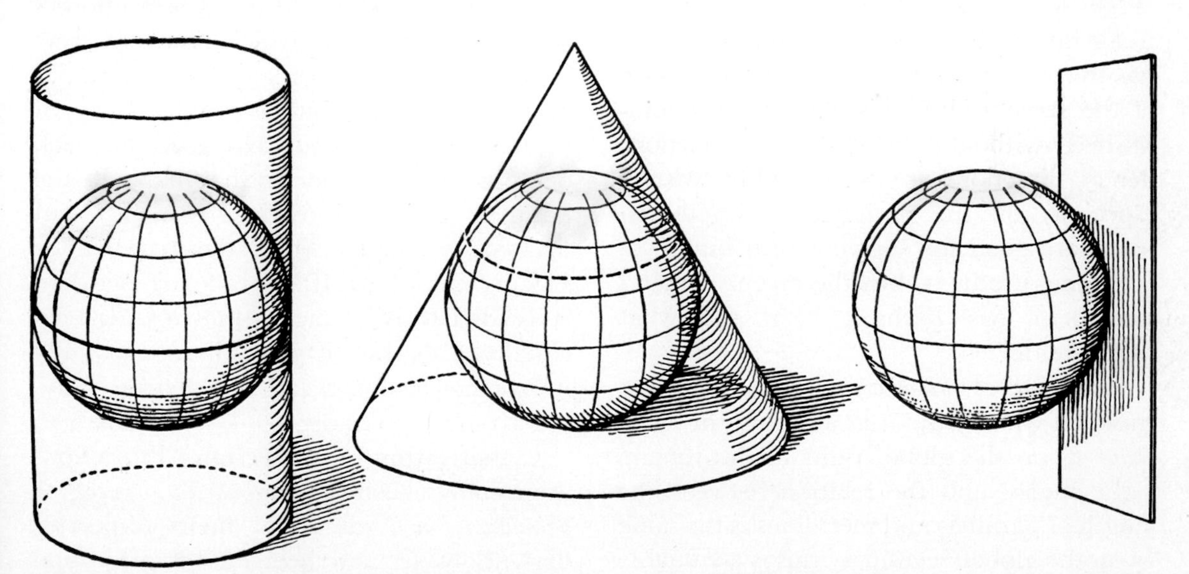

**Figs. 40, 41, 42** Most map projections are related to a cylinder, cone, or plane. The actually used projections are usually modified from the original geometrical conception.

A projection, then, as we use the term, can be defined as *any orderly system of parallels*

[1] In the following discussions the mathematical treatment of projections is restricted to a minimum, since otherwise it would not be understood by the average student of geography for whom this book is intended. For those who are interested in the mathematics of projections the books listed in the Bibliography, Appendix 4, are recommended.

*and meridians on which a map can be drawn.* There are hundreds of ways in which such systems can be constructed, but they are not equally good—some are good for one purpose, and some for another. However, there is no one projection that is the best for every map. An intelligent choice of projection is an important problem for a cartographer.

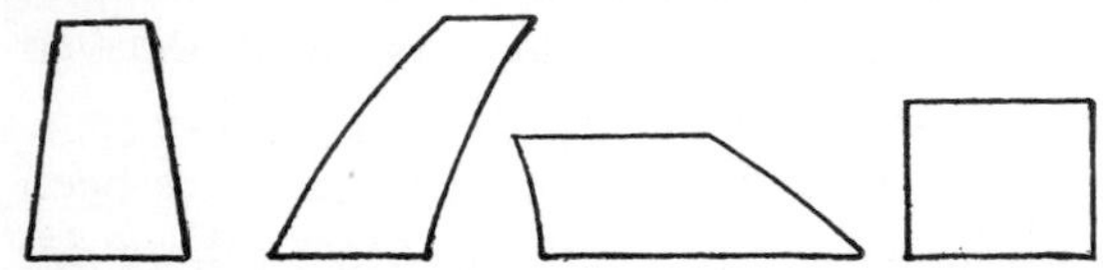

**Fig. 43** Equality of area is often achieved by bad distortion of shape.

*Equal-area*, or *equivalent*, projections are those in which any region, large or small, has the same area on the map as on a globe of the same scale. This cannot be accomplished without considerable distortion; hence, directions are considerably twisted, especially on the peripheries. Equal-area maps are good for showing distribution of economic products, but the recent demand for them has perhaps been somewhat overemphasized.

*Conformal*, or *orthomorphic*, projections are those on which any *small* area has the same *shape* as on the globe: right angles remain right angles, and the relation between the length of parallels and meridians is the same as on the globe. Seemingly this is a valuable property; unfortunately, however, in order to construct such a projection, the scale has to be varied considerably. Conformal projections are good in showing directions. Their chief use is in navigation. It is obvious that no projection can be at the same time equal-area and orthomorphic; only a globe has these properties, and a globe cannot be flattened without distortion. There is no perfect projection.

From a mathematical point of view, conformality and equality of area are highly valued properties of projections, and their construction constitutes a stimulating problem in geometry. For a practical geographer, however, they are less important. He often prefers a projection which, being midway between the conformal and the equal-area map, distorts neither the shape nor the scale to any great extent.

**Construction of Projections.** In any projection system, only the parallels or only the meridians or some other lines can be *true*—which means that they are of the same length as on a globe of corresponding scale. All other lines are too long or too short. If all the parallels and all the meridians were true, we would have a globe and not a map. It is most important, in the construction of projections, to know which lines are true, because these lines are laid out first. If it is said that the meridian is divided truly, it means that we lay out 69.2 miles for each degree on the scale of the map. If the parallels are truly divided, we lay out 69.2 cos $\varphi$ lengths along the parallel for spacing meridians. If a parallel or meridian is divided truly, it means that it is divided equally also, but if it is divided equally it does not always mean it is divided truly For cosines, see Table A · 4, Appendix 3.

**Classification of Projections.** Projections are usually classified as *cylindrical*, *conical*, or *azimuthal*, according to their respective derivations from a geometrical projection upon a cylinder, a cone, or a plane. It is a historical fact, however, that most projections were not developed in this manner but, rather, were invented in an accidental sequence. Some of them cannot be related at all to a cylinder, cone, or tangent plane; so, in order to avoid misconceptions, they may be divided into the following groups:

1. Projections with horizontal parallels
2. Conic group of projections
3. Azimuthal and related projections
4. Other unrelated projections

## Projections with Horizontal Parallels

**Cylindrical and Related Projections.** In this group the parallels are horizontal straight lines, and places in the same latitude appear on the map at the same height. This is a valuable property, because latitude and climate are closely related, and the east-west relationship is correctly shown. So accustomed are we to curved parallels that nearly half of the author's students thought that the southernmost part of the United States was a point in Texas rather than in Florida because on most maps the former point seems to be lower down.

Another advantage of this horizontal system is that the parallels and meridians can often be omitted, and their position indicated only on the sides of the map. It is also convenient that the lettering need not be curved along the parallels. Projections with horizontal parallels are especially good for simple, diagrammatic maps, or for any kind of map in low latitudes. Often the term "cylindrical" is confined to those projections which have horizontal parallels and vertical meridians. In this group the meridians are always spaced evenly, and they differ only in spacing the parallels.

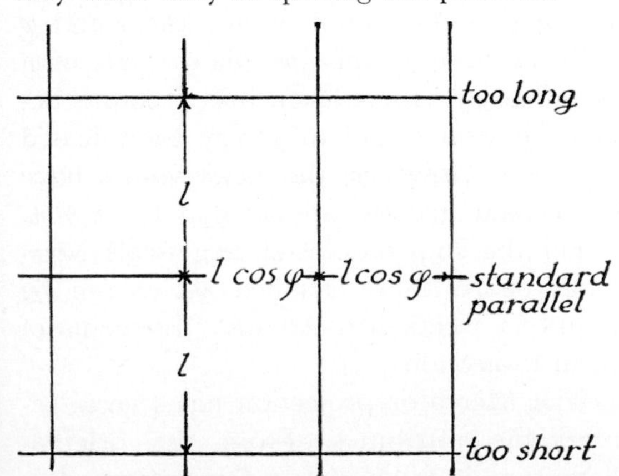


**Fig. 44** In the equirectangular projection the scale is true along the standard parallel and along all meridians. The rest of the parallels are either too short or too long.

**Equirectangular Projection.** This is the simplest of projections—a network of evenly spaced horizontal and vertical lines for parallels and meridians. The central parallel of the map is chosen as standard and is divided true to scale, in the same way as on a globe of equal scale. On the globe the length of 1° of longitude at latitude $\varphi$ is

$$1° \text{ long.} = 1° \text{ lat. } \cos \varphi$$

First we lay out the parallels, a set of horizontal lines spaced at true distances. Then we select the standard parallel, divide it according to the foregoing formula, and draw a set of vertical lines for meridians.

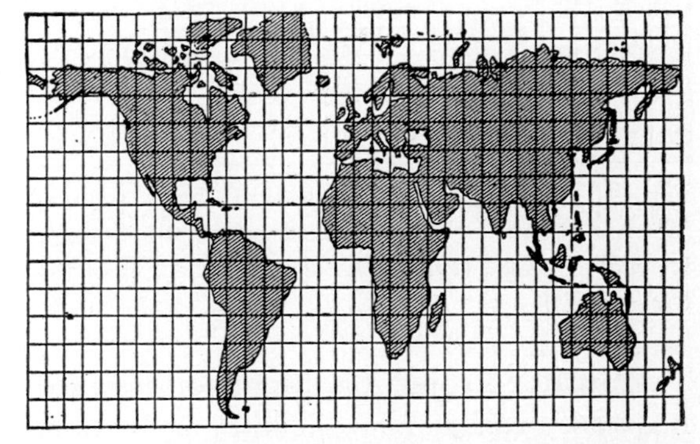

**Fig. 45** Map of the world in equirectangular projection. The standard parallel is 48° latitude. (*Modified from U.S. Coast and Geodetic Survey Spec. Pub.* 68.)

The scale is true on all meridians and on the central parallel; but the northern parallels are too long and the southern parallels are too short. The directions, east, west, north, and south, remain the same on the map; all other directions are changed.

The equirectangular projection is practical because of its simplicity. It is used mostly for maps of cities, small counties, or states. Figure 45 shows the map of the world in this projection, with latitude of 48° as standard parallel. The projection is neither equal-area nor conformal, but the areas are less exaggerated than in the Mercator projection.

When the standard parallel is the equator, we have a network of even squares, and maps in this projection are called "plane charts" (plate carrée). This projection was used on the chart of Marinus of Tyre (*ca.* A.D. 100). It was apparently also employed on the portolan charts, although it seems that these maps were first drawn without any thought of a projection, and that the network of lines was later superimposed.

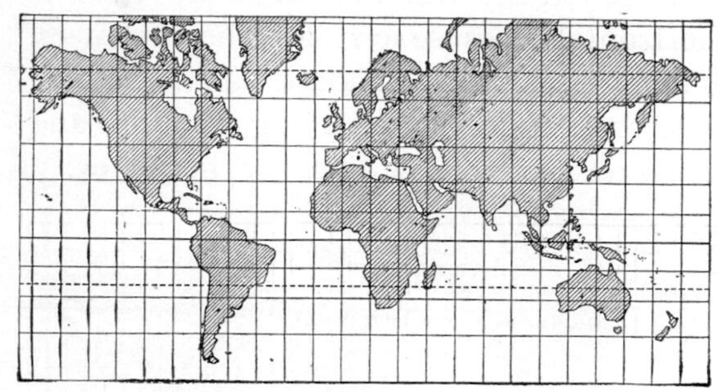

**Fig. 46** The Mercator projection shows a great increase in scale at higher latitudes. Only the equator is true to scale. (*From Finch-Trewartha, "Elements of Geography."*)

**Mercator Projection.** Mercator designed his 1569 world map in this projection, describing its principles and properties on the map itself. This projection has horizontal parallels and vertical meridians. The meridians are placed evenly, so that their spacing is true to scale on the equator. The parallels are spaced so that, taking any small area, the relation of scale along the meridians and along the parallels is the same as on the globe. For instance, at latitude 60° the parallels are twice as far apart as on the equator. Therefore, since the meridians are the same distance from each other at every latitude, the scale of the map is doubly exaggerated at 60°. At 80° the amplification of scale is sixfold. It is obvious, then, that the pole cannot be shown in this projection at all, because the expansion would be infinite. The Mercator projection was not derived from the projection of the globe upon a cylinder, but it is a modification of that idea.

On the globe the parallels become shorter toward the poles, and their length is proportionate to the cosine of latitude. In the Mercator projection the parallels are all equally long. This means that any parallel is increased $1/\cos \varphi = \sec \varphi$, where $\varphi$ is the latitude in degrees. In order to have the same scale along the parallels as along the meridians, each degree of latitude must also be increased by the secant of the latitude.

For any parallel, the distance $y$ from the equator is the sum of the secants of the latitudes:

$$y = \sec 1' + \sec 2' + \sec 3' + \cdots + \sec \varphi$$

There is also a simpler formula for $y$ which is derived from the general formula for all conformal projections, given here without its derivation:

$$y = R \cdot \log \text{nat.} \tan \left(45° + \frac{\varphi}{2}\right)$$
$$= R \cdot 2.302585 \log \tan \left(45° + \frac{\varphi}{2}\right)$$

where $R$ is the radius of the Earth and $\varphi$ is the latitude. In this formula the flattening of the Earth is not taken into account, because it would lead to a very complicated equation. However, the exact values have been calculated and are given in Table VII.

For the construction of large-scale Mercator charts more detailed tables can be found in Deetz and Adams' "Elements of Map Projection."[1]

The Mercator projection has several remarkable attributes. From the original definition it follows that the projection is

[1] DEETZ, C. H., and O. S. ADAMS, Elements of Map Projection, *U.S. Coast and Geodetic Survey Spec. Pub.* 68, 5th ed., pp. 117–136, 1934.

conformal, *i.e.*, taking any small area, the shape of the regions is the same as on the globe. However, since the scale varies to a considerable extent, the shapes of large areas are greatly distorted. For instance, on the Mercator projection Greenland has a larger area than South America, whereas on the globe it is only about one-eighth as large.

The most significant property of this projection is that it is the only system which *shows all compass directions, or loxodromes, as straight lines.* This is an important feature in navigation. Loxodromes are lines on the globe that constantly retain the same compass direction and cross each meridian at the same angle. Since the meridians converge at the poles, the loxodromes appear on the globe as curved lines, spiraling around the poles, which they never reach in a mathematical sense.

**Table VII** Mercator Projection Table
Distances of Parallels from the Equator in Minutes of Longitude on the Equator Taken in Account of the Earth's Ellipticity as $\frac{1}{294}$

| *Degrees* | Υ | *Degrees* | Υ | *Degrees* | Υ |
|---|---|---|---|---|---|
| 1 | 59.596 | 27 | 1672.923 | 54 | 3845.738 |
| 2 | 119.210 | 28 | 1740.206 | 55 | 3948.830 |
| 3 | 178.862 | 29 | 1808.122 | 56 | 4054.537 |
| 4 | 238.568 | 30 | 1876.706 | 57 | 4163.027 |
| 5 | 298.348 | 31 | 1945.992 | 58 | 4274.485 |
| 6 | 358.222 | 32 | 2016.015 | 59 | 4389.113 |
| 7 | 418.206 | 33 | 2086.814 | 60 | 4507.133 |
| 8 | 478.321 | 34 | 2158.428 | 61 | 4628.789 |
| 9 | 538.585 | 35 | 2230.898 | 62 | 4754.350 |
| 10 | 599.019 | 36 | 2304.267 | 63 | 4884.117 |
| 11 | 659.641 | 37 | 2378.581 | 64 | 5018.419 |
| 12 | 720.472 | 38 | 2453.888 | 65 | 5157.629 |
| 13 | 781.532 | 39 | 2530.238 | 66 | 5302.164 |
| 14 | 842.842 | 40 | 2607.683 | 67 | 5452.493 |
| 15 | 904.422 | 41 | 2686.280 | 68 | 5609.149 |
| 16 | 966.296 | 42 | 2766.089 | 69 | 5772.739 |
| 17 | 1028.483 | 43 | 2847.171 | 70 | 5943.955 |
| 18 | 1091.007 | 44 | 2929.594 | 71 | 6123.602 |
| 19 | 1153.893 | 45 | 3013.427 | 72 | 6312.610 |
| 20 | 1217.161 | 46 | 3098.747 | 73 | 6512.071 |
| 21 | 1280.835 | 47 | 3185.634 | 74 | 6723.275 |
| 22 | 1344.945 | 48 | 3274.173 | 75 | 6947.761 |
| 23 | 1409.513 | 49 | 3364.456 | 76 | 7187.387 |
| 24 | 1474.566 | 50 | 3456.581 | 77 | 7444.428 |
| 25 | 1540.134 | 51 | 3550.654 | 78 | 7721.700 |
| 26 | 1606.243 | 52 | 3646.787 | 79 | 8022.758 |
| | | 53 | 3745.105 | 80 | 8352.176 |

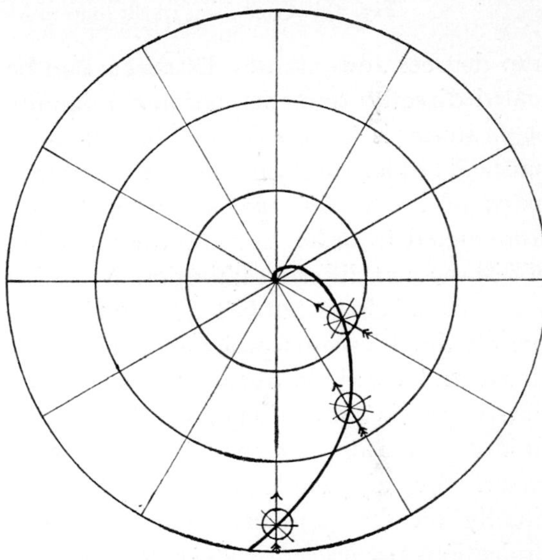

**Fig. 47** Loxodromes, or rhumb lines, are lines that have the same compass direction all along their lengths.

The shortest route between two points on the globe is the "great circle," but, in order to follow this course, a ship continually has to change its compass direction. Therefore, for shorter distances ships usually follow the straight rhumb lines, or loxodromes. The navigator connects his point of departure with his point of destination by a straight line on a Mercator chart. He reads the compass direction of this line, with the help of compass roses, printed on the chart, and sets his vessel on her proper course with due allowance for winds and currents.

Since exaggeration of the Mercator chart increases rapidly toward the poles, the usual types of scales cannot be used. Nautical charts which show larger areas have no scale, but the border of the chart is divided

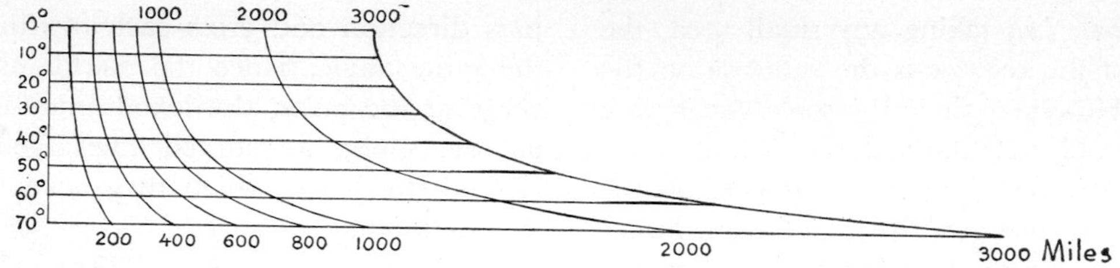


**Fig. 48** Scale for a world map in Mercator projection. The curves are sinusoids.

into degrees and minutes. Distances can be scaled directly from this, because 1 minute of latitude is approximately equal to a nautical mile. For small-scale Mercator maps of the world, special scales can be constructed in order to show the variation of distances at different latitudes.

Almost all charts published for navigation are on the Mercator projection. The U.S. Coast and Geodetic Survey formerly used the polyconic projection but has changed to the Mercator in recent years. Even in charts for air navigation, which were usually on the Lambert conformal conic projection, preference is given by both the British and American navies to a set of Mercator charts on uniform median scale.

In the past decades the Mercator projection was too often used for world maps. Even for statistical purposes where an equal-area map should be required, the Mercator projection, with its extreme regional distortion, is still used. There may be several reasons for this. Doubtless the ease of construction is one factor, and the convenience of horizontal parallels and vertical meridians is another. Perhaps the chief cause of this popularity, however, is the distortion itself. Every cartographer knows how difficult it is to label "Netherlands" or "Switzerland" on a world map; consequently, he welcomes any projection that exaggerates the higher latitudes. Nevertheless, the Mercator projection leads to such erroneous impressions of areas and distances in high latitudes that its use should be restricted. In recent years a transverse form of the Mercator projection has been also used, the discussion of which will be taken up later.

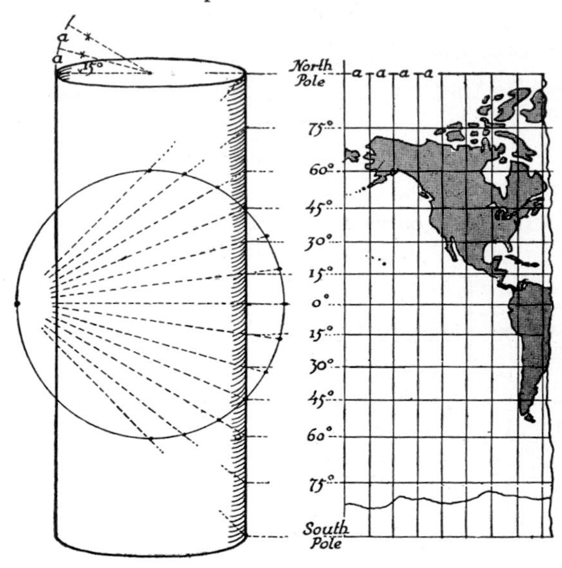


**Fig. 49** Gall's cylindrical projection derived from a cylinder cutting the globe at 45°. The parallels are projected from the antipodal point on the equator to any meridian.

**Gall's Projection.** In this projection it is assumed that a smaller cylinder cuts the globe at the 45°N and 45°S parallels. The meridians are straight vertical lines spaced truly on the two 45° parallels; the parallels are horizontal, and their spacing is determined by projecting each meridian from its antipodal point on the equator upon the secant cylinder. Only the two 45° parallels are true to scale; in the equatorial regions the map is reduced in scale; toward the poles the scale is exaggerated increasingly but not so much as on the Mercator projection.

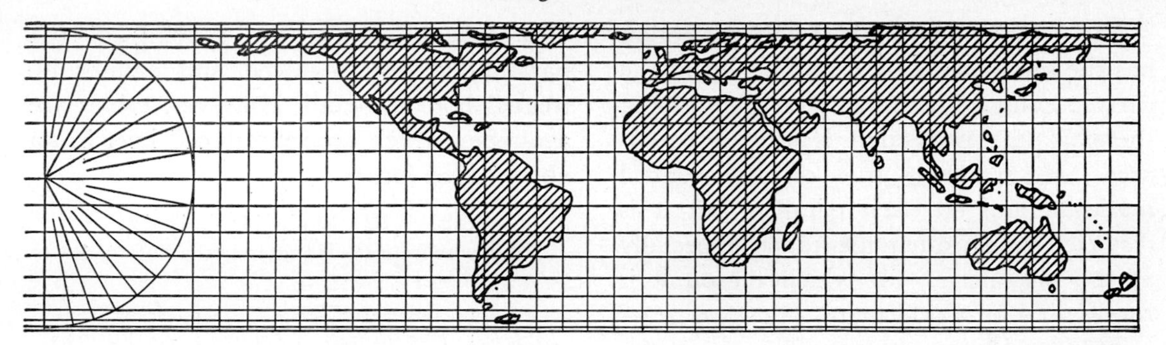

**Fig. 50** Cylindrical equal-area projection of the world. (*From Finch-Trewartha, "Elements of Geography."*)

The *central-cylindrical projection* is formed by projecting the surface of the globe from its center upon a cylinder tangent to the equator. The cylinder is then cut open along one of the meridians and laid out flat. This projection exaggerates high latitudes even more than Mercator's, and it is used only for astronomical purposes.

The *cylindrical equal-area projection* is developed by projecting the surface of the globe, with horizontal rays from its axis, upon a cylinder tangent to the equator. This, too, is rarely used because of its extreme distortion in higher latitudes.

There are a great many cylindrical projections possible, and for further study O. M. Miller, Notes on Cylindrical World Map Projections, *The Geographical Review*, Vol. 33, pages 424 to 431, 1943, is recommended. O. M. Miller has also developed several of his own projections.

**Sinusoidal (Mercator-Sanson-Flamsteed) Projection.** This projection has straight, horizontal parallels spaced truly. The central meridian is straight, and the others are curves which are derived from a true division of each parallel. The lengths of the parallels are obtained from

$$1^\circ \text{ long.} = 1^\circ \text{ lat.} \cos \varphi$$

where $\varphi$ is the latitude in degrees. The meridians can also be constructed as shown in Fig. 52. It can be proved from the construction that the meridians are sine curves, or sinusoids (more correctly, cosine curves), from which the projection is named.

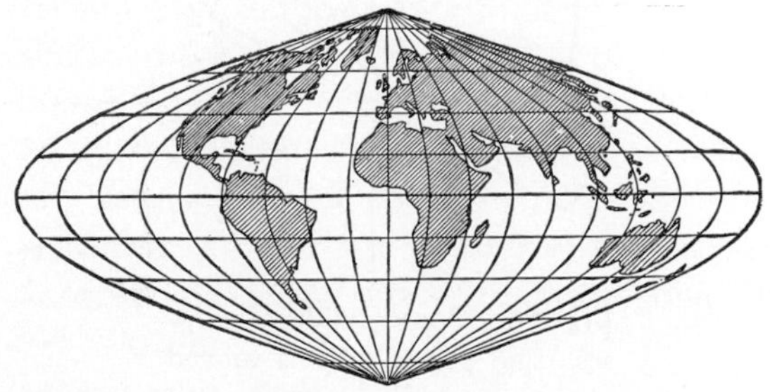

**Fig. 51** Sinusoidal projection is good in the tropical regions but distorts the high latitudes. (*From Finch-Trewartha, "Elements of Geography."*)

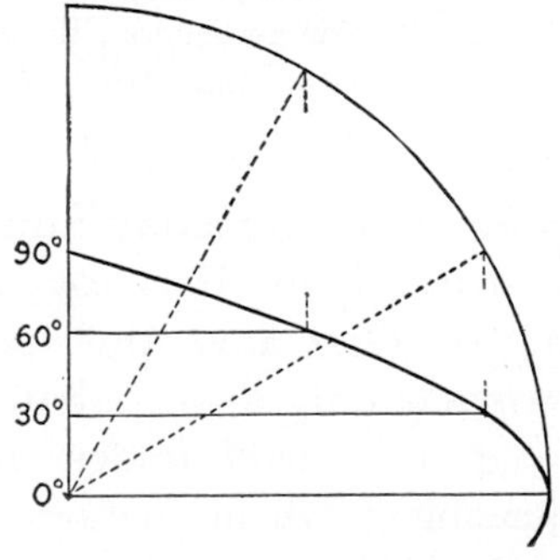


**Fig. 52** Construction of sine curves for the sinusoidal projection.

At one time this grid was called the "Sanson-Flamsteed projection" in honor of Nicholas Sanson, the famous French cartographer, and Flamsteed, the English astronomer. Sanson's map of Atlantis Island (Fig. 21) is in this projection. This name, however, had to be abandoned when it was found that Mercator and others had used this projection at an earlier date.

Each small quadrangle in this projection has the same base length and height as the corresponding quadrangle on the globe; therefore the projection is strictly equal-area. The scale is true on the central meridian and on each parallel, but it is distorted on all other meridians, especially at the peripheries, for which reason it is rarely used for world maps.

This projection is extensively used for maps of the equatorial regions and for the continents of South America, Africa, and Australia. It is also good for smaller countries in middle latitudes, provided that they extend in a north-south direction.

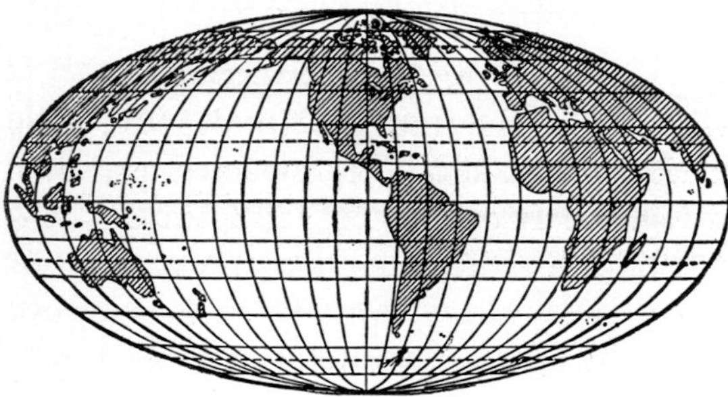

**Fig. 53** The Mollweide projection, if centered on America, distorts Europe and Asia. (*From Finch-Trewartha, "Elements of Geography."*)

**The Mollweide (Homalographic) Projection.** Invented in 1805 by Karl B. Mollweide of Germany, this projection became popular only after J. Babinet had reintroduced it in 1857 under the name "homalographic," which in Greek means "evenly drawn." It has horizontal, straight parallels and elliptical, equal-spaced meridians.

The equator is twice as long as the central meridian and is divided evenly. The meridians themselves can easily be constructed, for they are all ellipses, and the hemisphere is represented by a circle. Parallels are horizontal and are spaced so that each zone confined by two of them has the same area as the corresponding belt on the globe; this makes the projection equal-area. The calculation for the spacing of the parallels is very involved and cannot be treated here in detail. However, tables are available, which are reproduced here in an abbreviated form.

**Table VIII** Mollweide Projection
Distance from the Equator to the Pole = 1

| *Latitude* | *Distance of parallels from the equator* | *Latitude* | *Distance of parallels from the equator* |
|---|---|---|---|
| 0° | 0.000 | 50 | 0.651 |
| 5 | 0.069 | 55 | 0.708 |
| 10 | 0.137 | 60 | 0.762 |
| 15 | 0.205 | 65 | 0.814 |
| 20 | 0.272 | 70 | 0.862 |
| 25 | 0.339 | 75 | 0.906 |
| 30 | 0.404 | 80 | 0.945 |
| 35 | 0.468 | 85 | 0.978 |
| 40 | 0.531 | 90 | 1.000 |
| 45 | 0.592 | | |

A more extensive table for every half degree is to be found in Deetz and Adams, "Elements of Map Projection." The ellipses can be constructed according to several methods, one of the simplest of which is shown in Fig. 54. Another method of draw-

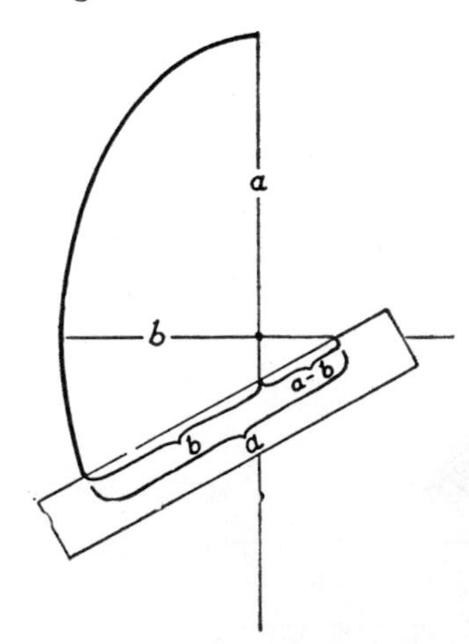


**Fig. 54** Construction of ellipses. The paper strip is moved along so that the end points of *a-b* are always on the axes of the ellipse.

ing the meridians is to divide the parallels evenly within the circular hemisphere. The parallels are spaced closer together near the poles than at the equator, the difference amounting to about 25 per cent. If we consider a globe of the same area as the map, only the two 40°40′ parallels are of true scale. The equator is slightly too short. Peripheral distortion is great but less so than in the sinusoidal projection.

In Europe this projection is used extensively for world maps, for, if Europe is placed in the center, the other continents are conveniently distributed. North America, however, suffers great distortion under this arrangement, and for that reason the projection has never become popular here. The projection can be recommended for hemisphere maps.

**The Goode Interrupted Homalographic Projection.** We have seen that in world maps constructed on the sinusoidal or the Mollweide projection North America is badly distorted if Europe is placed in the center. On the other hand, it is not convenient to put North America in the center, because Asia is then cut in half and the best part of the projection is occupied by the Pacific Ocean as shown in Fig. 53. In order to overcome this difficulty, Paul Goode, late professor of cartography in Chicago, developed his "interrupted" projection. Figure 55 explains its principle.

The equator is divided evenly, and the parallels are placed as in the Mollweide projection. Instead of one central meridian, each continent has a convenient central meridian of its own from which the other meridians are laid out to left and right as before. The projection is obviously equal-area and, at the same time, the shapes are realistic, because only the best part of the system is used. This same principle can also be applied to the sinusoidal and the Eckert projections. Goode later developed his homalosine projection, in which the lower latitudes as far as the 40th parallel are in the sinusoidal and higher latitudes are in the Mollweide projection.

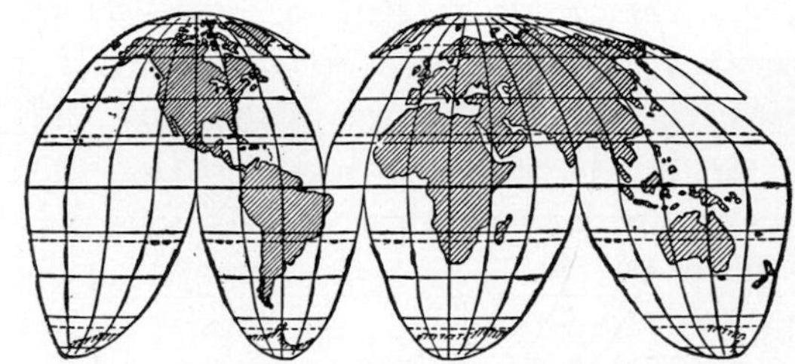

**Fig. 55** Goode's interrupted homalosine projection combines equality of areas with little distortion in shape. (*From Finch-Trewartha, "Elements of Geography."*)

The interrupted homalographic projection is a good one for the representation of statistical distribution, but certain world relationships cannot be shown on account of the discontinuity of the oceans. For oceanographic maps, these gaps can be chosen so that the continents are cut open while the oceans remain more or less intact.

**Table IX** Spacing of Parallels in the Eckert IV Projection (After A. Robinson)

| *Latitude* | *Distance of parallels from equator* | *Latitude* | *Distance of parallels from equator* |
|---|---|---|---|
| 0° | 0 | 50 | 0.718 |
| 5 | 0.078 | 55 | 0.775 |
| 10 | 0.155 | 60 | 0.827 |
| 15 | 0.232 | 65 | 0.874 |
| 20 | 0.308 | 70 | 0.915 |
| 25 | 0.382 | 75 | 0.950 |
| 30 | 0.454 | 80 | 0.976 |
| 35 | 0.525 | 85 | 0.994 |
| 40 | 0.592 | 90 | 1 |
| 45 | 0.657 | | |

[1] Eckert, Max, Neue Entwürfe für Erdkarten, *Petermanns Mitt.*, Vol. 52, pp. 97–109, 1906.

**The Eckert Projection,** Professor Max Eckert of Aachen, Germany, inspired by Apianus of the sixteenth century, developed a set of projections[1] in which the poles, instead of being the customary points, are

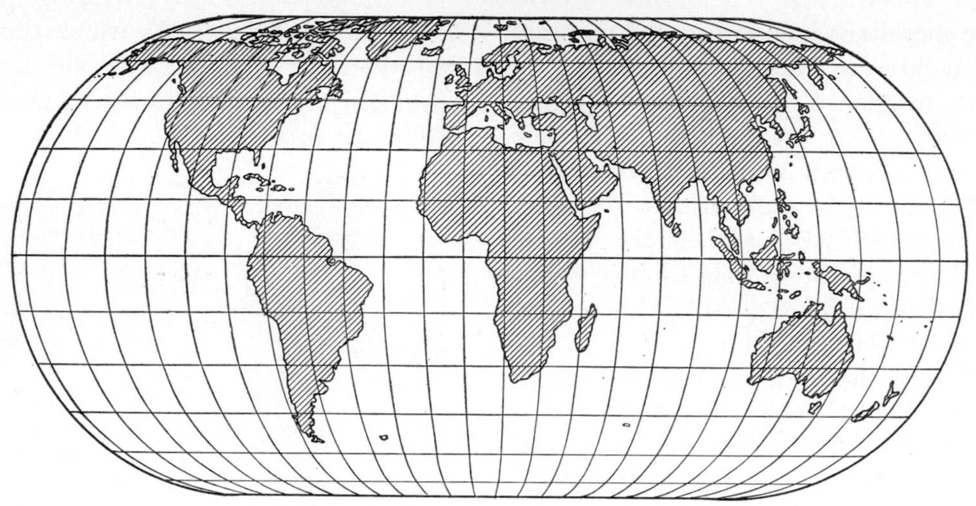

**Fig. 56** The Eckert IV projection. The poles are represented by lines half the length of the equator.

represented as parallels which are half the length of the equator.

Eckert proposed six projections, the fourth of which is becoming quite popular in Europe: In the first and second, the meridians are straight lines; in the third and fourth, they are ellipses; and in the fifth and sixth, they are sinusoids, all evenly spaced on the equator or any parallel. In Nos. I, III, and V the parallels are equally spaced; and in Nos. II, IV, and VI they make the projection equal-area. Since the meridians converge to a lesser degree than in the sinusoidal and Mollweide projections, the temperate latitudes are not greatly distorted.

# CHAPTER 7: *The Conic Group of Projections*

This group is derived, with some modifications, from the projection of the globe upon a tangent cone. Each conic projection has circular parallels and radiating meridians. They are particularly well adapted to countries in temperate latitudes.

**Simple Conic Projection.** This is formed by projecting the surface of a globe from its center upon a tangent cone, which is then cut open along one of its elements and laid out flat. The parallels are concentric circles, and the meridians are radiating straight lines that are evenly spaced on each parallel. This projection, however, is never used in its original form because the parallels would be spaced unevenly. In the actually used simple conic projection the parallels are spaced evenly at their true distances.

The construction of a simple conic projection is relatively easy. We choose a standard parallel near the center of the map, draw a cone tangent to this parallel, and thus determine $r$, the radius of the circle representing the standard parallel of the projection (see Fig. 57). It is unnecessary to obtain the length of $r$ by construction, because it can be calculated easily. For every $\varphi$ latitude

$$r = R \cot \varphi$$

where $R$ is the radius of the globe. Values of $r$ are given in Table X.

**Table X** Radii of Standard Parallels in the Conic Projection
$r = R \cot \varphi$
The Earth's Radius: $R = 1$

| | | | |
|---|---|---|---|
| 0° | ∞ | 50° | 0.8391 |
| 5 | 11.430 | 55 | 0.7002 |
| 10 | 5.671 | 60 | 0.5774 |
| 15 | 3.732 | 65 | 0.4663 |
| 20 | 2.747 | 70 | 0.3640 |
| 25 | 2.145 | 75 | 0.2679 |
| 30 | 1.732 | 80 | 0.1763 |
| 35 | 1.428 | 85 | 0.0875 |
| 40 | 1.192 | 90 | 0.0000 |
| 45 | 1.000 | | |

The length of 1° of longitude on the standard parallel is true

$$\frac{2\pi R \cos \varphi}{360}$$

In the simple conic projection the scale is true along the standard parallel and all

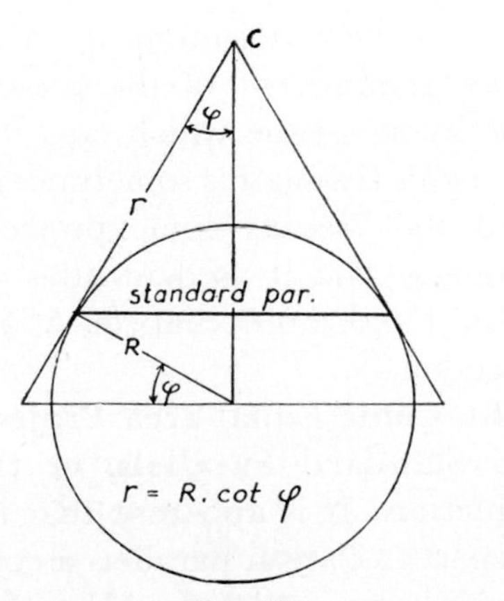


**Fig. 57**

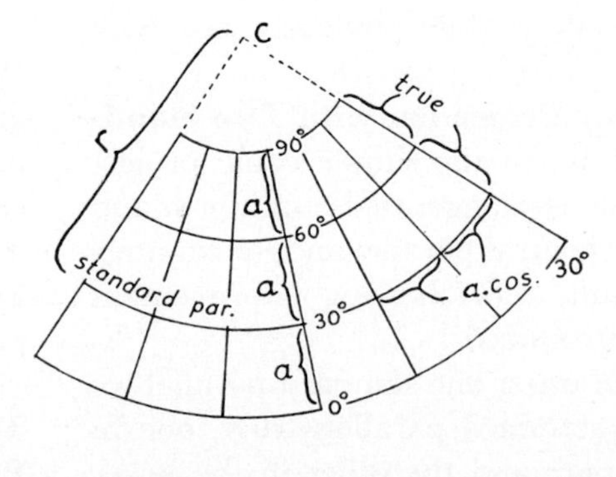


**Fig. 58**

**Figs. 57 and 58** The simple conic projection: Fig. 57, finding the radius of the standard parallel; Fig. 58, layout of the projection.

meridians. The pole is represented by a circular parallel at its true distance from the standard parallel. North and south of the central parallel the scale is exaggerated. It is not advisable to extend this projection too far north or south from the standard parallel, because of increasing distortion. This projection is neither equal-area nor conformal, but the parallels and meridians are at right angles and it is fairly accurate for small countries.

If the standard parallel is the equator, the tangent cone becomes a cylinder, and the consequent projection becomes a plane chart. If the standard parallel is the pole, the tangent cone becomes a plane, and the result is called the "polar azimuthal equidistant projection."

The conic projection is often used for atlas maps, not only because of its simple construction and relative accuracy but also because a map in this projection is divisible into sections. It is thus a great convenience to the map maker, for he can draw an entire region on one sheet, which can then be sectioned off and fitted to subsequent pages of an atlas. In the conic projection any meridian can be chosen as central meridian. This property is shared with the equirectangular, Mercator, cylindrical, and polar projections, but obviously not with any others.

**The Conic Projection with Two Standard Parallels.** In the simple conic projection the scale is exaggerated both north and south of the central parallel and, to counteract that fault, the following improvement has been introduced:

Instead of using one standard parallel we divide two standard parallels truly, one in the upper part and the other in the lower part of the map. The greatest accuracy is obtained if the selected standard parallels enclose two-thirds of the height of the map. The standard parallels are their true distance apart and their center point and radii are found according to Fig. 59. The parallels are arcs of circles drawn from the center point at their true distances. The meridians are straight lines through the division points of the standard parallels. A check on the construction is that the meridians have to meet in $O$. The scale will be slightly reduced along the central parallel and somewhat exaggerated along the marginal parallels. This scale error is very slight in small countries; even in a map of the United States it would nowhere exceed 2 per cent.

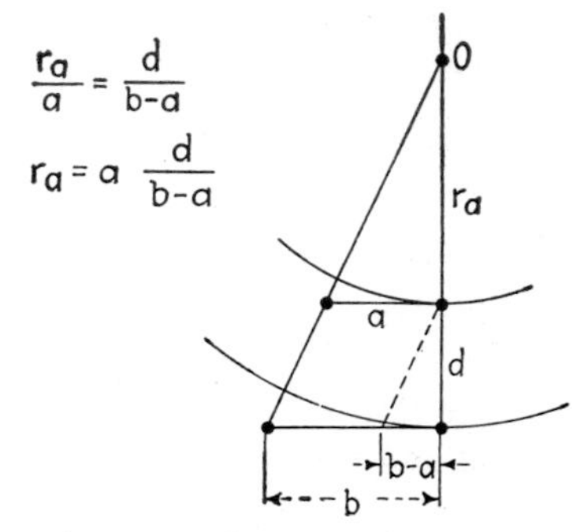


**Fig. 59** Finding the center $O$ for the conic projection with two standard parallels. $a$ and $b$ are the true lengths of the parallels or parts (say, 10°) of the parallels; $d$ is the true distance between the standard parallels.

The above projection is, to a certain extent, reminiscent of the projection of a globe upon a cone which cuts slightly into it. For this reason it is sometimes incorrectly called the "secant conic projection." We frequently find it used in atlas maps. The British 1:4,000,000 map of Asia is in this projection.

**The Conic Equal-area Projection with Two Standard Parallels, or the Albers Projection.** It is apparent that by varying the spaces between parallels a conic projection can be made equal-area. Such an equal-area projection with one standard parallel was constructed by Lambert in

1772, and another with two standard parallels was proposed by H. C. Albers of Gotha in 1805.

The latter projection, which combines a small scale error with equality of area, was used by several great surveys. It has concentric parallels and meridians that radiate from the center of the parallels. Two standard parallels are chosen, so that about two-thirds of the map is encompassed by them, and their radii are calculated so as to make the projection equal-area. This computation is quite involved.[1] Table XI contains the values for a map of the United States, to which country this projection is particularly well adapted. The standard parallels are then divided truly, and the points are connected with straight-line meridians. A check on the construction is the fact that all meridians must meet at the center of the parallels. The poles will be represented by parallels.

On a map of the United States the distortion of scale does not exceed 1 per cent in the center and 1.25 per cent on the margins; this is hardly any greater than the contraction and expansion of the paper with the change of humidity.

Extensive tables for the Albers projection are found in the *U.S. Coast and Geodetic Survey Special Publication* 130, 1927. The system has been used for a 1:750,000 map of Europe, published in Vienna, and also by some surveys in Russia. The formulas for the radii of the standard parallels are given here without their mathematical derivation.

$$r_1 = kR \cos \varphi_1$$

and

$$r_2 = kR \cos \varphi_2$$

where $r_1$ and $r_2$ are the radii of standard parallels; $\varphi_1$ and $\varphi_2$ are their latitudes; $R$ is the earth's radius; and

$$k = \frac{1}{\sin \frac{\varphi_1 + \varphi_2}{2} \cos \frac{\varphi_1 + \varphi_2}{2}}$$

The general formula for any radius is

$$r^2 = \tfrac{1}{2}(r_1^2 + r_2^2) + 2R^2(1 - k \sin \varphi)$$

[1] *U.S. Coast and Geodetic Survey Spec. Pubs.* 68 and 130.

**The Lambert Conformal Conic Projection with Two Standard Parallels.** This is the most common projection for air-navigation charts, as it has a small scale error and relatively straight azimuths within a few hundred miles. In this projection the concentric parallels are spaced so that every small quadrangle has the same proportions as on the globe. The meridians radiate from the center of the parallels and are placed truly on the two standard parallels. The radii of the parallels can be computed by the following formulas:

$$r_1 = m(\tan \tfrac{1}{2}\psi_1)^n \quad \text{and} \quad r_2 = m(\tan \tfrac{1}{2}\psi_2)^n$$

where $\psi$ is the colatitude,

$$n = \frac{\log \sin \psi_1 - \log \sin \psi_2}{\log \tan \frac{1}{2}\psi_1 - \log \tan \frac{1}{2}\psi_2}$$

and

$$m = \frac{R \sin \psi_1}{n(\tan \frac{1}{2}\psi_1)^n} \quad \text{or} \quad \frac{R \sin \psi_2}{n(\tan \frac{1}{2}\psi_2)^n}$$

There are several modifications of this projection, which have been developed recently for aeronautical charts.

The values of $r$ are tabulated for a map of the United States and for certain other regions, in the *U.S. Coast and Geodetic Survey Special Publication* 52. For the United States, 33° and 45° are chosen for standard parallels, and this results in a 0.5 per cent scale error in the center, and a 2.25 per cent scale error in Florida. If a more generally distributed scale error is desired, 29° and 45° can be chosen as standard parallels. This will reduce the scale error to 1.2 per cent in Florida but will increase it in the central regions. The projection was used also for

**Table XI** Table for the Construction of a Map of the United States on Albers Equal-area Projection with Two Standard Parallels at 25° and 45°

| *Latitude* | *Radius of parallel* | *Spacings of parallels* | *Longitude from central meridian* | *Chords on latitude* 25° | *Chords on latitude* 45° |
|---|---|---|---|---|---|
| | Meters | Meters | | Meters | Meters |
| 20° | 10 253 177 | | 1° | 102 184.68 | 78 745.13 |
| 21 | 10 145 579 | 107 598 | 5 | 510 866.82 | 393 682.00 |
| 22 | 10 037 540 | 108 039 | 25 | 2 547 270 | 1 962 966 |
| 23 | 9 929 080 | 108 460 | 30 | | 2 352 568 |
| 24 | 9 820 218 | 108 862 | | | |
| | | 109 249 | | | |
| 25 | 9 710 969 | | | | |
| 26 | 9 601 361 | 109 608 | | | |
| 27 | 9 401 409 | 109 952 | | | |
| 28 | 9 381 139 | 110 270 | | | |
| 29 | 9 270 576 | 110 563 | | | |
| 29°30′ | 9 215 188 | 110 838 | | | |
| 30 | 9 159 738 | | | | |
| 31 | 9 048 648 | 111 090 | | | |
| 32 | 8 937 337 | 111 311 | | | |
| 33 | 8 825 827 | 111 510 | | | |
| 34 | 8 714 150 | 111 677 | | | |
| | | 111 822 | | | |
| 35 | 8 602 328 | | | | |
| 36 | 8 490 392 | 111 936 | | | |
| 37 | 8 378 377 | 112 015 | | | |
| 38 | 8 266 312 | 112 065 | | | |
| 39 | 8 154 228 | 112 084 | | | |
| | | 112 065 | | | |
| 40 | 8 042 163 | | | | |
| 41 | 7 930 152 | 112 011 | | | |
| 42 | 7 818 231 | 111 921 | | | |
| 43 | 7 706 444 | 111 787 | | | |
| 44 | 7 594 828 | 111 616 | | | |
| | | 111 402 | | | |
| 45 | 7 483 426 | | | | |
| 45°30′ | 7 427 822 | 111 138 | | | |
| 46 | 7 372 288 | | | | |
| 47 | 7 261 459 | 110 829 | | | |
| 48 | 7 150 987 | 110 472 | | | |
| 49 | 7 040 925 | 110 062 | | | |
| | | 109 592 | | | |
| 50 | 6 931 333 | | | | |
| 51 | 6 822 264 | 109 069 | | | |
| 52 | 6 713 780 | 108 484 | | | |

the maps of the western war zone in the First World War, because its scale error did not exceed 0.5 per cent for that area.

The projection was developed by J. H. Lambert (1728–1777), a German mathematician who was chiefly responsible for placing the science of map projections on a mathematical basis and for introducing the ideas of conformal and equal-area projections. He also invented several other important projections.

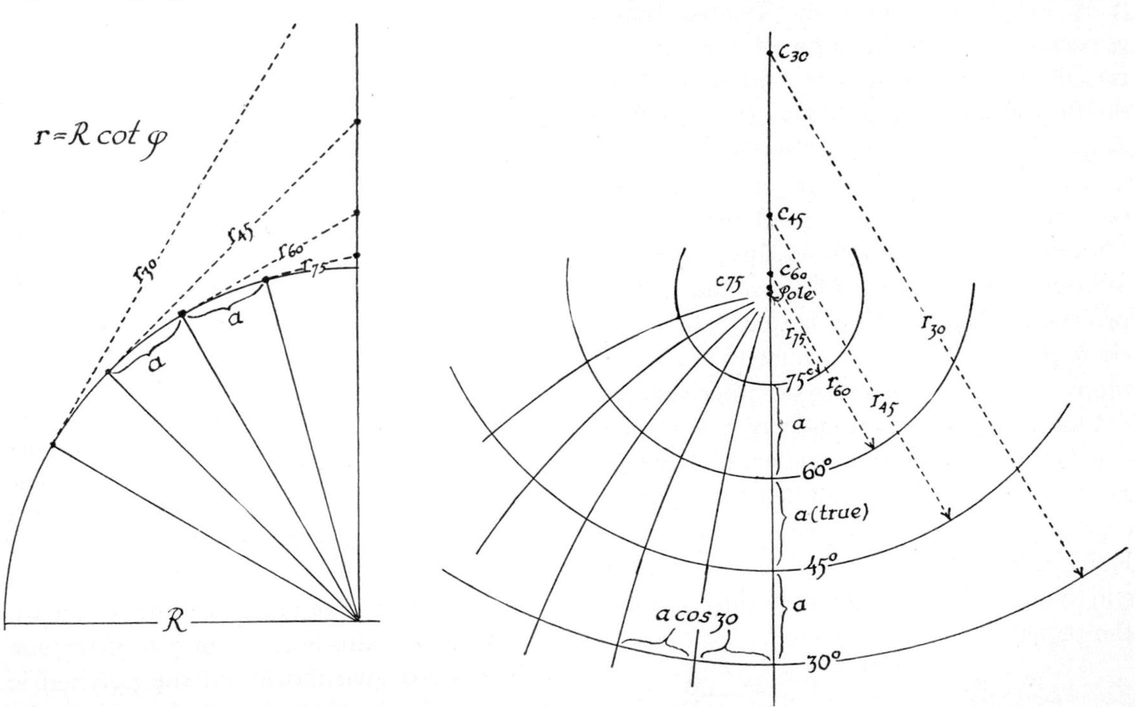


**Fig. 60** The polyconic projection has a truly divided central meridian, with nonconcentric circular parallels. The parallels are truly divided for the meridians.

**Polyconic Projection.** If we divide the earth's surface into narrow belts of latitude and draw to each of them a strip of a tangent cone upon which the surface of the globe is projected from its center, we arrive at the basic idea of the polyconic projection. The projection actually used, however, is a modification of this principle.

The polyconic projection has a straight, vertical, central meridian which is divided truly for the parallels; and the parallels themselves are nonconcentric circles, the radii of which can be constructed according to Fig. 57, or calculated ($r = R \cot \varphi$), as in the conic projection. Each of them is divided truly, and the curves which connect division points form the meridians. From this construction it follows that the equator will be a straight line, and the pole will be a point at a true distance from the equator, as measured on the surface of the globe. The distortion of scale is small near the center of the projection but increases rapidly at the peripheries.

The polyconic projection is neither conformal nor equal-area, but near the central meridian it has characteristics of each. The scale error is less than 1 per cent at any point within 560 miles of the central meridian.

This grid is eminently suitable for topographic maps when each sheet must be plotted independently. The construction is not difficult when a table has been prepared for the vertical and horizontal coordinates of each intersection. Such tables are published in the *U.S. Geological Survey Bulletin* 809 and in the *U.S. Coast and Geodetic Survey Special Publications* 5 and 57.

The polyconic projection is used on the U.S. Geological Survey topographic sheets, on the earlier sheets of the U.S. Coast and Geodetic Survey, by the Great Lakes Survey, and by various army surveys. Indeed, it is so popular with the United States government that, in spite of the curving meridians and the 6 per cent scale error on the peripheries, it is also employed for maps of the entire United States. Inasmuch as private cartographers like to copy government sheets, almost all maps of the United States are drawn on this projection, although for most purposes the Albers projection would serve better. The polyconic projection is also used for the 1:50,000 maps of France and by some other surveys.

One of the disadvantages of this projection is that only those sheets which have the same central meridian can be fitted together correctly. Fitting in the east-west direction is imperfect, but across only a few sheets it still remains within the stretching limit of the paper.

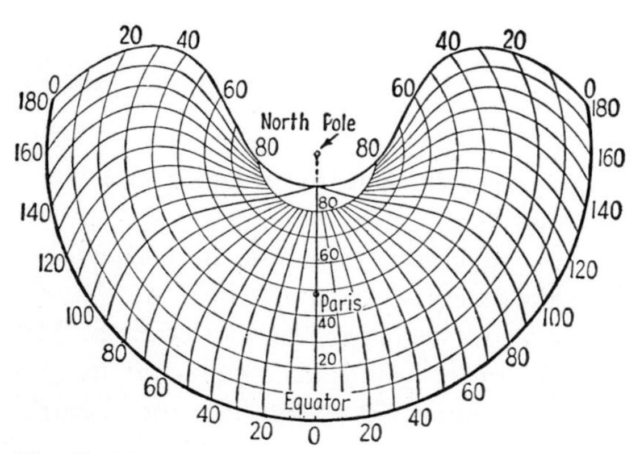


**Fig. 61** Hemisphere in Bonne projection centered on Paris. Note that the pole is not identical with the center of the parallels. (*From Deetz and Adams, "Elements of Map Projection."*)

The polyconic projection was devised in 1820 by Ferdinand Hassler, the organizer and first director of the U.S. Coast Survey.

An interesting modification of it is used on the 1:1,000,000 map of the world, each sheet of which covers 4° of latitude and 6° of longitude. The radii of the limiting parallels are calculated as before, but their distance is true only on the second and fifth meridian and somewhat too short on the central meridian. The limiting parallels are divided truly, and the division points are connected with straight lines to form the meridians. All other parallels are circles which divide the second and fifth meridian truly and the other meridians proportionately. Tables for the construction of such sheets by means of rectangular coordinates can be found in Deetz and Adams, "Elements of Map Projection."

The advantage of this projection lies in its small scale error, which does not exceed 1/1,300 on each sheet. The straight-border meridians and the circular parallels enable us to fit together any number of maps in the north-south and east-west directions, but in no other directions. Practically, however, it is possible to fit together about nine adjacent sheets with a slight amount of stretching.

**Polyhedric Projections.** The German, Austrian, Italian, and Spanish topographic sheets are drawn mostly on the polyhedric grid, in which small spherical quadrangles are projected upon a plane trapezium with identical corners. This projection has horizontal parallels and straight, converging meridians. Modifications of the principle are common; the central parallel and meridian can each be of true length and subdivided equally. Within the limits of one topographic sheet, the polyhedric projection is hardly distinguishable from the polyconic.

**The Bonne Projection.** This system was designed by Rigobert Bonne (1727–1795), a French cartographer, although similar projections had been used at an earlier date.[1] It has a straight central meridian which is crossed by a circular standard parallel, the radius of which is $r = R \cot \varphi$. The central meridian is divided truly, and all parallels are concentric with the standard one. Thus far, it is identical with the simple conic; the difference is that each parallel is divided truly, and the curves which connect these divisions constitute the meridians.

Every small quadrangle in the Bonne projection has both base and height true to scale and, therefore, the system is equal-area. Shapes are accurate along the central meridian; distortion increases toward the sides. The pole is a point that is not coincident with the center of the parallels. It is possible to draw either one hemisphere or the entire world in this projection, but because of excessive lateral distortion it is rarely used for more than one continent. With a 15° standard, however, it makes a fair world map.

[1] The author noticed this projection used in an anonymous French map, 1699.

The Bonne projection is utilized on the 1:80,000 sheets of France in such a way that one grid is prepared for the entire country. Individual sections are later cut from this network, with the result that on most sheets all parallels and meridians curve the same way. The Bonne system is used also for the topographic sheets of small countries, such as the Netherlands, Belgium, and Switzerland. Moreover, in atlas maps the continents of Asia and Europe are usually shown in this projection, in spite of the fact that it cannot be cut in sections similar to those of the conic-projection maps. For this reason, and because of its large distortion of scale, the Bonne grid seems to have lost prestige in recent years, and its place has been taken largely by the azimuthal group of projections.

If the standard parallel is the equator, $r$ is infinite, and the parallels are horizontal, equidistant lines, divided truly—the projection becomes identical with the sinusoidal projection.

# CHAPTER 8: *The Azimuthal Projections*

The azimuthal, or zenithal, networks are developed by projecting the surface of the globe upon a plane from some eyepoint. Different eyepoints make different projections. The eyepoint of the gnomonic projection is in the center of the globe; in the stereographic projection it lies in the antipode; in the orthographic projection it is in infinite distance, which means that the projecting rays are parallel. Other azimuthal projections, such as the equidistant and equal-area developments, are modifications of this process. All members of this group, however, have the following properties in common:

1. All great circles passing through the center of projection are represented as straight lines and have correct bearings or azimuths—hence the name "azimuthal."
2. All points equally distant from the center of the projection are also equally distant on the map. A circle connecting these equidistant points is called the "horizon circle," because it represents the horizon from a certain altitude above the center of the projection. All horizon circles remain circular on the map.
3. All places equally distant from the center have equal distortion.
4. All azimuthal projections differ from each other only in the length of the radii of the horizon circles, and thus they can easily be transformed one into the other. The scale of radial distortion can be obtained from the spacing of the parallels in the polar cases of the various azimuthal projections (see Fig. 75).

In the cylindrical and conical projections the axis of the cylinder or cone usually coincides with the earth's axis; oblique

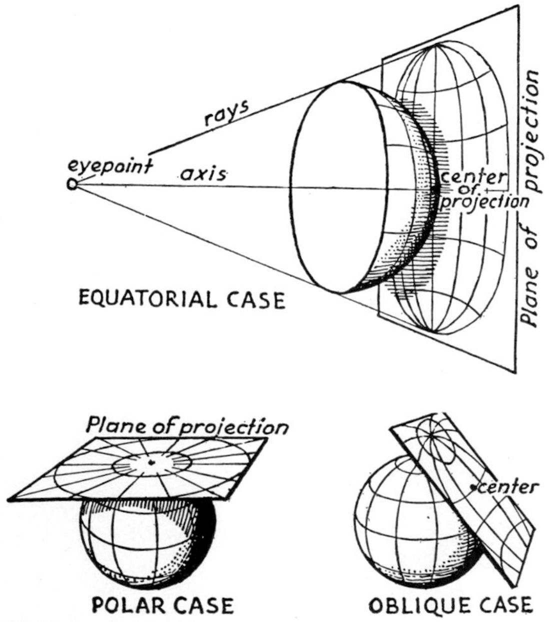

**Fig. 62** Azimuthal projections are drawn from any point of view. The plane of projection need not be tangent. (*C. S. Hammond & Co.*)

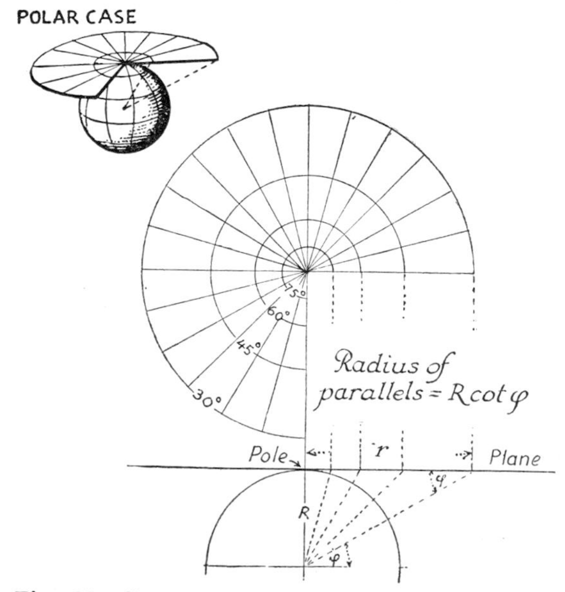


**Fig. 63** Construction of the gnomonic projection, polar case.

forms are rarely used. Azimuthal projections are common in all three positions:

1. *Polar*, with the plane perpendicular to the earth's axis
2. *Equatorial*, with plane perpendicular to the equatorial plane
3. *Oblique*, with plane in any other position

**Gnomonic Projection.** This projection is derived by projecting the surface of the globe, from its center, upon a plane. This plane is not necessarily tangent because maps projected on other planes parallel to a tangent plane would differ only in scale. Photographs of the stars are in gnomonic projection.

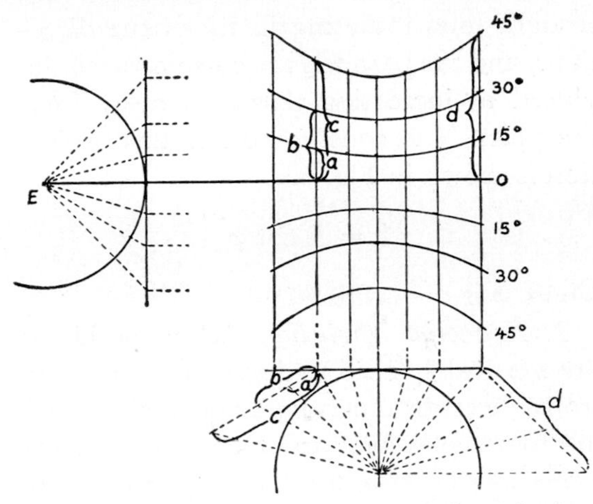


**Fig. 64** Construction of the gnomonic projection, equatorial case.

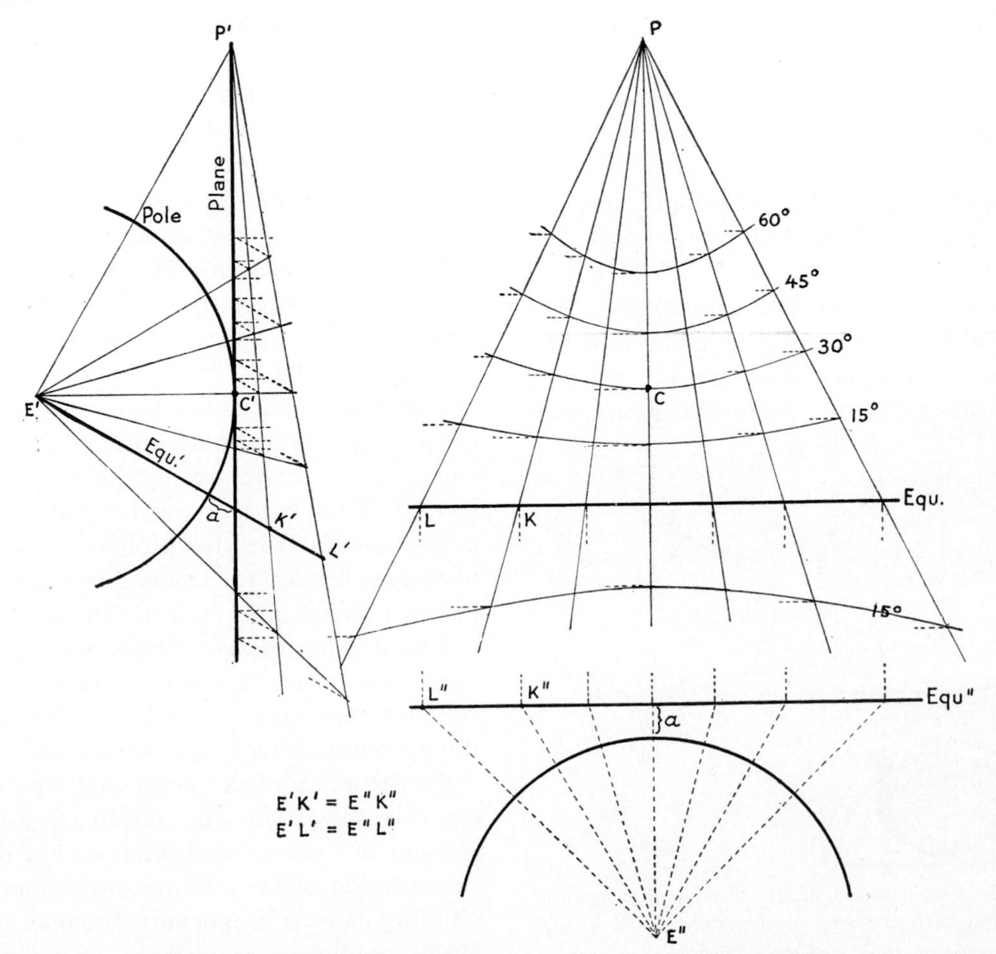


**Fig. 65** Construction of the gnomonic projection, oblique case.

1. *Polar Projection.* The meridians are straight lines radiating in their true directions, and the parallels are concentric circles placed at increasing distances away from the poles. The construction of this projection is shown in Fig. 63.

$$1 = R \cot \varphi$$

where $\varphi$ is the latitude.

2. *Equatorial Projection.* The meridians are verticals placed at increasing distances from the central meridian, and the parallels are hyperbolas with asymptotes of the same angle as the latitudes. The construction of this projection is shown in Fig. 64.

3. *Oblique Projection.* Construction of the oblique gnomonic projection is shown in Fig. 65. On the left is the side view of the globe; and the plane of projection, which is perpendicular to the paper, shows as a vertical line. In the bottom figure the plane of the equator lies turned down into the plane of paper. The meridians and the equator, being great circles, are represented by straight lines on the map. The parallels are hyperbolas, and their intersections with the straight meridians must be located first on the side diagram and then carried over to the main figure. In the side figure each

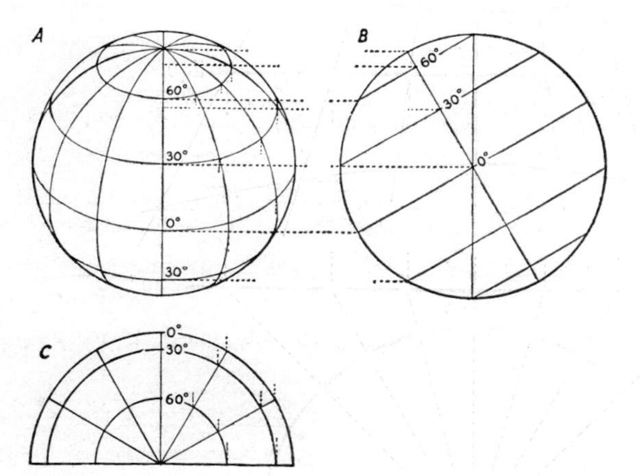


**Fig. 66** Construction of the oblique orthographic projection with the axis of the globe tilted at 60°. Note the visual quality of the projection.

meridional plane is turned down around the $E'P'$ axis onto the surface of the paper, and turned back again in place after the piercing point of the projecting rays has been found.

The chief merit of the gnomonic projection is that *all great circles are represented as straight lines.* These great circles define planes that pass through the center of the globe, and if extended as far as the plane of the projection the intersection of the two planes will be a straight line.

This property is of the greatest importance in navigation, because the shortest route between two points is that of the great circle. For that reason the U.S. Hydrographic Office has published charts of all oceans in the gnomonic projection. To plot the course of transoceanic voyages, the navigator draws a straight line on a gnomonic chart. The steering of the vessel, however, is done with a compass, and it is customary to transfer the great-circle route from the gnomonic to a Mercator chart, on which it will appear as a curve. As it is impracticable continually to change the compass directions, this curve is usually divided into shorter sections of straight compass directions.

Gnomonic charts are used also in connection with radio and seismic work, for the waves travel more or less on great-circle routes. The mathematical limit of this projection is the hemisphere, and the distortion becomes extreme if it is extended to more than a quarter of the globe.

**The Orthographic Projection.** In this the surface of the globe is projected by parallel rays upon a perpendicular plane, the eyepoint being in infinite distance.

Construction of the polar and equatorial cases is shown in Fig. 66 by *C* and *B*. Neither of these is used often except in the construction of the oblique projection. The oblique case is important because of its visual qualities, for it looks like a globe.

The parallels are ellipses, the major axes of which equal the diameters of the parallels. The minor axes can be projected across from the side figure. The meridians are also ellipses, and their intersections with the parallels can be carried up from the polar projection. If the projection is symmetrically arranged, only one-half need be drawn, for the other half can be copied with a transparent tracing paper.

The oblique orthographic projection of the globe is widely used in art and advertising, and its value for school maps is becoming more appreciated. Although the distortion along the peripheries is extreme, the eye does not perceive it, because we imagine that we see a globe instead of a map. This projection can be focused on any continent, which will then appear large in the center of the map; the relationship to other continents can be noted along the sides. It is useful in the earliest stages of geographical instruction for introducing the idea of maps to children.

The mathematical qualities of this projection, however, are less pleasant. It is neither equal-area nor conformal, and it is limited to the representation of one hemisphere. The radial scale decreases rapidly toward the peripheries, and the scale is true only along circles centered on the center point of the projection.

The orthographic projection was used occasionally during the early Renaissance (Stabius drew a large hemisphere map), but in later times it was rarely employed. Only recently has it been revived for artistic and school maps. It became very popular at the beginning of the Second World War, as it was easily understood by people not accustomed to interpretation of world maps. The popular term "global" maps usually means either the orthographic projection or a photograph of a globe.

**Orthoapsidal Projections.** In this group of projections a parallel and meridian system is applied to any solid other than a globe, and an

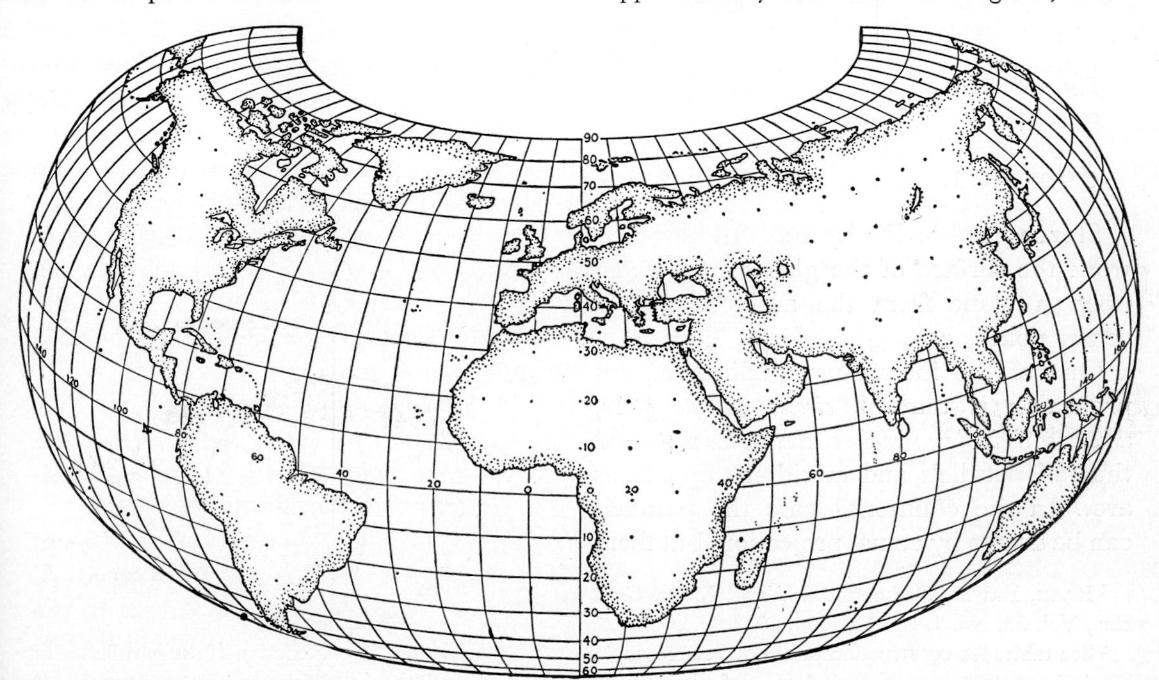


**Fig. 67** The armadillo projection got its name from the little Mexican animal that coils itself into a sphere if frightened. The construction of the map is similar to the orthographic projection. (*Courtesy of Geog. Rev.* Vol. 33, p. 133, 1943.)

orthographic view forms the map. Orthoapsidal maps[1] can be drawn upon a toroid, hyperboloid, bifolium, trifolium, etc. The advantage of these projections is that the whole earth can be shown instead of a hemisphere. Although the distortion on the sides is very great, the eye does not perceive it because it sees the picture of a three-dimensional body instead of a map. The armadillo and the half-ellipsoid projections, if tilted about 15°, are perhaps the world maps with the largest land area proportionate to their size; thus they became popular for maps of world relationships.

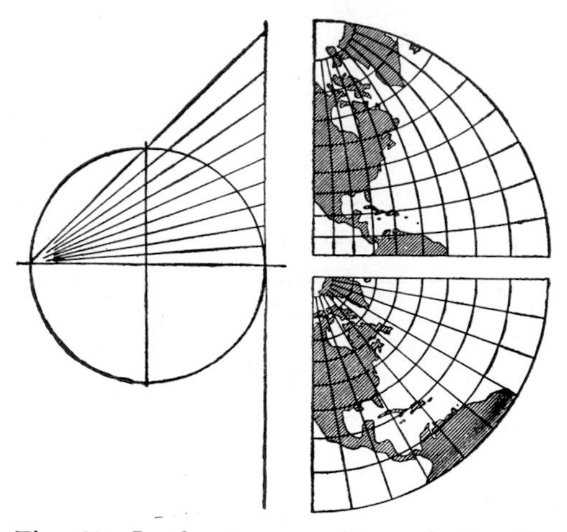

**Fig. 68** In the stereographic projection the scale is increasing from the center toward the peripheries. (*From Finch-Trewartha, "Elements of Geography."*)

**Stereographic Projection.** In this network the surface of the globe is projected upon a plane from the antipode of the center point.

One of the interesting qualities of this projection is that *all circles on the globe, whatever their size, remain circles on the map*, and thus all parallels and meridians appear as arcs. In the equatorial case the parallels can be drawn by actual projection, but there is an easier method: the center of the parallel circle is at a point (Fig. 69) which we obtain by drawing a tangent with the angle of the latitude, and from this construction it follows that

$$AO = R \operatorname{cosec} \varphi$$

The construction of meridians is shown in Fig. 69.

$$OF = R \cot \lambda$$

In olden times stereographic hemisphere maps were used almost exclusively, but in recent years they have lost popularity because of their great variation in scale. The parallels and meridians are much closer together in the center of the map than near the peripheries. The projection is conformal, as all meridians are at right angles to the parallels, and their scale relationship is correct in any small area.

The constructional details of the oblique stereographic projection are shown in Fig. 70. The construction is based on the fact that even in the oblique case, the meridians and parallels are circular arcs. This projection is often used in atlases to show water and land hemispheres, and also as a stage of transformation into more difficult oblique azimuthal projections.[2]

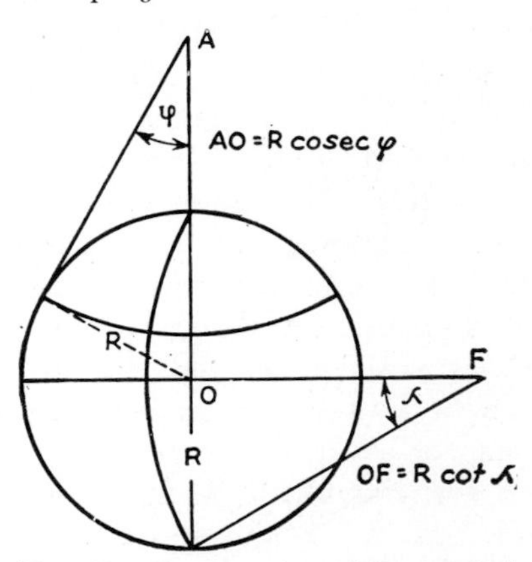


**Fig. 69** Construction of the parallels and the meridians in the equatorial case of the stereographic projection.

[1] RAISZ, ERWIN, Orthoapsidal World Maps, *Geog. Rev.*, Vol. 33, No. 1, pp. 132–134, 1943.

[2] See tables for construction of oblique stereoscopic hemispheres for every second degree of tilt, *Harvard Univ. Inst. Geog. Exploration*, 1942. 28 pp.

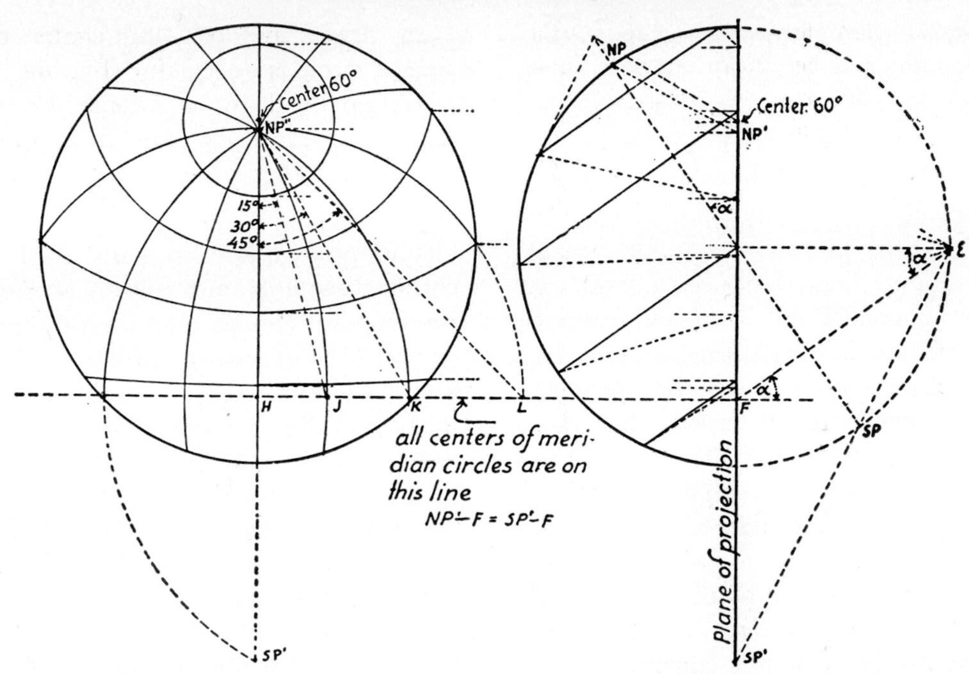


**Fig. 70** Construction of the oblique stereographic projection. On the right is a side view of a tilted globe, halved by the plane of projection. *E* is the eyepoint. Each point is projected from the eyepoint upon the plane of projection and then carried over to the map on the left. *H* is the horizontal parallel and locus of the centers of meridians. South of *H* the parallels curve the other way.

**Other Azimuthal Projections.** In the orthographic projection the peripheries are too small in scale, whereas in the stereographic the peripheries are too large. However, we can choose the eyepoint of an azimuthal projection so that the distortion is more evenly distributed. Clarke's minimum-error projection has the eyepoint between 1.65 and 1.35 radius distance from the center of the globe, depending on the area to be represented. In LaHire's network the eyepoint is 1.71 radius distance from the center of the globe. These maps are similar in appearance, and on both somewhat more than a hemisphere can be shown. If England is placed in the center of the projection, almost the entire land surface of the earth can be included in an extended hemisphere map.

If the eyepoint is still farther, the projection will look like a photograph of a globe. This is often used by artists instead of laborious construction and is called "perspective projection."

**Azimuthal Equidistant Projection.** In this projection not only has every point a

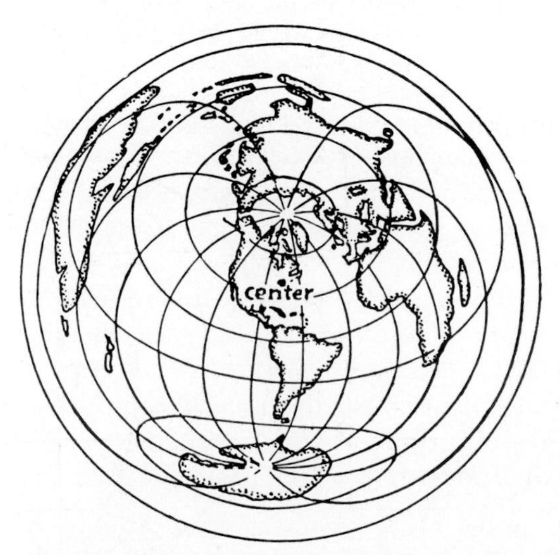


**Fig. 71** In the azimuthal equidistant projection, every point is at its true distance and in the right direction from the center. (*C. S. Hammond & Co.*)

true direction (azimuth) from the center, but the distance of each point from the center is also true. However, distances and directions between other points are distorted. Such a map, however, cannot be obtained by actually projecting, from any eyepoint, the globe's surface upon a plane.

*Polar Case.* This is the most commonly used projection for the Arctic and Antarctic. The meridians are radiating straight lines, and the parallels are equidistant circles placed at their true distances. The radius of the equator is a half meridian. This projection obviously creates an exaggeration of scale along the parallels, which increases toward the peripheries.

The equatorial case of this projection is rarely used, but the *oblique case* is important because, if a projection is constructed for a certain city, all distances and globe directions will be true from that place. No other projection could do the same.

This projection has a relatively small scale error if we do not go beyond a hemisphere. However, it is possible to show the entire earth, although the distortion increases rapidly toward the peripheries. The antipodal point opposite the center of the projection is represented by a circle, the diameter of which equals the earth's circumference.

The projection has many uses. Great-circle directions and distances from the center point can be read directly for flying or navigation. Radio broadcasting beams are laid out on maps centered on the transmitting station. The location of earthquakes can be measured off directly if such a chart is constructed with the earthquake recording station as the center. This is also the best projection for isochronic maps and for certain cartograms. It has been used also for continent maps, for instance, the National Geographic Society maps of Asia and Europe.

**The Azimuthal Equal-area Projection.** This network, designed by J. H. Lambert in 1772, has gained in popularity in recent years. Its construction can best be understood in the polar case. From Fig. 72 it

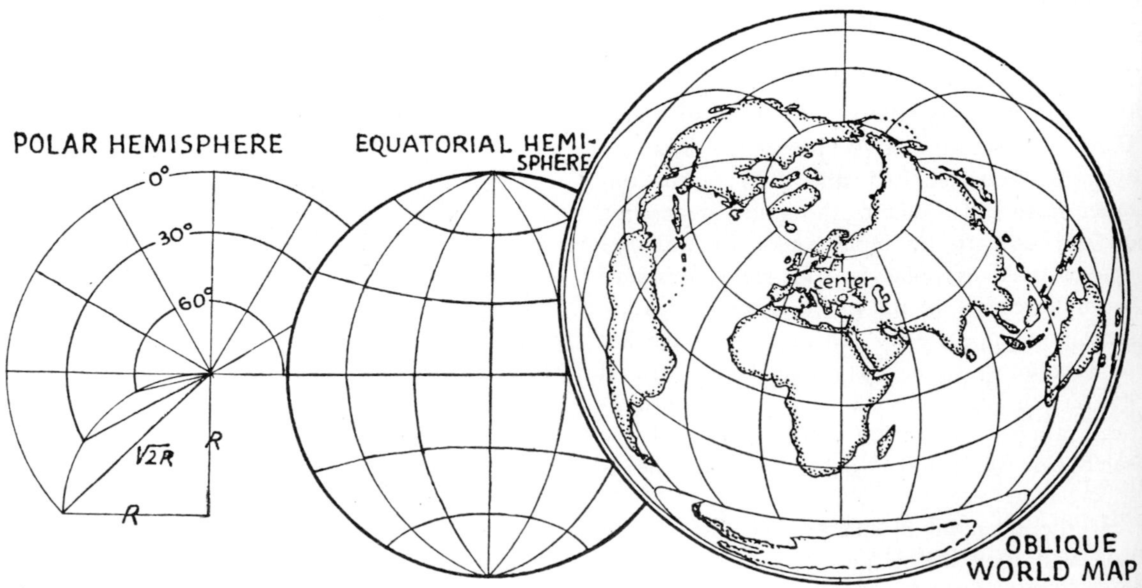


**Fig. 72** The azimuthal equal-area projection is commonly used for continents and "air-age" maps. The oblique map can be centered on the center point of all lands. (*C. S. Hammond & Co.*)

can be seen that the radius of the hemisphere equals the length of the secant between the pole and the equator. The radius of the map of a hemisphere is $r = R\sqrt{2}$, and its surface equals $r^2\pi = 2R^2\pi$, the same as the surface of a half globe. $R$ is the radius of the globe. Similarly, it can be proved that every parallel belt has the same area on the globe as on the map.

The polar case is often used for polar maps. The north polar map is often extended to include the whole earth or at least all continents. The South Pole will be a circle with a radius of $2R$. This map is widely used to show world air lines. It makes a good counterpart for a Mercator map.

The equatorial case of this projection is often used for hemispheres. Its construction is somewhat complex, but tables were prepared by Lambert himself.

The oblique case is much favored for continents. The construction of a network centered on parallel 40 is tabulated in the *U.S. Coast and Geodetic Survey Special Publication* 68. The parallels appear as arcs that are flat in the center and curve sharply toward the sides, and the meridians are nearly elliptical. The scale error of this projection is very small; nowhere on a map of the United States does it exceed 2 per cent. An oblique projection centered on the center of all lands in southeastern Europe makes a compact world map (see Fig. 72). The construction of oblique projections in general is discussed below.

**Aitoff Equal-area Projection.** This system is often used for world maps. The earth appears as an ellipse, and the central meridian is half the length of the equator. The parallels and meridians are obtained by taking a hemisphere in the Lambert azimuthal equal-area projection and doubling the horizontal coordinates of every intersection, leaving the vertical coordinates unchanged. The Aitoff projection also resembles to a certain extent the Mollweide network, but the parallels are slightly curved, and the angles are somewhat less distorted. It is obvious from its construction that the projection is equal-area.

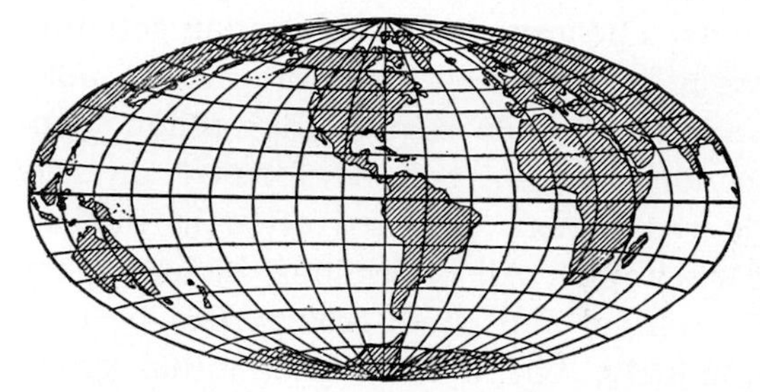

**Fig. 73** The Aitoff projection is the same as the Lambert azimuthal equal-area projection with the horizontal component of each point doubled. (*From Finch-Trewartha, "Elements of Geography."*)

**Transverse Projections.** These projections are related to a globe that is turned 90° to its usual orientation. Some authors use the term "transverse" in the same way as the term "oblique," thus causing confusion. The term "meridional" is also used, which is an even more confusing term. Most transverse projections are polar cases of the equatorial projections.

*Transverse Mercator Projection* (*Gauss Conformal Projection*). The easiest way to understand this projection is to relate it to a horizontal cylinder tangent along a meridian (or to a smaller cylinder cutting into the globe) in the same way that the usual Mercator map is related to a vertical cylinder tangent at the equator. On the usual Mercator map, the scale is true along the equator, and the pole cannot be shown; on the transverse Mercator, the scale is true along the meridian and points $A$ and $B$ cannot be shown. The projection is used by the Ordnance Survey of Great Britain and is also used as a base map for state grids in the United States. The projection continues to be conformal but loses the quality of straight rhumb lines.

**The Construction of Oblique Projections.** The great centers of human activities are not centered on the equator or the pole, and thus it is no wonder that oblique projections, which can be focused on any desired region, are used often in modern cartography. All projections, including the cylindrical and conic groups, can be used obliquely, but it is the azimuthal group where this is the most common. The construction of oblique projections is laborious. The three most commonly used methods are the following:

1. *Transformation from the Oblique Stereographic.* This method can be applied to azimuthal projections only. First an oblique stereographic projection with the required tilt is constructed; this can be drawn according to Fig. 70 with great accuracy, as the parallels and meridians are circular arcs. Tables are available for the centers of the circles for every 2° of tilt.

The transformation into the azimuthal equidistant and equal-area projections is done with a specially prepared radial scale. Every point in the equidistant projection will be the same radius from the center as in the stereographic, but its distance from the center will differ. The scale is a meridian divided into degrees of latitude in the polar projection. We draw both scales in different colors on the same strip of paper and pin the 0 point very exactly with a fine needle on the center of the stereographic map. Reduction or enlargement is possible. We read the radial distance of an intersection to $\frac{1}{10}$° accuracy in the stereographic pro-

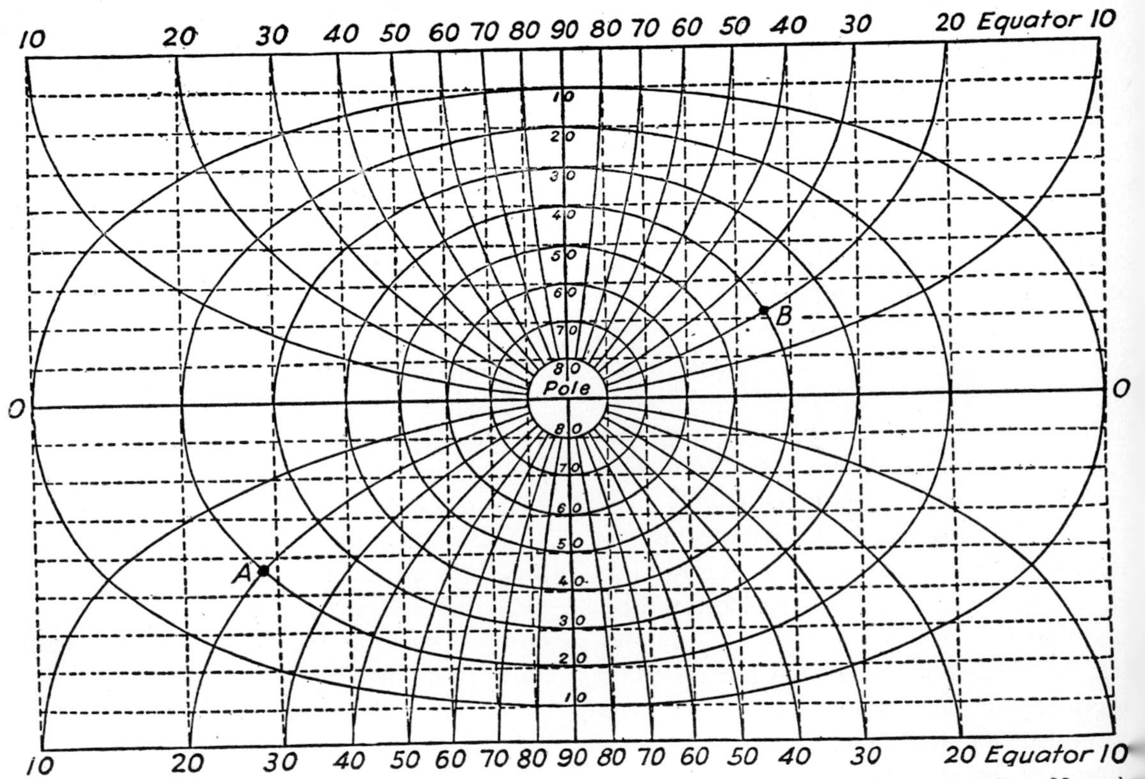


**Fig. 74** The transverse Mercator projection can be related to a cylinder tangent along a meridian. Near the central meridian it makes a good conformal projection. (*After Deetz.*)

jection, and prick the same number of degrees in the other projection along the same radius.

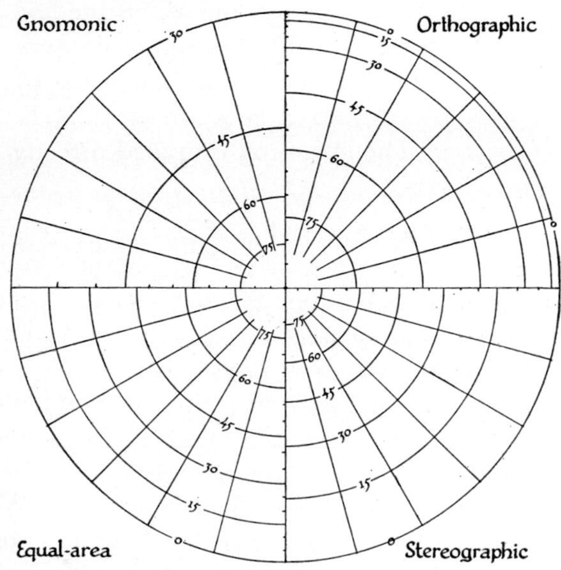


**Fig. 75** All azimuthal projections differ from each other only in the radii of their horizon circles. They can be transformed into each other according to the radial scale.

In the stereographic projection it is not practical to go much beyond the hemisphere, but the whole world can be shown in the equidistant projections. Considering that the distance between an intersection and its antipodal is constant and equals 180°, the outer points can be easily pricked by sliding a straight paper strip on which 180° are marked along the central needle. In the azimuthal equal-area projection where the radial scale is variable make a 360° long graduated paper strip, pivot it around the center, and mark off $l$ and $180° \, l$ from each intersection (see Fig. 76).

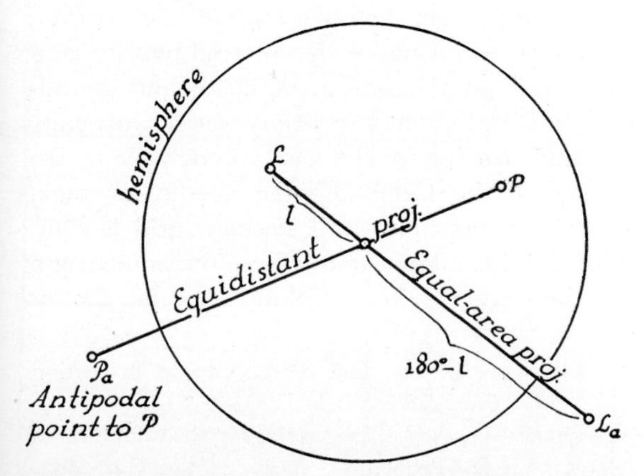


**Fig. 76** In the construction of azimuthal equidistant or equal-area projections, the antipodal points to any point will be on a line passing through the center of projection, 180° apart.

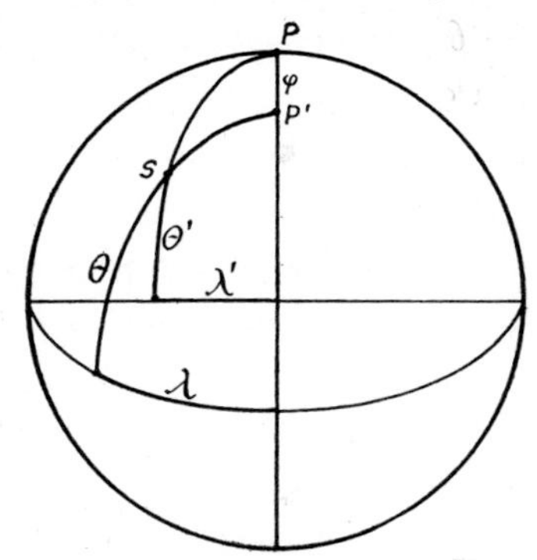


**Fig. 77** Transformation of one spherical coordinate system into another.

2. *Transformation by Spherical Coordinates.* First an equatorial (or polar) projection is drawn; then the intersections of the parallels and meridians in the oblique system are located by their coordinates in reference to the equatorial system. The points are then connected to form the new parallels and meridians.

It is convenient to take the central meridian as prime meridian for both projections. When the network is completed, any meridian can be taken as prime.

Let us assume that the new pole is shifted with $\varphi°$ in respect to the old pole on the central meridian. The solution of the spherical triangle $PP'S$ gives the following results for any point $S$:

$P'$ = old pole
$P$ = new pole
$\varphi$ = degrees of shift
$\theta$ = latitude in new system
$\lambda$ = longitude in new system

$\theta'$ = latitude in old system
$\lambda'$ = longitude in old system
$S$ = intersection of any parallel and meridian in the new system

We are interested in getting $\theta'$ and $\lambda'$, the latitude and longitude in the equatorial system for every $S$ point. By the law of cosines

$$\cos (90° - \theta') = \cos \varphi \cos (90° - \theta) + \sin \varphi \sin (90° - \theta) \cos (180° - \lambda)$$

from which

$$\sin \theta' = \sin \theta \cos \varphi - \sin \varphi \cos \theta \cos \lambda$$

from which $\theta'$ can be obtained. From the law of sines

$$\frac{\sin (180° - \lambda)}{\sin (90° - \theta')} = \frac{\sin \lambda'}{\sin (90° - \theta)}$$

which gives

$$\sin \lambda' = \frac{\sin \lambda \cos \theta}{\cos \theta'}$$

from which $\lambda'$ can be obtained. Thus for each intersection, $\lambda'$ and $\theta'$ can be tabulated. However, the laying out of the points is not easy. The distances have to be measured off along curved lines, and the longitude scale especially is very variable. Tables for every 5° of tilt were published by E. Hammer, "Uber die geographisch wichtigsten Kartenprojektionen . . . ," Stuttgart, 1889.

*Rotation Method.* This is in certain cases the fastest and most accurate method of transforming an equatorial azimuthal projection into an oblique one. The method was described for the stereographic projection by S. L. Penfield,[1] and analyzed by A. J. Dilloway,[2] and extended in use by R. E. Harrison.[3] The following is quoted directly from Harrison.

To illustrate the procedure, the construction of an orthographic projection tangent at 35°N will be described. This is the procedure followed in making any azimuthal projection, with only minor and rather obvious differences.

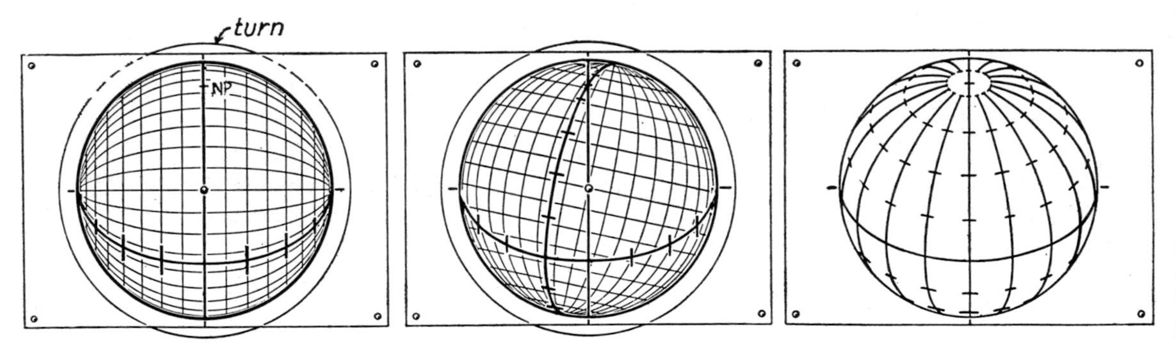


**Fig. 78** Three stages in the construction of an orthographic grid from a nomograph. Light lines show the nomograph; heavy lines, the construction on the tracing paper. (*Courtesy of Geog. Rev.* Vol. 33., p. 656.)

The circular nomograph is placed on a drawing board and covered with a rectangular piece of tracing paper that overlaps the nomograph on the sides but not at the top and bottom, and is tacked on the board. A needle, or round-shanked thumbtack, is firmly thrust vertically through tracing paper and nomograph at the center of the latter. As the needle, or tack, remains in position until the new grid is completed, it is well first to reinforce the nomograph at the center with cellulose tape or similar

[1] Penfield, S. L., The Stereographic Projection . . . , *Am. Jour. Sci.*, Vol. 11, 1901.

[2] Dilloway, A. J., The Cartographical Solution of Great Circle Problems, *Royal Aeronautical Soc.*, January, 1942.

[3] Harrison, R. E., The Nomograph as an Instrument in Map Making, *Geog. Rev.*, Vol. 33, pp. 655–657, 1943.

material. The nomograph is first rotated so that its equator is upright (stage I, Fig. 78). The intersections of the equator and the central meridian with the circumferential margin are then lightly marked on the tracing paper. Thirty-five degrees are counted off below the center along the equator of the nomograph; the meridian passing through this point becomes the equator of the new grid. This is traced freehand or with appropriate curves, and the intersections of the parallels of the nomograph with the new equator are marked at the desired interval of the grid. This should be done so that the angles of the intersections are correctly preserved, because of a remarkable feature of the nomographic method: instead of providing horizontal and vertical coordinates to establish the points of crossing as in mathematical and other graphic procedures, it gives not only the point but the correct angle of any intersection on the projection. Before changing the orientation of the nomograph, the North Pole is marked by counting 90° from the new equator along the upright center line. (When making an azimuthal equidistant or equal-area projection, the South Pole is also marked.)

At this stage we have the North Pole and an equator on which the meridional intersections are marked (stage I, Fig. 78). We can now add all the meridians to the map grid. This is accomplished in the same manner as finding a great circle nomographically, namely, by rotating the nomograph until the North Pole and the meridional intersection of the equator are on the same nomograph meridian or occupy the same relative position between two meridians. The meridian is drawn in its entirety, and while in this position the appropriate crossings of the parallels (with their proper angles of intersection) are noted on the meridian (stage II, Fig. 78). Since the intersections rarely coincide exactly with the parallels on the nomograph, it is generally necessary to interpolate. However, in working with a one-degree nomograph the proper intersections will be so close to a parallel that they can be drawn directly with little loss of accuracy. Furthermore, one often finds a simple means of checking the accuracy of the interpolations. For example, on the orthographic projection advantage can be taken of the fact that all lines connecting the intersections of parallels along any two meridians are parallel. With a parallel ruling device the intersections along any meridian can be ticked off from the corresponding intersections along the central meridian, since these are already established.

The nomograph is then rotated to obtain the next meridian, and so on, until all are drawn in. At this stage the grid consists of an equator and a complete set of meridians marked with the crossings of the parallels (stage III, Fig. 78), and it is a simple matter to complete the parallels, since these crossings form an almost continuous curve of short, straight segments. The grid can be drawn first in pencil and later in ink, or it can be inked directly. It is a most satisfying experience to draw a brand-new grid in ink without the necessity for any previous pencil drawing, to say nothing of not having to erase horizontal and vertical construction lines. A similar procedure in the case of cylindrical maps involves translation along the equator instead of simple rotation.

## Other Conventional Projections

This group of projections includes those which cannot be classified with any of the previous groups.

**The Globular Projection.** This projection was devised by Nicolosi in the seventeenth century. It is often used for hemispheres, and its construction is very simple. The central meridian, the equator, and the peripheral circle are each divided equally, and the points are connected with arcs of circles. This network is obviously neither equal-area nor conformal, but it has no unpleasant proportions and is true to scale on the central meridian and the equator. On all other places the scale is exaggerated.

**Table XII** Key to Projections

| | *Parallels* | *Meridians* | *Projection* | *Merit* | *Use* |
|---|---|---|---|---|---|
| 1 | Horizontal, spaced equally at true distances | Vertical, spaced equally, true on standard par. | RECTANGULAR | Easy to construct | City maps, less exact maps |
| 2 | " " closer near equator | " " " " " equator | MERCATOR | Conformal<br>Straight loxodromes | Charts, world maps |
| 3 | " " equally, at true distances | Sine curves, " " " " each par. | SINUSOIDAL | Equal-area | Tropics |
| 4 | " " closer near poles | Ellipses, " " " " equator | MOLLWEIDE | " " | World maps, hemispheres |
| 5 | " " " " "<br>(poles are lines half length of equator) | " " " " " "<br>Sine curves, " " " " " | ECKERT 4<br>6 | " " | World maps |
| 6 | Concentric circles, spaced equally | Radiating straight lines, " " " " one or two standard par. | CONIC | Small distortion | Middle latitudes, series maps |
| 7 | " " closer at N and S ends | " " " " " " " | ALBERS | Equal-area | Maps of U. S. |
| 8 | " " wider " " " " " | " " " " " " " | LAMBERT'S CONFORMAL CONIC | Conformal | Aeronautical charts |
| 9 | " " equally, at true distances | Curves, " " " " each par. | BONNE | Equal-area | Middle latitudes |
| 10 | Nonconcentric circles, " true on central meridian | " " " " " " " | POLYCONIC | Tables available | Topographic sheets |
| 11 | " " " " " "<br>spaced equally on periphery | Circles, " " " " equator | GLOBULAR | Easy to construct | Hemispheres |
| 12 | " " closer near center | " " closer near center | STEREOGRAPHIC | Conformal | Oblique transformations |
| 13 | Ellipses, " " " periphery | Ellipses, " " " periphery | ORTHOGRAPHIC | Visual | Hemispheres, continents |
| 14 | Curves, spaced closer near poles on central meridian | Curves, spaced closer near sides of equator | AZIMUTHAL EQUAL-AREA | Equal-area | Hemispheres, continents |

Polar projections, interrupted, and rare projections are not included.

**Fig. 79** In the globular projection the equator, the central meridian, and the peripheral circle are divided into even lengths.

**Van der Grinten's Projection.** This projection is sometimes used for world maps. Its construction is shown in Fig. 80. The globe is represented by a circle, and the parallels and meridians are flat arcs of circles. The scale is true on the equator, but expands rapidly toward south and north. This increase, however, is less than in the Mercator projection, and the angles are not greatly distorted. The projection was invented by Van der Grinten in 1905 and for some time was widely used in America.

**Fig. 81** B. J. S. Cahill's butterfly projection.

**Star and Other Interrupted Projections.** In these systems the Northern Hemisphere is usually shown in a polar projection, and the southern continents are starlike appendages. The members of this group are particularly useful in climatology and biogeography. Figure 81 shows Cahill's ingenious butterfly projection, which is developed from an octahedron.

It is beyond the limit of this book to discuss the various ingenious interrupted projections that have been invented in recent years. Attempts have been made to show the earth in the form of a triangle, a trapezoid, or even in a spiral form. Few of them have won wide popularity, although many embody noteworthy features. All in all, several hundred projections have been

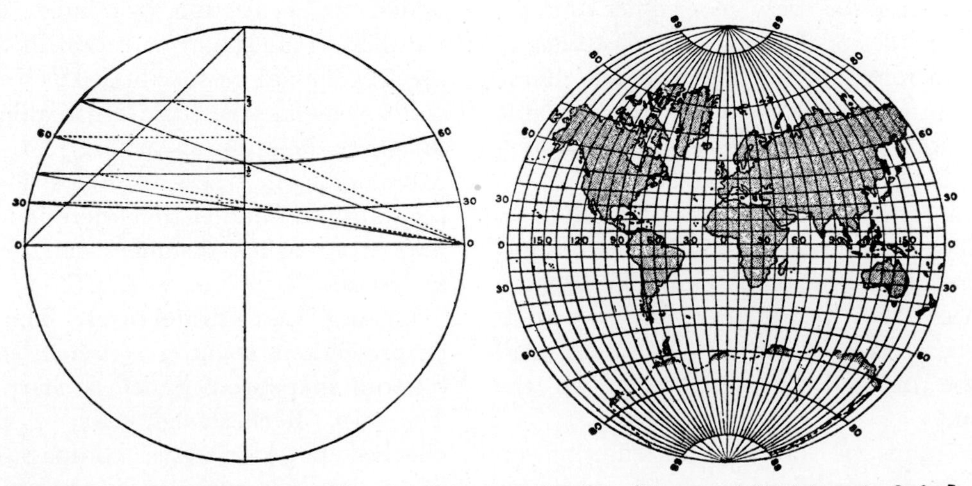


**Fig. 80** Construction of the Van der Grinten projection. (*Courtesy of Bartholomew's Oxford Atlas.*)

invented in the last century, but more than nine-tenths of all maps are drawn in projections that have been described in the foregoing chapters.

**Identification of Projections.** On modern maps and atlases it is customary to indicate the name of the projection, but on smaller maps it is often necessary to find it out ourselves. With the help of the key the various projections can be identified by the simple measurement of parallels and meridians. There are, however, certain rarely used systems that are not listed in the key because their identification is too complex. For instance, the oblique azimuthal equidistant projection, if used for smaller areas, is difficult to differentiate from a modified globular projection. It is also especially hard to distinguish between the projections of maps of small areas, such as topographic sheets, but in this case the differentiation is relatively unimportant, because all projections have practically the same appearance. Choice of projection becomes important only on maps of large areas, especially world maps.

**The Choice of Projections.** This depends chiefly on the purpose for which the map is intended (see the key to projections). It is essential for every geographer to know the principles of the various projections, in order to make an intelligent choice. Time spent in the construction of a suitable projection, instead of copying existing maps, is usually worth while.

As a general principle, it is advisable on simple diagrammatic maps to use the projections with horizontal parallels, because on these the lettering does not have to be curved, and the latitude-longitude grid can be omitted or shown only on the borders.

For maps of statistical distribution an equal-area projection should be used, although from a practical standpoint this is less important, because for individual countries all projections are quite similar. Most existing statistical maps of the United States are in the polyconic projection, which is not equal-area. For the entire world the equal-area maps have too much distortion; here, the Eckert projections may be used to advantage.

For maps of continents, when it is desirable to emphasize their relationships with other continents, the oblique orthographic projection is useful. The great educational advantages of this projection have already been pointed out. Many magnetic, climatic, and biologic relationships can best be understood from maps in polar projections; their use should be encouraged. For more exact maps of the United States the conic projections, especially the Albers network, are recommended.

**Distortion of Projections.** As we have seen, only a limited number of lines on a map are true to scale, *i.e.*, the same length as the corresponding globe; all the other lines are too long or too short. On small maps of small regions the scale distortion is small, and a good scale can be given. Not so with world maps. If a scale is given at all, it should be the scale of the globe to which the projection is related, and the parallels or meridian or radial lines which are true should be specified. Diagrammatic scales showing the scale error along other lines are helpful, as in Fig. 48, for the Mercator. The users of maps should be constantly reminded that there is no world map from which distances can be simply scaled off.

**Laying Out Projections.** The layout of projections requires extreme accuracy. Smooth shapeproof paper, a sharp pencil, T-square, steel straightedge, a properly checked large triangle, compass divider, and a circular protractor are the equipment. The paper is fastened to the board. First a central vertical is drawn with a T-square, and then a horizontal reference line is laid out with a triangle. Next comes the laying out of parallels and meridians. If the central meridian is truly divided, we lay out the whole length and divide it into degrees, rather than measuring off single degrees

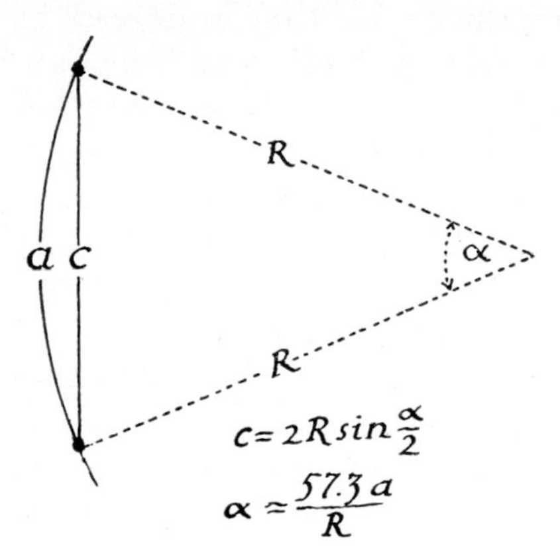


**Fig. 82** If arc distances are known, chord distances can be laid out accordingly.

and having a large cumulative error. An error that is barely visible will be serious if added eighteen times. If there are truly divided parallels, they come next, their length being calculated as the cosine of the latitude. A common difficulty is the laying out of distances along curved lines. This can easily be done by a flexible scale, a paper scale used edgewise; otherwise the length of a chord can be calculated.

$$\text{Chord} = 2R \sin \frac{\alpha}{2}, \text{ where } \alpha = \frac{57.3a}{R}$$

where $a$ is the arc distance and $R$ is the radius of the circle. A very common problem is to lay out very flat circular parallels and meridians so that the center is inconveniently far away. If three points, $A$, $B$, and $C$, are known, a three-point compass can be made from two strips of paper. Pencil at $B$ will describe a circular arc if the strips are moved along $A$ and $C$.

In constructing projections, very often a number of lines converge in a single point. This point soon becomes smudged, a bothersome source of inaccuracy. Every such point should be finely pricked and always kept clean by erasing.

Most world projections are symmetrical on a central meridian and on the equator. It is sufficient to construct one quarter with great care and to draw a new equator and central meridian on a clean paper and to prick every intersection, reversing the paper around the equator and central meridian. Save the original construction for future use. This also saves erasing pencil lines.

**Measuring of Distances on Maps.** The shortest distance between two points is the great-circle route. These great-circle distances are not truly shown on maps except along certain specified lines. The simplest way to measure them is to use a globe, but this is limited by the accuracy of the globe. A scale can be prepared by cutting a paper strip to the half circumference of the globe and dividing it into 124.4 parts for

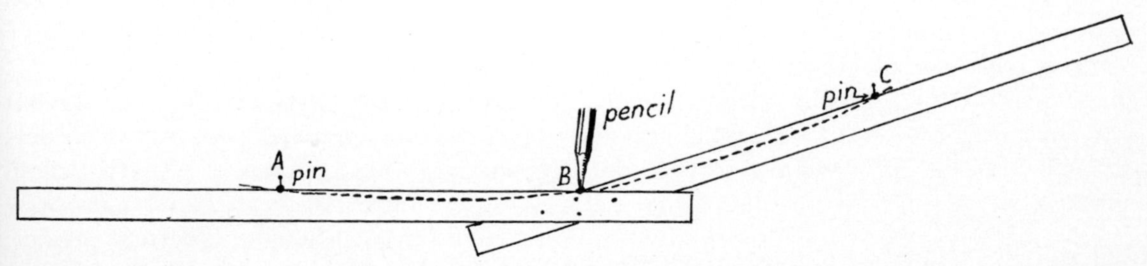


**Fig. 83** A circular arc can be drawn through three known points by moving the cardboard strips along the two pins in $A$ and $C$.

each hundred miles. Mark the 1,000-mile divisions first, and subdivide them.

A more exact method of preparing a scale is to solve the spherical triangle

$$\text{hav}\, d = \text{hav}\,(\varphi_2 - \varphi_1) + \cos\varphi_1 \cos\varphi_2\, \text{hav}\,(\lambda_2 - \lambda_1)$$

where $d$ is the distance in degrees (of 60 nautical miles), $\varphi$ is the latitude, and $\lambda$ is the longitude of the respective points. [Hav is short for haversine, which is a useful function in geodesy.

$$\text{hav}\,\alpha = \tfrac{1}{2}\,(1 - \cos\alpha)$$

A table of haversines is contained in books on geodesy and navigation.] For exact calculations the ellipsoidal form of the earth has to be reckoned and the formulas are more complex.

A third method, used mostly on cylindrical projections, is to superimpose upon an equatorial map a transverse projection on the same scale. The meridians will then be a set of great circles, and if the central meridian is shifted along the equator of the original map until the two points are on the same transverse meridian, the distance can be read off in degrees by the parallels that mark off equal distances from the meridians. In Fig. 74 on the Mercator map shown by dashed lines, points $A$ and $B$ are 120 latitudinal degrees apart. There are some other ingenious methods also. See Graphical Determination of the Distance between Two Given Points on or Near the Surface of the Earth, by Gen. M. Uzefovich, *School Science and Mathematics*, Vol. 28, pp. 853–958, 1928, or Simple Computations of Distances Over the Earth, by Litterly and Pierce, *Navigation*, Vol. 1, pp. 62–68, 1946.

# CHAPTER 9: *Symbols*

Almost every feature on a map is symbolized. If real pictures were used, many significant elements would be microscopic. On a standard topographic sheet a 25-foot-wide road would show as a very thin line $\frac{1}{200}$ inch wide. Since topographic sheets show roads by double lines about $\frac{1}{40}$ inch apart, it is obvious that we use a symbol. On a page-sized map of the United States, the Mississippi River would be a microscopic, meandering line 1/2,000 inch wide. If for this we substitute a wavy line one hundred times wider, we also use a symbol.

*A good symbol is one which can be recognized without a legend.* Such a symbol should either be reminiscent of the feature it represents or be sanctioned by centuries of use. Most of our symbols date back to very early maps. Symbols should be small, distinctive, and easy to draw.

There is a difference in the use of symbols, depending on the scale of the map. On small-scale maps, roads are often represented by a single line instead of the double line of topographic sheets. On small-scale maps, cities are usually shown by circles; on large-scale maps, by their streets. In the choice of symbols it is a common error to force large-scale symbols into small-scale maps and thus overburden them. Most cartographers like to use a single system of symbols in all their maps, regardless of difference in scale, but they do not always have fortunate results. Symbols used in colored maps will necessarily differ from those used in black-and-white maps.

The symbol content of a map can be divided into three groups: (1) man-made features, or *culture;* (2) water features, or *hydrography;* and (3) relief features, or *hypsography.* In modern maps a fourth feature, *vegetation,* is often added. Besides these, many special symbols may be used on scientific and statistical maps.

For the well-established convention of colors, blue indicates water; black and red usually designate culture; various shades of brown represent relief features; and green obviously is the color for vegetation.

## Cultural Features

Man-made features are particularly emphasized on maps. Cities, roads, and railways are very important, and thus they are represented far beyond their actual size. Many maps contain little more than cultural symbols.

**Cities.** In the earliest maps, cities are shown by small, pictorial, bird's-eye views. Since the early walled cities were usually round, on small-scale maps their representation was either reduced to the more or less circular layout of the wall or was symbolized by a circle. The circle as a city symbol survives up to the present time, although there is now little analogy between a small circle and a city.

It is possible that the origin of the city circle was different. It was customary in early Renaissance maps to designate a city by a small pictorial group of houses. But since this group was very much larger than the size of the city, the exact location of the latter was shown by a small circle within the group of houses. In small-scale maps the group of houses was omitted, and only the circle remained. At present we still show cities by a small circle or by several concentric circles, the size or complexity of which varies with the population of the city.

On large-scale maps, where the actual extent can be shown, the city can be represented better by crossed lines indicating a street system, even though it does not exactly follow the actual pattern. Since this symbol has no sharp outline, it symbolizes the modern city that gradually merges into country better than does the round circle so characteristic of walled towns. It has been attempted to show cities by means of ovals in which the size of the population (in thousands) is lettered.

The selection of cities to be represented on small-scale maps is usually made according to population. The number of people, however, is not a sure indication of the importance of a city. For instance, Fairbanks, Alaska, with its few thousand people is far better known, being an outpost of civilization and a center of a huge region, than is a town of similar population in Ohio. Ports, railroad junctions, capitals, cultural and historic centers, spas, and frontier towns are shown even if inhabited by fewer people than other less important places.

**Roads.** Even in the earliest maps it was customary to show roads by a double line, which was often further accentuated by rows of trees along it. The symbol is so obvious that it has changed but little up to the present time. On large-scale maps the various types of roads are shown by different thicknesses of lines; on small-scale maps, however, where only the most important roads can be shown, this differentiation is not often made and, to avoid overcrowding the map, a single line is preferable to a double line. If color can be used, roads may appear in red or black—usually in a different color from the railways.

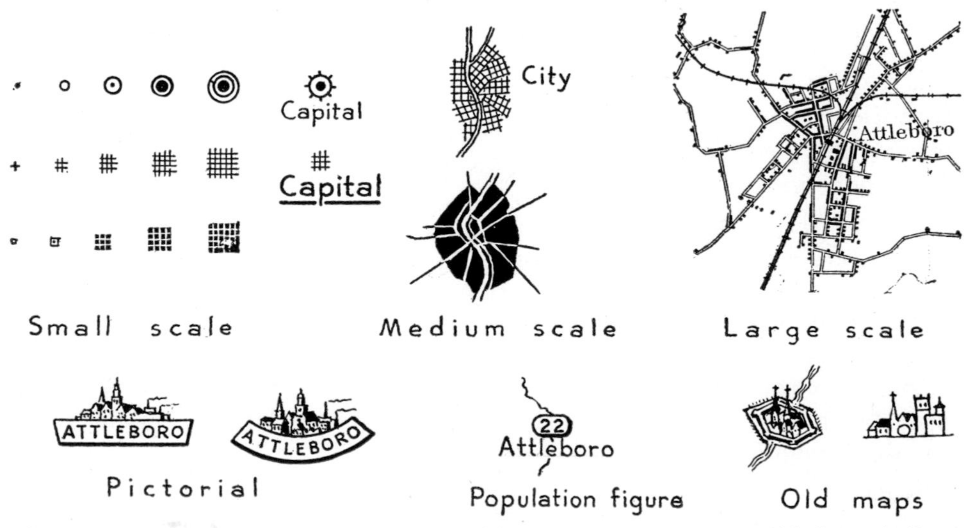


**Fig. 84** City symbols vary with the scale and style of the map. They should always indicate the size of the city.

Modern automobile road maps have a different and more detailed symbolism to indicate a great variety of road types. A convenient instrument with which to draw roads is a double-ruling pen specifically designed for that purpose. If only a limited number of roads are shown, they are selected according to importance and not their type. The unpaved Alaska Highway will be shown when many paved roads in the East are omitted.

**Railroads.** On the older lithographed maps railroads were usually shown by two parallel lines with alternating black-and-white spaces. In photoengraved maps, however, the little white squares were easily clogged up with ink, and thus the crosstie symbol, which is now in common use, was adopted. As we use this symbol at the present time, the crossties are too far from each other and only slightly reminiscent of their origin.

It adds much to the value of a map if the railroads are shown by different thicknesses of lines, according to their importance. Such lines resemble the arterial system of the human body and afford a vivid picture of the flow of traffic, which is preferable to the usual network of lines of even thickness. It is most important that the gauge of railroads be indicated, if they are not the standard size, either by symbols or by lettering. Transloading stations and boundary stations for customs inspection are indicated to help travelers.

**Boundaries.** The conventional symbol for boundaries consists of alternating dashes and dots which, being an artificial type of line, represents an artificial feature well. Varying thicknesses of lines may differentiate town, state, and international boundaries. Their usual color, as for all cultural features, is black or red.

In black-and-white maps the presentation of river boundaries is somewhat of a problem, because the boundary symbol cannot be superimposed upon a river. The line cannot be put on one side of the river, for this would indicate that the river belonged to one political unit whereas the

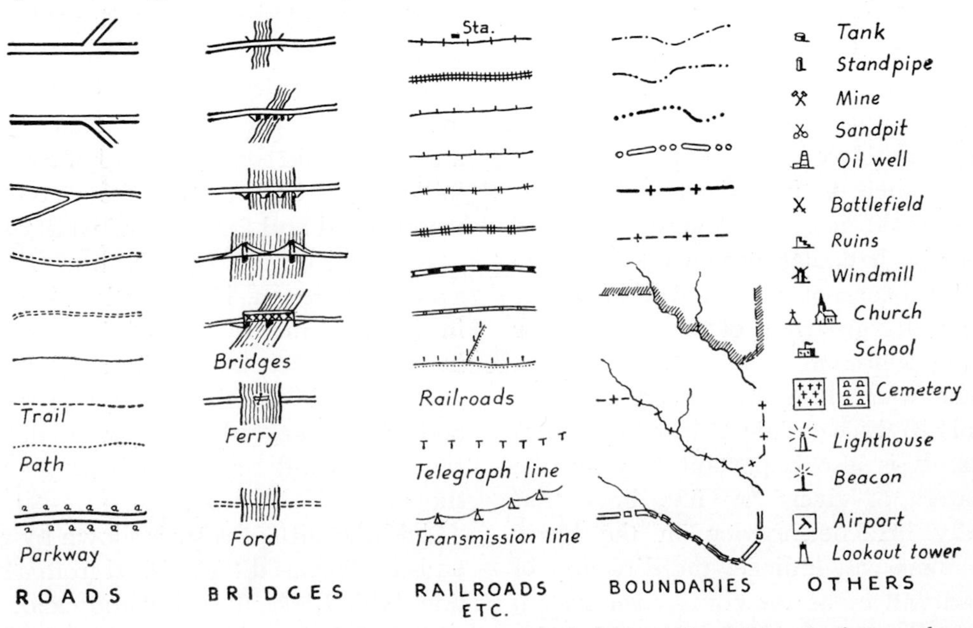


**Fig. 85** Examples of cultural symbols. They should suggest, if possible, the feature they represent.

boundary itself may be the center of the river. There are different ways to overcome this difficulty. The most common is to barb all boundary lines whether formed by rivers or not; the barbing will indicate that the river serves as the boundary. Another method is to use small crosses as boundary lines; these crosses will show even where the boundary is a river. In colored maps there is no such difficulty, for the blue rivers can be overprinted with red or black boundary lines.

A certain problem arises in showing international boundaries over the seas and oceans. Boundaries are often carried outside the 3-mile limit to show sovereignty over island groups. This, of course, is incorrect according to international law; therefore, to indicate that these are not actual boundaries, the line should be broken. Another problem arises from disputed and undelineated boundaries. These can be shown with interspersed question marks; disputed areas should be marked as such. Boundary changes are frequent, and they help to date undated maps.

**Small Cultural Symbols.** Most small-scale maps do not contain any cultural symbols besides cities, roads, railroads, and boundaries, but on large-scale maps various other features, such as farmhouses, mines, parks, and ruins, are shown. The symbols usually derive from the vertical view of the object, but it is admissible to use side views if they are more easily recognized. Crosses for cemeteries, crossed hammers for mines, and tiny lighthouses are well-established conventions; but for landing fields, schools, golf links, etc., the cartographer is free to design his own symbols.

## Hydrography

When we lay out a map, we draw first the shore lines and the rivers as the most important features in the outlining and orientation of a region. The conventional color for all water features is blue, and this practice is rarely departed from.

**Rivers.** On large-scale maps, rivers are shown by their actual width and course; on small-scale maps, however, they are shown by an irregular, somewhat wavy line which is in excess of the actual width of the river. The irregularities of the line may or may not represent actual curves; in a black-and-white map such a line often is used only to differentiate a river from other features. It is also important to show the headwaters of rivers by fine lines that gradually become heavier on the lower course. This will indicate the direction of flow and will make the entire river system stand out. Some rivers, such as the Colorado, actually diminish by evaporation, but rarely is this fact brought out on maps. On small-scale maps, the main rivers only are shown and many tributaries are omitted. The branches of the rivers that are shown should be carried to their headwaters to indicate the divides. Different types of anchors should show the head of navigation, indicating whether it is the wet- or dry-season head and for boats of what draft.

It would be of great advantage, even on small-scale maps, if distinction were made in the three major types of rivers, as shown in Fig. 87, such as (1) the actively down-cutting; (2) the balanced, meandering; and (3) the aggrading, or braided, type of river. This differentiation is as yet seldom shown.

An intermittent river is shown by a dash-and-dot line, as distinguished from a dashed line, which indicates that the exact course of the river is not known. The headwaters of every river are intermittent, and the

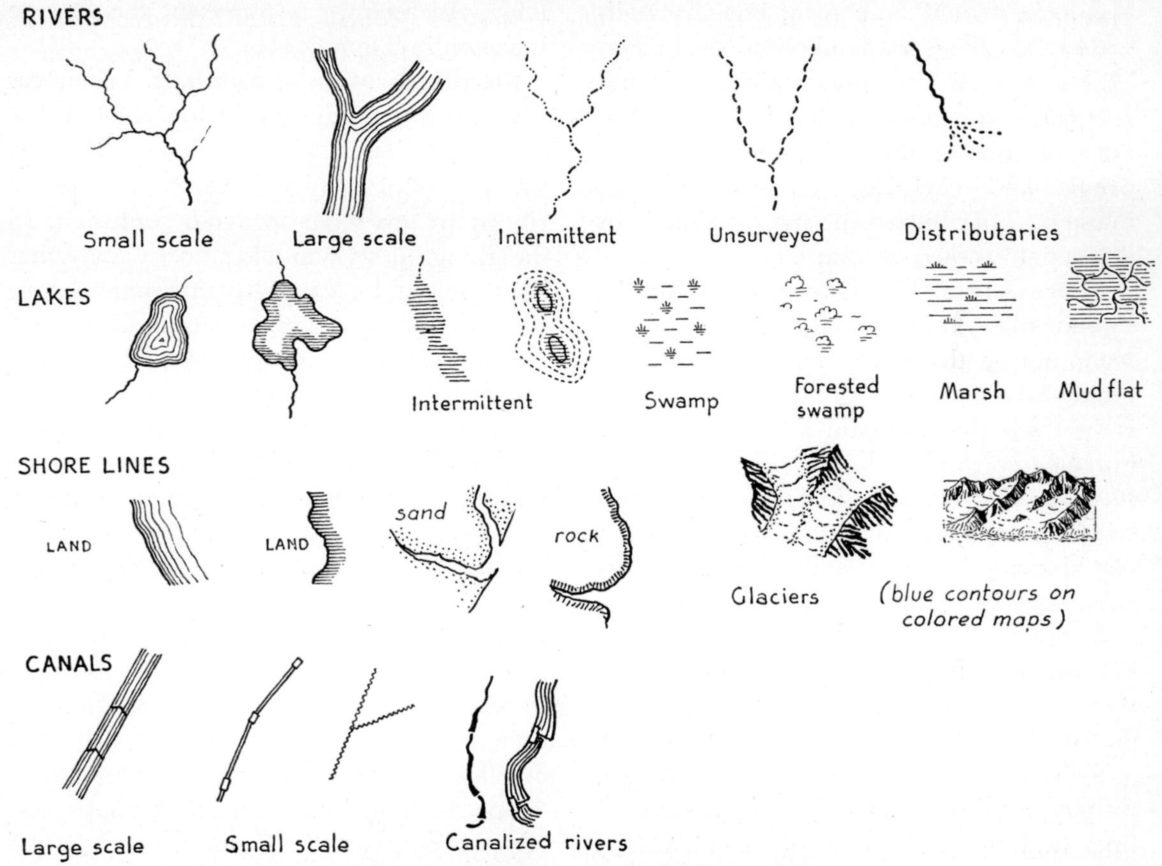


**Fig. 86** Examples of hydrographic symbols.

symbol should be carried up the hillsides to the place where the river flows at least half the year. In some parts of the world,

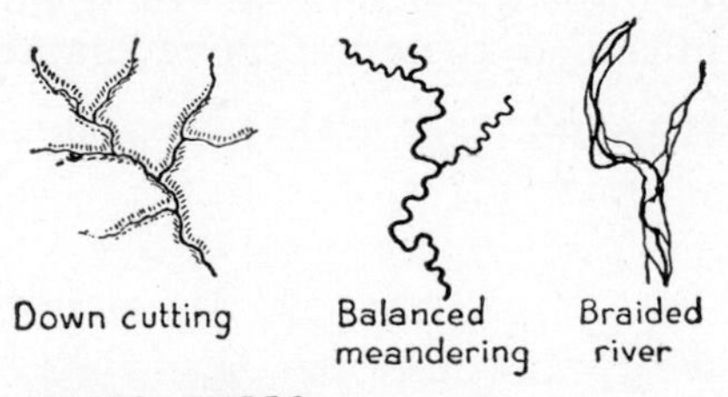


**Fig. 87** The types of rivers can be shown even on small-scale maps.

with strong seasonal variation in rainfall, even large rivers may dry up in summer, as do most of those in southwestern United States. Hence, it is customary to restrict the intermittent river symbol to those rivers which in most years are dry for more than 3 months.

**Canals.** On colored maps canals are indicated by straight, blue lines, but there is a particular lack of agreement as to how they should be shown on a black-and-white map. The straight, black line used by the National Geographic Board is not distinctive enough. In European maps it is customary to show canals by a line barbed on one side. This symbol, however, is so similar to the railway symbol that its use cannot be encouraged. The vibrating line that the U.S. Geological Survey uses for ditches (see Fig. 86) seems to be more satisfactory.

Canalized rivers should be shown as such. Preferably the exact location of the dams and locks should be shown, but on small-scale maps they are symbolized, as in Fig. 86. If a river is only straightened and deepened, this also can be indicated. On detailed maps, the minimum depth of canals and canalized rivers should be marked. This important information is as yet seldom shown on maps.

**Shore Lines.** On large-scale maps the shore is marked by its actual line; on small-scale maps, this line must be somewhat generalized. On black-and-white maps, it is desirable that the land masses shall stand out clearly, and this can be achieved in several ways, as shown in Fig. 86. On maps where mountains are shown, distinction can be made between sandy and cliffed and complex shore lines.

Intermittent lakes or lakes with greatly varying levels should not have a definite shore line. A horizontal line tint with no outlines serves best.

**Swamps and Marshes.** Swamps are usually represented by short, horizontal lines and by reeds reflected in the water. This symbol is derived from Europe, where most of the swamps are open, but it is not so acceptable when the swamp is forested. No satisfactory symbol has yet been generally adopted for forested swamps, which are sometimes of enormous extent, as on our coastal plain, or in the Siberian taiga. An attempt to represent this feature is shown in Table XIII.

**Standardization of Symbols.** Whenever a series of maps is started, one of the first matters attended to is the delineation of a set of symbols, which have to be followed rigidly in this series to avoid confusion. In designing these symbols, the cartographer does well if he carefully investigates how the symbols on similar sets worked out, similar not only in the type of country but also in scale and method of reproduction. Some important sets of maps—including our own—suffer from ill-designed symbols, often delineated generations ago for other scales and purposes. The British Ordnance Survey's custom of bringing out a new edition of new symbols about every generation is commendable. Cartography is a kind of language, and the symbols are its words. We like to have a dictionary to understand one another, but we also want our language to live, grow, and expand.

Special maps and small-scale maps usually serve a variety of purposes and rigid standardization is impossible. It is a major part of the cartographer's art to select expressive, harmonious, and easily read symbols. The social and economic maps especially offer an open field to the cartographer's imagination, and some suggestions are offered in their respective chapters.

# CHAPTER 10: *Relief Features*

The representation of relief features, such as mountains, plateaus, cliffs, and valleys, is one of the major problems of cartography. The essential difficulty comes from the fact that we are accustomed to view mountains from below and that their aspect, seen vertically from above, is unfamiliar. When looking straight down from an airplane, one cannot recognize even good-sized mountains; vertical airplane photographs testify to this fact.

Representation of mountains was the last development in cartography. Up to the middle of the eighteenth century this was best done by showing a row of hills pictorially. Little attempt was made to indicate their nature, and rarely were they made proportionate to their height. The exact altitude of mountains was not then known, and thus the most erroneous conceptions prevailed. The Alps were estimated to be over 90,000 feet high. Only after the invention of the barometer and the perfection of the theodolite were more exact data available. Progress was slow; at the beginning of the nineteenth century, Humboldt listed only about 120 peaks whose altitudes had been measured.

**Hachuring.** Hachuring is a method of hill shading by closely set parallel lines. A scientific system of hachuring came into use at the end of the eighteenth century; its principles were laid down by the Saxon major, Lehmann. In this method the slopes are indicated by parallel lines drawn in the direction in which water would run on that surface. Roughly, there should be the same number of lines to the inch but, where the slope is steeper, the lines are heavier. The thickness of the lines can be mathematically determined as shown in Fig. 88.

The relation between the black lines and the intervening white spaces is proportionate to the angle of slope; a slope over 45° is shown entirely black. The steeper the land is, the darker will it appear on the map. In actual drawing an exact contour-line map is first made and, from the density of contour lines, the angle of the slope is determined. The lines of various thicknesses are then drawn by hand. It takes a great deal of practice and skill to make a satisfactory hachure map. The generation of highly trained artists who did this kind of work is slowly dying out.

The Lehmann system of hachuring greatly appealed to the military. The great advantage of such a map is that mountains can be visualized even by untrained persons. This system, however, does not work out so well for the very purpose for which it was designed. The angle of slope is important for artillery and for other military purposes, but actually it cannot be read because of the difficulty of measuring the thickness of the lines, which, even if they could be measured, are not put in with sufficient accuracy.

The hachuring method was adopted by most military surveys of the nineteenth

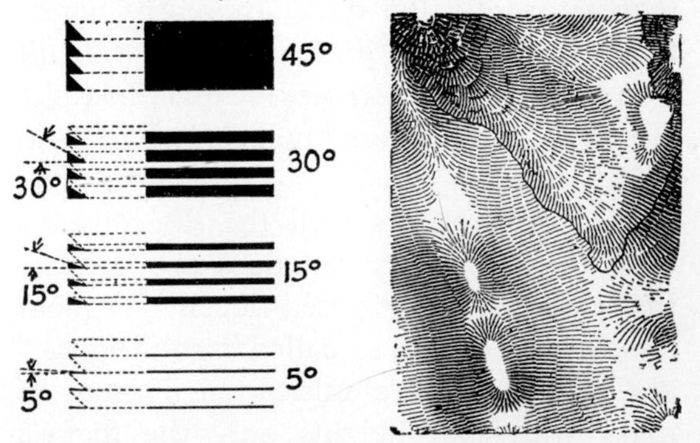


**Fig. 88** Lehmann system of hachuring. The lines are strongly magnified. In this system of hachuring, the thickness of lines is proportional to the tangent of slope.

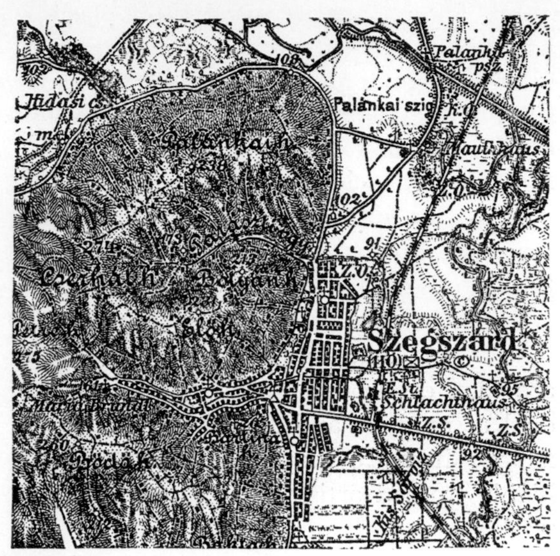


**Fig. 89** Typical black-and-white hachured military map of the nineteenth century (*From the* 1:75,000 *Spezialkarte of Austria-Hungary.*)

century, and formed a popular representation of relief up to the 1870's, when the introduction of color printing made clear contour-line maps possible. The hachuring method is well adapted to show flat regions. River terraces, small ridges, sinkholes, etc., are easily lost in contour-line maps, where they may fall within the contour interval. The method is fairly adequate for rocky, mountainous country also, but, when representing rolling, hilly terrain, the resulting map is usually too dark. In places where there are no rivers it is sometimes difficult to tell which way the slope dips. Sinkholes are distinguished from knolls only by means of little arrows.

Hachuring shows well the slope conditions of the country but does not indicate the elevation above sea level. Frequent figures of elevation, so-called "spot heights," are helpful. It is a misleading custom to mark with spot heights only the highest peaks; altitudes of railroad stations, lakes, and landing fields are often more important. Approximate spot heights are indicated by figures in parentheses.

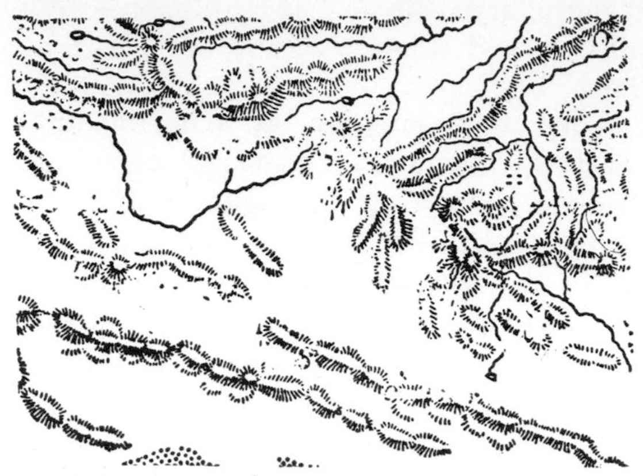

**Fig. 90** In small-scale maps hachure lines often deteriorate into "hairy caterpillars."

The hachuring method is not well adapted to small-scale maps. The Lehmann system cannot be used, for individual mountains cannot be shown thereby. In the nineteenth century, a certain method was worked out, sometimes referred to as the "caterpillar and pine branch" system, by which we can differentiate dissected plateaus (pine branches), mountain chains

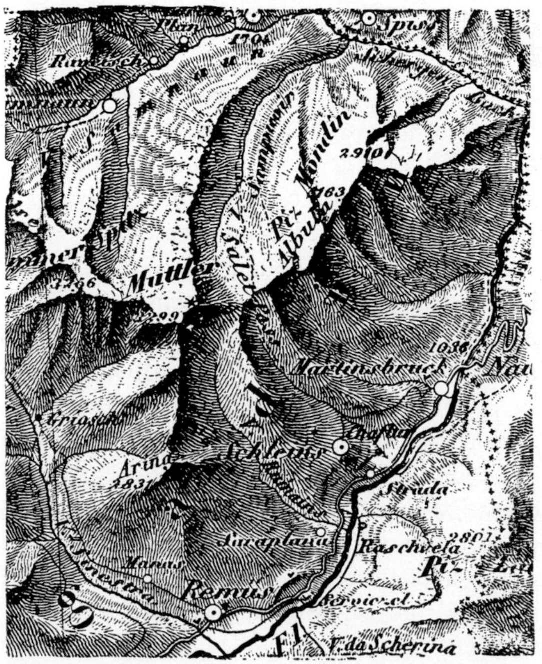


**Fig. 91** Hachuring with oblique illumination is effective in mountainous country. (*From the Dufour map of Switzerland.*)

(caterpillars), single ridges (half caterpillars), and single peaks (short radiating lines).

Attempts were made to make the hachures lighter on the north and west, and darker on the south and east slopes, thus giving the appearance of oblique illumination. The Dufour maps of Switzerland, drawn in the middle of the last century, are the outstanding examples of such a system. These maps are wonderfully plastic, and perhaps mark the high point in the art of hachuring. The system has its disadvantages, for it is necessary to use a different scale of darkness on one slope than on the other; also, it is not well adapted to low, rolling country.

At present the use of hachuring has declined. Its place is being taken chiefly by contour-line maps and plastic shading.

## Plastic Shading

In this system we regard the map as a photograph of an uncolored relief model, taken vertically from above. Plastic shading became possible with the introduction of lithography. In older times half tones could not be reproduced.

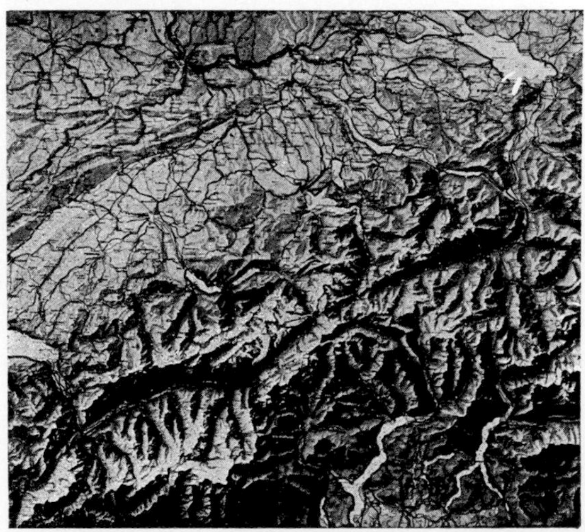

**Fig. 92** Plastic shading with oblique illumination. (*From Finch-Trewartha, "Elements of Geography."*)

**Fig. 93** Lakes on a glacier look elevated unless we turn the page upside down. (*Photograph by Bradford Washburn.*)

**Vertical and Oblique Illumination.** Whether vertical or oblique illumination should be used is a much discussed question. In vertical illumination somewhat less light falls upon slopes than on horizontal land. The effect of shading in this system is similar to hachuring in that the steeper the slope the darker it appears on the map. Strictly speaking, this is not correct, because in vertical illumination exactly the same amount of light falls on every part of the map, although where the land is sloping, a larger area is represented.

In oblique illumination the map is regarded as a picture of a relief model lighted from the northwest. Such a map, especially of mountainous countries, is very effective. It was questioned whether the illumination should be from the southwest or from the northwest, because in most of the northern hemisphere the light actually comes from the south. Nevertheless, it is not satisfactory to use southern illumination, since, for optical reasons, the map appears to be negative, *i.e.*, the mountains appear as valleys if the light falls from behind the spectator, and it would be necessary to turn the map around to correct this impression.

At present plastic shading is widely used, chiefly in combination with other methods. The French and English surveys use it; the U.S. Geological Survey has published several state maps made by this method. Plastic shading is used on the topographic sheets of many countries where detailed contour survey is not available, as on the 1:500,000 maps of Mexico. It is preferred to hachures or dashed contours as it can easily be generalized. The shading is usually in brown or gray, so as to allow overprinting of black lettering.

Plastic shading is applied by various means: watercolor (wash), crayon, soft pencil, or smudging graphite powder. It is reproduced by the half-tone process. If Ross board or coarsely kerneled paper is used, the half-tone process is not necessary. In lithography all shades of gray can be obtained by smudging the kerneled surface of a lithographic stone with crayon.

## Contouring

Contouring is by far the most common method of showing relief features on topographic maps. Contours are lines that at certain even intervals connect points of equal elevation. For a better understanding of this method let us consider the zero contour line to be sea level. If the sea were to rise 10 feet, the new shore line would be the 10-foot contour line. Similarly, the 20-, 30-, 40-, etc., foot contour lines could be determined. Contour lines will be closer together where the slope is steep, and mountainous areas will appear dark on the map. It is obvious that a contour will always be horizontal and perpendicular to the direction of running water on that surface. Within the limits of the contour interval the height of every point can be read directly from the map, and the angle of slope can easily be determined.

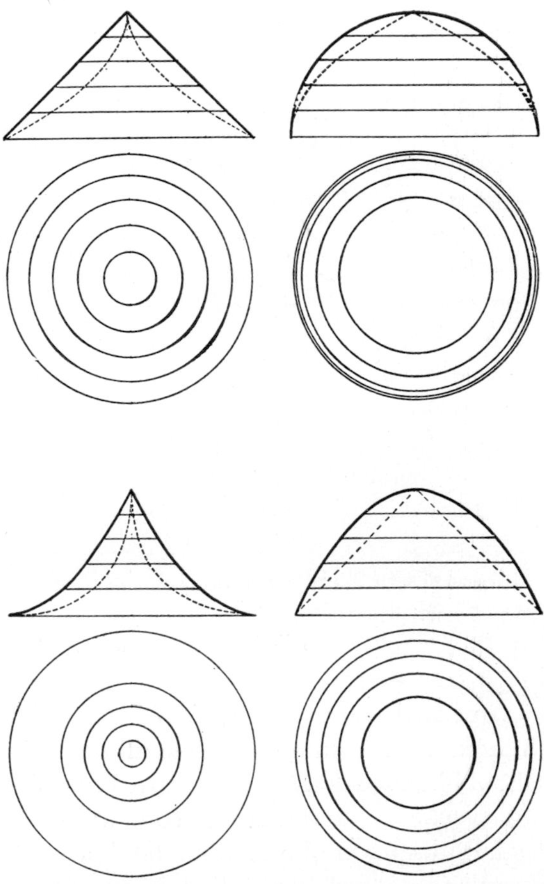

**Fig. 94** Geometric forms expressed in contour lines. The dotted lines are hypsographic curves (see Chap. 24).

**Contour Interval.** The choice of the contour interval depends on the scale of the map, the amount of relief, and the accuracy of the survey. Some topographic sheets of the southern Texas irrigated areas have 1-foot contour intervals. The Great Valley of California has been mapped with 5-foot contour intervals on the scale of 1:31,250.

The most common contour interval on the 1:62,500 topographic sheets is 20 feet; in high mountain areas it is occasionally 50 feet. On the 1:125,000 maps the contours are usually 50 feet apart. As a rough rule, in regions of medium relief a contour interval in feet equals 25 times the miles-per-inch scale of the map; in rugged regions the interval is larger; in flat regions it is smaller. On smaller scale maps, like the 1:1,000,000 map of the world, a variable contour interval is adopted; the contours are spaced closer at lower elevations. The intervals chosen are 100, 200, 300, 400, 500, 700, 1,000, 1,500, 2,000, 2,500, 3,000, 3,500, and 4,000 meters. On small-scale continent maps the usual intervals are 500, 1,000, 2,000, 3,000, 5,000, 7,000, 10,000, and 15,000 feet. This differentiation is necessary since otherwise important features of lesser height would be lost in densely settled lowlands, and too frequent contour lines would clog the map in the high, rugged mountains. On the other hand, on a high plateau even a 1,400-foot range may be missed entirely. Close contour intervals add greatly to the plasticity and accuracy of the map but often require more detailed surveying than is available.

The bottoms of the seas and lakes can also be shown by contour lines. This was really the original purpose of such lines.

**History.** So far as is known, contour lines were first used by the Dutch engineer, N. Cruquius (1728 or 1730), to show the bottom of the Merwede River for the purpose of navigation. In 1737, Buache used contour lines to indicate the various depths of the English Channel. However, contour lines were not used for land maps for a long time. The first important contour map was made by Dupain-Triel in 1791; it showed France. In the precise military surveys of the nineteenth century, contour lines were generally used but only on the plane-table sheets; on the sheets that were actually published they were replaced or combined with hachure lines, because these are less confusing on a black-and-white map. After the invention of lithography, the British Ordnance Survey experimented with shaded contour lines and gray altitude tints (see Fig. 106). Before that series was finished, color printing was perfected, and in 1878 the usual system of brown contour lines, blue hydrography, and black cultural symbols was adopted by the U.S. Geological Survey. At the present time almost every country publishes its contoured topographic maps with or without combination with other methods.

**Datum Plane.** The usual datum plane for surveys is the mean sea level. This level is determined by a series of observations which, if properly taken, should extend over 19 years. The mean sea level is not perfectly horizontal; it varies with the configuration of the shore and with the tide conditions, and it depends also on the geodetic interpretation of the term "horizontal," depending on the type of spheroid adopted. So long as the variation does not exceed a few inches, the problem is of only theoretical importance. Contour lines showing depths of the sea bottom are, for obvious reasons, usually reckoned from mean low-water level. Altitudes in charts are often reckoned from mean high-water level, chiefly because this line is clearly visible.

**Drawing of Contour Lines.** Contour lines are, as a rule, drawn in the field by the plane-table parties themselves. Only the important points—hilltops, knobs, road crossings—are measured; and, in accordance with these measured points, the contour lines are drawn. Where the slopes are even, usually every fifth contour line only is drawn in the field, and the intervening contour lines are drawn in the office. Much depends on the topographic sense

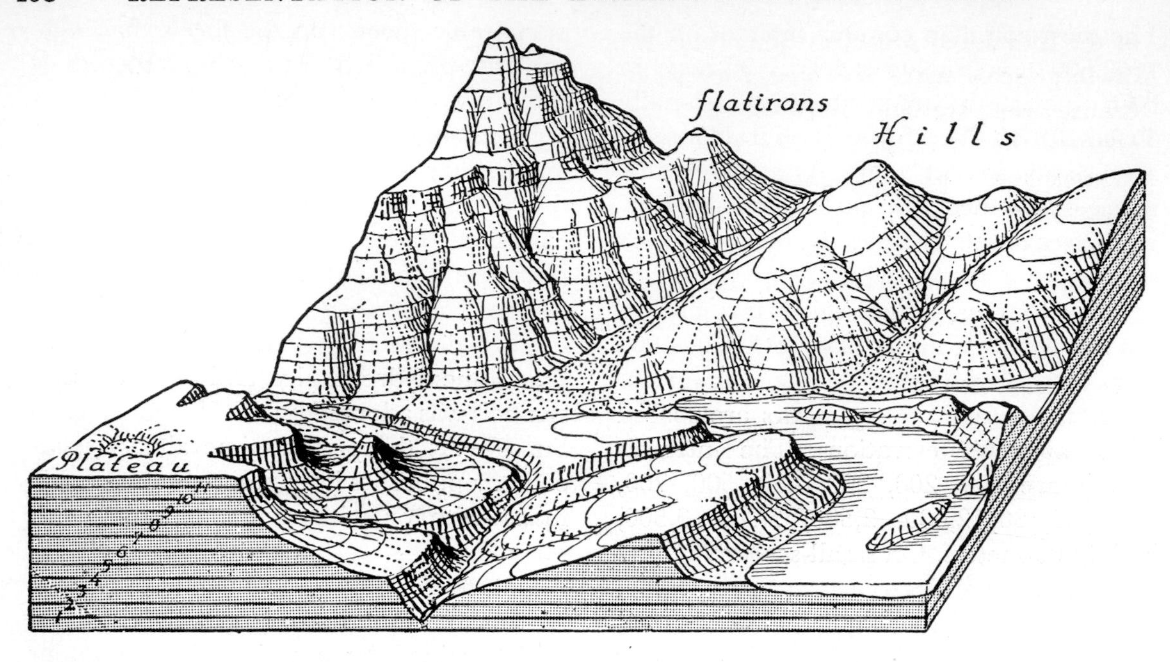


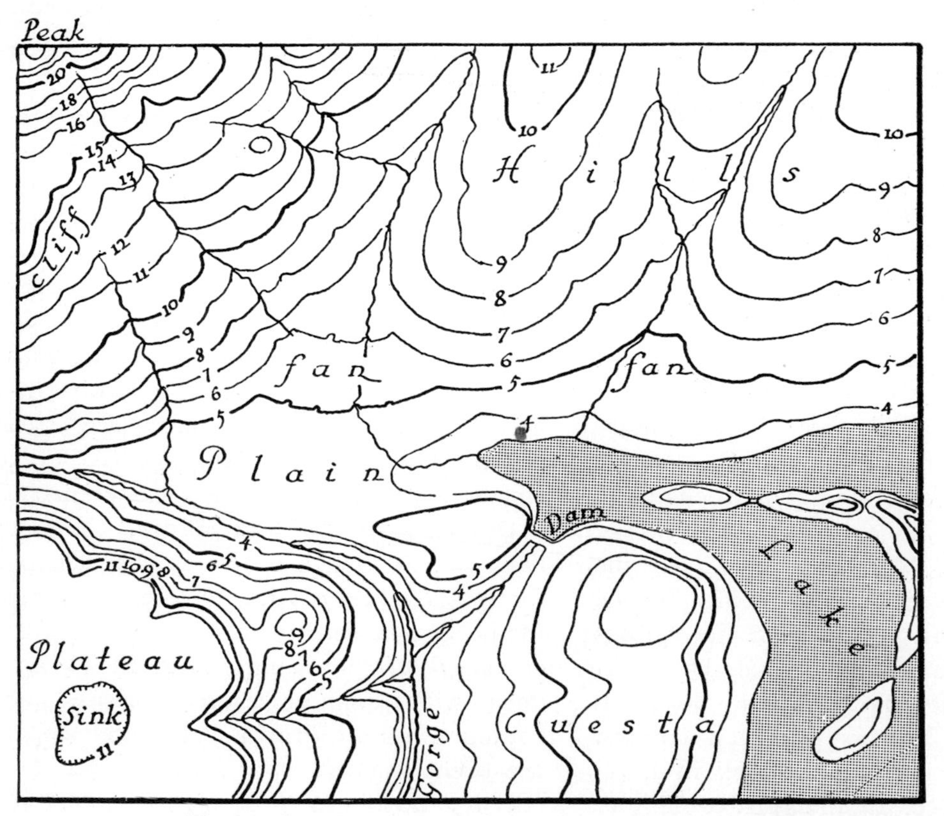


**Fig 95** It takes a great deal of analysis to visualize a contour-line map.

of the individual surveyor. Sometimes even on large-scale maps it is necessary to generalize the contour lines of a rugged country. But even in this case they should express the type of topography. For instance, in badland type of dissection it would be impossible for the topographer to measure exactly every small rill, but he would give less information by generalizing the contour lines into smooth curves than by drawing the lobate contour lines characteristic of badlands, even if the rills were not exactly in place at every point. Similarly, lava beds are often expressed with jagged contour lines. There is altogether too great a tendency to make the contour lines round and even. By this tendency to generalize, many sharp cliffs and precipitous ravines are lost on maps. How far generalization can go is shown in Fig. 96 by comparison of an early reconnaissance sheet of Springfield, Mo., with the adjacent sheet of more recent years.

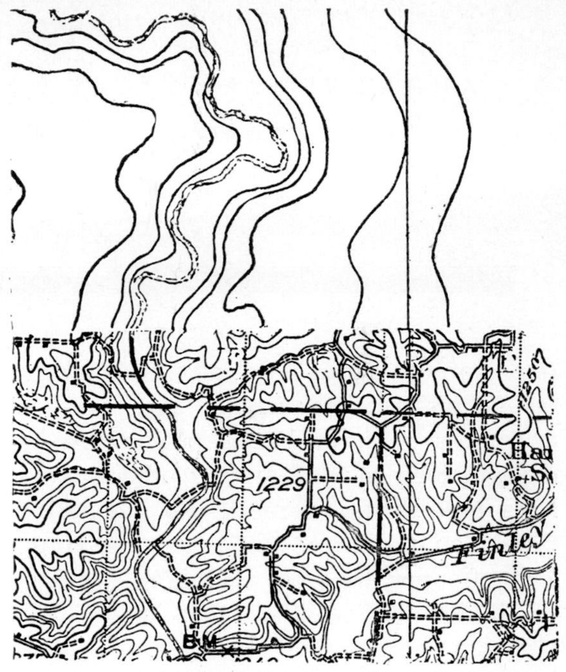


**Fig. 96** Contour lines are often generalized. Above are shown two adjacent areas in the same scale and contour interval.

Generally, contour lines are inked in with a so-called "pivot pen" (Fig. 136), which, if properly handled, makes very fine and even lines. Every fifth contour line is made heavier, thus making the map easier to follow; but, on the other hand, it may emphasize a certain elevation that actually has no distinction. One disadvantage of the use of the pivot pen is that it tends to make the lines rounded and expressionless. Many contour-line maps suffer from this defect, and one may wonder whether sometimes it would not be better to sacrifice the elegance of line and give it more character by using an ordinary drawing pen.

Contour lines should be labeled frequently with *figures of elevation*, which, if possible, should be placed on the southern slopes so as to read upward. To facilitate finding them, they are placed, if possible, in a row one above another. Important small features, like river terraces, mounds, and eskers are sometimes shown by dotted auxiliary contour lines that mark half the contour interval. By the definition of contour lines, every line must be a closed curve but not necessarily within a single map, if this map shows less than an island or continent. For instance, the 80-foot contour line runs clear around America from northern Alaska to and from Punta Arenas in Chile. It is impossible for contour lines to go in spiral or to cross each other. Actually, they would cross each other in the case of an overhanging cliff, but when the cliffs are nearly vertical, they are shown by a cliff symbol. The same contour has to appear on both sides of a river.

**Profiles.** The solution of almost every practical problem connected with contour lines is accomplished with the help of drawing profiles or vertical sections. A profile gives the most easily conceivable expression of slope along a certain line. If there is a trend in the topography, the

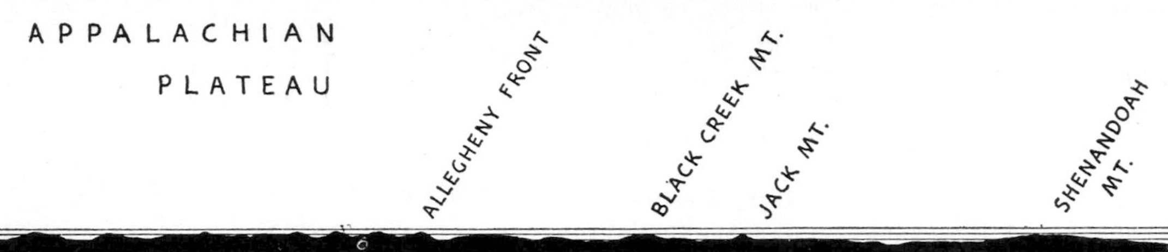


**Fig. 97** A profile across the Appalachian Mountains

line of profile is usually selected perpendicular to this trend, as in Fig. 98. This line usually is straight, but a profile can be drawn along a road or any other curved line, too. First, we mark the line of the profile on the map. Then, on a separate strip of paper, we draw a straight base line, or datum line, of the same length. We choose a vertical scale on which usually $\frac{1}{10}$ inch represents a round number of feet. Then, at frequent intervals we mark, in the chosen vertical scale, the vertical elevation perpendicular to the base line. The points so obtained and connected will give the profile of the land.

For the drawing of profiles cross-lined "section" or "profile" paper is often used. Such paper can be bought in any store carrying engineering supplies, but its use is by no means necessary.

In most cases some *vertical exaggeration* is necessary, especially in small-scale profiles. On a 1:500,000 profile the Appalachian Mountains would be only $\frac{1}{10}$ inch high and thus hardly perceptible. The amount of vertical exaggeration depends on the scale. On 1-inch per mile maps little or no vertical exaggeration is necessary except in flat regions. On 1:1,000,000 scale it is necessary to exaggerate at least five to ten times in order to notice the characteristic features. Much also depends on the purpose of the profile; for the construction of a reservoir much greater exaggeration is required than for a geological section. Strictly speaking, for geological sections no vertical exaggeration should be used at all, for the layers would have a false dip. Flat land requires greater exaggeration than mountains. As a rough rule, for average hilly country the

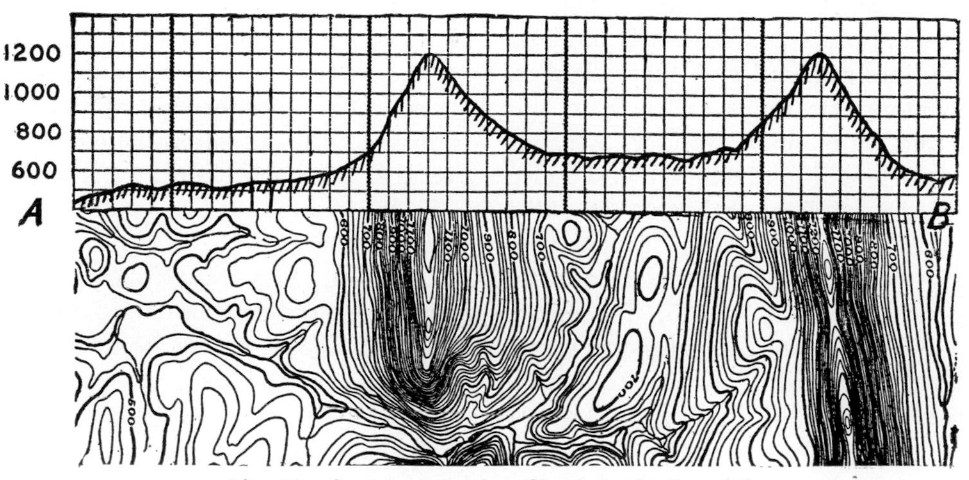


**Fig. 98** Construction of profile along the line *A-B*.

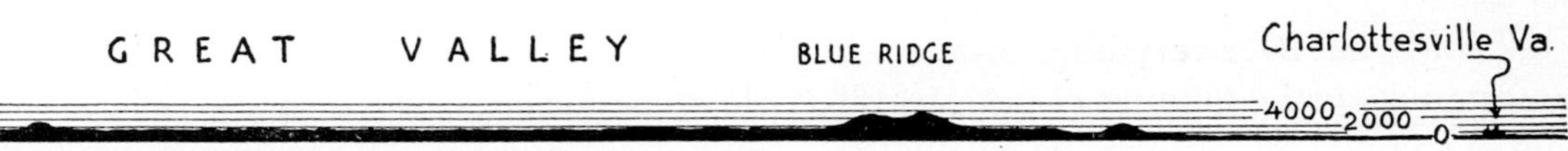


without vertical exaggeration looks too flat.

following figures apply:

| *Scale* | *Vertical Exaggeration** |
|---|---|
| 1 mile per inch | 2 times |
| 2 miles per inch | 3 times |
| 4 miles per inch | 4 times |
| 8 miles per inch | 6 times |
| 16 miles per inch | 8 times |
| 64 miles per inch | 16 times |

* Vertical exaggeration = $2\sqrt{\text{mile per inch}}$.

Profiles are supplied with a horizontal and a vertical scale, and often the amount

**Fig. 99** Vertical exaggeration changes the character of a profile.

of vertical exaggeration is stated. Vertical exaggeration is usually calculated by comparing inches on the profile with feet in nature. Thus, on a 1:62,500 profile with $\frac{1}{10}$ inch to every 200 feet of elevation:

Horizontally 1 inch represents 62,500:12 = 5,208 feet

Vertically 1 inch represents 10 × 200 = 2,000 feet

Vertical exaggeration is 2.6 times

It should be kept in mind that vertical exaggeration not only increases but also changes the character of the profile, as shown in Fig. 99. It really creates a caricature of the topography; for instance, volcanoes ten times exaggerated will show up as sharp spines.

*Laying Out Roads and Railroads.* For roads and railroads a maximum slope is usually specified. The laying out of such roads on a contour-line map is shown in Fig. 100. Wherever the contour lines are closer together than the maximum gradient of the road, the necessary length to reach the next contour is scaled off slantingly with a compass. For railways a minimal radius of curvature is also prescribed, for which we cut out small celluloid circles in the proper scale.

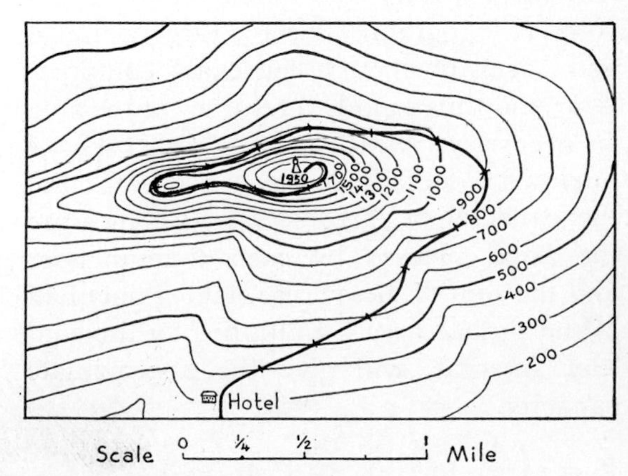


**Fig. 100** The layout of a motor road of even grade. Several alternatives are possible.

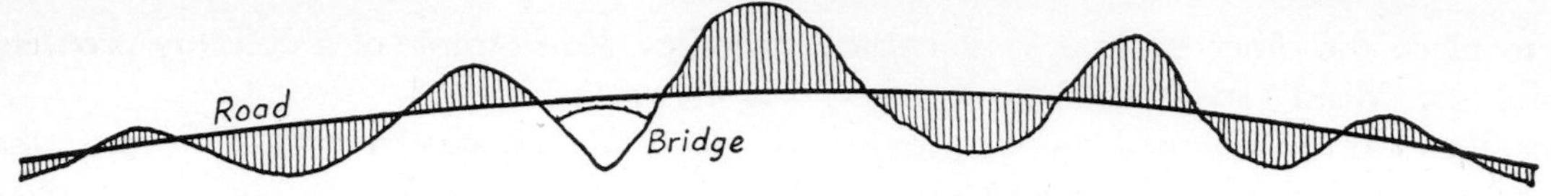


**Fig. 101** Cutting and filling should even up along a railroad or motor road.

*Cut and Fill Problems.* If a road or railroad has to be laid out over very hilly country, it is important that the amount of cut and fill should even up. This can best be calculated by constructing a profile along the proposed line of the road. Then, a so-called "give-and-take" line is laid out, which bisects the mass of hills so that the mass above the line is the same as that below.

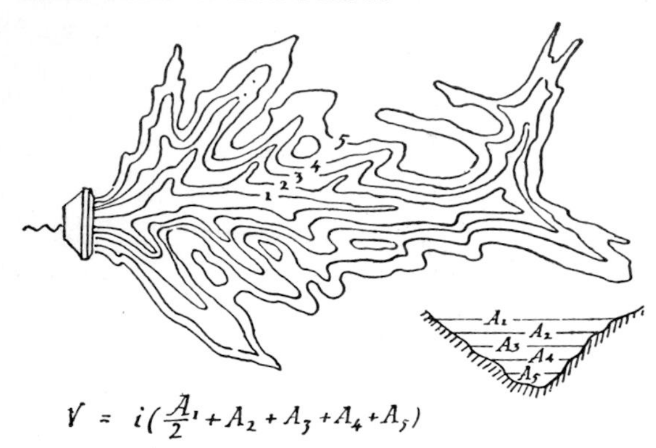

$V = i(\frac{A_1}{2} + A_2 + A_3 + A_4 + A_5)$

**Fig. 102** The volume of reservoirs is calculated from exact contour maps with small contour intervals.

*Reservoir Problems.* Contour-line maps are indispensable in the figuring of dam sites and the capacity and extent of the reservoirs. A topographic sheet is rarely detailed and accurate enough for exact computation; and thus usually a resurvey of the area is necessary, with more closely spaced intervals, generally not over 5 feet. To get the capacity of the reservoir, we measure the area enclosed by each contour line; and the sum of these areas (taking only half of the surface area), multiplied by the contour interval, will give the approximate capacity.

$$V = i\left(\frac{A_1}{2} + A_2 + A_3 + A_4 + \cdots + A_n\right)$$

*Irrigation Problems.* Successful irrigation often depends on utilizing the gentlest slopes of land, for which very exact contour lines are necessary. All major projects have been mapped by the U.S. Geological Survey and by the Bureau of Reclamation with a very small contour interval, such as 5 feet, or even 1 foot.

It would go far beyond the limits of this book to discuss more illustrations of the need for contour-line maps to aid in engineering problems. Mention should be made, however, of some of its military uses.

*Visibility Problems.* In locating artillery observation stations it is important to know which areas will be visible from a lookout

**Fig. 103** The visibility from an observation point is ascertained by radiating profiles. Invisible areas are shaded.

and to place the other stations so that the invisible or "dead" space shall be a minimum. This can be planned on a contour-line map by drawing profiles radially from the lookout point; then tangents to the tops of the hills will determine the dead spaces. How close the radiating profile lines should be spaced depends on the topography. It will soon be found that only a moderate number of profiles will be necessary if the terrain is properly visualized. For instance, the observer is not able to see beyond a hill which is higher than the lookout, to any place which is lower, and all such places may be darkened in without drawing profiles. An example of a visibility problem is shown in Fig. 103.

*Ballistic Problems.* In modern warfare, the artillery fires at an invisible enemy over hills of considerable height. The curve of the projectiles is superimposed upon a set of profiles of the terrain taken radially from the battery, and the striking points can easily be determined. Sometimes even infantry fire is thus calculated, for it is possible to shoot with rifles over low ridges into the hidden positions of the enemy.

*Drawing of Landscapes.* Good contour-line maps enable us to draw a landscape from a certain point without actually going to the

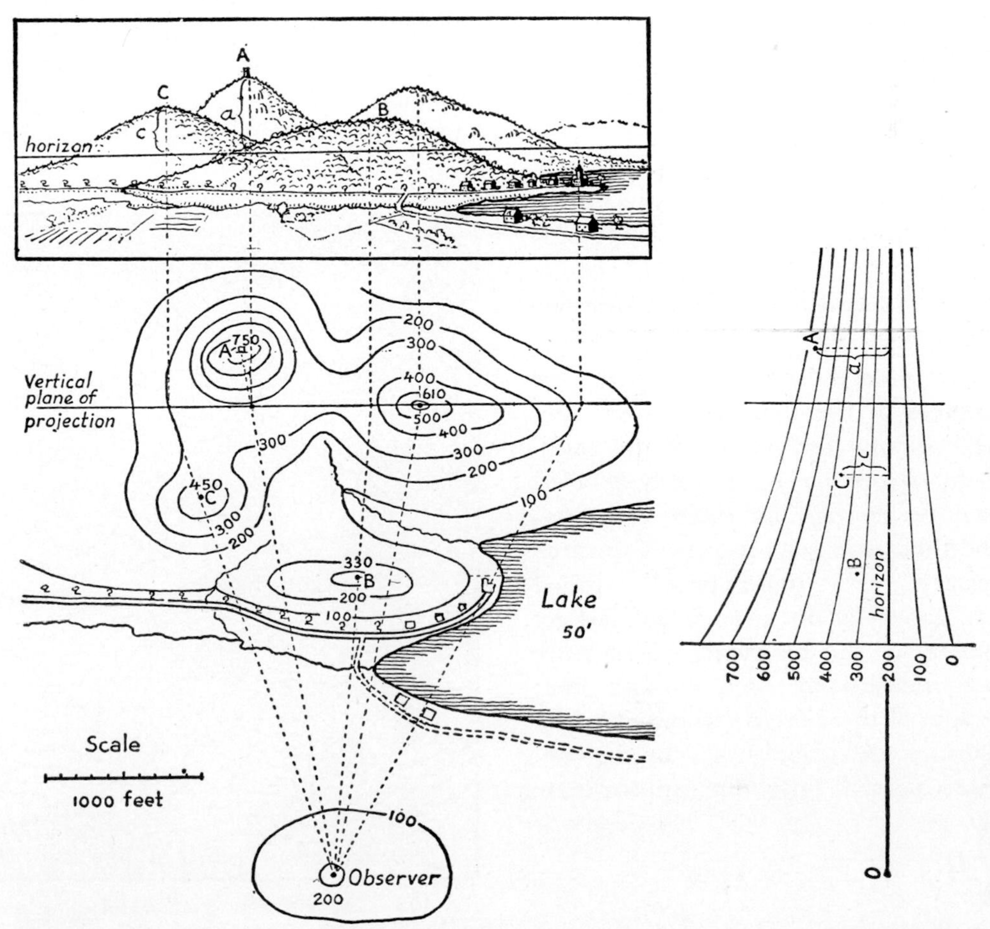


**Fig. 104** The landscape visible from any point can be outlined from a contour-line map. The vertical scale consists of hyperbolic curves.

place. A vertical plane of projection is drawn on the map at a chosen distance from the observer. The closer this plane, the smaller the landscape. Every important point is projected upon this plane with rays from the observer. This vertical plane is turned down flush with the paper to show the landscape. We draw a horizon line that represents the level of the observer, and the height of each point above or below the horizon is determined by the help of a hyperbolic vertical scale. This scale is constructed so that when a hill is twice the distance from the observer, it should appear one-half the height. A small vertical exaggeration of scale is permissible in flat countries. The solution of such a problem can best be understood from Fig. 104.

# CHAPTER 11: *Other Relief Methods*

**Altitude Tints (Hypsometric Coloring).** In small-scale maps mountains cannot be shown individually, and considerable generalization is necessary. In maps on a smaller scale than 1:500,000, the contours are usually drawn at increasingly larger intervals at higher altitudes. For instance, contours of 500, 1,000, 2,000, 3,000, 5,000, 8,000, 12,000, and 18,000 feet are a common sequence of contour lines on small-scale maps. Such greatly generalized contour lines cannot give good visualization of the country; the only information they really convey is the general elevation above sea level.

Contour lines on small-scale maps were not used until the middle of the nineteenth century. With the perfection of lithography and color printing, General von Hauslab in Vienna and others experimented with altitude tints, coloring each zone within adjacent contour lines with a slightly different color. In the first experiments the darker colors were used for low elevations, but that made the densely settled lowlands too dark and they reversed the system. In the present conventional color scheme, greens are used for elevations under 1,000 feet, browns ranging from light to dark for higher lands, and sometimes white for over 15,000 feet. The symbolism of such an arrangement is twofold. First, the greenish tints remind us of fertile valleys, the browns the bare rock, and the white the snow. Second, according to the rule of perspective, the nearer an object is to our eyes, the warmer should be the color that is used for painting it. Since a map is a picture of the earth as seen from above, the mountain tops are nearer to the imaginary observer, and so they are shown in warm, reddish brown, and the more distant valleys in a colder, green tint.

This symbolism has its dangers. For instance, much of the Sahara Desert is under 1,000 feet in elevation, and on many maps it is shown in bright green, thus conveying to untrained people the impression of fertile lowlands. For this reason a new color scheme was tried using gray or olive instead of green for low elevations; this made

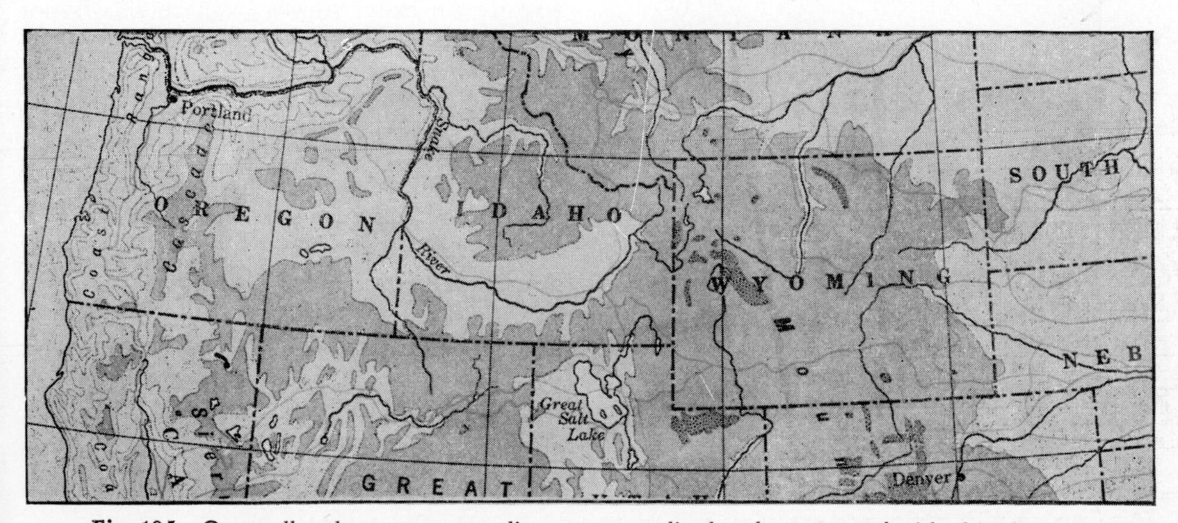


**Fig. 105** On small-scale maps contour lines are generalized and accentuated with altitude tints.

less brilliant but also less misleading maps. Another danger of altitude tints is that they may overemphasize certain lines which are not significant in nature. In most of our school maps the 5,000-foot line marks the change from light brown to dark brown, and is very conspicuous. Since this line just misses the Rocky Mountain front and happens to cross the most featureless parts of the Great Plains, many school children obtain an erroneous idea about western topography (see Fig. 105). With modern engraving methods it is possible to make *merged altitude tints*, gradually going over from one color to the other. This method has been successfully tried on the latest British Ordnance Survey sheets, and also can be well adapted to small-scale maps.

**Stereographic Method.** Professor Karl Peucker of Vienna perfected the altitude-tint method as follows: The tints graded from a greenish-gray in the valleys to a bright orange-brown at high altitudes. These were combined with contour lines and violet oblique plastic shading and a generous application of the cliff symbol. The result was such striking plasticity that the method was named stereographic. This is perhaps the most advanced method of showing relief at the present time. The Peucker method is excellent for use in mountainous countries, but in lowlands it has little advantage. It is with good reason that this method is most used in Switzerland and Norway.

**Fig. 106** Illuminated contour-lines give a "terrace" effect. (*British Ordnance Survey*, 1866.)

**Illuminated Contour Lines.** Experiments have been made in making gray altitude tints and combining them with contour lines, which are white in the northwestern sector and black in the southeastern sector. The land looks like layers of cardboard placed one above the other. The British Ordnance Survey published in the 1860's a set of maps in this method. These were very striking but of such "terraced" effect that their use was soon abandoned (see Fig. 106).

This method was recently improved upon by Tanaka Kitiro, who made the shadows of uneven thickness, proportional to the actual light received in standard oblique illumination. These contours can readily be drawn with a stub pen and give vivid relief effect.

**Horizontal Form Lines.** Contour lines require an exact survey. Where this is not available, horizontal form lines may be used. In exploratory reconnaissance of a country, mountains can be sketched in by using broken horizontal lines drawn in the same direction as contour lines would run. Steepness is expressed by closer spacing of the lines. Since the lines are not connected and cannot be counted, it is more correct to call the method "hachuring with horizontal lines" or "horizontal form lines" than contour lines.

**Kantography.** Doctor R. Lucerna of Prague developed an interesting method to make large-scale contour-line maps more

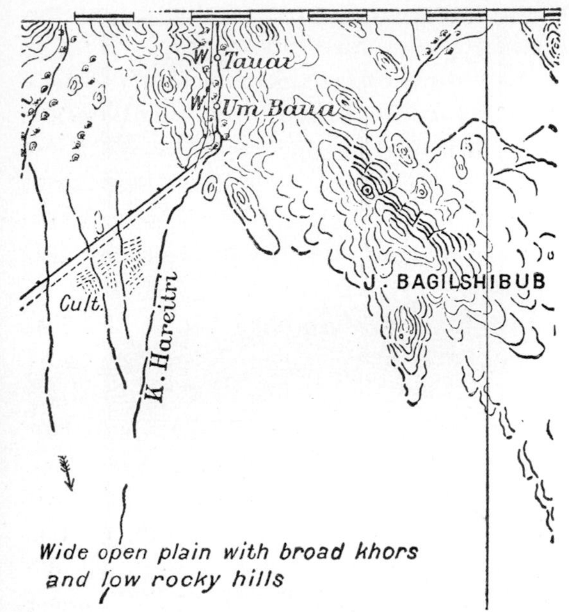


**Fig. 107** Horizontal form lines are used in reconnaissance maps. (*British War Office*, 1: 250,000, *Sudan.*)

expressive (Kante-edge).[1] He contends that every edge or break in the topography signifies an event in the Earth's history. This break may be convex as in crests or terraces, or concave as in gorges. Thus, he differentiates between crests, rock edges, terrace edges, river edges, and edges developed along the contacts of different geological formations. Break lines are drawn with heavy single lines. All contour lines change their direction at the break lines.

Kantographic representation is of greatest significance in mountainous and glaciated countries. In smooth hilly regions, relatively few edges can be drawn unless the map is on such a large scale that even the breaks caused by different vegetation are included. The method is recommended for geographic or geomorphologic field work, mapping relatively small areas with the plane table. Airplane photographs also help in discovering break lines in the topography.

[1] LUCERNA, DR. R., Neue Methode der Kartendarstellung, *Petermanns Mitte.*, p. 13, 1928; also *Petermanns Mitte.*, p. 17, 1930; and Fazettierung, *Petermanns Mitt.*, p. 1, 1931. See also, *Comp. Rend. Intern. Geog. Cong.*, Vol. 2, Cartography, pp. 101–103, 1938.

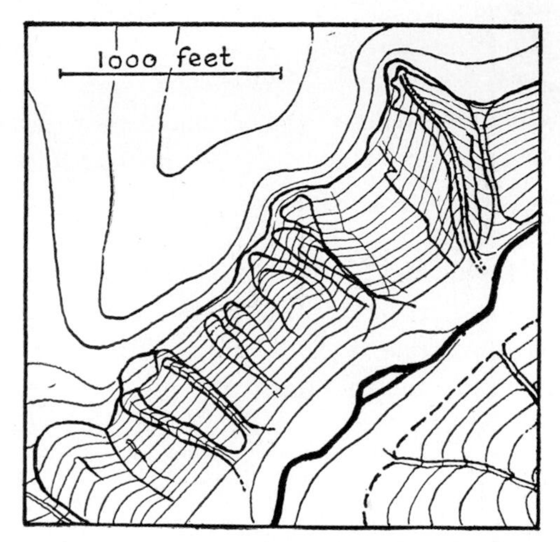


**Fig. 108** Example of kantographic representation of a small region. All break lines in nature are indicated. (*After R. Lucerna.*)

**The Kitiro Method of Showing Relief.** Professor Tanaka Kitiro of Japan has devised an ingenious method of transforming contour lines into a form of plastic shading. The contour-line map is ruled with fine parallel lines spaced at even distances. Beginning with the intersection of a horizontal line with the lowermost contour line, we connect this point with the intersection of the next higher contour line, with the next horizontal line, etc., as shown in Fig. 109. It should be noted that the lines thus obtained are not subsequent profiles; they are, rather, subsequent contour lines cut out by parallel planes, the datum plane of which is not horizontal but inclined. If the spacing of the horizontal lines equals the contour interval, the planes are inclined 45°. The effect of these lines is quite pleasing and gives a good impression of relief, especially when the map is turned so that the "shadows" fall toward you.

Fig. 109*a*

Fig. 109*b*

**Fig. 109*a* and *b*** Kitiro method of showing relief. The effect of the crater is better if the book is turned upside down. (*Courtesy of Geog. Jour., Vol.* 79, 1932.)

## Combinations

Contour lines give exact information about slope and elevation; hachuring and plastic shading bring out visibly the forms of mountains; altitude tints emphasize elevation above sea level. These advantages are often combined in one map. The most common combination of relief methods is contour lines with oblique plastic shading. Various European surveys use them, notably the 1:50,000 French maps. An interesting attempt was made by the U.S. Geological Survey and by the Army Engineers to print some of the Pennsylvania sheets with red-brown contour lines, blue hydrography, a dark greenish-gray lettering, and oblique plastic shading in this same color. The reddish contour lines stand out brilliantly on the lighted sides of the hills; the grayish shadow gives plastic relief to the topography. It is to be hoped that this method will be adopted for other mountainous areas.[1] In the Norwegian 1:100,000 maps the contour lines are combined with plastic shading using vertical illumination, which is appropriate to show the fjord land with equally steep slopes on both sides of the fjord.

Hachures and contour lines are often combined. In the old 1:75,000 Austrian maps, 50-foot contour lines were added to the hachuring (see Fig. 89). In later maps, when contour lines were used as the main method, the hachures were often overprinted in a fainter color. The most elaborate combination is on the new British Ordnance Survey sheets with brown contour lines, gray hachuring, purple plastic shading, and brown, merged altitude tints. The hachure lines, however, are used only because the plates of the earlier editions are still available.

On small-scale maps, the most frequent

[1] Instructors are advised to show the students the topographic sheets of various nations and let them describe the methods of showing relief used therein.

combination is that of contour lines with altitude tints, the disadvantages of which have already been mentioned. In most European maps altitude tints are combined with a type of generalized hachuring which is superior to the tinted contours. A few attempts have been made to combine hachures or physiographic symbols with faint merged altitude tints; this is perhaps a promising method for the future.

## Morphographic, or Landform, Maps

This method is designed primarily for small-scale maps. Both hachuring and contour lines are satisfactory on large-scale maps, but on small-scale ones, where we cannot show every mountain individually, both systems have to be generalized to such an extent that they lose expressiveness. The morphographic method approaches the problem from an entirely new angle; instead of showing slopes or elevations, it shows the type of the landscape with more or less pictorial symbols which are derived from airplane views.

This method is an outgrowth of the block diagrams used to illustrate physiographic principles by William Morris Davis and others in the late nineteenth century. A block diagram is a perspective view of a part of the earth's crust, on the sides of which the geological structure is shown, and the surface is handled pictorially. To show the various surface types a certain symbol system was adopted which was found to be applicable to vertically seen maps, too. Such maps were prepared by William Morris Davis himself. The first major map of this kind was A. K. Lobeck's "Physiographic Diagram of the United States" (1921). The method was systematized by the author in 1931,[1] the earth's surface being classified into 40 morphologic types as shown in Table XIII.

If we regard such a map as a systematic application of a set of symbols instead of as a bird's-eye view, we do not violate cartographic principles even though the symbols are derived from oblique views instead of from vertical views, just as our present swamp symbol is derived from side views of water plants.

In a morphographic map the existing conventional symbols for roads, rivers, and cities can be used without change. First we draw the major rivers and locate the outstanding peaks, and fill in this skeleton with symbols. Where the relief is high, higher, steeper, and darker symbols are used than on lower regions. Shading on one side adds greatly to the plasticity.

We can also show the vegetation types on the flat areas; all three major elements of the geographic landscape—relief, vegetation, and culture—are present on a small-scale, black-and-white map. It is important,

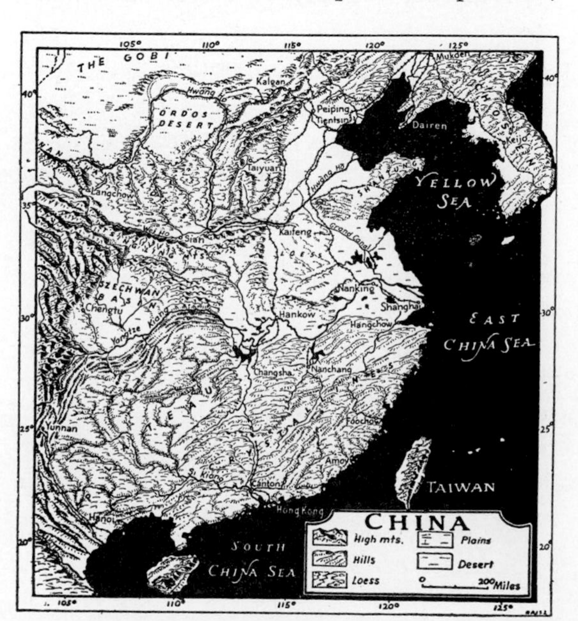


Fig. 110 Landform maps are easy to visualize.

[1] RAISZ, ERWIN, The Physiographic Method of Representing Scenery on Maps, *Geog. Rev.*, Vol. 21, pp. 297–304, 1931.

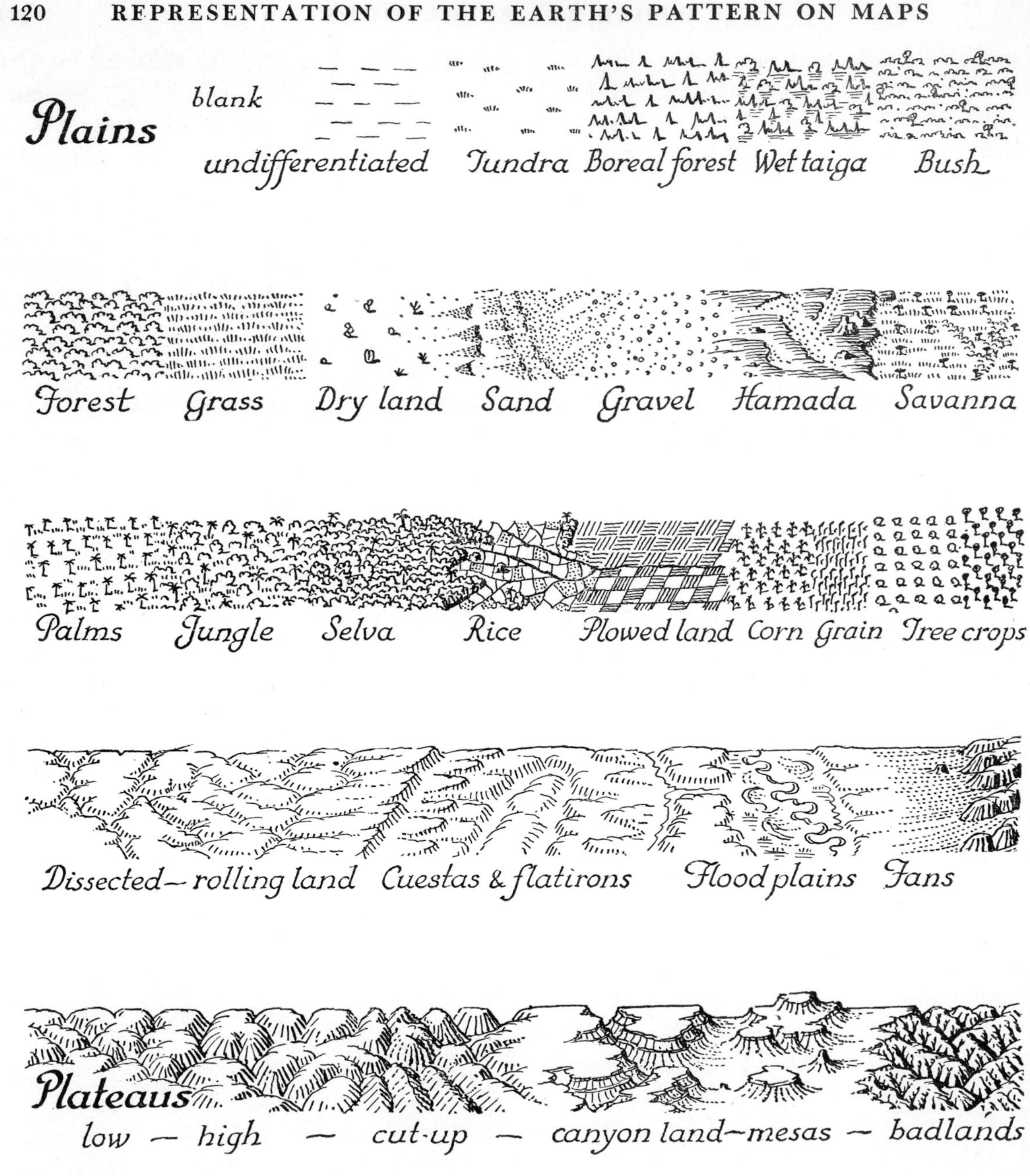

Table XIII Physiographic Symbols

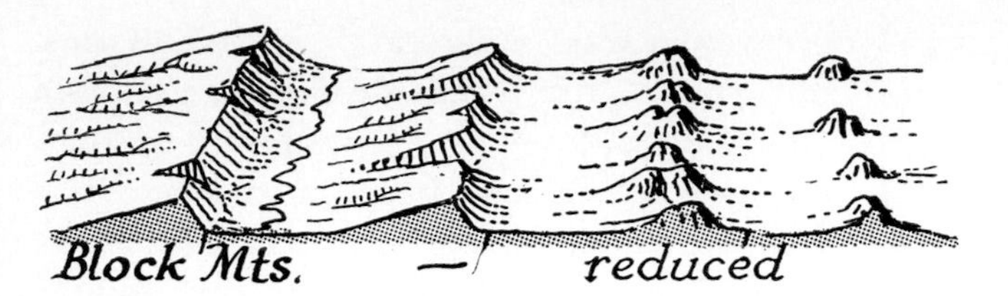

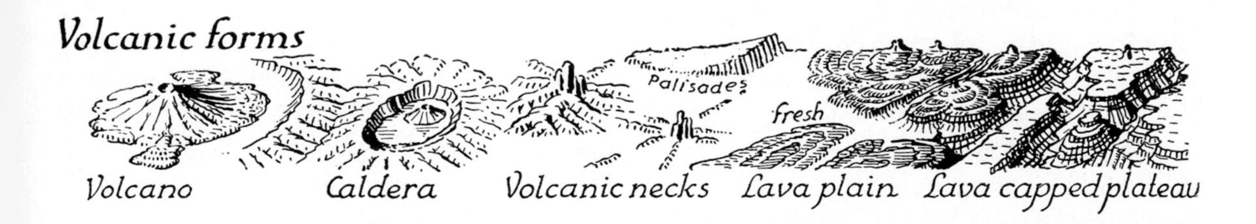

**Table XIII Physiographic Symbols** (*Continued*)

**Fig. 111** A landform map with vegetation symbols may be called a "land-type" map. (*From P. E. James, "South America," Doubleday & Company, Inc.*)

however, that the mountains should be drawn very heavy, so as not to compete with the vegetation symbols (see Fig. 111).

A disadvantage of landform maps is that the symbols used are derived from oblique views; therefore, on the northern slopes the perspective has to be drawn out. Again, the method gives no information about the elevation above sea level. If colors are used, this deficiency can be overcome by combining the landform maps with merged altitude tints. Otherwise, frequent spot heights may help.

The advantage of the landform map is that it appeals to the average man. It suggests actual country and enables him to see the land instead of reading an abstract diagram. It works on his imagination even if he is not able to recognize the exact geomorphologic types. It is a method that makes mountains look like mountains. This type of map is adapted for representation of regions where only reconnaissance surveys have been made. It can be rendered with pen and ink and reproduced in black-and-white line cut, but often it is made with crayon or wash and reproduced in half tone. Blue hydrography, black culture, and brown morphography make very pleasant maps.

It should be kept in mind that landform maps are designed only for small-scale maps. The distortion resulting from the oblique view is not then disturbing, because peaks of the highest mountains are not displaced more than a small fraction of an inch. On large-scale maps, where the displacement is appreciable, it is necessary to use actual block diagrams.

The method had many names. Lobeck called his a "physiographic diagram," although this is the least diagrammatic of all relief methods. The author earlier called it the physiographic method. The term "morphographic," however, is preferred here as it indicates the geomorphographic origin of the method. The informal term "landform map" seems to express the direct appeal of the method. Landform maps have become very popular; this is the almost universal method used in newspapers and magazines, and even theaters of war were rendered this way. The "terrain diagrams" made by the U.S. Geological Survey for strategic uses were either block diagrams or landform maps.

**The Trachographic Method.** The ruggedness of a region is the result of the height and steepness of the mountains. The height from valley to peak is the "relative relief," and the steepness is expressed by the "average slope." The trachographic method combines a measurable representation of relief and average slope with a pictorial effect that can be easily perceived and remembered. It has the advantage, also, that it can be easily applied to a general map showing railways, roads, rivers, etc. It is designed for small-scale maps only.

The fundamental element of the method is a hill-shaped curve, the height of which is made proportionate to the relative relief, and the width to the average slope. The symbol does not have to be drawn completely everywhere; its possible applications are shown in Fig. 112. If the relative relief is reached by gradually increasing slopes, this fact can also be presented.

This method, combined with a few geomorphologic symbols, such as sand, lava, swamps, and volcanoes, will give a vivid picture of the slope conditions of a country. This type of map can be made by persons who have but little drawing experience. Care should be taken not to draw "fish scales," which can be avoided by varying the spacing. The entire method, for which the name "trachographic" is here tentatively proposed, is still in an experimental stage.

Although a trachographic map is similar to a morphographic map, the two have entirely different origin. While the landform symbols are derived from pictures of genetic types of surface features, the trachographic method uses a single symbol and varies it according to the height and steepness of any kind of mountain. Landform maps tell more about the land, but trachographic maps are easier to draw and serve well enough for simpler maps.

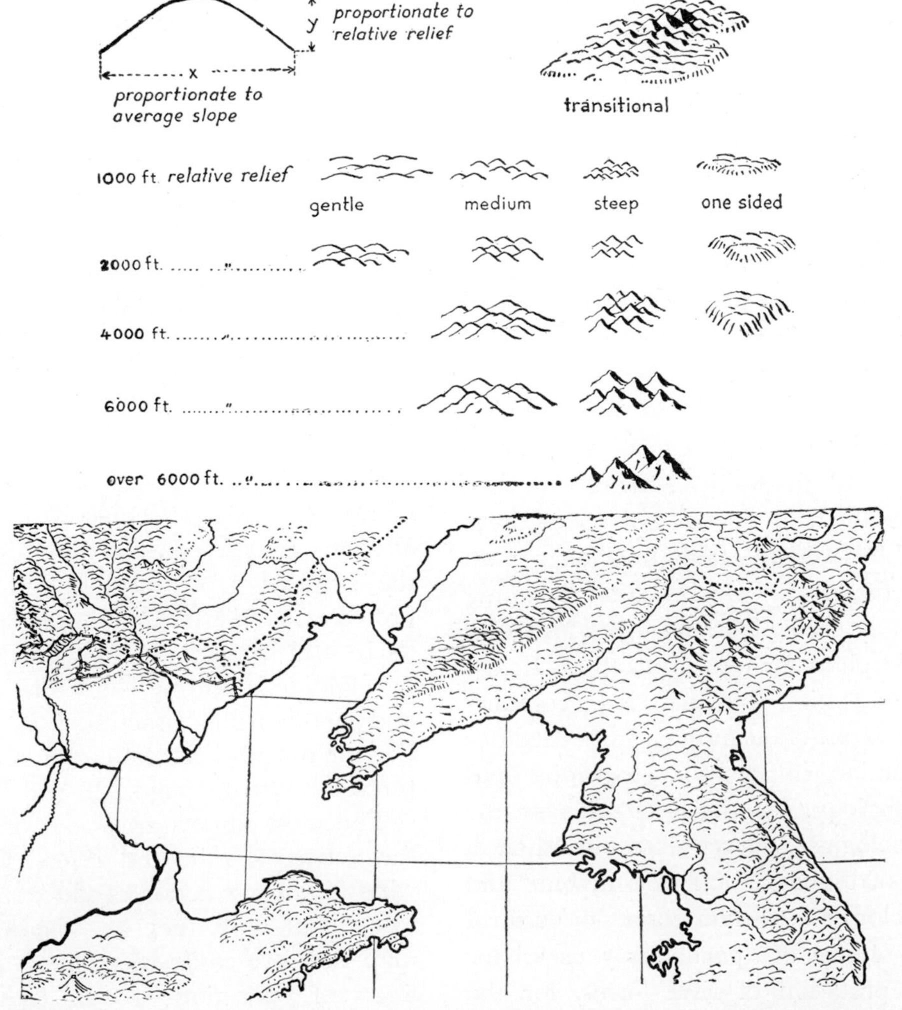


**Fig. 112** Simplified trachographic symbols for small-scale maps showing ruggedness of land.

# CHAPTER 12: *Map Reading*

The reading of contour-line maps is not easy for untrained people. Nature has no lines that are reminiscent of contour lines (except in some plateaus with horizontal layers), and the visualization of a contour-line map needs careful study and power of imagination. Figure 94 shows some geometrical figures expressed in contour lines, which may help in an understanding of the natural forms. After some training, however, a contour line will give a clearer conception of and more reliable information about the land forms than any other method.

A man with a keen sense of analysis and some knowledge of geomorphology and geography can read an astounding number of facts from a contour-line map. Not only can he recognize the geologic structures but he can make a fair guess as to the possible utilization of the land and social conditions therein. In many cases the morphology of the land can be more easily recognized from a contour-line map than from actual travel through the country.

Map interpretation is useful in many ways. An oil prospector can recognize certain types of favorable structures before going into the field. A geologist is sometimes better able to locate fault lines on a map than in the field. Governmental planning boards may recognize land types and thus formulate plans for land utilization. In the field of education the analysis of contour-line maps is one of the most effective methods of instruction in general geography and geomorphology. For the latter purpose the U.S. Geological Survey has published a number of topographic sheets in blue and brown color only, without names or cultural symbols. These are particularly useful for the interpretation of land forms, for the students are not influenced by previously acquired knowledge.

The ability to read maps is vital for soldiers. Military operations have to be planned on maps, perhaps into unseen territory of the enemy, and the men have to be able to recognize the natural objects from maps. For instance, a good map reader can tell ahead of time from a contour map whether a certain stream is likely to be of hard or muddy bottom and whether or not he can risk fording it.

The first step in the analysis of contour-line maps is to visualize the land. It is convenient to divide the map into regions of the same pattern, and to analyze each region separately. The scale and contour interval have to be found. The slopes can be read from the density of the contour lines. Contour-line density corresponding to a 100-foot slope per mile represents flat country; a 500-foot slope represents steep, hilly country; and a 1,000-foot slope represents rugged and mountainous country. The field study of various average slopes will help more than any theory.

For further analysis of the land forms the *structure-process-stage* sequence is followed. *Structures* are the constructional land forms, the original land built up by geologic processes, such as (1) plains and plateaus of horizontal strata; (2) mountains, derived by folding, faulting, igneous intrusions, and metamorphic processes; (3) volcanoes. For the diagnosis of the various basic structures the key on page 125 will be helpful.

The most important *process* of erosion is the action of rain and rivers. Glaciation, wind, and wave action produce such typical forms that once they are diagnosed on a map they are easily recognized again. The *stages* of dissection—youth, maturity, old

Key to the Recognition of Land Forms on Contour-line Maps

| | | | |
|---|---|---|---|
| No trend | | | |
| (dendritic drainage) | Symmetrical valleys | Even dissection; low relief | *Plain* } of horizontal |
| " " | " " | " " high " | *Plateau* } strata |
| " " | " " | Uneven " | *Massive, unglaciated* |
| " " | Asymmetrical peaks | " " | *Massive, glaciated* |
| Elongated ridges | Strongly asymmetrical | The same ridge of even | *Cuestas; gently folded* |
| (trellis drainage) | ridges | height | *mountains* |
| " " | Symmetrical ridges | " | *Steeply folded mountains* |
| Radial-annular drainage | Asymmetrical ridges | " | *Domes* |
| Subparallel trend | " " | Of uneven height | *Gneissic; schistose mountains* |
| Several trends | " " | " " | *Slaty mountains* |
| Trend chopped off | " " | " " | *Faults* |
| Radial drainage | Conical or subconical | Isolated | *Volcanoes* |

age, peneplanation, second cycle with rejuvenation—all produce typical forms that can best be recognized by drawing profiles either actually or in the imagination. Care should be taken not to confuse the stage of development of the major rivers with the stage of dissection of the land masses, *i.e.*, the percentage of the original land that was carried away by erosion in the present cycle.

Obviously, landforms are not always pure types. They are often transitional or very complex, and their diagnosis is not always easy, especially in crystalline rocks. It is also assumed that the contour lines are exact in every detail, which is not always true. An effort should be made to recognize the 12 typical landforms on pages 126 to 128 without turning to the "Explanation."

**Map Reading of Land Use.** The geomorphologic analysis is only a part of map reading; just as important is the interpretation of the human uses of land. With some knowledge of geography one may learn a great deal of the life of the people from maps. The use of land depends on slope, climate, soil, resources, social, political, and economic factors, etc. Our topographic maps as we have them now show little of this kind of information; in the future we hope for maps from which it will be possible to tell whether the land is used and if so for what. At present we can only speculate.

One of the limiting factors of land use is its *slope*. In general, slopes steeper than 200 feet per mile are rarely cultivated. The rough limit of hayfields and orchards is 500 feet per mile, while rough pasture can be still steeper. This does not mean that every flat land is cultivated, but it does mean that only some of it can be cultivated, while steep land cannot be. The above limits are applicable only to the eastern United States. In the wet tropics incredibly steep slopes are not only cultivated but are preferred to bottom lands.

Equally important in limiting cultivation is the effective *rainfall*. The climate can be estimated from the frequency of rivers. A river may have its origin in near-by mountains and flow through a desert; only the rivers that have their source within the topographic sheet count. Every river is intermittent in its headwaters, but if it does not become permanent within a few miles of its origin the climate is likely to be dry. The landforms themselves give indications of the dry climate. The prevalence of alluvial cones, high-level fans, bolsons,

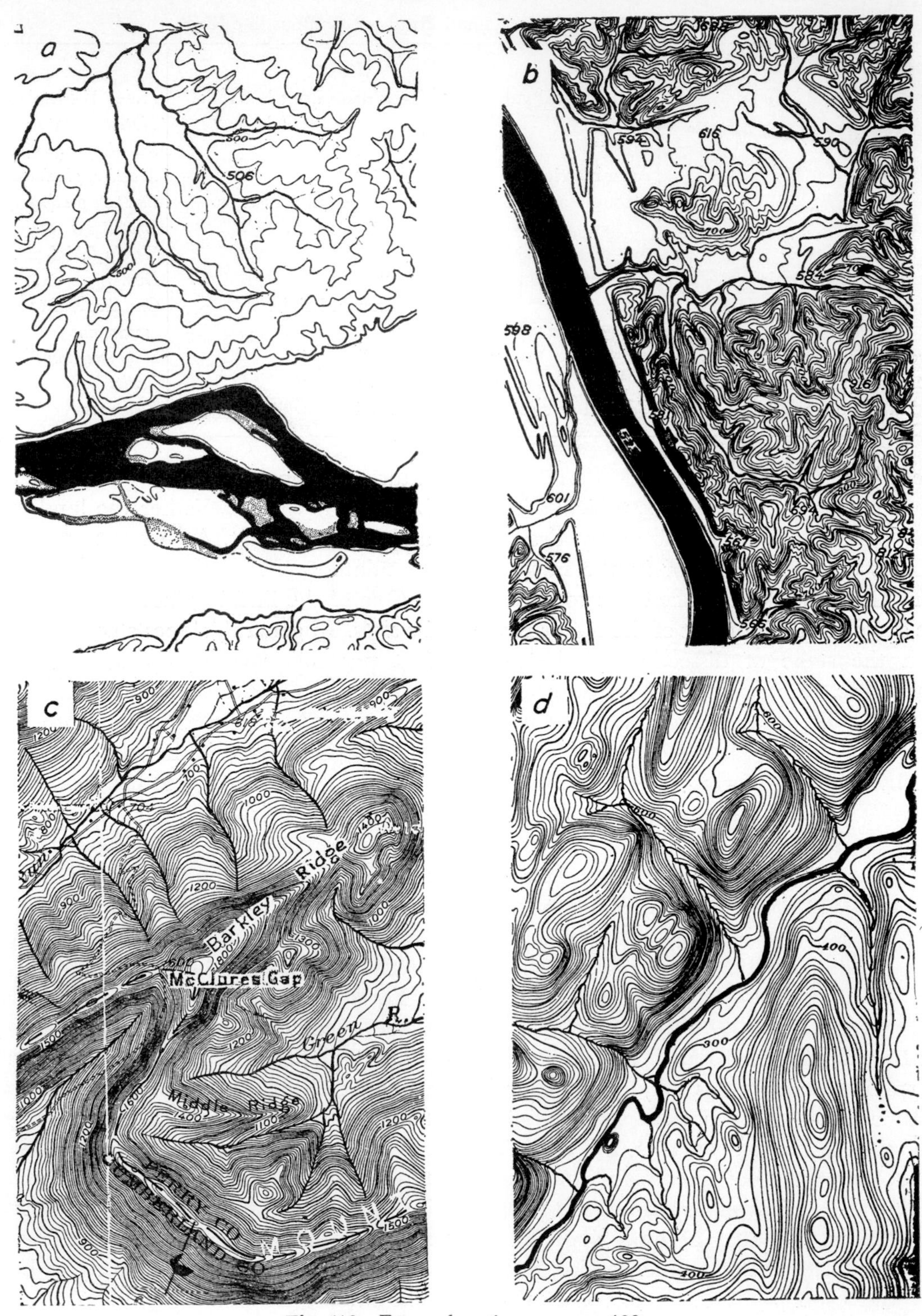


Fig. 113 For explanation see page 129.

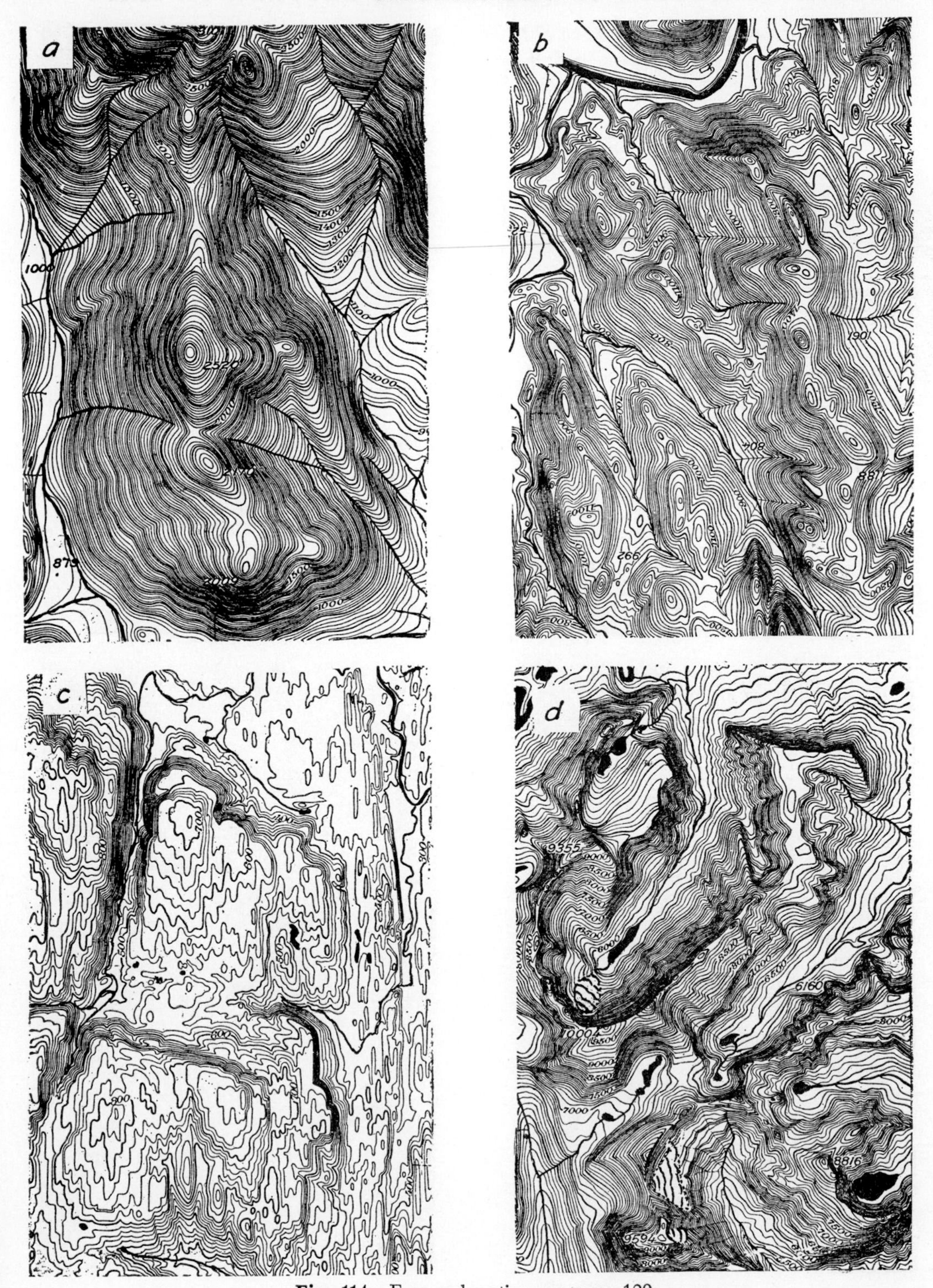


Fig. 114 For explanation see page 129.

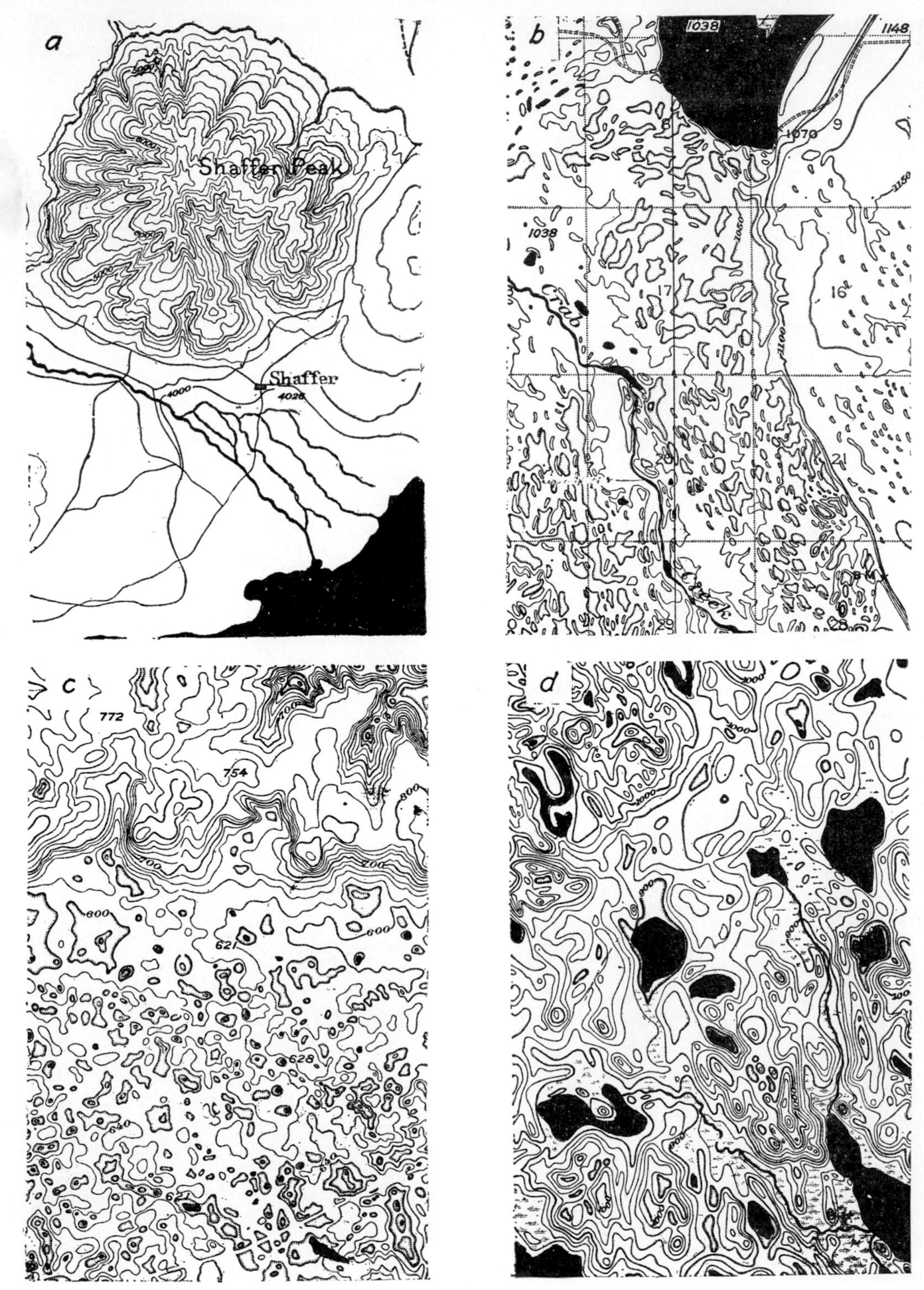


**Fig. 115** For explanation see page 129.

arroyos, and playas are indications of dryness. Dry climate does not preclude settlement, but it is likely to be limited to ranching unless irrigation is employed.

If the climate is humid, the best indication of the density of settlement is the *road pattern.* In ranching regions or forests, the roads will be farther apart, while in corn, cotton, truck farming, and tobacco areas the roads are closer together. Truck farmers are likely to cultivate the black soil of flat bottoms of former lakes or swamps. In deserts the density of roads is often surprising in view of the sparse habitation. Their presence is due more to the ease of building, absence of bridges, and cheapness of upkeep than for their use. West of the Appalachians, all the United States was once public land, and it is divided into townships of 36-square mile sections. In wheat lands or less intensive farming regions a road is found at about every mile.

The *density of population* can be figured from the number of farmhouses; if the average number of houses is eight per square mile, the average farm is 80 acres and the population is likely to be 50 to 60 per square mile, a fairly dense rural population. In ranching regions, however, the number of people on a ranch may be many more than on farms. Suburban populations with more than 20 houses per square mile may be judged by allowing four to five people per house.

The *population of towns and villages* can be roughly calculated from the size of the

EXPLANATION

**Fig. 113** *a. Maturely dissected plain* interrupted by the flood plain of a river. The large river is hemmed in by its valley and is not able to meander freely. Thus it is in submature stage of development. The river is slightly aggrading (many islands). Note Yazoo type of river at the southern side of the flood plain. (O'Fallon, Missouri-Illinois, quadrangle; 1:125,000.)

*b. Maturely dissected plateau* interrupted by the flood plain of a large river. The river is in the second cycle of development in which it has reached the submature stage. Note the abandoned high-level meander flat. (Ravenswood, West Virginia, quadrangle; 1:62,500.)

*c. Folded ridges peneplained and redissected.* Barkley Ridge is an anticline (the inside of the curved end is steeper). Green River occupies the bottom of a syncline (the outside of the curved end is steeper). (Loysville, Pennsylvania, quadrangle; 1:62,500.)

*d. Fault line scarp* separating the upper region with NE-SW trend, from the lower region with a N-S trend. A river flows along the fault line. (Ramapo, New York-New Jersey, quadrangle; 1:62,500.)

**Fig. 114** *a. Massive, glaciated mountains,* maturely dissected, with dendritic drainage and steeper southern slopes. The texture (spacing of rivers) is coarse. (Crawford Notch, New Hampshire, quadrangle; 1:62,500.)

*b. Complex gneissic mountains,* peneplained and maturely redissected with subparallel trend. Note river terraces. (Randolph, Vermont, quadrangle; 1:62,500.)

*c. Complex slaty hills,* peneplained and redissected, with joint-controlled trends. (Coxsackie, New York, quadrangle; 1:62,500.)

*d. High mountains maturely dissected by local glaciation.* Note cirques, tarn lakes, glacial troughs, trough lakes, faceted spurs, Alpine peaks, arrêtes, and flat uplands, remnants of preglacial surfaces. (Chief Mountain, Montana, quadrangle; 1:125,000.)

**Fig. 115** *a. Submaturely dissected volcano* with radial drainage on a flat plain. (Honey Lake, California, quadrangle; 1:250,000.)

*b. Sand dunes.* Crescent-formed barchans on the two sides and irregular dunes and blowholes in the center. Note the N-S bluff marking the course of a former river. (Moses Lake, Washington, quadrangle; 1:62,500.)

*c. Sinkholes in limestone* in the southern half, covered by a locally perforated sandstone cap on the northern half of the map. Note the absence of rivers and the many small lakes. (Mammoth Cave, Kentucky, quadrangle; 1:62,500.)

*d.* Irregular young *morainic hills* with many lakes, kettle holes, and swamps and undeveloped drainage system. (Minneapolis, Minnesota, quadrangle; 1:62,500.)

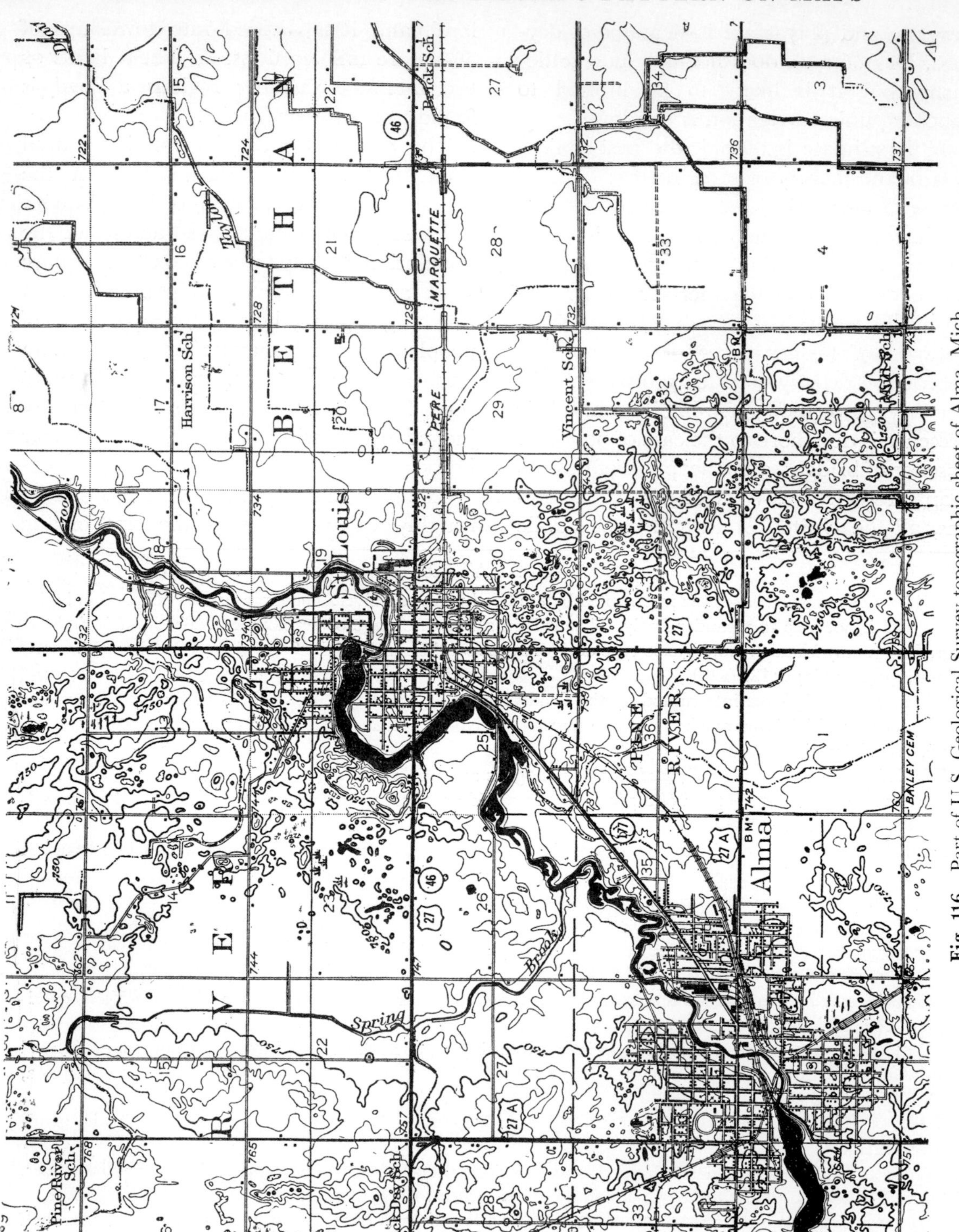


**Fig. 116** Part of U.S. Geological Survey topographic sheet of Alma, Mich.

built-up area. Towns of about 1 square mile have about 1,500 to 2,000 people. The density of population is larger in larger cities. It ranges for small towns from 3,000 to 8,000 per square mile, denser in the manufacturing East, less dense in the spreading Western and Middle Western cities. In large cities the density is 8,000 to 10,000 per square mile, while in the great Eastern metropolitan areas it may reach 15,000. An exact survey of city densities is very desirable. Always the entire built-in area of a city within its suburbs has to be taken into account, exclusive of larger parks and water surfaces. The actual density in some sections of Manhattan is more than 100,000 people per square mile. These figures are far from true in European and Asiatic cities, which are much more congested.

*The functional types* of cities and parts of cities, such as business centers, ports, railroad centers, manufacturing cities, capitals, resorts, mining and lumber towns, college towns, etc., can also be read from the map. A large building with a railroad siding is likely to be a factory. A great number of factories and small closely set houses are typical for a manufacturing city. Lumbering and mining cities show up well because of the uniform evenly set "company" houses, even if the mine symbol does not indicate it clearly. Railroad centers and port cities are obvious on a topographic map. Colleges and hospitals often are similar on maps, although hospitals are more likely to have a regular pattern. First-, second-, and third-class residences are recognized by their spacing and their distance from the center of the city. The business sections in the center and subcenters of cities are preconditioned by the road system and are usually obvious. Closely set houses around the business center often represent slums and the poorest parts of American cities.

**Alma, Michigan.** For a sample analysis, let us consider the Alma, Mich., sheet, the northwestern part of which is reproduced here.

In considering the scale first, it is well to compare the area shown on the map with similar-sized areas in our own neighborhood. The next step is to divide the map into parts that appear to be of similar pattern. The map is easily divided into a regular eastern and more complex western region.

Let us consider the eastern part first. The river system is dense enough to indicate that the region has a medium rainfall. Plenty of intermittent rivers do not indicate dryness but indicate the headwaters of rivers of very low gradient. The rectangular east-west and north-south pattern of the rivers is curious, but this means simply that the farmers ditched the preexisting rivers to the edges of their fields. The only larger river is meandering and has a low gradient. Direction of flow could be established from the contours, from elevation figures, and from the joining angle of the tributaries if the two dams would not have given it away. The river is obviously entrenched about 20 feet. A discussion of meandering rivers may clear up many puzzling questions in the student's mind.

Examination of the contour lines reveals that the average slope of the plain is about 10 feet per mile to the northeast. This is an extremely flat country, which indicates a plane of relatively recent deposition of sediments, most probably a former lake bottom with black soil. Coastal plains would also be very flat, but this is, at an altitude of 700 feet, not possible in the United States.

A complete road pattern indicates intensive farming. There are, on an average, 10 farmhouses in a square mile, which, averaging about 7 people per farm, gives 70 people per square mile, a rather dense rural population. The average size of farms is 64 acres—too small for wheat but a sizable farm for corn, legumes, and rotation crops. The black soil is excellent for vegetables, and some truck gardening and considerable dairying can be expected.

The average number of rural schools is one for every 3 miles; each schoool thus serves about 9 square miles, or about 600 people, of which about 100 are children of school age. The maintenance of a complete rural school system, the total occupation of the land, which has excellent soil, and the many paved roads indicate prosperous, well-educated, independent farmers, who are somewhat more likely to vote against the governing party than are wheat farmers or farmers of marginal lands or irrigation districts, who depend more on government support in lean years.

The city of Alma occupies about 2 square miles; according to page 131, it should have a population of about 6,000. (Actually the town had 7,200 people in 1940; the difference is partly due to growth since the map was made in 1934.) The several railroad sidings to large buildings indicate considerable manufacturing. (There are several oil refineries, sugar mills, and automobile-trailer factories, and several packing houses. Its Consumers Power Company employs 175 people. The various industries employ 1,200 people.) It can safely be inferred that the chief function of the town is business or professional services—catering to the farmers. It is also a railroad center with warehouses, sheds, and elevators for farm products. The town is likely to have a college, if the name "Alma" came from "Alma Mater." (The large building on the north end of town, however, is not the college but the Masonic Home.) Whether the low dam, as the contour lines indicate it, is used for water power is not clear from the map, but it may have started the manufacturing.

The distance between St. Louis and Alma is smaller than is the average distance between towns in that part of the country. The close proximity of the two cities is a result of historical rivalry.

The country around Alma, and north and south of St. Louis, shows thousands of small hills of variable height, 10 to 50 feet high, as if they had been strewn accidentally over the landscape. That is what actually happened, for this is the typical pattern of a moraine dumped here in the Ice Age. This land is obviously much poorer than the flatlands of the eastern part. There are fewer farmhouses, and the network of roads is incomplete. Much of the land is poorly drained; some of it seems to have a slope of more than 300 feet per mile, too steep for cultivation.

NOTE TO INSTRUCTORS: Map reading should be practiced whenever possible. At first maps of the familiar neighborhood should be chosen. Later, more distant and foreign lands should be studied. It is a good plan to read maps on the very first meeting to find out about the previous map experience of the students and to introduce the fundamental terms.

# CHAPTER 13: *Lettering and Geographical Names*

Lettering is one of the most baffling problems of cartography. The essential trouble is that lettering is not a part of the picture of the earth's pattern but is a necessary addition for the identification of features. The names by their bulk cover up many of the important elements of the real landscape and prevent the reader from seeing the map as a picture of the earth. On small-scale maps, city names often cover hundreds of miles in length, even if printed in the smallest readable type, and their least disturbing placement is a trial to cartographers. The development of expressive cartography has been hindered more by lettering than by any other cause.

**History.** Even in the earliest times, manuscript maps were clogged with lettering, whether with Chinese characters, Arabic script, or, as on the Aztec maps, with pictures of foxes, eagles, and the like. The Middle Ages produced wonderfully rich romanesque and gothic script letters, especially on Spanish and Italian maps. In the early woodcut maps lettering was often set up in type and stamped in separately, sometimes even in a different color—a custom that was not resumed until the middle of the nineteenth century. The style of lettering changed profoundly with the copper-cut maps of the Dutch masters. Mercator introduced the inclined *italic* lettering for smaller features and used a beautifully proportioned roman lettering for the larger letters. This lettering was still further perfected by his successors, and their style is imitated even now. The Royal Geographical Society uses the lettering of Hondius as the model for its maps.

**Fig. 117** Fancy swash lines were often used as space fillers on old maps.

Dutch cartographers liked to cover the blank parts of their maps with lettering adorned with graceful swash lines; such lettering is one of the chief characteristics of the seventeenth-century maps. In the eighteenth century the style of map lettering became less fanciful. The daring strokes of swash lines were gone, and the letters were accurate, clearer in type, and smaller in size. This finesse reached its perfection in the tiny letters of the early nineteenth century. The atlases of Cary of England, and the maps of Benjamin Tanner, are good examples of this style.

The introduction of wax engraving in 1841 allowed the stamping of lettering, and the consequent ease with which lettering could be applied resulted in overlettering, which is still a characteristic of the

American maps. Only in the most modern maps is a tendency evident to reduce the amount of lettering and to emphasize natural features.

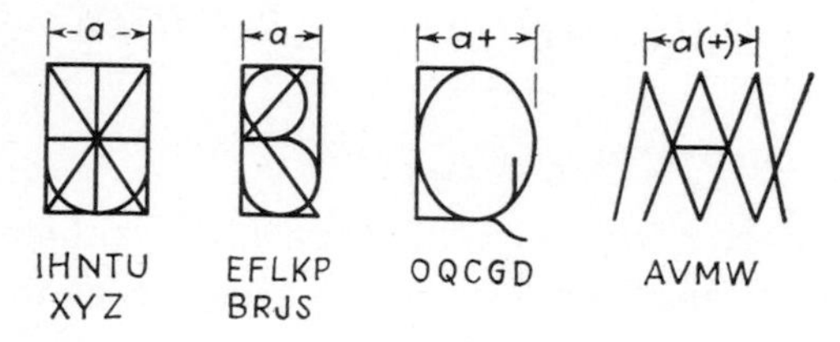


**Fig. 118** Letters can be classified into normal, narrow, wide, and unusual forms.

**Types of Letters.** Our present system of writing derives from the Roman capitals. These letters were written with a stub-pointed stylus in wax or were chiseled into stone. Either instrument would produce wide vertical and narrow horizontal lines, and to give distinct ending to the lines an extra stroke produced the "serif." Medieval scribes, using a reed pen or quill, modified the roman letters and added the lower-case letters to the alphabet. This book is printed in roman. The Renaissance produced the inclined "*italic*" lettering, which is easier to write. The simple, **sans-serif** and **gothic** lettering of lines of even thickness became fashionable much later. Many variations of these basic types of letters are used on maps. The most common types are

Roman of variable thickness and serifs

*Italic* of variable thickness and serifs, inclined

Gothic of even thickness, no serifs

Lightface Roman of even thickness with serifs

*Lightface Italic* of even thickness with serifs, inclined

***Inclined gothic or gothic italic*** of even thickness, no serifs, inclined

Variable thickness, no serifs, as **Lydian**

**Sans serif** more modern gothic types

Cursive Manuscript a kind of roman produced by stub pen

**Phantom** produced by double lines

We can differentiate between the various geographic features by the types of lettering used. For instance, the U.S. Geological Survey topographic sheets use italics for hydrography, gothic for hypsography, and roman and some inclined gothic for culture. The most economical on space are the various gothic types, and in modern maps the tendency is to use the vertical and inclined sans-serifs for all features. Vertical gothic for culture, heavier vertical gothic for mountains, and inclined gothic for water features make a good combination.

The rough rule is to use lower-case letters if the name is outside the feature, *i.e.*, if the feature is smaller than the name (small cities, for instance). Capitals are used if the name is inside the feature, meaning that the feature is larger than its name. In this case, the letters have to be *spread* from one end of the region to the other. We often depart from these rules for the sake of uniformity. For instance, names of countries will usually be capitals, even if we are forced to have the name outside the land, as with the name "NETHERLANDS" on very small-scale maps.

**Size of Letters.** By the size of the letters we can express the importance of the features. CEYLON, for instance, in Fig. 120, has a larger name than Sabaragamuwa. There is, however, a definite lower limit to the size of letters. The smallest readable capital letter is 5 point ($\frac{5}{96}$ inch high), which makes the waist height (:) of a lower-case letter $\frac{1}{30}$ inch. In small world maps, we may have to use minimum-size letters, even for the largest cities, otherwise

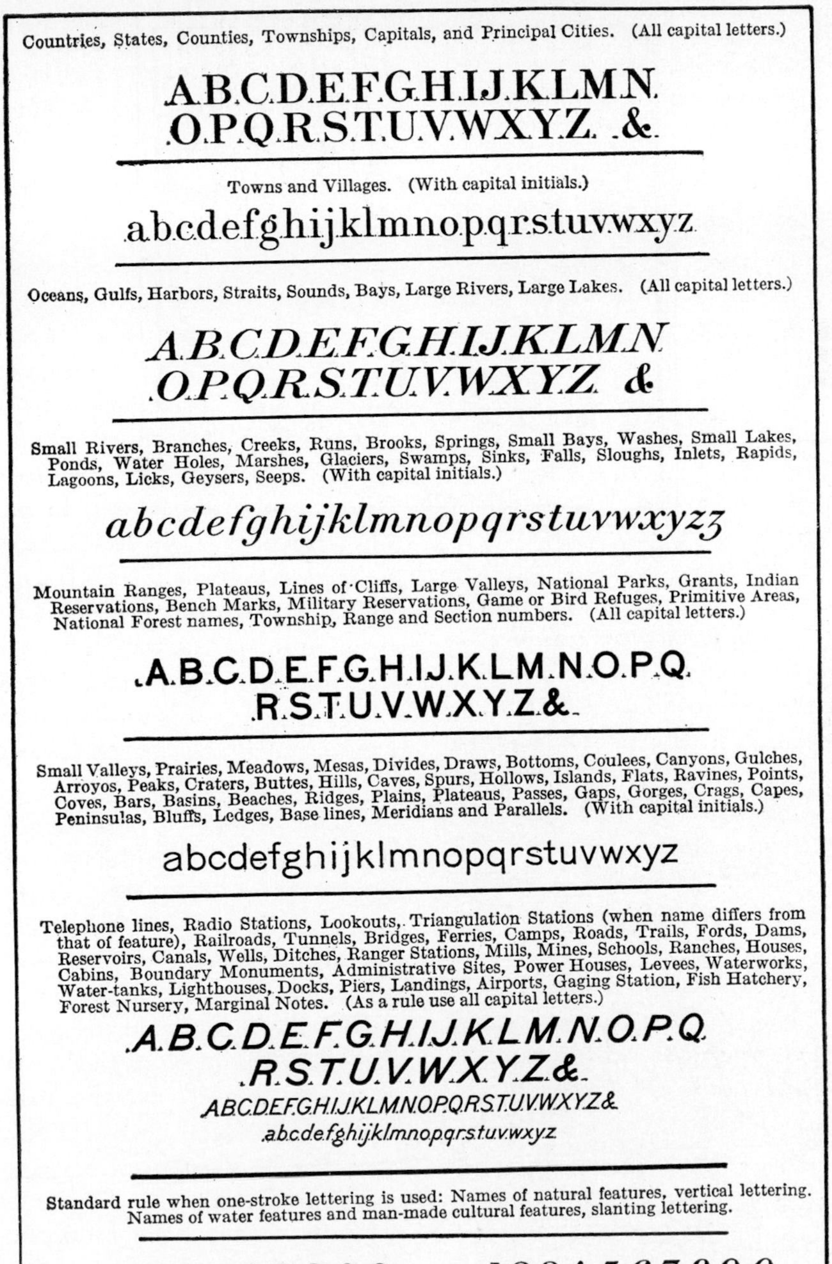

Countries, States, Counties, Townships, Capitals, and Principal Cities. (All capital letters.)

A.B.C.D.E.F.G.H.I.J.K.L.M.N.
.O.P.Q.R.S.T.U.V.W.X.Y.Z. .&.

Towns and Villages. (With capital initials.)

a.b.c.d.e.f.g.h.i.j.k.l.m.n.o.p.q.r.s.t.u.v.w.x.y.z.

Oceans, Gulfs, Harbors, Straits, Sounds, Bays, Large Rivers, Large Lakes. (All capital letters.)

*A.B.C.D.E.F.G.H.I.J.K.L.M.N.*
*.O.P.Q.R.S.T.U.V.W.X.Y.Z. &*

Small Rivers, Branches, Creeks, Runs, Brooks, Springs, Small Bays, Washes, Small Lakes, Ponds, Water Holes, Marshes, Glaciers, Swamps, Sinks, Falls, Sloughs, Inlets, Rapids, Lagoons, Licks, Geysers, Seeps. (With capital initials.)

*abcdefghijklmnopqrstuvwxyzz*

Mountain Ranges, Plateaus, Lines of Cliffs, Large Valleys, National Parks, Grants, Indian Reservations, Bench Marks, Military Reservations, Game or Bird Refuges, Primitive Areas, National Forest names, Township, Range and Section numbers. (All capital letters.)

.A.B.C.D.E.F.G.H.I.J.K.L.M.N.O.P.Q.
.R.S.T.U.V.W.X.Y.Z.&.

Small Valleys, Prairies, Meadows, Mesas, Divides, Draws, Bottoms, Coulees, Canyons, Gulches, Arroyos, Peaks, Craters, Buttes, Hills, Caves, Spurs, Hollows, Islands, Flats, Ravines, Points, Coves, Bars, Basins, Beaches, Ridges, Plains, Plateaus, Passes, Gaps, Gorges, Crags, Capes, Peninsulas, Bluffs, Ledges, Base lines, Meridians and Parallels. (With capital initials.)

abcdefghijklmnopqrstuvwxyz

Telephone lines, Radio Stations, Lookouts, Triangulation Stations (when name differs from that of feature), Railroads, Tunnels, Bridges, Ferries, Camps, Roads, Trails, Fords, Dams, Reservoirs, Canals, Wells, Ditches, Ranger Stations, Mills, Mines, Schools, Ranches, Houses, Cabins, Boundary Monuments, Administrative Sites, Power Houses, Levees, Waterworks, Water-tanks, Lighthouses, Docks, Piers, Landings, Airports, Gaging Station, Fish Hatchery, Forest Nursery, Marginal Notes. (As a rule use all capital letters.)

*.A.B.C.D.E.F.G.H.I.J.K.L.M.N.O.P.Q.*
*.R.S.T.U.V.W.X.Y.Z.&.*
*A.B.C.D.E.F.G.H.I.J.K.L.M.N.O.P.Q.R.S.T.U.V.W.X.Y.Z.&.*
*.a.b.c.d.e.f.g.h.i.j.k.l.m.n.o.p.q.r.s.t.u.v.w.x.y.z*

Standard rule when one-stroke lettering is used: Names of natural features, vertical lettering. Names of water features and man-made cultural features, slanting lettering.

1 2 3 4 5 6 7 8 9 0 *1 2 3 4 5 6 7 8 9 0*
1 2 3 4 5 6 7 8 9 0 *1 2 3 4 5 6 7 8 9 0*

**Fig. 119** Lettering types of the United States government maps. (*From U.S. Forest Service Manual.*)

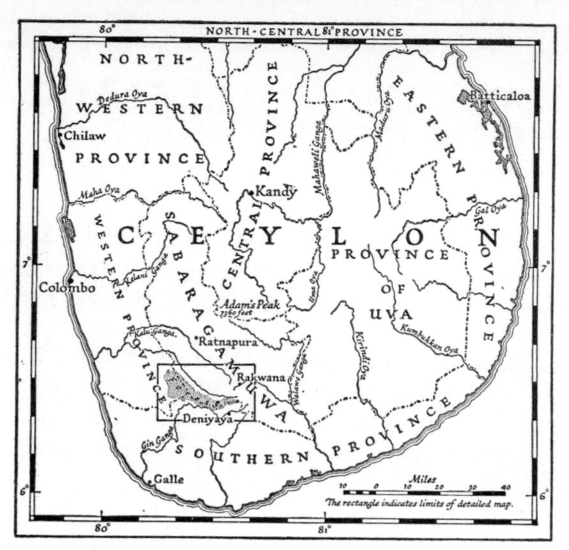


**Fig. 120** The maps of the Royal Geographical Society are artistic and simple. Most of the lettering is made with quill pens. (*Courtesy of the Royal Geographical Society.*)

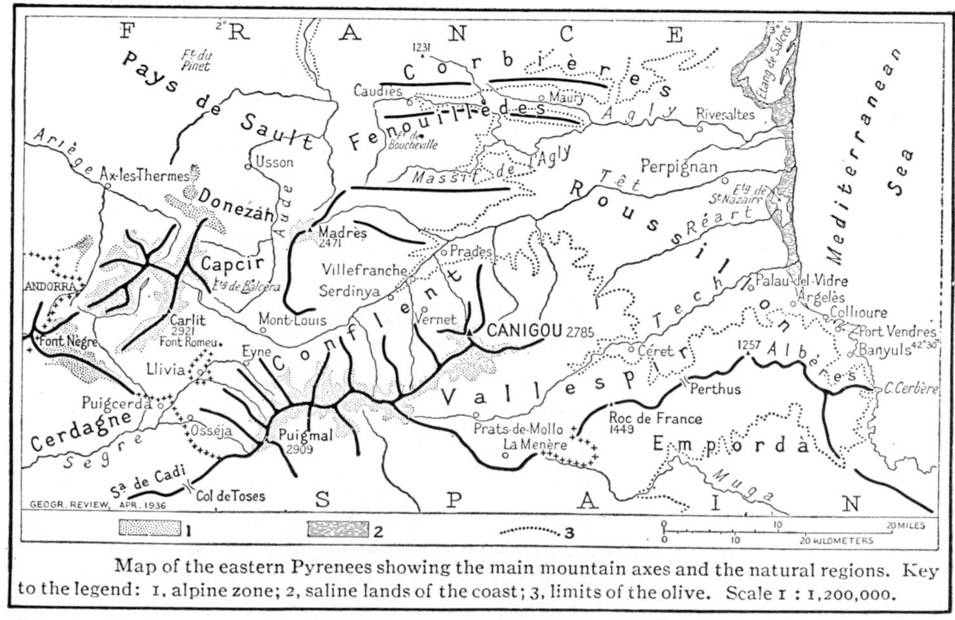


Map of the eastern Pyrenees showing the main mountain axes and the natural regions. Key to the legend: 1, alpine zone; 2, saline lands of the coast; 3, limits of the olive. Scale 1 : 1,200,000.

**Fig. 121** Precision and simplicity characterize the maps of the American Geographical Society. Note the sans-serif and lightface roman lettering.

the name Copenhagen might easily reach over into Russia. If pressed for space, it is customary to use condensed types.

**Practice in Lettering.** Contrary to general opinion, almost everybody can, with some effort, learn good hand lettering. The following rules give in concise form some steps to follow:

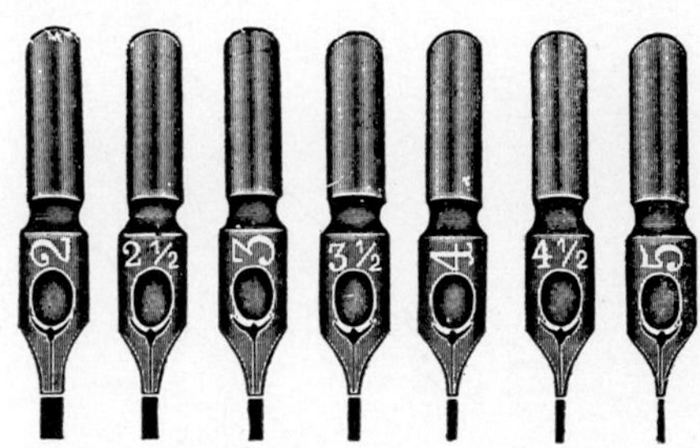


**Fig. 122** Stub-pen lettering is fast and effective.

## Rules of Lettering

1. Sit erectly and comfortably, rest body on left arm, and place the paper in the most convenient position.

2. Draw fine, sharp guidelines with pencil. In lower-case letters the guidelines indicate the waist height. Clear and sharp guidelines can be made with a special instrument that has two pencil points, or, lacking this, by two pencils whittled down on one side and fastened together with an elastic band; their spacing can then be regulated by placing a peg or strips of paper between them.

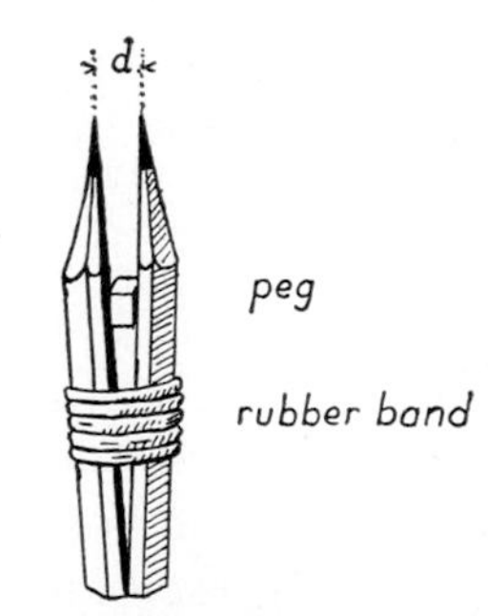


**Fig. 123** Device for drawing guidelines for lettering.

3. Letters are made up of several strokes, and each stroke should be clearly defined. First, place your arm in resting position above the supposed *end* of the stroke. Mark the point. Stretch your hand a little beyond the *beginning* of the stroke; aim and bring down your pen in the proper direction.

4. Make the strokes with the motion of the full arm and not with the motion of the fingers or wrist.

5. After each stroke "follow through," lifting your pen in the same direction as the stroke.

6. Curved letters can be made in from two to four segments; but do not go over the same line twice. Do not "paint" your letters.

7. Keep your eye on the point where you want to go and do not look at your pen point.

8. Ink is supplied to the pen point through a slit that requires cleaning every few minutes. Dust off your paper before inking.

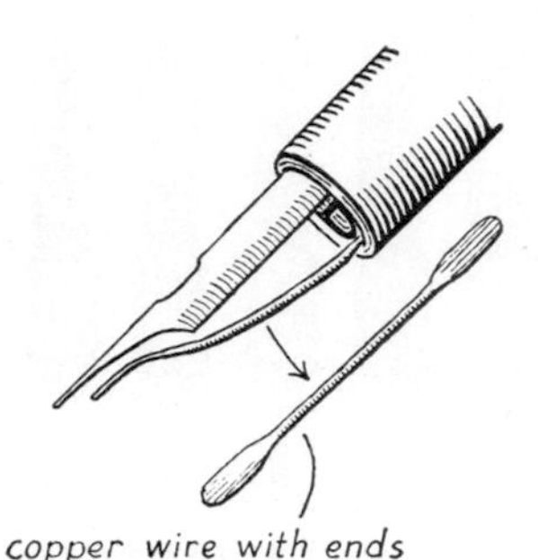


**Fig. 124** An ink retainer provides an even flow of ink.

9. Space letters so that the space between them *appears* even, although the actual distance is variable. There is a smaller space between OO than between II. Between two words leave a place corresponding in size to the letter *o*. The distance between two letters is less than the width of an average letter. Beginners usually spread their letters too much.

10. Keep up an even but slow rhythm in lettering. This gives a feeling of poise and relaxation but does not mean a let-up in utmost concentration on your work.

The beginner is especially warned to adhere strictly to the rule that lettering should be made with the motion of the whole arm and not merely with the wrist or fingers; this rule will at first make his lettering worse but will lead to greater perfection later. The rule of "follow-through" motion is also very important. It is better to learn well the straight and inclined block lettering only than to spend time learning the roman and italic types; for simple maps the block lettering is sufficient.

**Placing of Lettering.** The placing of lettering is one of the major difficulties for a map designer. As a general rule the name should unmistakably refer to the feature it designates. It should be clearly readable without overcrowding.

The *direction* of the letters indicates the trend of the feature. The name of a mountain range should follow its trend; the name of a river parallels the river. If the lettering refers to a point, as the name of a city on a small-scale map, or if there is no special trend, as, for instance, in naming France, the lettering should be horizontal. *However, "horizontal" on a map means parallel to the parallels, whether or not the parallels are shown.* The letters, however, bear no relationship to the meridians. Difficulties arise in polar projections. Here the lettering has to be turned along the horizontal meridian, so that the names do not overhang in the upper half of the map. In large, loose polar maps, which may easily be turned, all lettering may have its top toward the pole. Similar problems arise in world maps in oblique projections.

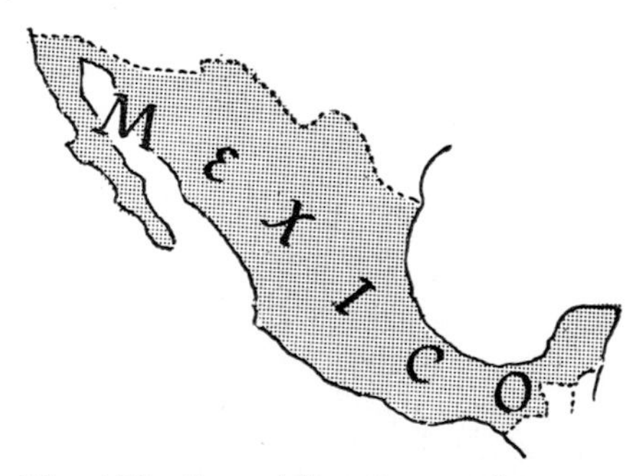


**Fig. 125** Spread lettering conforms to the trend and size of the land.

The *spacing* of lettering should express the extent of an area. All lettering designating an area and placed inside the area should be spread from one end to the other. Usually one unit distance is left on the two ends, and the letters are evenly spread, as in Fig. 125. In "spread" lettering, the two end letters are laid out first, then the center letter, and then the other letters are similarly placed.

*City Names.* On a topographic sheet, a city may be shown several inches across. The name, in all capitals, is spread inside the city. Small cities, and cities on small-scale maps, carry the name outside the city with lower-case letters. The best place for a city name is centered under its symbol; the second choice is on the right and the third choice is above the symbol. If it must be placed to the left, it is advisable to put it above or below the city symbol in order to avoid collision should the length of the name be miscalculated. If the city names are too crowded, it is not bad practice to curve the name in a gentle arc, so that one end of it points directly to the city symbol. Names of harbors are preferably in the sea, and it is better to have the name of the city on the proper side of a river.

**Fig. 126** City names are preferably centered below the symbol; second choice is to right or above. If it has to go on the left, it should be slightly above or below the symbol.

*River Names.* If the name is inside the river, it should be capitalized, but lower case should be used if the name has to go outside. River names are *not spread.* The names of rivers should follow their courses. It is better to place the lettering on the northern side of the river. When the river happens to be exactly north-south, it is advisable to letter it on the western side, because otherwise the inclined italic lettering will overhang. Overhanging lettering should in general be avoided, but sometimes this is very difficult, as in the case of the Mississippi River on small maps. The names of lakes, swamps, etc., should be either entirely inside or entirely outside. The same rule applies to islands, peninsulas, etc.

*Mountain peaks* are difficult to name, especially on black-and-white maps, because such a map is in most cases dense in mountainous regions. It is a good practice to name mountain peaks on a circular arc above each peak, and altitude of the mountain can be marked underneath. Names of mountain ranges should follow very closely and should emphasize the crest line of the range. The letters should be heavy and narrow, to stand out but not to obscure the relief.

In modern maps there is an evident tendency to *reduce lettering to the minimum.* It does not seem necessary to write "United States," "Atlantic Ocean," "Pacific Ocean," etc., on every map of the United States, for these features would be familiar to most persons who are able to read a map. On special maps for more advanced study, it is better to omit all names that have no direct bearing on the purpose of the map. For instance, on a map of oil production in the United States it is not necessary to name the states or the rivers.

**Abbreviations.** The use of abbreviations may help a great deal to prevent overcrowding. As a general rule, a good abbreviation is one that can be recognized without a key. Special abbreviations, however, should be listed in the legend, especially those of foreign names. An abridged list of the authorized abbreviations of the U.S. Geological Survey is given here.

| | |
|---|---|
| Ave. | Avenue |
| Bdy | Boundary |
| Br | Branch, Bridge |
| Bk | Brook |
| Can | Canyon |
| C | Cape |
| Cem | Cemetery |
| Ch | Church |
| Co | County |
| Cr | Creek |
| Dist | District |
| E | East |
| El | Electric, Elevated |

| | |
|---|---|
| Fy | Ferry |
| Fd | Ford |
| F, For | Forest |
| Ft | Fort |
| Gl | Glacier |
| Hbr | Harbor |
| Hy | Highway |
| H | House |
| I, Ind | Indian |
| I | Island |
| Is | Islands |
| Junc | Junction |
| L | Lake, or Little |
| LH | Lighthouse |
| Mid | Middle |
| Mi | Mile |
| Mil | Military |
| Mon | Monument |
| Mt | Mount |
| Mts | Mountains |
| N, Nat, Natl | National |
| N | North |
| Pk | Peak |
| Pen | Peninsula |
| Pt | Point |
| Pd | Pond |
| PO | Post office |
| PH | Power house |
| RR | Railroad |
| R | Range, River, Run |
| Res | Reservoir, Reservation |
| Rd | Road |
| Rk | Rock |
| Sch | School |
| Sd | Sound |
| S | South |
| Spr | Spring |
| Sta | Station |
| Str | Stream, Strait |
| St | Street |
| Val | Valley |
| WW | Waterworks |
| W | West, Water |

**Mechanical Means of Applying Lettering on Maps.** Even on the earliest printed woodcut maps, lettering was set up in type and stamped on the map. Stamping lettering was still the practice of the Army War College maps until the Second World War. Type stamped into wax is the basic feature of wax engraving.

*Stick-up Lettering.* Pasting printed lettering on manuscript maps has also been done for centuries. The simplest method is to have the lettering printed on thin paper backed with Duco cement. Then cut it out closely and paste it on the map with acetone applied with a brush. This method has an advantage in that the opaque paper will cover up lines on the map that would interfere with lettering.

Some years ago "float" lettering became popular: The lettering is printed on thin, transparent Japanese tissue, and when in place it is wetted with a brush, using a sticky liquid that filters through the paper and attaches it firmly to the base. The tissue will be hardly visible and can be easily drawn over. The method is patented and a permission fee has to be paid to the owner when it is used. More recently, *cellotype* lettering has been used to a considerable extent wherever the lettering has to be on transparent paper, as, for instance, on blueprints. The lettering is printed on the underside of a cellophane sheet that is covered with a sticky substance of paraffin base. The lettering is cut out and simply rubbed on the place. It holds firmly enough but care must be taken not to keep the map in a hot place because the paraffin melts and the letters fall off. Cellophane lettering will be printed according to the cartographer's instructions by the Monsen Company in Chicago and delivered for use.

There are on the market various lettering devices (Wrico, Le Roy, Ames, etc.) with which lettering can be applied by means of perforated templets and special pens. Except for titles and labels, their use for map making is limited. It is difficult to use them for large "spread" letters, and for city names even the smallest templets are too large unless the drawing is made two or three times the publication size. A professional cartographer will use these devices relatively rarely, but a geographer making an occasional map finds them helpful.

Fig. 127 Wrico lettering uses perforated templates.

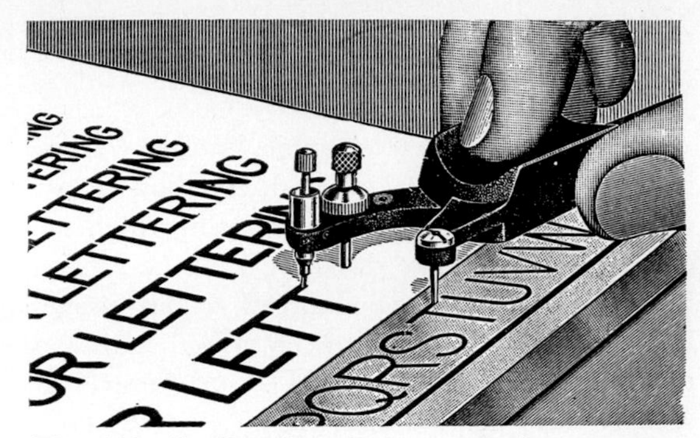

Fig. 128 Le Roy lettering set uses the same embossed guide for vertical or slanted letters.

## Geographic Names[1]

Geographic names are of concern to the cartographer because they are necessary for the identification of places and features symbolized on maps. It is virtually impossible to refer to individual places on maps without employing place names.

Toponymics, the science of place names, is a field of knowledge based on specialized training in geography, linguistics, and history. Few cartographers fully comprehend the complexity and specialized character of place-name problems or have the necessary facilities and training to deal with them in detail. Most persons engaged in the field at the scientific level are in the service of governments that undertake extensive mapping programs.

To cope with the problems of place names many governments have set up agencies, committees, or boards that study place-name usage, formulate place-name policy, and exercise varying degrees of place-name authority. This function is exercised in the United States by the Board on Geographical Names in the U.S. Department of the Interior. Among the foreign countries may be mentioned Canada, Brazil, Argentina, South Africa, New Zealand, and many European countries. Of special interest to American cartographers is the Permanent Committee on Geographical Names for British Official Use, the only one other than our American agency that has concerned itself extensively with names outside its own territory.

**Principles of Geographic Nomenclature.** The cartographer will do well to acquaint himself with the following general principles that govern the work of the Board on Geographical Names:

1. The names of major territorial divisions, such as countries, self-governing dominions, colonies, and protectorates, shall regularly be spelled in accordance with conventional English usage. The use of local official names (in the language of the country concerned) is permissible, however, when such practice is clearly preferable. *Examples:* The regular practice is to use Germany instead of Deutschland, Finland instead of Suomi, Hungary rather than Magyarország, and Japan rather than Nippon or Nihon.

Conventional English names may have various derivations; they may be complete or partial translations, respellings in terms of English or some other language, or they may be spellings in the official language, or

[1] Quoted from a statement of the U.S. Board on Geographical Names.

one of the official languages, of the country or countries concerned.

2. The names of geographic features (rivers, mountains, deserts, lakes, etc.), common to two or more major territorial divisions in which the official languages are different, shall be spelled in accordance with conventional English usage, but the local official form employed within a given country may be used . . . wherever it seems desirable. *Example:* Danube is the conventional name for the river known to the Germans and Austrians as Donau, to the Hungarians as Duna, to the Yugoslavs and Bulgarians as Dunav, and to the Rumanians as Dunărea.

In small-scale mapping of large areas, such as continents, hemispheres, or the world, conventional English names generally will be available for all features within the scope of this rule that are capable of being shown and named. On the other hand, in large-scale mapping it may be desirable to name some features of this category for which there is no true conventional English name.

3. Local geographic names in each country, dominion, colony, protectorate, or possession, in which a Latin alphabet is habitually or alternatively used, shall be spelled in accordance with local official usage, except in cases where there is a conventional English form which differs from the official name, in which case either may be used. *Examples:* Seine; São Paulo; Roma (Italian), Rome (English); Wien (Austrian), Vienna (English).

For geographical features in the United States and its possessions the board is able to determine local usage with more ease and greater assurance than it is able to do for those of most foreign countries. Direct information from local inhabitants in areas of American sovereignty usually can be readily obtained, whereas for foreign areas it is necessary to rely on official publications of the governments concerned and other secondary sources for evidence of local usage. This has the effect of emphasizing official, more than local, usage in the latter areas.

4. In the geographical names of countries employing the Latin alphabet extra or modified letters, accents, and diacritical marks of all kinds, when regularly used in the language concerned, should be retained. *Examples:* København, Curaçao, Åbo, Łódz, Köln, São Tomé, Sète, and Saône.

| | | | | | | | | | |
|---|---|---|---|---|---|---|---|---|---|
| 1 | А | а | a | | 18 | Р | | р | r |
| 2 | Б | б | b | | 19 | С | | с | s |
| 3 | В | в | v | | 20 | Т | | т | t |
| 4 | Г | г | g | | 21 | У | | у | u |
| 5 | Д | д | d | | 22 | Ф | | ф | f |
| 6 | Е | е | e | | 23 | Х | | х | kh |
| | Ё | ё | e | | 24 | Ц | | ц | ts |
| 7 | Ж | ж | zh | | 25 | Ч | | ч | ch |
| 8 | З | з | z | | 26 | Ш | | ш | sh |
| 9 | И | и | i | | 27 | Щ | | щ | shch |
| 10 | І × | і | i | | 28 | Ъ | × | ъ | omit |
| 11 | Й | й | i | Omit after ы, и, or і, | 29 | Ы | | ы | y |
| | | | | at the end of a word. | 30 | Ь | | ь | omit |
| 12 | К | к | k | | 31 | Ѣ | × | ѣ | e |
| 13 | Л | л | l | | 32 | Э | | э | e |
| 14 | М | м | m | | 33 | Ю | | ю | yu |
| 15 | Н | н | n | | 34 | Я | | я | ya |
| 16 | О | о | o | | 35 | Ѳ | × | ѳ | f |
| 17 | П | п | p | × obsolete | 36 | Ѵ | × | ѵ | i |

**Fig. 129** Russian writing developed from the Greek. Obsolete letters are commonly found in older maps. (*Courtesy of U.S. Board on Geographical Names.*)

5. Geographical names in countries which use a non-Latin alphabet or a nonalphabetic writing system should be treated in accordance with approved transcription and transliteration systems.

Transliteration systems, *i.e.*, systems in which each letter of a non-Latin alphabet is replaced by a letter or combination of letters representing approximately the same sound in English, are used for such languages as Russian, Bulgarian, and Arabic. For languages written with a great number of silent letters, such as Siamese, Mongolian, and Tibetan, and for nonalphabetic languages, such as Chinese, transcription systems are used. In the latter, the sounds of the foreign language are represented by Latin letters, combinations of letters, and letters provided with diacritical marks in such a way that the sounds of the foreign language are approximately reproduced, with consonants as in English and vowels as in Italian.

The transliteration and transcription systems in use for rendering names into the Latin alphabet may have official approval of the country concerned, or, if there is no officially approved system or if the system approved is inadequate or otherwise unsatisfactory, systems of American authorship are used.

**General Procedures.** The cartographer concerned with the problem of obtaining place names in accordance with the above principles should keep in mind a general caution. Few maps or other materials are so reliable in their geographic nomenclature that they can be safely used as sources for place names without comparison with other materials. Many place-name source materials are faulty because of careless compilation or inadequate compilation data; others because their name information is out of date. Place names are not static. They change for numerous reasons: (1) change of official language or languages resulting from change in sovereignty, (2) change of spelling, both by evolution and by law, (3) change in official transcription and transliteration systems, and (4) official renaming by the country concerned. This situation calls for precise information in regard to current sovereignty, laws affecting place names, and pertinent linguistic data. It is necessary not only to use the proper source materials for names but also to compare the sources used.

Small-scale maps of large areas usually show only such major features as countries, cities, large rivers, mountain systems, seas, and gulfs. The required names for such maps can be selected most conveniently by comparing the names to those on similar maps, and in desk atlases, geographical dictionaries, general gazetteers, and comparable materials. Names in agreement in several sources and in accord with the principles outlined above should be chosen for use.

Large-scale maps allow the inclusion of many geographical names which will not be found on small-scale maps and for which spellings in the language of sovereignty are recommended. For some foreign areas, names have been worked out for maps except at the largest scales and are available in the lists of the Board on Geographical Names and on recent maps published by Federal agencies. For other names, two or more reliable sources of recent date in the language of sovereignty should be compared. If the language of sovereignty uses the Latin alphabet, names should be taken without modification as determined by comparison of the sources. If the official language is not written in the Latin alphabet, suitable transcription or transliteration systems, such as those of the Board on Geographical Names, should be used to render the names in the Latin alphabet.

There are available on request from the Board on Geographical Names lists of decisions on domestic and foreign names and directions and guides for the treatment of geographical names for separate countries. The board also maintains voluminous files of names on which research has been done, formulates and publishes geographical-name transcription and transliteration systems, and furnishes advice on matters of place names related to cartographic problems.

# CHAPTER 14: *Composition and Drafting of Maps*

Most small-scale maps show an irregular area that has to be fitted to a rectangular page or sheet. The proper composition of the sheet is not always easy. There will always remain empty spaces that can be filled up with title, legend, and insets; or, if this is not enough, a characteristic picture or quotation may enliven the map. The old Dutch cartographers of the seventeenth century were masters of producing well-balanced and beautifully composed sheets; a study of the maps by Janszoon and Blaeu is recommended, for we still use the same style in the make-up of our maps.

**Title.** The title of the map designates the name of the land represented, the type of map, possibly its author, the scale, the year of preparation, pertinent remarks, etc.

The scale should be in a round number of miles. On simple maps a graphic scale is sufficient, because a numerical scale may be easily rendered untrue by photographic processes.

It is preferable to put the title into a simple or decorative frame, called a "cartouche." The lettering within the frame is usually centered; therefore, in order to determine the extent and size of the letters, a vertical axis is drawn, and the title is laid out very roughly and lightly. Then guidelines are drawn, and the letters counted; each space between words counts as a letter. Beginning with the central letter on the axis, the letters to the right are drawn first, and then those to the left, lettering backward. The graphic scale is also centered on the axis. After all writing has been laid out, the frame is drawn; it can follow in form more or less the extent of the lettering.

**Legend.** Whether to use the term "Legend," "Key," "Reference," or "Explanation" depends on individual taste. All four are commonly used. The legend may be included in the title cartouche but, if more extensive, it is placed separately. It is not necessary to include in the legend obvious features that will be clearly understood by prospective users of the map. Thus, a road, railroad, or boundary symbol rarely need be explained. Unusual abbreviations should be listed, but it is not necessary to list standard ones.

**Border.** Most maps are framed within a rectangular border. This may be a simple line, but often elaborate frames are used, consisting of two or more parallel lines. A double line at least $\frac{1}{4}$ inch wide makes a good frame; between the two lines the numbers for parallels and meridians may be placed. In order to save space, it is customary to interrupt the inner border for projecting corners of the land. The outermost line of the border, however, should not be interrupted, since this would create difficulties for the engraver, especially when the map is published within a text.

Decorative borders are common. A simple and appropriate border can be made attractive by marking the degrees with alternate black-and-white bars (see Fig. 120). These bars will vary in length with the lengths of the degrees. Sometimes, for decorative purpose only, a black-and-white bar is made in even division and in no relation to the parallels and meridians (see Fig. 130). In Victorian times, frames were often overdecorated, but at the present time taste is simpler.

**Parallels and Meridians.** The drawing of parallels and meridians is necessary only when they promote a better understanding of the map. In simple maps they can often be omitted and designated only on the borders. If, however, we use a projection with strongly curved parallels, it is often essential to draw the whole network in order to indicate distortion. Often parallels and meridians are omitted on land and drawn over the seas and oceans only.

Parallels and meridians are fine hairlines, drawn with a sharpened ruling pen, on carefully cleaned and dusted paper. They are drawn from intersection to intersection, along a straight or curved ruler.

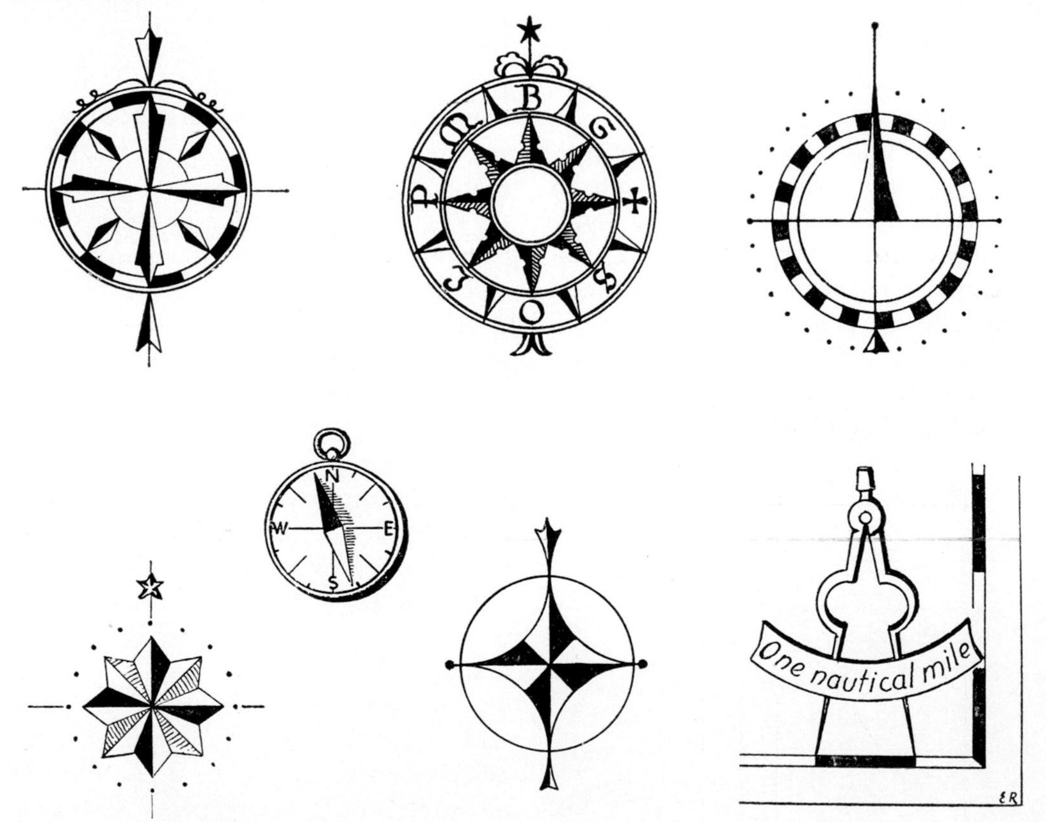


**Fig. 130** Decorative compass roses have been common on maps since the time of the portolan charts. (*From Morison, "Admiral of the Ocean Sea"* Little-Brown, 1942.)

**Compass Roses.** These are common accessories for maps—a survival from the time of the portolan charts. Even the rhumb lines of the portolanos are often imitated in decorative maps. Although this is an appropriate decoration, actually a compass rose or any indication of the north direction is necessary only when the map is oriented other than to the north and when the parallels and meridians are not drawn. In most projections the north direction varies over the map, so that it is advisable to place several compass roses.

On large-scale maps it is usual to indicate the true north by a star, and the magnetic north by a half arrow, and to state the exact amount of the magnetic declination.

**Insets.** The empty spaces on maps are well taken care of if used for insets. One inset may show a significant portion of the main map on a larger scale or it may be a small-scale general map showing the location of the main map. The inset map should be regarded as an independent small map; it should have its own border, central meridian, title, etc.

An exception to this rule is made when

the inset map shows a peripheral portion of the main map that was chopped off to save space. In this case the inset is regarded as a retracted part of the main map. Such insets should have the same scale, and the parallels and meridians should be in the same direction as on the main map. Long Island on maps of New York State and the Panhandle of Oklahoma are often shown in this way.

## Drafting of Maps

The preparation of a map proceeds through various stages. First, the material must be collected. Small-scale maps are usually compiled from already existing maps; large-scale maps may be based upon original surveys or airplane photographs. Next, the scale and projection must be considered. The scale is usually determined by the page size of a book or by the practical size of a sheet. In considering projections, cartographers are often too willing to accept existing maps and to copy them rather than to construct their own projections. Often, however, the construction of a suitable projection amply repays the cartographer for the time spent on it.

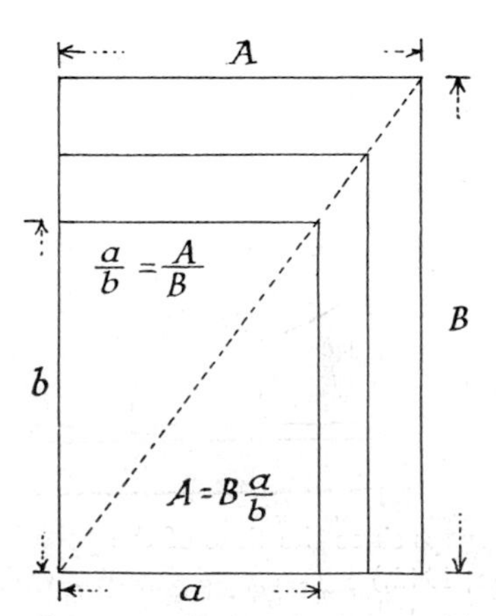


**Fig. 131** The proportions of the enlarged drawing can be figured either by a diagonal or by calculation with the help of a slide rule.

Maps are drawn larger than the size in which they are to be reproduced. The photographic reduction of the engraving processes will make them appear finer. This exaggeration in size varies from $1\frac{1}{2}$ times in length on simple maps to double on more formal ones. A draftsman with unsteady hands will use larger exaggeration, because, after reduction, the slight irregularities of line will be less conspicuous. However, it is not advisable to use too large exaggeration as one may lose the sense of proportion and the reduced map may appear too weak.

The size and shape of the map are usually ascertained from existing maps. The desired area is squared in by the use of a tissue overlay, so that the central meridian is vertical. A diagonal line makes possible the drawing of larger or smaller rectangles in the same proportions as the map itself. After the approximate size of the map has been decided, a piece of paper is cut large enough to allow for a few inches of margin.

**Pencil Drafting.** In the actual process of drawing, the projection is constructed first (provided that the map is not copied) on a separate paper, and then the parallels and meridians are transferred, usually by pricking through with a needle. It is advisable to use a hard pencil so that these lines shall not disappear entirely after every erasure. Next, the hydrography is drawn—the shore lines, rivers, and lakes. Shore lines are drawn with great exactness, since they are well known from larger scale maps, and any deviation therefrom is readily noticed. The same accuracy is important in the drawing of rivers and lakes, because these are the main reference lines for locating cities, mountains, and other features.

With the help of shore lines, rivers, and a few boundary lines it is usually possible to ascertain the exact extent of the map, so that a frame can be laid out. The sides of the frame should be parallel to the central meridian. It is well to draw the frame in an early stage of preparation, so as to ensure better composition.

Next the boundaries, railroads, roads, and cities are drawn. Care must be taken even on small-scale maps to draw cities on the correct side of rivers. All these features are as yet unlettered. Next come the mountains, whether represented by contours, shading, or the landform method.

The final step is the layout of lettering and the make-up. Names of countries, mountains, and large political divisions are lettered first because they are the most difficult to place. Names of cities come next, as there is some choice in placing them. Last come the names of rivers, which, except in the case of small streams, can be placed anywhere along their course.

Lettering is first outlined lightly with pencil; then sharp guidelines are drawn with harder pencil. Experienced letterers do not draw out the small lettering precisely, since this involves using ink over graphite, which affects the quality of the line. Large lettering, however, should be penciled. Title, scale, insets, legends, and other accessories complete the pencil work on a map.

When the whole map has been outlined in pencil, it is ready for inking. First, the map is rolled over with a kneading eraser or, better, with powdered eraser, in order to remove superfluous graphite. This is important because the layer of graphite may prevent the penetration of the ink when the drawing is finished, and the ink lines may rub out easily. The map is erased until the lines are faint but still clearly visible. (An eraser can be easily powdered with a kitchen grater, and the powder can be used over and over again.) Then the paper is thoroughly cleaned with a duster—a wing of a goose or a sea gull is particularly good for this purpose—so that no trace of dust shall remain.

**Inking.** The inking of a map is usually done in the reverse sequence of the pencil work. The thumbtacks are removed, so that the paper may be shifted into convenient positions for pen work. Lettering is inked in first; then the symbol content of the map; and, finally, the parallels, meridians, borders, and accessories. This order is important, because lettering has the right of way over everything else, and the parallels, meridians, and border have to be interrupted where any symbols require the space.

After all inking has been done, the remaining traces of pencil lines are erased. It is dangerous to bear down too heavily with the eraser lest the ink lines also be weakened. A final checking—touching up with ink or painting out the imperfections with white—is always necessary. The map is then trimmed, mounted on cardboard, covered with cellophane, and delivered flat. Colored maps need special treatment, which will be discussed in the chapter on methods of reproduction.

**Fig. 132** Graceful scrolls with good typography add much to the beauty of a map.

# CHAPTER 15: *Drawing Tools and Materials*

Proper tools in their proper places and in proper condition cut in half the time spent on map drawing. The best eraser is worth little if it reposes under the table, and the finest pen will not work if clogged with dried ink.

**Papers.** Paper used for fine maps must have a smooth finish. It should not have loose fibers that clog the pen, and it must be able to stand considerable erasing. It is especially important that it should not change its size and shape with change of humidity. Only the best tub-sized or gelatin-impregnated cotton or rag papers fulfill these conditions.

Maps are usually drawn on *Bristol board. Strathmore board* is excellent, but the largest sheet is only 23 by 29 inches. This paper comes in various thicknesses from one-ply to four-ply. The two-ply is simply two one-ply sheets pasted together. It comes in smooth and in "kid" finish. The latter is too coarse, and the former perhaps a little too smooth. The thin one-ply paper can be used if the map has to be copied over a lamp; otherwise two-ply paper is recommended.

For large maps, rolled papers are used. There is always the danger with rolled paper that it will contract and expand differently lengthwise from crosswise, thus causing distortion. It is also difficult to lay roll papers out flat. The best method is to roll them in reverse around a paper pipe. There are several good grades of rolled drawing papers on the market.

*Transparent tracing papers* are made of a straw and cornstalk base and are used in map work for sketching, for copying, and for tissue overlays that indicate various colors and tints. Transparent tracing papers will expand easily on humid days; they should, therefore, not be used for precise work. It is not good practice to finish a map on transparent paper, for the engraver photographs the map under strong side lights, and the lines cast a shadow (penumbra) on the plate that underlies the transparent paper, thus causing the fine lines to appear heavier. Mechanical tints especially fare badly if on transparent paper.

*Vellums* are semitransparent papers that are slightly impregnated with oil. The oil prevents the expansion and contraction of the paper with changes of humidity. Vellum is often used for colored maps where each color is drawn on a separate sheet and has to register perfectly. It is not easy to draw on vellum, for the lines are uneven, and the pen does not make ready contact with the paper; many map makers therefore prefer to use thin drawing paper. Moreover, vellum turns yellow in a few years, and yellow paper is not satisfactory for reproduction. It is claimed that some modern brands of vellum retain their whiteness.

*Tracing cloth* is excellent for engineering drawings but is rarely used in fine map work, because it clogs a fine pen. It is used for thick-line work, chiefly in engineering maps and for blueprints, or for maps reproduced by the Ozalid process. It is especially recommended if the manuscript map is to be subjected to rough handling.

**Special Papers.** There are several special papers used in map making. Various *profile papers*, *cross-section papers*, and *coordinate papers* are used to make profiles, diagrams, and cartograms and to measure map areas. They are printed on either transparent or opaque paper. They are also available in blue; and a drawing on this paper can be reproduced without showing the printed cross lines.

*Carbon papers* are used for copying, but it is

important to try them out first, as most commercial carbon papers are greasy and not easily erased. It may be necessary to prepare special drafting carbon paper by smudging one side of a thin paper with a soft pencil or stick of graphite. Carbon paper is used for copying maps which are printed on both sides and on which, therefore, the tracing glass cannot be used.

*Cellophane*, *Tracilin*, etc., are used where perfect transparency is essential, as in tracing details from airplane photographs. Drawing on cellophane with special ink is quite easy. Cellophane is also used to cover and protect finished drawings.

*Ross board* is used when mountains are shown with plastic shading. It will be described in the next chapter.

*Celluloid sheets*, both transparent and nontransparent, are often used. They take very fine lines both in pencil and in ink. Since they are washable, they can be used over again. Unfortunately, they are not perfectly shapeproof.

*Drawing paper mounted on muslin* is used for country, town, and other manuscript maps that have a permanent value. Mounting drawing paper on cloth does not make it shapeproof.

*Transparento*, *translux*, and similar oily liquids make paper somewhat transparent. They can be used for making direct blueprints from drawings that were prepared on drawing paper instead of on vellum or tracing cloth. They are applied only when the drawing is completed.

*Blueprint papers* are used when only a few copies of a map are desired, in which case the drawing is prepared on transparent paper, vellum, cloth, or celluloid. The drawing is put into a frame in contact with a sensitized paper and exposed to sunlight for 4 or 5 minutes. A negative imprint is thereby obtained, usually on blue paper. This is fixed and washed, and thus made permanent. By the same process positive blueprints are made from the negative print. Blueprints can be easily bleached out by a special liquid eradicator.

Direct positive prints can be made by the *Ozalid* process. Ozalid paper does not require washing; it is fixed dry over ammonia vapor.

*Shapeproof drawings* are made on zinc or aluminum sheets painted with white oil paint, on vellum mounted on glass, or on specially prepared sheets of various plastics.

**Pencils.** Pencils are made from mulsified powder of graphite mixed with fine clay and binding substances and are encased in cedar wood. Graphite is soft, and the more clay that is mixed with it, the harder the pencil. A good pencil should write an even, dark line; it should not wear down too rapidly or break easily. Such contrasting qualities are not readily obtained, and only a few brands of pencils are satisfactory for map work.

Pencils are made in various grades of hardness, ranging from 9*H* (the hardest) to *HB* (medium) and 6*B* (the softest). The paper determines which grade of hardness to use. Smooth paper requires a softer pencil; on smooth-finish Bristol board an *HB* should be used for sketching, and a 2*H* or 4*H* for fine drawing. On vellum pencils at least two grades harder are used. A softer pencil than *HB* is rarely used in map work. An equipment of *HB*, 2*H*, 4*H*, and 6*H* is ample, and in this group the harder pencils will outlast the softer.

Some map makers prefer metal-encased mechanical pencils with lead fills, as they do not require a knife for sharpening. Special thin leads are often used in mechanical pencils, but even the thinnest lead must constantly be sharpened.

Sharpening is done with a knife, a fine sandpaper, or a steel file; the file is preferable. Mechanical sharpeners are convenient, but only the better types make points long and sharp enough for map work.

Colored *wax crayons* are used in the layout of colored maps. Light-blue crayons are used for sketching maps to be reproduced by the half-tone process. Blue does not photograph; so blue markings will not show on the printed map.

**Erasers.** Since many erasers contain sand or emery, they will destroy the smooth surface of the drawing paper. For this reason only soft artgum and "soap" eraser should be used to eradicate pencil lines. Hard erasers are used only for ink lines. If only a small part of the inked drawing has to be erased, an erasing shield is used—a thin steel plate containing various-sized holes. A kneaded eraser that is molded in the hand to form a sharp point is very useful.

**Pens.** The most commonly used pens are the Gillott Nos. 290 (soft), 291 (hard), 303, and 404. For superfine lines the Gillott No. 1,000 may be used, but its use is not recommended for drawings that will be further reduced by engraving. A good penholder in which the pen fits firmly is essential. For longer sustained and more even flow of ink, the pen supplied with an ink retainer is best. This is a small, narrow strip of metal that can be cut out from an ordinary tin can; it should be about $\frac{1}{16}$ inch wide and set in the penholder so that its tip almost, but not quite, touches the pen. Even better is a piece of thin copper wire about 1 inch long, hammered flat on both ends. When cleaning the pen, the ink retainer is pushed sideways (see Fig. 124).

Each pen should have its own penholder and should be kept conveniently in a glass tumbler in the bottom of which is a silk rag for absorbing the superfluous ink.

Ink is supplied to a pen point through the slit in its center. If this is clogged by minute particles of carbon, the flow of ink will be restricted and will not easily make contact with the paper. For this reason the pen has to be kept very clean. Every few minutes it should be dipped into water and wiped off with a piece of rag or chamois.

For heavier lines, the so-called "ball-point" pens may be used, but the map maker does well to invest in some of the more expensive special pens, such as the *Payzant*, *Le Roy*, or similar products, since these give a steadier and more even line.

Many map makers like to use *round writing pens*, called also "stub" pens or "manuscript" pens. Lettering with a stub pen is fast and distinctive. For very small lettering, the tip of a No. 290 Gillott pen may be chopped off. For very heavy lettering in the same style, the *Esterbrook Drawlet* and similar pens can be used. For fine work, engineers like to use a very small pen, called "crow-quill," which does not require the use of an ink retainer. It is harder than the No. 290 Gillott.

Lettering devices are not further discussed here, since their merits and disadvantages were explained in the previous chapter.

**India Ink.** India ink is still sold in China and Japan in the form of small cakes from which the ink is rubbed into a small cup and diluted with water. This ink in older times came to us from India—hence the name. As sold today, it is already dissolved. It consists of very fine carbon particles (lamp-black) suspended in a liquid composed of various ingredients. This liquid has the same specific gravity as the carbon, and thus the carbon does not settle. India ink is deep black, has excellent photographic qualities, and, when dry, is waterproof. It dries quickly—a little too quickly for fine map work.

When not in use, ink bottles should be kept closed. It is practical to buy a large bottle of India ink and from it to half fill a small bottle, which can be washed out and refilled every few weeks. This is better than adding water, which spoils the ink.

Several brands of waterproof *colored inks* are on the market, to be used for colored maps. Most of them have the tendency to coagulate in a short time. Special heavy opaque waterproof inks are available for work to be blueprinted.

*Reproduction White.* Unnecessary ink lines can be removed by (1) painting them over with white; (2) scratching them out with a razor blade; or (3) erasing them with an ink eraser. The first method, applied with a fine sable brush, is the fastest. Reproduction white has the quality of preventing photographic reproduction even in a thin layer, semitransparent to the eye. It is important to cover nothing but the black area with the paint. Since waterproof inks repel water, the wet paint easily runs off the black line if the adjacent paper surface is made wet.

**Water Colors.** Map makers use water colors chiefly to cover a surface with an even tint. Ordinary water colors that come in tubes or cakes, or the Japanese water colors, are made for artists for a different purpose. Since they contain much glue, they stick well to their place and do not spread. For even tints, ordinary powdered aniline dyes may be used. These can be dissolved and kept in small bottles, always ready in standard hues.

**Brushes.** Map makers use fine *sable brushes* for painting. A No. 2 sable brush is good for painting with India ink and reproduction white; and either No. 6 or No. 8 is good for coloring large surfaces. It is important to clean the brushes after use, for some colors corrode their fine hairs.

For *painting a surface* the map should be slightly tilted and the work should proceed downward. Before beginning to paint, the surface is divided into sections, each of which can be painted rapidly. For instance, in painting the blue sea, the open ocean can be one section, and the small seas and embayments other sections. Each is painted separately, and a white line is left between adjacent sections, which can be filled in later with a half-dried brush. This is much better than to overlap the paint. Parallels and meridians will often help to divide the map into convenient sections. The brush should always be well filled, so that the paint will flow freely, and the progressing front of the paint should never be allowed

**Fig. 133** Painting maps with transparent water colors. (1) Mix enough paints. (2) Fix drawing on inclined board. (3) Divide drawing in sections and decide direction of painting. (4) Clean drawing thoroughly. (5) Always paint downhill. (6) Carry a "wet front." (7) Don't change inclination of board before paint is dry. (8) Pick up extra paint with blotter.

to dry during the work. The paper cannot be turned until the paint has dried because it may flow back. It is not advisable to wet the surface beforehand, because this will cause the paper to swell and the paint will run unevenly. Speed, combined with precision, is essential for an even coloring. It is very difficult to correct faulty, uneven painting. Dark places can be lightened with an eraser; too light spots can be dubbed with a half-dry brush.

**Fasteners.** The map maker fastens his paper when making borders or when constructing a projection, but most of the time his map will lie loose on the table. For fastening, he uses thumbtacks, or dry-sticking Scotch tape, over which a ruler rides more easily.

**Paste.** The best paste for temporary use is *rubber cement*, which is rubber dissolved in benzene. It comes in either a can or a tube; the latter is preferable. This rubber cement is applied to both surfaces, and only when they are almost dry are they pressed together. The unnecessary paste can be rubbed off with the fingers or, better, with a kneading eraser. Rubber cement will not swell or curl the paper. Unfortunately, in a few years it disintegrates and is liable to leave grease spots. Hence, for permanent use, liquid *glue*, which comes in tubes, is preferable to pastes, mucilages, and cements.

**T-squares and Triangles.** Ordinary maple T-squares are sufficient for map making. Complex T-squares with rotating heads are rarely necessary. A small and a large 30° triangle and a medium-sized 45° triangle are sufficient for most map work. There are on the market heavy celluloid triangles about $\frac{1}{10}$ inch thick, which are more than worth their somewhat higher price. A steel *straightedge* with inch and centimeter divisions is an essential part of a map maker's equipment. A large *right-angle iron* is also important for squaring the borders. *French curves* are convenient for drawing parallels and meridians, but some prefer an adjustable *flexible curve.*

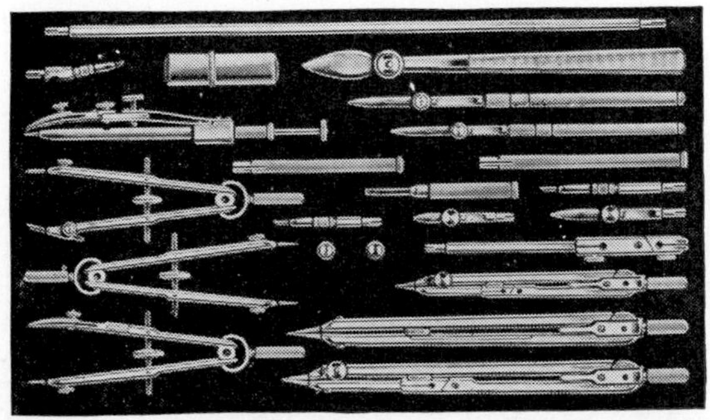

**Fig. 134** Drawing instrument set. (*Charles Bruning Company, Inc.*)

**Drawing-instrument Sets.** Most drawing-supply manufacturers produce sets of drawing instruments, consisting of compasses, dividers, and ruling pens. These assortments are sometimes very elaborate. A map maker will select a set consisting of a good compass, a divider, a compass elongator, a drop-spring bow for small circles, and a ruling pen.

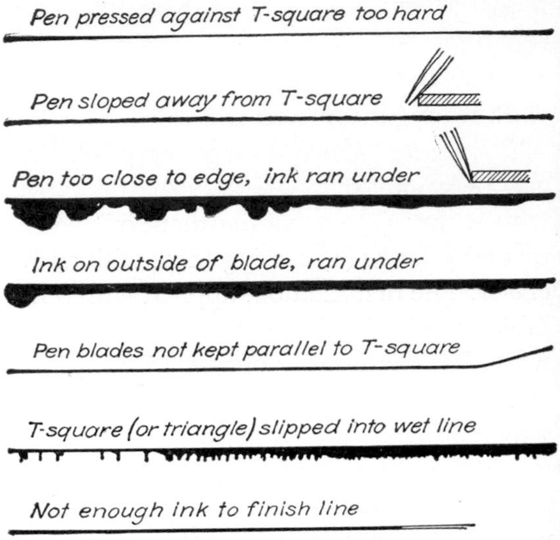

Pen pressed against T-square too hard

Pen sloped away from T-square

Pen too close to edge, ink ran under

Ink on outside of blade, ran under

Pen blades not kept parallel to T-square

T-square (or triangle) slipped into wet line

Not enough ink to finish line

**Fig. 135** Beginners' common faults in the use of ruling pen. (*From French, "Engineering Drawing."*)

A good *ruling pen* is very important. The ink is supplied between the two blades with a quill, and care should be taken that no ink sticks on the outside. The lines are drawn with the pen held lightly in a perfectly vertical position. The two blades should never press against each other, for the ink must flow easily. If the pen is pressed down, it may clog with fibers of the paper. If contact with the paper fails, or the line becomes thick, the pen must be cleaned. If sufficiently fine lines cannot be obtained, the ruling pen should be sharpened on a fine honing stone. A strong magnifying lens helps in sharpening not only ruling pens but also other pens and tools.

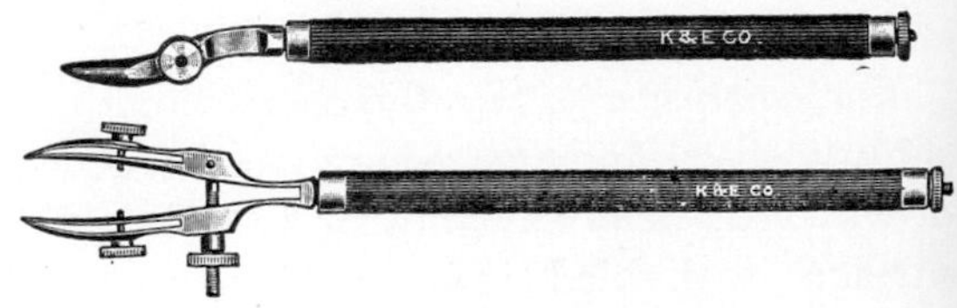


**Fig. 136** Road pen and pivot ruling pen (contour pen). (*Keuffel and Esser Company.*)

There are a few instruments that a map maker should add to the standard set. First among them is a *road* or *double-ruling pen*. This consists of two ruling pens fastened together and is used to make close parallel lines. This is a very useful instrument, but it requires a certain skill, for, in order to make equal lines, the two blades must have equal pressure on the paper. The pen should be held in a vertical position. A similar instrument, but with pencils instead of pens, is used for making guidelines for lettering.

A *proportional divider* is useful for copying maps on reduced or enlarged scales. It is not an inexpensive instrument, but it will, in the long run, repay the purchaser. This instrument is shown in Fig. 134.

A map maker often uses a *beam compass* for circles of long radii, as for parallels in conic-projection maps. Ready-made beam compasses can be bought up to 6 feet in length.

*Protractors* are used for measuring or laying out angles. They usually consist of a metal, paper, or celluloid circle or half circle, divided into degrees. Elaborate protractors, with three arms, vernier, and magnifying lens, are used to lay out angles of triangulation, but for ordinary cartographic work, radiating lines printed on transparent paper give the best results.

Several wooden, metal, or celluloid *scales* for measuring distances are necessary: the map maker uses a triangular scale divided into tenths of inches, and one with millimeters. It is convenient to use a strip of cross-section paper as a scale. Paper makes closer contact with the drawing, and therefore the error deriving from oblique vision is minimized. It is important, however, that the length of such a strip of cross-section paper be checked on a reliable ruler, for it may be in error as much as $\frac{1}{20}$ inch per foot length. Most scales are 12 to 18 inches long, but a good steel yardstick is useful in laying out larger maps.

*Parallel rulers* are used chiefly for laying out parallel lines and also for tinting with closely set parallel lines. In larger offices, more elaborate instruments called "section liners" are used for parallel ruling.

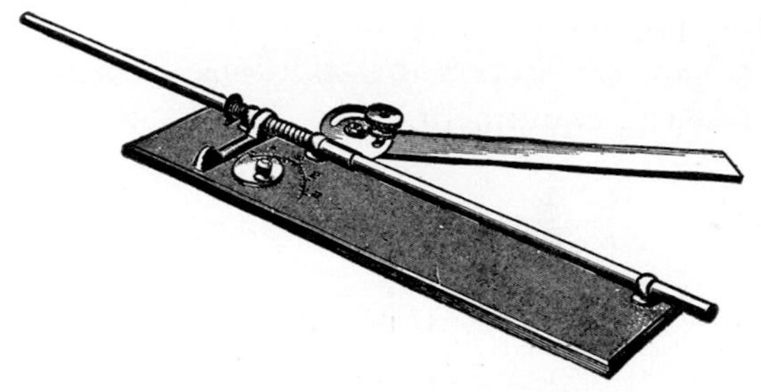

**Fig. 137** Section liners for parallel lining are indispensable for map makers. (*Keuffel and Esser Company.*)

In former times a large precision *pantograph* was almost symbolic of a cartographer's office, but now, since most enlargement and reduction is done photographically, the pantograph has lost its importance. The principle of the pantograph is based on the rule of parallelograms and can be understood from Fig. 35. It is not advisable to enlarge more than four times with a pantograph, because the smallest irregularities are magnified enormously.

*Cameras.* For enlargement of maps a large-sized photographic *enlargement camera* can be used. The ground glass is replaced by ordinary glass and covered with transparent paper, upon which is traced the image of the well-lighted map in front of the lens. It is not difficult to rig up a camera that will reduce instead of enlarge. It is even possible to reduce or enlarge maps with the help of mirrors or prisms so that, in a darkened room, their image will appear conveniently on the drawing paper.

*Other Instruments.* There are a number of other instruments that are useful to a map maker. A *slide rule* will enable him to make rapid calculation of reductions and enlargements. *Fixative* and an *atomizer* will help to preserve crayon and pencil drawings. A *duster* made of a sea-gull or a goose feather will remove eraser powder and dust, and its other end can be sharpened and used to fill the ruling pen.

A *cutting machine*, a large *chest of drawers* for paper and reference maps, and a *filing cabinet* are important additions to a map maker's equipment.

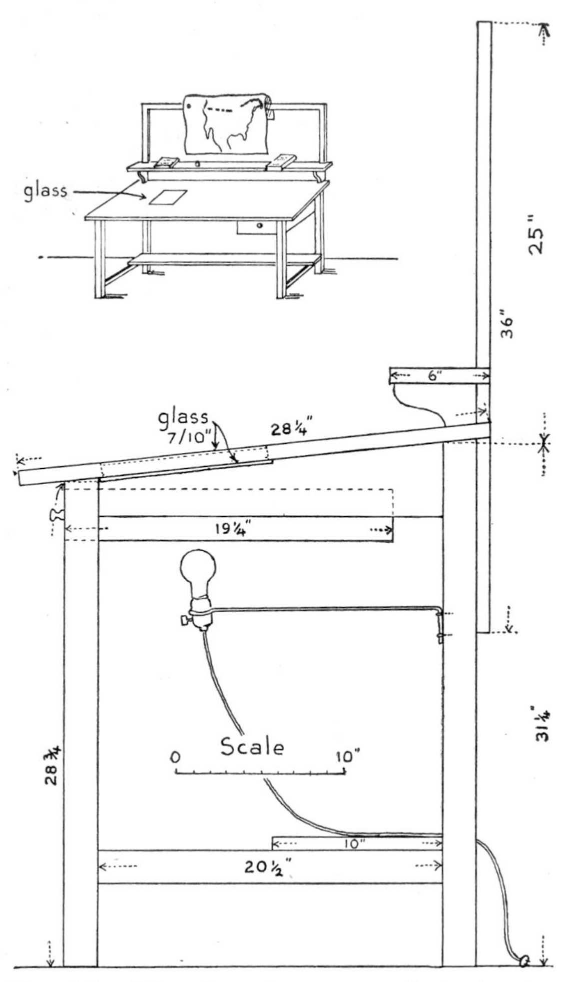


**Fig. 138** Side view of a cartographer's drawing table.

**Drawing Table.** A map maker compiles his materials from maps, atlases, books, field sketches, and airplane photographs. All these references must be within his easy reach. For fine work and precise lettering he has to sit conveniently. He cannot do good lettering while leaning over a faraway corner of the drawing. He has to shift his drawing around, at least while he is inking it in. No reference material or instruments, therefore, should interfere with the free movement of the paper. For this reason, a map maker's table is different from an architect's, an engineer's, or a surveyor's table. The design shown in Fig. 138 has been worked out by the author and found to be serviceable. The table has a frame at the back on which to tack large reference maps; small reference material, books, and atlases are on the small shelf. The drawing paper can be freely moved under the shelf and can hang down on the outer side. The drawing instruments are in a drawer far enough to the side so as not to interfere with the knees of the draftsman. Some map makers will prefer to have a tray attached to a movable arm, in which to keep instruments for immediate use. The drawing board is the top of the table, and is made of 1-inch plywood with a precisely straight front edge. A short T-square is used, on the front of the table rather than on the side. Triangles, straightedges, etc., hang on the side of the table. Small bags filled with shot are used to weight down the drawing so that it will not shift too easily. A mercury light is fixed to the top of the frame.

For copying purposes, an 8- by 10-inch

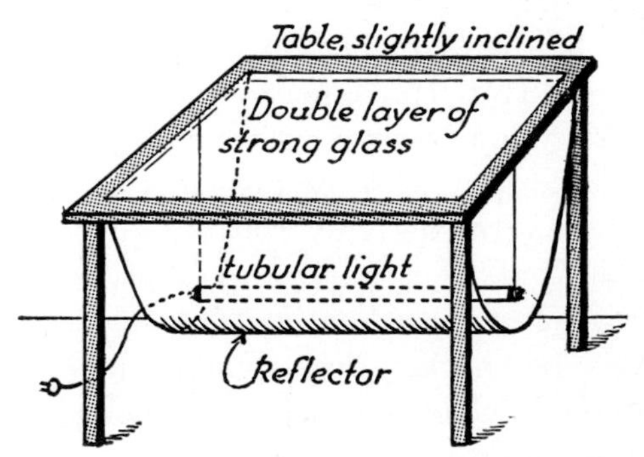


**Fig. 139** Copying maps and drawing color overlays is best done over the transparent table.

hole is cut in the top of the drawing table and is covered with thick glass, flush with the rest of the table. Underneath this glass is a lamp. A second glass underneath the board prevents excessive heating. The drawing paper—preferably one-ply—is attached over the original map with Scotch tape, and is moved around freely over the glass. This is a simpler arrangement than the large *tracing table* with a glass top and a number of lamps.

All the foregoing instruments should be part of the geographic drafting room of every university. For individual students of cartography, who do not want to go into map making professionally, the following equipment is sufficient for a regular year's course:

1 *HB* pencil
1 2*H* pencil
Gillott pens, Nos. 290, 303, and 404
3 penholders
1 instrument set, consisting of a compass, a divider, and a ruling pen
1 soft eraser
1 celluloid triangle 8 inches long
1 wooden T-square
1 bottle of India ink
1 No. 4 sable brush
2 sheets of one-ply Strathmore board, smooth finish, large size
2 sheets of two-ply Strathmore board, smooth finish, large size
1 Xacto knife
1 roll of transparent Scotch tape
1 paper protractor
1 set of water colors
1 set of colored crayons
1 set of colored inks: brown, blue, red, and green
1 block of transparent tracing paper } for every six students
1 bottle of reproduction white } for every six students
1 roll of cross-section paper } for every six students

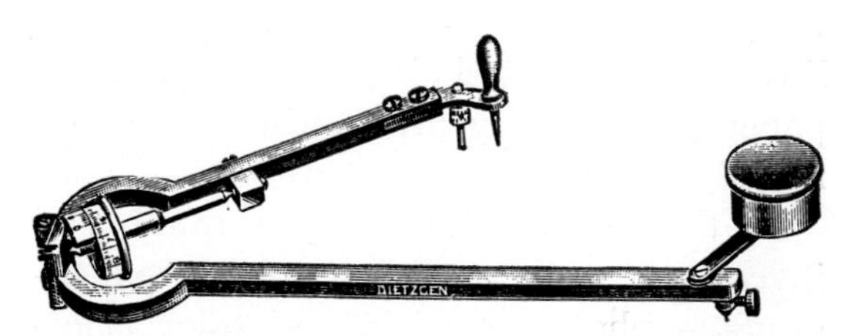


**Fig. 140** Planimeters are used for measuring areas on maps. (*Eugene Dietzgen Company.*)

If the making of topographic models is included in the curriculum, the laboratory should be equipped with an electric jig saw with a very wide arm. (Round jigsaw blades can be bought in dental-supply stores.) Cardboards, molding plaster, plastiline, stapling machine, boards for frames, shellac, oil, green soap, paints, brushes, turpentine, nails, and hand tools should also be included. The use of these is described in Chap. 30.

# CHAPTER 16: *Methods of Map Reproduction*

Until the 1830's, maps were reproduced by the copper-engraving process. The map was drawn reversed in mirror fashion on a polished copper plate, and lines and lettering were cut into the copper with a burin or groover. Printer's ink was then rubbed into the grooves of the plate, and the surface was cleaned. The plate was pressed against damp rag paper, and an impression was thus obtained. After about 3,000 impressions the plate had to be reengraved. The printed lines were sharp and clean-cut, and the fine paper gave quality and distinction to the maps.

In the nineteenth century, a number of inventions, such as lithography, wax engraving, photoengraving, and color printing, simplified the work of the map maker and made maps less expensive, but the great increase in demand and quantity of map production was not always accompanied by a higher standard of quality.

For reproduction, maps may be prepared in any one of the following ways:

1. Line
2. Line and tint
3. Half tone
4. Flat colors
5. Merged colors

They can be reproduced by the following processes:

1. Photoengraving
2. Wax engraving
3. Lithography (offset)

Modern engraving is a highly diversified, complex industry; hence only a brief outline of it can be given in the following pages.

**Photoengraving.** This is the most commonly used method for engraving smaller maps, especially those which appear in books. A drawing submitted for line engraving should be done with India ink $1\frac{1}{2}$ to 2 times the size in which the map will be printed. All lines should be solid black and not closer to each other than $\frac{1}{100}$ inch. Dots should be large; the dot over the letter *i* is often lost in reproduction. Care should be taken not to overerase the drawing, for the ink may fade to such an extent that the lines will not photograph.

In the process of photoengraving, the drawing will first be photographed to the proper size. The negative will then be placed, in the darkroom, over a sensitized zinc plate, and a contact print will be made under a lamp. The sensitized zinc plate is covered with bichromate of albumin, which has the property of becoming hard and insoluble when exposed to light. The black lines of the drawing are transparent on the photographic negative. By lighting this through, an insoluble line is made on the sensitized zinc plate. The unaffected albumin is washed away, the lines are strengthened by burning into them acid-resisting resin, and the zinc plate is then ready for etching.

Etching consists of four or five "bites" of nitric acid. After the plate has been etched deep enough, it is cleaned, squared, and mounted on a wooden block, type high (0.912 inch). The larger nonprinting portions are "routed," or further deepened; otherwise they may get some ink from the roller. Several proof prints are made, and the block is delivered to the customer. Printing is usually done in another establishment. A "line cut" (a very misleading term), prints from raised surfaces as does type and can be printed along with the text. Most figures in this book are line cuts.

Instead of zinc, a copper plate can be

used, the process being the same except for the use of different chemicals. Copper cuts are much finer; the lines thereon can be closer together, and can also be crosslined, which is not advisable on zinc, on which such lines easily clog. The cost of copper engraving is about twice that of zinc.

If a large number of prints is required, the printing is not done from the original plate but from electroplated copies, or "electros."

**Tints.** It is often essential on maps that certain areas be covered by even shadings or tints. In line engraving only black (or any *full* color such as red or blue) lines and dots can be printed. The illusion of gray tints is created by closely set lines and dots.

1. *Hand-drawn Tints.* Tints consisting of closely set dots can be drawn by hand on the original drawing. They can be made in regular rows, but, since this requires great care and accuracy, it is better to place the dots irregularly though in even density. This "regularity in irregularity" will give a more even impression.

Parallel line tints can be best applied with an instrument called a "section ruler" or "parallel ruler," a standard piece in a map maker's office. It is possible to make them with a T-square, but this demands careful attention. Crosslining should be used with caution; a too close network may clog in printing unless it is reproduced in copper.

2. *Cellophane Tints.* By a more modern method a cellophane sheet, with tints already printed thereon, can be pasted on the map. Various such cellophane tints are available (Craftint, Burgess, etc.). The tints are on top of the sheet and are removable; where they are not needed they may be easily scraped off. It should be borne in mind, however, that the tints will be reduced photographically and will appear much finer on the printed map. Special cellophane sheets with white lines can be applied to black surfaces. In the *Zip-a-tone* process the lines are at the bottom of the cellophane, and thus they cannot be removed; but their effect is more reliable, since the lines are in close contact with the paper.

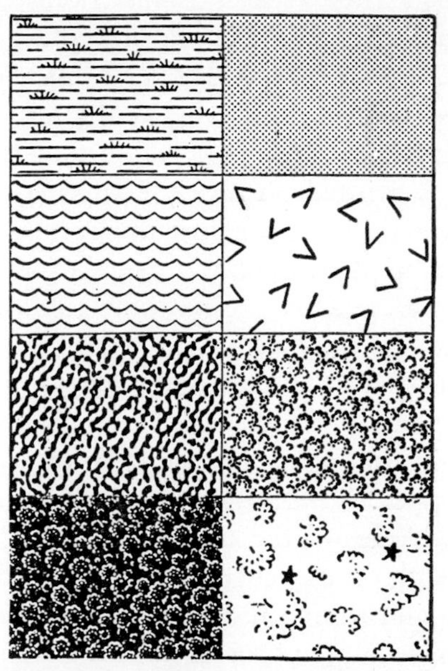

**Fig. 141** Mechanical patterns are used on maps for differentiating type areas. (*Para-Tone Company.*)

3. *Ben Day Process of Tinting.* In this process the tints are applied to the copper or zinc printing plate by a trained operator, before the plate is etched. A specially prepared tint sheet is placed over the printing plate and acid-resisting ink is pushed through it with a small roller. To keep the tints exactly within their limits, the area is outlined on the plate with a yellow protecting paint called "gamboge." This is then washed off with water, which will not remove the ink. After etching, the ink lines or dots will stand out and print in the same way as the other lines.

In preparing a drawing for the Ben Day process, all the cartographer has to do is to place a transparent paper or *tissue overlay* on the drawing and outline thereon the areas to be tinted, indicating the number of the tint from his Ben Day book of patterns. If the tints consist of parallel lines, the direction in which these lines should run must also be indicated.

The map maker has to keep in mind that the Ben Day process is not done on the original drawing but on the plate itself, which is already reduced to publication size, so that the tints appear the same as in the tint book. It is regrettable that the tint book is printed on highly coated paper, so that the tints appear finer than on the usual papers used in books. Because of this, unpleasant surprises are not uncommon.

There is no difficulty in applying several Ben Day patterns to the same map; they can even be printed over each other. However, in that case, they must be reproduced in copper. The skilled operator can vary the darkness of the tint by slightly shifting one end of the sheet with a micrometer screw and rolling it over again with ink. By a more complex process he can also make a negative of each tint.

The Ben Day process is expensive. Even a small amount of Ben Day work may double the price of the plate. The so-called Ben Day "half-tone" tints, however, are well justified. They consist of about 100 dots per inch (10,000 dots per square inch) and give the effect of an even, light gray which cannot be attained by other methods.

4. *Single- and Double-tone Sheets* (*Craftint*). These are sheets of drawing paper upon which the dots are printed with invisible ink. The map is drawn on these sheets as on ordinary paper, and a developer applied with a brush will bring out the dots in black wherever desired. Double tone has two shades brought out by two developers.

**Half-tone Process.** A photoengraved plate prints black and it cannot print gray. Consequently, photographs and wash drawings cannot be reproduced by direct line cuts. The reproduction of half tones is possible only if the gray surfaces, or half tones, are broken up into minute black dots, so that the larger the dots, the blacker the appearance of the surface. This is accomplished by photographing the picture through a screen. This screen consists of two pieces of glass, into each of which fine parallel lines are grooved. The two glasses are cemented together crosswise. The screen is placed in the camera in front of the negative plate. If the picture is photographed through this screen, the light reflected by the picture will be broken up into minute rays; the lighter parts will affect the photographic plate more than the darker ones. Such screens vary from 60 to 175 lines to the inch; the usual one is 120. Finer screens require more smoothly finished paper.

After a negative has been obtained through the screen, it goes through a process identical with that of a copper line cut. Zinc is used only with very coarse screens. The appearance of a half-tone print is somewhat duller than the original. The high lights of the original appear light gray, showing the "screen effect." There is no clear white on a half-tone print, unless tooled out in finishing. The best idea of what a half-tone print will look like can be obtained by viewing the original drawing through a transparent tracing paper. Fine black lettering will also appear duller in a half tone, and the edges of the lines will be somewhat fuzzy on account of the screen. For all these reasons, half tones are rarely used for maps except for plastic shading. Figures 1 and 15 are reproduced in half tone.

**Ross Board.** Ross board is a paper with an enameled surface that has tiny raised eminences. If drawing is done on Ross board with a crayon, only the tops of these eminences will be darkened—more or less, according to the pressure of the hand—and the surface will be dissolved automatically into tiny dots. From this the engraver can make an ordinary copper cut and the effect of a half tone is thus obtained without the application of a half-tone screen. Since there is no screen, the white surfaces remain white. Unlike half tones, the printed pictures will appear more strongly contrasted and darker than the original.

Ross board is used for maps that show relief in plastic shading or for maps in the morphographic method. Lettering, rivers, boundaries, etc., can be inked on Ross board and will appear strong and clean-cut in the reproduction.

The preparatory sketching of a map on Ross board has to be done with a blue pencil; and copying has to be done with blue tracing paper, because even the faintest black sketching lines may photograph. A Ross-board drawing cannot be much reduced unless a very coarse pattern is chosen. A great advantage of Ross board is that it can be used fully as well as scratchboard; white lines can be cut into a blackened surface with the greatest of ease. In skillful hands Ross board is a promising medium for black-and-white maps. Its greatest disadvantage is that the enamel clogs the pen.

**Surprint Half Tones.** This process is used to avoid the fuzzy edges of black lines in ordinary half-tone prints. Two drawings are made, one (a key plate) containing all line work, the other showing mountains and other half tones in wash or crayon. The engraver will make an ordinary negative of the line work, and a half-tone negative of the other, and then will make a contact print of each *on the same* sensitized copper plate. The plate will be etched in the usual way, and the resulting print will have clear-cut black lines and solid black surfaces over the half tones, but the high lights will be covered by a light-gray screen effect.

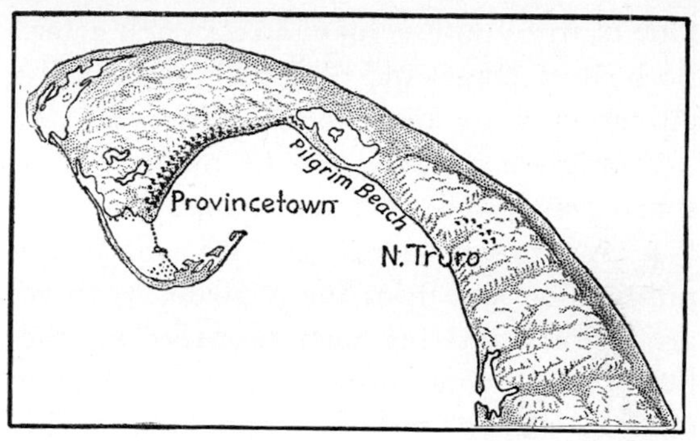


**Fig. 142** Line cut of a map drawn with ink and black crayon on stippled (Ross) board.

**Flat Colors.** Many maps are reproduced in flat colors; *i.e.*, various colors may be printed over each other, but there is no gradation in tone and strength within the same color. Maps are prepared for flat-color printing by various methods:

1. A separate drawing is made in black ink for each color. Each drawing is engraved separately, and they are printed over each other. The drawings are usually made on vellum because it does not change its shape and size with humidity. All drawings have to be on the same kind of paper. Each drawing must have register marks for perfect overprint. The correlation of colors is usually done over a glass table lighted from below.

2. If the artist wishes to see the final effect and wants to ensure perfect registration, only one drawing is made in all the colors of the final map. From this the photographer makes as many so-called "silver prints" as there are colors present. On each silver print the lines that are desired in any one color are drawn over with waterproof India ink. The silver print is then bleached out with an acid solution of potassium bichromate until only the inked lines remain.

3. As it is not pleasant to work over photographic paper, so-called "light-blue pulls" are printed from the original drawing on nonphotographic blue for each color.

One of these pulls is inked in for each color. Both silver prints and blue pulls are usually on larger scale than the publication size. The original drawing can be made with a sharp pencil and colored crayons.

4. As many negatives are made in publication size from the drawing as there are colors, and on each negative all the lines (appearing transparent) are made opaque except those of one color. The original drawing must be completely inked, and no colors other than black, red, brown, and olive green can be used.

5. If only pure red, green, purple, and yellow colors are used on the original, the photographer can use filters that block out all colors but one, and the negative thus obtained can be used directly by the engraver. It is not necessary for the colors to be the same as those in which the map is later printed.

In all flat-color maps it is advisable to have a *key plate,* usually the black plate, which contains the border and all the important lines. This helps to line up the tints in all other colors. Often all the line work of the map is printed in black only. The other colors are used for altitude tints or to differentiate between sea and land or between various countries.

**Three-color Process.** In most paintings all hues and gradations of colors are used and they are usually reproduced by the three-color process. Maps have often been made by this method in recent years. This process is based on the fact that all pigments can be mixed from red, blue, and yellow. Three negatives are made of the painting: through a purple, through a green, and through an orange filter. A half-tone screen is used with each filter. The purple filter lets through all colors but yellow, and thus records all yellows in negative; the green filter records the reds; and the orange filter, the blues. Thus, we have three half-tone negatives, from each of which a copper plate is made. Then each plate is printed in its own color, and a faithful reproduction of the original color is obtained, but because of the half-tone-screen effect the print will be less brilliant than the original. To darken it, it is customary to add a fourth, black, plate to the reproduction made through a yellow screen. In preparation of paintings for three-color-process reproduction, it should be kept in mind that even with an orange (minus blue) filter blues photograph very poorly; therefore, in order to obtain the right result, this color must be made darker than finally desired.

**Lithography.** In 1796 Alois Senefelder discovered that a certain dense limestone of Kelheim, Bavaria, had an unusual property. If lines were drawn upon this stone with a greasy ink or crayon and the stone soaked in water and then rolled over with a greasy printing ink, the ink would adhere to the lines only and it would be repelled by the bare, wet stone. Coating the stone with gum arabic greatly improved the process. The stone was then pressed against paper, and an impression was made. The process can be repeated several thousand times. In recent years it was found that, instead of expensive, heavy lithographic stone, a finely kerneled zinc or aluminum plate could be used in the same way, with the further advantage that a speedy rotary press could be used instead of the flat lithographic press.

Few maps are drawn directly on stone, since this would require working in publication size and in mirrorlike reverse. Usually, an ordinary drawing is made on paper in larger size and then photographed. The negative is placed over a paper sensitized with bichromate of gelatin, and a contact print is made in the same way as in photoengraving. The paper is then soaked and rolled over with greasy ink, which will adhere to the lines only. The greasy lines are transferred to a lithographic stone or zinc plate, which is wetted, rolled with ink, and printed. Tinting, half-tone work, and color printing are done in much the same way in lithography as in photoengraving.

A simpler form of lithography, where the zinc plate itself is sensitized and a direct contact print is made from the negative, is called "planography." A planographic plate is similar to an unetched plate in photoengraving.

*Offset Printing.* In this process the cylinder with the zinc plate prints first on an intermediate cylinder of rubber; then the rubber prints on the paper. This makes it possible to use a coarser and more absorbent paper upon which the lines appear very fine. The drawing on the zinc plate is straight and not mirrorlike. It reverses on the rubber cylinder, and it appears straight again on the paper.

Modern offset printing has come a long way from the original lithographic process. The kernelled zinc and aluminum plates can be made an enormous size—some offset presses are 6 or 7 feet wide. Automatic sucker-blowers deliver the paper to the rollers. Dozens of vibrating ink drums deliver the perfectly evenly distributed, thin layers of ink to the plate cylinder and the dampening is arranged with equal fineness by sets of rollers. The rubber or "blanket" cylinder contacts the plate cylinder with such precision that there is no widening of the finest line, after tens of thousands of impressions. The paper cylinder delivers the printed map to a chain delivery and drying system. In some presses the print is dried so fast that a second color is printed in the same operation. A single plate can deliver 50,000 impressions or even more in a few hours. The large sheets are delivered with such exactness that color overprints will register with perfect precision. Disregistration will occur more often in the preparation of the individual color plates than in the printing process.

Corrections on an offset plate are difficult and expensive and often a new plate is advisable. Careful work is done on the negative by touching up the imperfections with opaque ink and cutting the lines with sharp needles.

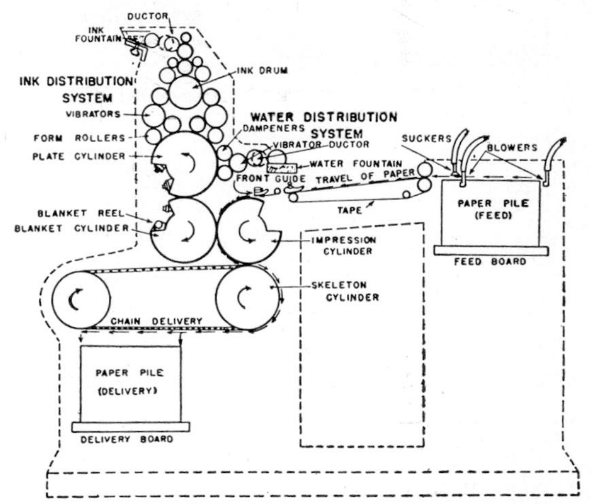


**Fig. 143** Offset printing presses can print the finest lines fast and economically. The printing is carried over to the impression cylinder by a rubber blanket. (*Courtesy of United States Army.*)

Almost all maps that are not printed in books are now reproduced by offset. The lines are finer and yet the process is much cheaper than photoengraving, and the rotary press allows incredible speed.

Contrary to the custom in photoengraving, the lithographer does the printing job himself. He sets the price for the whole job and does not deliver the stone or the zinc plate to the customer, since there may be several other jobs on the same plate. Corrections in lithography are somewhat difficult to make. It is easy to add thereto, but for removal of parts the stone must be shaved off as deep as the grease penetrated.

**Wax Engraving.** This is a special American process introduced in 1841 by Sydney Edwards Morse. The principle of wax engraving is very ingenious. Upon a highly polished copper plate a thin layer of wax is spread. Into this wax the lines are cut with a stylus, clear down to the copper plate, care being taken not to injure the copper itself. The wax is then powdered over

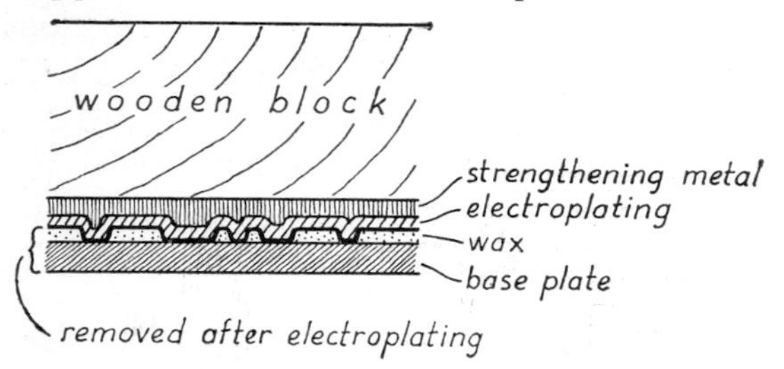


**Fig. 144** Wax engraving.

with fine graphite so as to make it electrically conductive, and the whole plate is submerged in an electrolytic bath which deposits a layer of copper on the wax. This copper layer is lifted out of the wax and, after strengthening and mounting, presents a good printing plate which prints from raised surfaces as do type or photoengraved plates.

The great advantage of wax engraving is the ease with which lettering can be set up in type and stamped into the wax. Tints can also be easily cut into the wax by a ruling machine. For this reason, wax-engraved maps have a tendency toward being overlettered and have a rather mechanical appearance (see Fig. 32). The typical American commercial maps are wax-engraved in flat colors, and the different political units are shown in all the colors of the rainbow, although such maps rarely have more than four printings. The colors are obtained by overprinting ruled tints of red, blue, yellow, and black.

One drawback of wax engraving is that the drawing must be done in the engraver's office. Even when a perfect drawing is submitted, it must be photographed on a sensitized wax plate and cut into the wax by the engraver. The engraver is rarely a geographer; he is, rather, a highly specialized and very conservative craftsman. Wax-engraved maps of today look exactly like those made a hundred years ago—mechanically perfect but uninspiring. The method, however, has possibilities in more progressive hands.

Wax engraving is a somewhat more expensive process than the other two. In preparing a map for wax engraving, it is sufficient to submit sketches in pencil and to leave the rest to the engraver. Half-tone or three-color-process work is not done in wax.

Other processes, such as photogelatin (rotogravure), "deep-set" printing, etc., are also used for reproducing maps, but the average cartographer rarely has an opportunity to use them.

**Duplicator Processes.** In these processes a drawing is reproduced in the same size without photography in a limited number of copies. These processes are more useful to the engineer, architect, and surveyor than to a cartographer; yet their knowledge is not only helpful but may open up new possibilities. Hundreds of patents are issued for the various processes; only the most important ones are mentioned here.

1. *Hectograph.* The map is prepared with writing ink or better with aniline dye and laid upon a moistened gelatin sheet. The gelatin absorbs some of the ink and it yields a few dozen copies before it wears out. Typewritten sheets and carbon copies can also be reproduced.

2. *Blueprinting.* No construction work was imaginable some years ago without quantities of blueprints; at present, however, it is largely replaced by black-and-white processes. The drawing or map is prepared on tracing cloth or paper and laid over blueprint paper in a special frame. The blueprint paper is coated with light-sensitive iron salts. Under exposure to a lamp or

sunlight the iron salt decomposes and turns blue if wetted. No change takes place under the shadow of lines on the drawing, and thus the lines remain white. Blueprints from a negative of a map are often used as "blue pulls" for color separation.

3. *Sepia prints* (*Vandyke process*) are similar to blueprints but a silver-iron-gelatin compound is used, a sensitizer which produces a clean, sharp, dark-brown negative print which in turn can be used to obtain positive prints. The prints are often used to obtain "proofs" from maps, which will stay for a short time without developing and fixing. For permanent use they have to be developed by water and fixed with a weak hypo.

4. *Black-and-white* (*B and W*) *Prints*. The B and W paper is sensitized with a diazo compound which will be bleached under light but which will form a dark line under the shadow of the lines of the map on tracing cloth or paper. It has to be dampened by a special developer, but need not be washed, and therefore it does not distort so much as a blue or sepia print.

5. *The Ozalid process* is similar to the B and W process but the developing is done dry with ammonia fumes.

6. *Mimeograph*. The map is prepared by drawing with a stylus upon a wax-coated fibrous stencil. This is placed over an ink drum and the ink filters through where the stylus cut the wax away. Several hundred impressions can be made on absorbent mimeograph paper.

7. *Lithomat* (*Photomat*) prints are produced on paper having lithographic quality —repelling printing ink where wet. Not only do the wet surfaces—the whites between the black lines—repel the ink but they also swell up, and the lines in between appear deeper and hold the ink as in "deep-set" lithography. Half tones can also be duplicated by the "photomat" process.

# BOOK TWO

# *Special Cartography*

## PART FIVE: SURVEYING ON THE GROUND AND FROM THE AIR

The purpose of cartography is to collect data and measurements of the earth's features and to represent them on such reduced scale that their pattern is discernible. This part of the book, however, deals with methods of making those measurements and surveys. Obviously the content of this part is not part of the body of cartography. It is presented here only because a cartographer needs to know a great deal about surveying methods if for no other reason than to understand their limitations. A professional cartographer's education is not complete without a regular course in surveying and geodesy. The subject as it is treated here represents the minimum amount of knowledge that a geographer should have. Outdoor surveying exercises will help him greatly to connect mentally the map with the country represented. To establish this connection is one of the fundamentals of a cartographer's education.

---

# CHAPTER 17: *Surveying*

Every point on the earth's surface can be related to any other part if its distance and direction is measured. The concept of distance and direction is a simple one in the case of areas which are so small that they can be regarded as plane. The problem will be much more complicated in larger areas where the curvature of the earth has to be taken into consideration. Measurements of distance and direction on a plane are called "plane surveying," in contrast to "geodetic surveying," which takes in account the earth's curvature.

**Distance.** When the surveyor speaks of distance, he means distance along a horizontal surface, because it will be this distance that will be recorded on maps.

For measuring distances, various units were used. Some came originally from the dimensions of the human body, as yard, and foot; some from pacing, as paces and miles (mille passuum); some others from the dimensions of the earth, as the meter and the nautical mile. These measurements have now been standardized, and the American surveyor uses the mile of 5,280 feet, and thinks in tenths of feet instead of inches. Older surveying records use also the furlong (length of a furrow) of 660 feet, the chain of 66 feet, the rod of 16½ feet, and the yard of 3 feet. The non-English world uses the meter as a unit of 39.37 inches (see Table A · 7, Appendix 3).

The crudest method of measuring distance is *pacing*. This is used only in rough traverses; yet for short distances between controlled points it is often remarkably accurate. Of course the strides of persons are very different and data have value only when the person's stride is known. This is usually measured along a 100-foot tape; the ratio being known, the steps can be converted into feet. Pacing should be uniform and at normal speed; it is a mistake to assume some unnaturally long steps for pacing. Paces can be counted every two or four steps (four steps being not far from 10 feet). A pedometer can be used if distances are great. Steps are slightly longer downhill and shorter uphill. There is an even larger difference between road, grass, or bush.

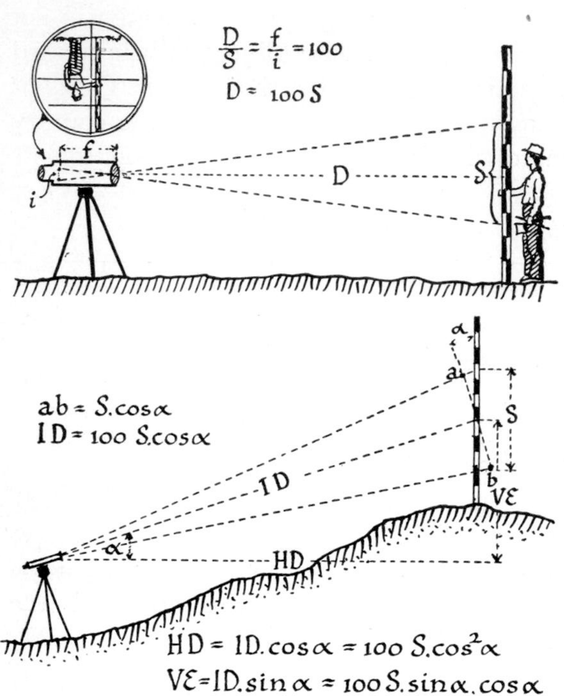


**Fig. 145** In the stadia method distances are observed by reading the length of the part of the rod's image that appears between the cross hairs.

The 66-foot chain was a standard instrument of old surveyors. Nowadays, however, a 100- or 200-foot steel tape is used mostly. The old surveyor's rod was $16\frac{1}{2}$ feet long; now 20-foot rods are more common. Very exact measurements, as bases for triangulation, are taken by Invar steel tapes, going back and forth several times. The largest error in direct measurements comes from slope. The rod has to be horizontal, and its "hanging" end is located on the ground with a plumb. Tapes sag down under their own weight and they have to be pulled with a specified force to measure correctly.

An object twice as far away looks half as large, and on this principle is based the *stadia method.* We look upon a vertically held graduated rod through a telescope that has two horizontal cross hairs. The farther the rod is, the larger portion of it is visible between the cross hairs. From Fig. 145, $D:S = f:i$. Instruments are usually made so that $f:i = 100$; thus $D = 100S$. The rod is graduated in $\frac{1}{10}$-foot divisions and each of these means 10 feet in distance. The measurement gets more complicated if it is on slope, but tables, nomographs, and special slide rules are available for quick calculation of vertical and horizontal distances.

*Sound* travels in air about 760 feet per second, while light travels so fast that it can be seen instantly over any practical distance. The difference between the light and sound of a flare will give the distance with good accuracy if wind velocity and atmospheric conditions are taken in account. Distances at sea are often measured by the echo of a directional radio beam, or radar, but more exactly by a sound signal that releases a radio response from a shore station of known position (radioacoustic reckoning).

A surveyor cannot measure every point in the landscape, and a great deal of interpolation of rough estimates will help to complete the map between measured points. Taking into consideration the size of trees, houses, people, etc., an average surveyor can estimate his distance within 10 per cent error in a landscape of familiar pattern. Estimating distances should be practiced on each field exercise.

**Direction.** Directions are usually related to the north or to a previously established direction. The angle, reckoned clockwise from the north, is called "azimuth." Angles are measured by a compass, sextant, alidade, or theodolite, or some special sighting instrument.

*Compass.* The simplest instrument for measuring horizontal angles is a sighting compass. A good sighting compass can be read to about half a degree, but care must be taken of near-by iron or steel. Especially elongated iron objects, such as rails, fences, etc., are dangerous. Reading a compass is not easy, as it is hard to keep it motionless. The magnet needle points roughly to the magnetic pole, which is in Northern Canada. The variation from the true north changes from year to year. It is now 24°W in Maine and 28°E in Seattle. The line of no variation passes through from Michigan to South Carolina. The amount of variation always has to be added or subtracted whenever true azimuths and not mag-

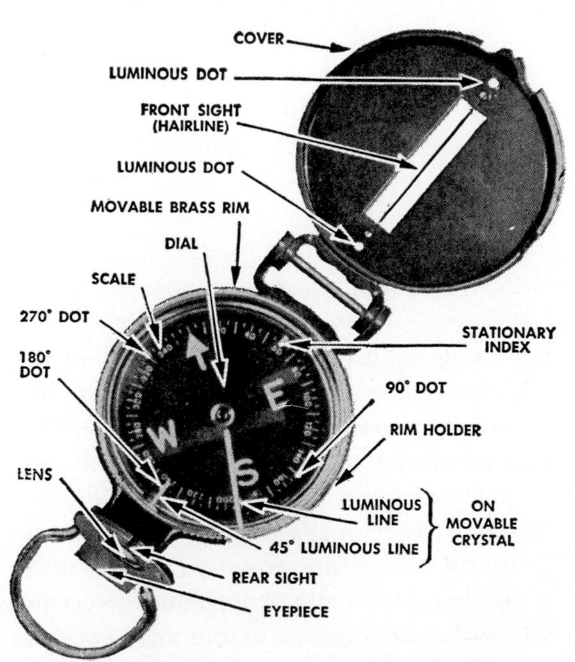


**Fig. 146** A good sighting compass can be used with about 1° accuracy.

netic azimuths are required. This variation changes in time; therefore only the latest data can be used.

*Sextant.* This is a seaman's instrument to measure the altitude of the sun above the horizon, but it can be used for measuring horizontal angles too. Livingstone used it in Africa, and it is handy for exploration or rough surveys. Figure 147 shows how a sextant works.

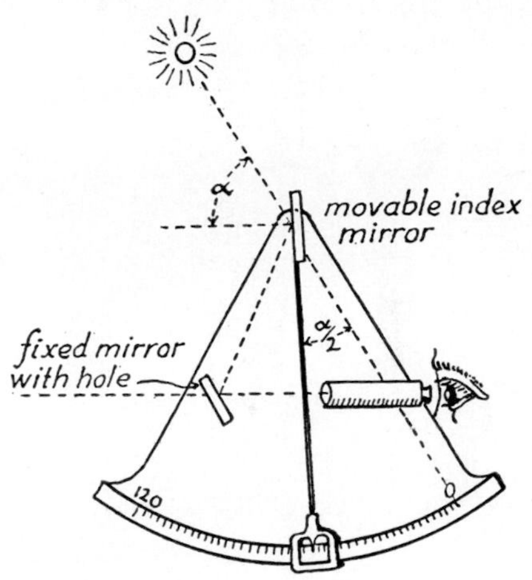


**Fig. 147** The sextant is used mostly on ships for measuring the altitude of the sun or stars. It can also be used to measure horizontal angles.

*Theodolite, or Transit.* This is a precision instrument for reading vertical and horizontal angles, and is the most important part of a surveyor's equipment. Its various adjustments are not discussed here, and the student is referred to a standard text on surveying. In reading horizontal angles, the instrument is first leveled with the help of two perpendicular spirit levels. The telescope is attached to an upper circle which has a vernier and which rotates over a lower circle which is graduated. By clamping the lower circle and turning the telescope and with it the upper circle in one direction and then another, the difference between the two readings will give the angle between the various directions.

Vertical angles are read on the vertical circle. Here, however, it is essential that we read from the exact horizontal, and for this purpose a highly sensitive spirit level is attached firmly to the telescope.

*Spirit Level.* The spirit level is a glass tube curved in an arc and filled almost full with a mixture of ether and alcohol. The remain-

**Fig. 148** A transit, or theodolite, can measure vertical and horizontal angles with great accuracy. (*Keuffel and Esser Company.*)

ing bubble is filled with the vapor of ether. If the bubble appears in the center of the axis, the level is horizontal. The greater the radius of curvature of the level, the more sensitive it will be.

*Vernier.* The vernier is an auxiliary scale that helps to read fractions of the smallest divisions of the main scale. It is used on precision instruments both for distances and for angles. The distance-measuring vernier usually has one-tenth smaller divisions than the main scale. It is generally attached to the moving part, or pointer, of the instrument. Its working can best be understood from Fig. 149. We read to the last divisions on the main scale, 52 in this case, then observe which line on the vernier coincides

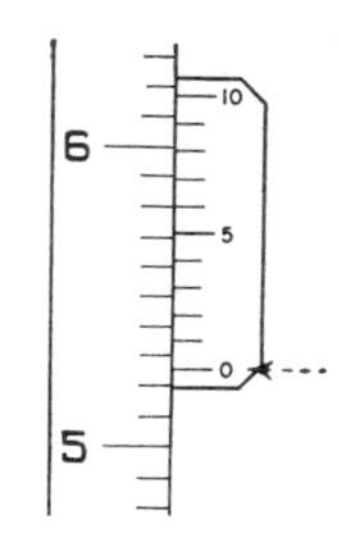


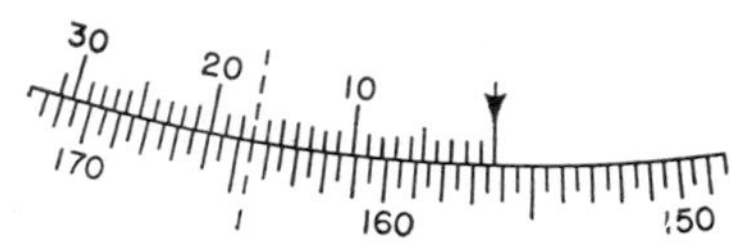


**Fig. 149** Verniers are used for exact reading of lengths and angles. The arrow is on the moving part. (*After Finch.*)

with a division on the main scale, and this will represent the decimals, so that the complete reading in this case will be 52.6. On verniers which are also used to read angles, as in Fig. 149, the circle is divided into half degrees; the vernier is divided into 30 parts, which are equal in length to 29 divisions on the main scale. Thus the vernier will give one-thirtieth of the least count of the main scale, namely, 1 minute. The last count on the main scale is 156°, and reading along the vernier it is seen that the best coincidence of lines is at 17. Thus the angle is 156°17′.

## Methods of Surveying

**Compass Traverse.** This is the simplest, but by no means the easiest, method of mapping. A traverse is a connected series of straight lines on the earth's surface, the lengths and bearings of which are determined. The earliest surveys were all traverses. This was the method of the portolan charts, which obtained directions from the compass and distances from dead reckoning. The same method was employed by the early explorers, perhaps improving the process by counting the steps of their horses, and in modern expeditions by reading the speedometer. The method is inherently rude, and is used for reconnaissance only. If an expedition proceeds from one camp to the next and keeps a compass traverse, it has no check on how good the survey was unless the location of the two camps was otherwise determined. This kind is an *open* traverse, in contrast to a closed traverse which returns to the starting point and in which case the results can be checked. Whenever it is possible, a closed traverse is made.

Compass traverses are recorded in a notebook only; no map is made in the field as there is no time for that along a marching column. First a sight is made with the compass at a point which seems a good point for the next station. The compass direction is read carefully, expressed in degrees reckoned clockwise from magnetic north 0 to 360°, and noted down in the first column at the bottom of the page. The barometer is read and recorded in the second column. The distance is then paced in a straight line to Station *B* and noted in the right column. The whole process is repeated leg by leg until the return to the starting point. Greater accuracy is obtained if at every station we sight both backward and forward. A compass traverse is not made for its own sake but for drawing a map, and features left and right from the route should be noted. If a lake is skirted or a river followed, the distance of the shore should be noted at each station and this should be written down on the side of the notebook on which the stream is.

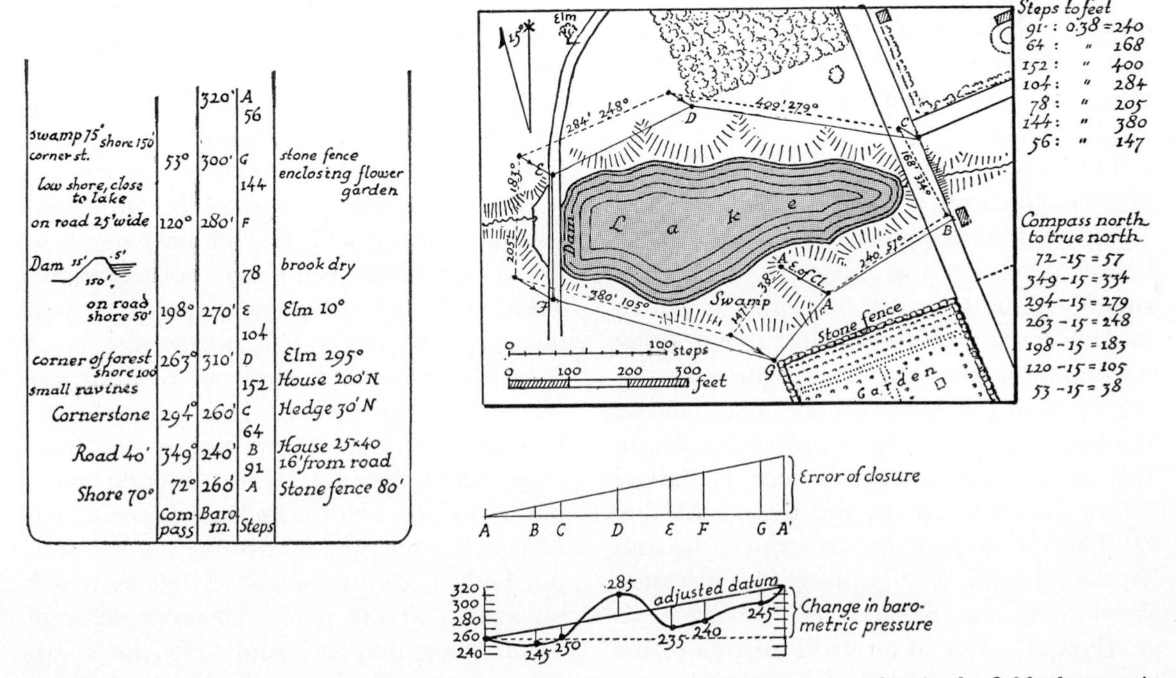


**Fig. 150** A compass traverse is for rapid reconnaissance surveys. Only notes are taken in the field; the map is drawn later.

Some rough triangulation can also be made: if a house, hill, or any other important feature appears near by, a compass reading to it can be made from a station and marked down on the side of the notebook on which the feature is. Then another compass reading to it is taken from a later station, and when the rectified traverse is plotted, the feature can be located. Flank detail even with estimated distances is most important. Most compass traverses fail not because of bad readings but because beginners are so engrossed in making the traverse that they forget that they are supposed to make a map and not only its skeleton.

A list of legs is made, and steps are transformed into feet. For this purpose a measurement is made of the length of the steps taken along a 100-foot tape laid out in the field in average terrain. If, for instance, 38 steps are made in 100 feet, all recordings have to be divided by 0.38 to have them in feet. A scale is prepared to lay out the distances. It is also a good idea at this stage to transform magnetic readings into true azimuths by adding or subtracting the local variation.

The preparation of the map is done at home or in camp. The scale is decided, and a paper of sufficient size is tacked on the board. The size and shape of the map is roughly visualized and Station *A* is put in its proper place. A vertical line representing north is drawn with a T-square up from this point; from this direction the first compass reading is laid out with a protractor. Upon this line the first distance in paces is marked off on the chosen scale, and there is Station *B*. Then a vertical line is drawn through Station *B* with the T-square; the direction is plotted; the distance of Station *C* is marked off; and so on until all legs of the traverse are completed. In a closed traverse, if the measurements have been absolutely correct, the last leg of the traverse returns to the starting point. A compass reading, however, can easily be off a degree or more, and the pacing may vary, especially in hilly and bushy land, and there always will be an "error of closure." If this error is too great, for instance, larger than 5 or 10 per cent of the length of the traverse, the survey has to be repeated. If the error is small, it may be distributed along the entire traverse, according to Fig. 150. A short line parallel to the error of closure is drawn from every station and $A_1$ is pushed up to $A$. Next $C$ is pushed up along the parallel line somewhat less, $F$ still less, etc. How much to push up depends on the distance. The legs of the traverse (usually reduced to one-fourth or one-tenth) are laid out in a straight line, and at the end the error of closure is drawn on a perpendicular. Perpendiculars from $B$, $C$, $D$, etc., will give proportionate lengths for the push. The idea is the same as if the traverse were laid out with a wire bent at every corner and then one end were pulled to the other. It does not matter which end is pulled to the other. If $A$ is pulled to $A_1$, the error of closure would be laid out on the left side, and the triangle would be reversed.

After the error of closure is eliminated and the traverse laid out, the next step is to fill in the detail from flank observations. Title, scale, lettering, etc., should be laid out perpendicular to true north.

In hilly country barometric readings are taken at every station. It is advisable to take along an aneroid barometer that indicates feet of elevation. If the exact elevation of the starting point is known, the pointer is turned to the proper altitude, but if it is not known, the barometer is left as it was on arrival at the place, however different the reading may be from yesterday's, because that may give a check by which to correct for weather from daily weather maps. It is quite possible that the reading will be quite different at the close of the traverse than it was at the start. This is compensated in a similar manner to that used in the case of the error of closure, as shown in Fig. 150. A profile is drawn according to the barometric readings, and if on returning to the starting point the reading is different, the end point is connected with the starting point and a new tilted base line is obtained from which the corrected altitudes can be measured off according to the vertical scale.

Compass traversing should be practiced by every cartographer. It gives good practice in appreciation of distances and directions and also in selection of features to be mapped. The judging of distances is particularly useful. It is advisable to start a day's field work by letting the students compete in guessing distances.

**Plane Tabling.** This is the most important type of field work that a cartographer should be able to do. It is far more accurate than a compass traverse, and it has an enormous advantage in that the map is drawn in the field. It is very exciting to see how the visible landscape is transformed into a map, and, as the connection between map and landscape is obvious, mistakes are rare.

The plane table is a drawing board on a tripod. A sheet of smooth paper is fixed upon the board. The best type of tripod has a spherical bearing by which the plane table is set horizontal with the help of a circular spirit level. It has two screws; when the upper screw is clamped, the plane table can still be rotated horizontally. When correctly oriented, the plane table is fixed rigidly with the lower screw.

Directions on the plane table are obtained by sighting along a ruler called the "alidade." Although a simple ruler with two vertical needles on the two ends would do the job, the work is accomplished faster and better with a modern telescopic alidade. This allows not only the measurement of distances with some accuracy, but also the measurement of vertical angles and the

**Fig. 151** Plane tabling is the standard method of filling in the detail into a network of triangles. The elaborate telescopic alidade with stadia wires is a long step from the ruler with two needles. (*C. L. Berger & Sons.*)

accomplishment of contour-line work as well.

Distances are measured with the help of a rod and stadia line (see Fig. 145). The rod is 12 to 20 feet long and divided into feet and tenths of feet (not in inches). As these small divisions, each corresponding to a distance of 10 feet, have to be seen from great distances, they are boldly painted in red, white, and black colors. First take a sight on the rod and bring it into focus; then with another screw focus the cross hairs so that they are clearly visible. This is done usually by placing the palm of the hand a few inches before the telescope against which the cross hairs stand out sharply when in focus. Then turn the telescope up or down until either the upper or the lower stadia line is aligned with an even foot division. In wooded country it is often possible to read only half of the stadia interval, and the reading has to be doubled with corresponding loss of accuracy. Obviously a 12-foot rod cannot be read for a distance greater than 1,200 feet, but in an emergency it is possible to read half-stadia intervals up to 2,400 feet; however, this reading might be as much as 50 feet off.

*Inclined Readings.* A telescopic alidade is an excellent instrument to use for obtaining both horizontal distance and difference in elevation. Indeed most of the contour-line work on U.S. topographic sheets was made on a plane table. If possible, look at the rod so that the center cross hair is at plane-table height. If the rod is looked at from any other height than that of the plane table, it is necessary to add or subtract the difference. Most telescopic alidades are equipped with a "Beaman arc" with which *HD* and *DE* can be obtained easily. The rod reading (not multiplied by 100, but in feet and tenths of feet) is multiplied by the numbers indicated by the pointer in order to obtain *DE* and the amount to subtract from *ID*.

*Progress of Plane Tabling.* First obtain some idea about the lay of the land that is to be surveyed by walking or riding or by studying the existing maps. Then select a good starting point (Station *A*) from which it is possible to see far and wide. Mark the station with a large peg, which should be visible from the other stations. Place the tripod over it, make the plane table horizontal, clamp the upper screw, and turn the plane table so that the elongation of the paper follows the elongation of the land, and then clamp the lower screw. The plane table is now rigidly fixed. Draw a line that indicates magnetic north. (Most telescopic alidades are equipped with a trough compass.) Select a scale of such size that the area to be surveyed will not run off the paper. This is one reason why it is necessary to have a previous estimate about the lay of the land. Scales range from 100 feet to 2,000 feet to the inch, but beginners should use the largest scale possible. Visualize roughly how the map will fill the paper, and locate Station *A* with a pin. Give instructions to the rodman as to where he is to go, and later instruct him with hand signals. The rodman, however, selects the spots with care for visibility and keeps the rod perfectly vertical and motionless until signaled to proceed. He carries along a number of small pegs and leaves one at each point he occupies. After the alidade man has marked all the readings radiating from Station *A*, which he cares for, he selects Station *B*, and takes a careful reading to it. He signals the rodman to wait for him, and he picks up the plane table and proceeds to Station *B*. At Station *B* he drives a large peg, sets the plane table horizontal, clamps upper motion, pricks the pin in Station *B*, and places the alidade on the line connecting Station *A* and Station *B*; he then turns the plane table until he has a backsight on the peg at Station *A*. The plane table is now "oriented," and the lower screw can be clamped. Then the rodman is sent to a new circuit, and the whole process is repeated. It is an excellent habit to make a rough compass traverse of the region first and to select the likely spots for plane-table stations.

While the rodman proceeds from point to point, the alidade man is busy sketching details between points. For instance, the rodman stops at only one corner of a house; the other corners are drawn in by sighting them through the telescope, but no distance reading has to be taken. Water courses also are drawn from relatively few points. Descriptions of points in extremely small handwriting with a well-sharpened pencil are most useful. Some surveyors have such small handwriting that it has to be read with a magnifying glass. Others use notebooks for the same purpose and refer to locations with a number.

Contour lines also are drawn in the field. Readings of *HD* and *DE* are taken at hilltops, shoulders, rims, and every point at which the topography breaks. On long and even slopes it is sufficient to draw in every fifth contour line, but in rugged terrain every line has to be completed in the field. A trained plane-tabler will soon develop a keen sense of contouring with relatively few points actually measured, but beginners will have considerable trouble, especially in forest areas where 60-foot trees easily conceal smaller topographic features. Deciduous forest areas are best surveyed in the spring.

Many points will be obtained by intersection of two rays from two stations, a form of rough triangulation. As the distance between plane-table stations is of the greatest importance, it should be read in both directions if possible. It is advisable to sight from every station to a conspicuous point within the sheet in order to be able to check on major errors. It is also advisable to check occasionally on the magnetic north. If there is a discrepancy, it should be noted for reference, but the orientation of the plane table should not be changed on this account. The discrepancy may be due to local magnetic disturbance. It is possible to sight with the alidade within a few minutes of accuracy, while the compass reading can be $\frac{1}{2}°$ off. Field work is not complete without obtaining all local information for place names, etc.

The above description of plane tabling will fill the needs of a geographer and student; professional surveyors use more accurate methods, more complete recording, and more precise control for the location of the area.

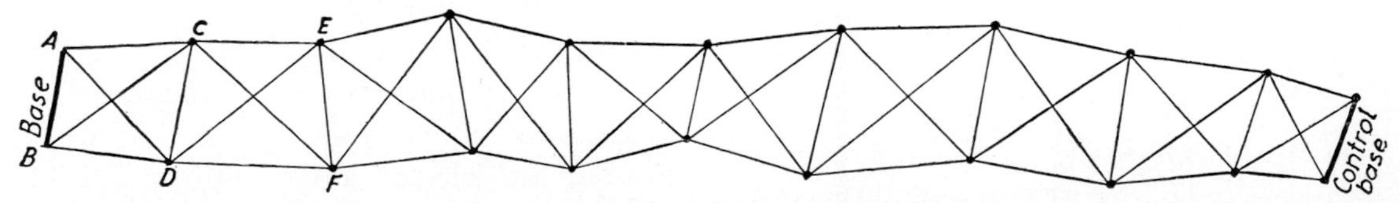


**Fig. 152** In triangulation only a few lengths are measured; all other points are fixed by reading angles.

**Triangulation.** The principles of triangulation were laid down as early as 1524 by Gemma Frisius, and the underlying geometry dates back to the ancients; yet the first practical application of the method as far as we know was by Willem Janszoon Blaeu about 1610. The triangulation of France under Cesar François Cassini was described in Chap. III. This was the first large-scale operation, and it was soon followed by most European states. At present less than one-half of the world's land area has been triangulated.

Every point on the earth's surface can be fixed by its direction and distance from a known point. If the point is within eyesight, its direction can be read within a few minutes with a transit with the greatest accuracy; to measure its distance, however, may take days and require a large party and great expense, and produce doubtful accuracy. No wonder the surveyor reads a dozen angles rather than measure distances.

In the method of triangulation only one distance is measured very accurately, and upon this "base" are built perhaps dozens of triangles. The base is normally measured along a long, straight beach, railway, or road, and it may be 5 to 15 miles long. From the two end points of the base line, *A* and *B*, the direction of some distant points, *C* and *D*, are read, perhaps dozens of miles away. As a side and two angles solve a triangle, the location of *C* and *D* can be drawn. From *C* and *D* the location of *E*, *F*, *G*, etc., can be fixed by measuring angles only, without any measurement of distances.

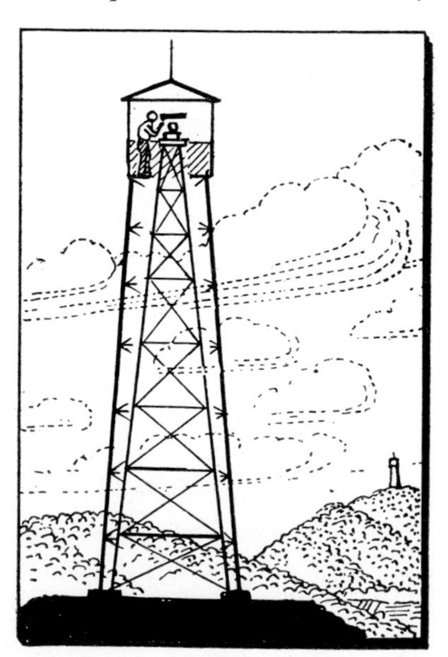

**Fig. 153** In triangulation towers, the theodolite and its observer are on two separate structures.

Obviously in these large, spherical triangles the sum of the three angles will exceed 180°. They have to be reduced to their plane for computing distances by deducting the "spherical excess" for each ($abm \sin \gamma$, where $a$ and $b$ are the lengths of two sides, $\gamma$ the angle between, and $m$ a constant depending on latitude). This first set of large triangles is called first-order triangulation. The points so determined, however, are too far apart for detailed mapping and require a second-order triangulation, which establishes points in between and on the sides. The two higher orders of triangulation are made by the U.S. Coast and Geodetic Survey. Third-order triangulation establishes points even closer, and fourth-order triangulation is usually done with plane table and stadia. This work is usually done by the U.S. Geological Survey or local agencies. While a first-order triangulation must be accurate to 1 unit in 25,000, the tolerance of error of second order is 1:10,000 and third order 1:5,000.

The general order of progress in triangulation is the following:

*Reconnaissance* for the best location of bases and stations. Bases are measured on beaches or along railways or highways; stations are selected along high intervisible points.

*Base Measurement.* Supports are erected or poles are driven along a selected line, and a 100- or 200-foot Invar tape is stretched under specified tension. The measurement is repeated back and forth until there is no undue discrepancy.

*Erection of Towers.* The Bilby steel tower used by the U.S. Coast and Geodetic Survey consists of an inner tripod supporting the theodolite, which is not touched by the outer tripod holding the observer, recorder, and light keeper. Maximum height of the tower is 130 feet, and it can be erected in 5 hours. As the triangulation party progresses, the rear towers are taken down, carried ahead on trucks, and reerected.

*Measurement of Angles with the Theodolite.* This is done with great accuracy. Main angles are read in first-order triangulation to 1.5 second, second-order to 3 seconds, and third-order to 6 seconds. The first- and second-order observations are usually made at night because there is less atmospheric refraction. In addition to the readings taken at the principal stations, a number of "intersection" readings are usually made during the day to points that are not occupied by an observer. Each point has to be observed from three main stations in order to have a check on them.

*Control Base Measurement.* As the length of the triangulation net progresses, the accuracy, called the "strength of figure," diminishes, and as a certain specified weakness is reached a control base has to be measured. To check triangulation results after 8 to 10 quadrilaterals, field observations of latitude and longitude are taken. Usually four stars are observed, the positions of which will give the latitude, the meridian, and the longitude. With the 60° astrolabe the observation of two good stars is sufficient. Unfortunately astronomical observations are dependent on the verticality of the plumb line. Large mountain masses or massive geological formations may throw the plumb line off, and thus the measurement may be off several seconds, in extreme cases 20 to 30 seconds. However, the deflection of the vertical can be determined by geodetic methods. Stations where this correction has been made are called "Laplace" stations.

*The adjustment of data* is done by special equations[1] on the principle of "least squares." The sum of angles must be made equal to 180° + spherical excess. The sides of the triangles and quadrilaterals must correspond to the angles, and the arc has to be made consistent with intermediate bases and Laplace stations.

*The latitude and longitude* of each station has to be computed together with the length and azimuth of each leg of the triangle. Before this calculation can be made a standard shape of the earth has to be formulated. The U.S. Coast and Geodetic Survey uses the Clarke spheroid of 1866, which has simpler equations than the International Ellipsoid (based on Hayford, 1909) accepted by the 1924 meeting of the International Geodetic Association.

Clarke spheroid of 1866:

equator radius, 6,378,206 meters
polar radius, 6,356,584 meters
flattening, $\frac{1}{295}$

International (Hayford) spheroid:

equator radius, 6,378,388 meters
polar radius, 6,356,912 meters
flattening, $\frac{1}{297}$

For computation of the latitude and longitude of triangle stations, there must be one station whose location is standard. For the United States the chosen station is Meades Ranch, Kans. (Lat. 39°13′26.686″—Long. 98°32′30.506″) because, being in the center of the country, the error resulting from deflection of the vertical can be more easily eliminated. Canada and Mexico adopted the same datum, which was called the "North American Datum." In 1927, the whole triangulation system of the United States was recalculated for better distribution of errors and the new positions are labeled "North American Datum of 1927." Meades Ranch retained the same position in this readjustment, and in the peripheries the changes in positions amounted to no more than about 100 feet, which shows the extreme accuracy with which the work is done.

[1] *U.S Coast and Geodetic Survey Spec. Pub.* 138.

The third aim of office computations is to *record the locations* so that they may be used by surveyors. The tables of the U.S. Coast and Geodetic Survey contain for each station its latitude, longitude, lengths of all lines of triangulation in meters and feet, and forward and backward azimuths. (The two azimuths are not exactly 180° apart because of the convergence of the meridians.) It is somewhat confusing that the azimuths have south as 0° and west as 90°.

*Marking the Stations.* On hilltops or near road intersections, small bronze disks are often found embedded in bedrock or in concrete blocks. These are either triangulation marks or bench marks, azimuth marks, gravity stations, etc. Triangulation marks show a small triangle in the center.

**State Grids.** Since 1932, most states have adopted plane coordinate systems something like a military grid system. States extending east-west use the Lambert conformal conic projection for base maps, and states elongated north-south prefer a transverse Mercator projection. Some larger states, such as Michigan, had to be divided into zones. All triangulation stations are now in the process of being recorded on these state coordinate systems, together with the grid azimuth. Back azimuths are not given because in these rectangular systems they are 180° from forward azimuths. For conversion of plane coordinates into latitude and longitude, and vice versa, tables are published by the U.S. Coast and Geodetic Survey. The state grids facilitate the work of the local surveyors who are not accustomed to make geodetic computations. Within a zone 158 miles wide the error caused by curvature does not exceed 1:10,000, the tolerance of second-order surveys. Local surveyors attach their own measurements on the nearest triangulation mark and record it in feet and grid azimuths.

## Leveling

Altitudes are determined on exploratory surveys with an aneroid, on plane-table surveys with an alidade, in triangulation with a theodolite, but for really precise leveling a special instrument, the spirit level, is used. Precise leveling is called "vertical control" survey, and its importance is just slightly less than that of triangulation or "horizontal control." Horizontal and vertical control surveys are usually independent of each other. Triangulation prefers mountaintops as stations, while precise leveling follows railroads and roads, which for the most part follow the valleys. According to accuracy we differentiate between first-order, second-order, and third-order leveling.

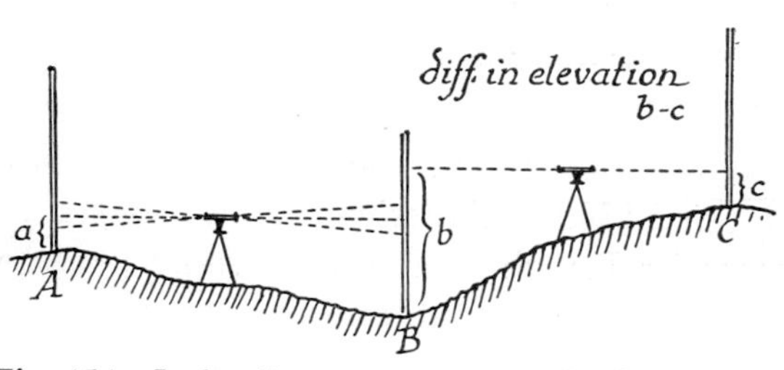

**Fig. 154** In leveling great accuracy is obtained by reading backward and forward. This eliminates the effect of possible slight departures from exact horizontality.

The leveling instrument is a telescope connected with an extremely sensitive level bubble. In the engineer's level, it rides on the top of the telescope and is called a "Y level." In the instrument used for first-order leveling (such as the Fisher level), the level and telescope are firmly attached, and the rod and level bubble may be seen at the same time with the help of a mirror. The instrument is made of Invar, which does not expand with heat. The graduations of the rods are smaller than the rods used in stadia measurements.

As the work progresses, a reading is made forward and backward from every station. At the next station the front rod becomes the rear rod. The length of a reading should not exceed 500 feet. In first-order leveling, sections of a few miles are run forward and backward, and the closing error should not exceed 0.017 foot $\sqrt{\text{miles}}$. The accuracy of leveling is amazing. First-order leveling carried across the continent and back may be off only a few feet. The main network of leveling lines, when completed, will leave no point more than 50 miles from a bench mark. Second-order leveling will reduce the greatest distance from a bench mark to 12.5 miles, and third-order leveling to even less. The tolerance for error in the second order is 0.035 foot $\sqrt{\text{miles}}$, and in the third order 0.05 foot $\sqrt{\text{miles}}$, but it should never be carried beyond 30 miles.

After the field notebooks are forwarded to Washington, existing surveys are checked and adjustments are made. The records are published in Special Publications of the Coast and Geodetic Survey.

**History.** First-order leveling in the United States was started in 1878 in connection with the First Transcontinental Arc of Triangulation. As instruments and methods improved, several general adjustments of the networks were made, as in 1899 and in 1903. After the Atlantic and Pacific were connected with a line of levels in 1907, the changes resulting from this check were so small that only a partial adjustment was necessary. In 1927, a special study of "sea level" was undertaken, and "the results seemed to indicate that the actual mean sea level surface as defined by the tide observations tends to slope upward to the north along the coast of the Atlantic and Pacific Oceans and upward to the west along the Gulf Coast. The actual mean sea level surface on the Pacific Coast appears to stand appreciably higher than the similar surface on the Atlantic Coast."[1]

By 1929, about 45,000 miles of first-order leveling was carried through. In this year a major general adjustment was made in connection with the 20,000 miles level net of Canada and the water-level nets of the Great Lakes, and the sea level was fixed at 26 tide stations. The results of this extensive adjustment cannot be published in a single book, but copies can be obtained for any special area from the survey. By 1940, 112,000 miles of first-order leveling made a net of about 100 miles interval, and 166,000 miles of second-order leveling closed the net to 25 to 50 miles, with 5- to 10-mile intervals in important areas. Releveling of lines, especially in the Pacific area, disclosed slow movements of the earth's crust, which are eagerly studied by structural geologists.

*Bench marks* of leveling are small bronze tablets with a bar engraved in the center. They seldom give the elevation of the mark because at every adjustment they have to be changed perhaps a few hundredths of a foot. Although the reluctance of the survey to display data of lesser accuracy can be understood, it is very annoying to find an unlabeled bench mark and to be unable to identify it promptly from a map. It would save a great deal of correspondence and loss of time if every bench mark were labeled with a serial number and the elevation according to the latest adjustment.

[1] *U.S. Coast and Geodetic Survey Spec. Pub.* 134, 1927.

# CHAPTER 18: *Sketching*

During the last half century landscape sketching, a cherished art of old-school geographers, fell into oblivion. Photography provides such a quick and effortless way of obtaining pictures of a landscape that very few geographers now carry a sketchbook. Yet field sketching has many advantages over photography, among which are the following:

1. It stimulates close observation, for many important features which may be lost to a photographer are discovered under the careful observation required by sketching.

2. It makes possible the omission of much of the foreground by emphasizing or even enlarging distant features, whereas by photography the incidental features of the foreground, such as trees and houses, loom up too large, and important features on the distant horizon show inadequately. The camera serves the biologist better than the geographer.

3. It facilitates the selection of significant features, whereas the camera takes in everything indiscriminately, so that often, especially in forested country, vegetation obscures all else.

4. Labels and explanatory notes can be placed directly on the picture. Where art fails, words help.

5. It can be reproduced in line cut, whereas a photograph must be reproduced in half tone. Half tones look dull compared with line cuts.

Many prominent geographers were excellent landscape artists. The sketches of William H. Holmes and William Morris Davis are classic in their exactness and simplicity of expression. Yet it is not necessary to be an artist in order to produce good field sketches. Observation of certain principles will enable anybody to do satisfactory work.

The equipment for field sketching consists of about 6- by 12-inch drawing paper attached to a cardboard pad, a pencil, an eraser, and an ordinary 12-inch ruler. The

**Fig. 155** Establishing reference lines for a field sketch.

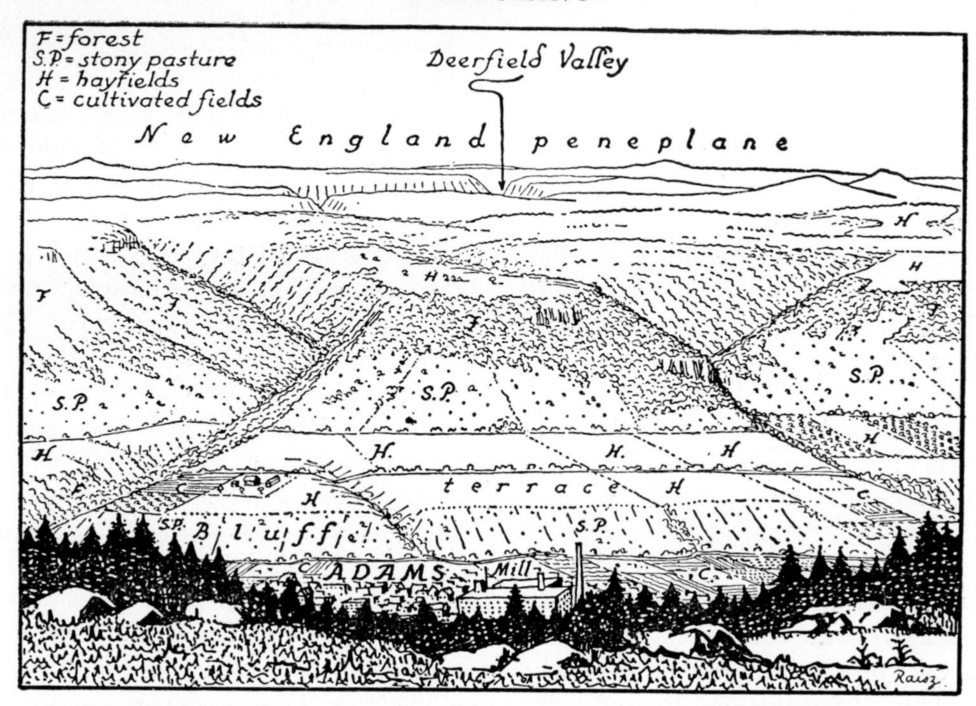


**Fig. 156** Field sketch showing land utilization. (*Courtesy of Geog. Rev.*)

size of the sketch pad depends on individual taste. William Morris Davis used 4- by 6-inch notebooks. Sun glasses will reduce the glare of the white paper.

The stages of producing a sketch are as follows:

1. *Size of Sketch.* Decide how wide a portion you want to include in the sketch. Choose a point as center of the sketch.

2. *Center Line and Horizon Line.* Draw a vertical center line on the pad and a horizontal line, which should correspond to the horizon or any other well-marked horizontal line in nature. (A distant lake shore or road will often serve as a good horizontal reference line.)

3. *Determination of Scale of Sketch.* Hold the inch scale horizontally at the distance of the outstretched arm and measure the width of the intended landscape. If this width has to be drawn on a 12-inch-wide paper, the scale can be calculated. It is convenient to use a scale in which 1 inch on the scale corresponds to $\frac{1}{2}$ inch in the sketchbook. Turn your whole body while measuring toward the various parts of the landscape. Your outstretched right arm is nearer to your eye looking left than looking right.

4. *Layout of Key Points.* Measure the horizontal distance from the center point, and the vertical distance from the horizon line of a few important points, and mark them on the sketch pad in the proper scale. Careful work in this stage of the sketching is amply rewarded later. The points will enable one to draw the major lines of the landscape.

5. *Drawing of the Detail.* The general rule for drawing the detail is to proceed from the large features to the smaller ones. If one begins in a corner and adds detail to detail, the drawing will probably be wrong. Use as few lines as possible. Differentiate the type of feature with the type of line; for instance, show bare rock with straight, crossed lines, and forest with lines characteristic of treetops. A certain amount of

symbolism may be used. Plowed fields, orchards, and single trees can be shown by an appropriate conventional pattern. A few housetops and steeples will indicate a village.

6. *Vertical Exaggeration.* It is a common experience for landscape painters to find that the vertical scale of very distant hills has to be exaggerated in order to appear natural. In a flat landscape the distant belt of 2 or 3° at the horizon represents a larger territory than all that is in its foreground. The eye is very keen to observe this narrow belt, and every painter involuntarily exaggerates it. One of the shortcomings of photography is that distant hills do not show up well. In field sketching it is quite permissible to draw this belt somewhat wider and to point out distant features more clearly. This exaggeration is especially recommended in sketches made from hilltops, and does not have to be used if no distant features are included.

7. *Designation of Depth.* Bringing depth into the picture can be accomplished by various means. Most landscapes have a coulisse effect; ridges and hills disappear beyond each other as do the coulisses of stage scenery. Hence it is important to show these coulisses distinctly.

Distance can be expressed by the weight of the line. Hills on the distant horizon are drawn with a very fine, or even dotted, line, and the lines are made increasingly heavier toward the foreground. Features of known size appear smaller with distance. It is advisable to draw distinctly a few trees, houses, men, or animals on the landscape by which to establish the scale. The curly line outlining forested hills should become smoother with distance.

8. *Lettering.* A field sketch can be richly annotated. Names of lakes and rivers can be placed inside the sketch; names of mountains, however, are usually placed directly above, with arrows pointing to the peaks. For possible later use in mapping, the width represented in the sketch should be noted. As a rough measurement, the width of the two outstretched fists is about 15°.

9. *Inking.* Sketches in the field are usually drawn in pencil only, and inked in later. Lettering is inked in first; next, the most distant hills (for which a Gillott No. 290 pen is recommended); then the middle ground (with a Gillott No. 303 or 404); and, lastly, the foreground, with the same pen born down heavily on the paper or turned around so that the point is flattened.

10. *Coloring.* After the sketch is inked, it is ready for reproduction in black and white. If colors can be used, a few touches of light wash will add greatly to the effectiveness of the sketch, but too heavy colors may spoil it. The haze of the air cuts out the warm reds and yellows, and the distant horizon appears in cold colors, such as blue and gray. The true color effect of a landscape can best be seen by turning the head sideways or by bending over. Kodachromes are very helpful.

The most distant regions are painted with very faint blue, and the colors become darker and warmer toward the foreground; but, in field sketches to be used in geography, even the closest foreground should not be in full color. Beginners will often find it necessary to wash off their first efforts with a sponge.

**Transformation of Photographs into Pen-and-ink Drawings.** Poor or hazy photographs become even less satisfactory by the half-tone-reproduction process; hence they are usually redrawn with pen and ink for reproduction in line cut. A student proficient in landscape sketching will have no difficulty in doing this.

First, the photograph is traced upon drawing paper. Often it is better to enlarge the photograph, either photographically or by the square method. Then a pencil drawing is made in which the essential elements of the photograph are clearly outlined. The incidental elements, such as trees in the foreground, which have no bearing on the matter and which would have been avoided by taking the photograph from a slightly different location, may be omitted or outlined in a rough way. Otherwise, the drawing proceeds along the same lines as in direct field sketching.

Vivid pictures can be obtained by blackening the shadow side and the cast shadow of features in the middle or foreground, and modulating their darkness with fine brush lines of white paint. A similar effect can be obtained by using Ross board or scratchboard.

**Blackboard Sketching.** The ability to draw rapid sketches on the blackboard is a great asset to teachers of geography. Blackboard sketches have to be simple, and a teacher need not be endowed with special artistic ability to draw sketches and diagrammatic maps. A few suggestions for improved chalk technique follow.

First of all, the use of colored chalks is recommended. Light blue is used for water features; for drawing hills yellow is preferable to white, because it is more brilliant and can be seen at a greater distance; red is good for cultural features; and green represents vegetation.

Shading of mountains can be done rapidly and effectively by holding a short piece of chalk flat, with its side to the board. Dotting can be quickly applied by holding a long piece of chalk by the end at an angle opposite to the direction in which the row of dots is to be marked, and forcing the end of the chalk to jump elastically, the distance between dots being regulated by the velocity of the motion. Double lines are drawn by holding two chalks together. Tinting can be done with the flat side of the chalk or by dabbing with the blackboard eraser. Black lines on white can also be made with the blackboard eraser. Roman and italic lettering can be made by sharpening the chalk to a flat edge. Chalk is such a versatile tool that every teacher may find new ways to use it.

**Blackboard Maps.**[1] The use of diagrammatic maps or cartograms in teaching geography is not a new idea. Indeed the very first school maps in history, made in the ninth to thirteenth centuries in Moslem countries, used this device to acquaint the pupils with the relative location of the various countries. In more recent times the mid-nineteenth-century geography textbooks often presented cartograms in which the outlines of countries and continents were pressed into geometrical forms. They used curved parallels, however, and were so complicated that they defeated their own purpose. The fundamental idea is sound, however, and blackboard maps add enormously to the interest of class and audience.

The purpose of these cartograms is to present simply and forcefully the basic geographic facts, such as climatic belts, vegetation zones, location of mountain belts, rivers, urban centers, agricultural regions, etc. The continental outlines are drawn according to a sinusoidal projection which, with its horizontal parallels and tapering meridians, gives the simplest outlines and preserves the exact areas. They are drawn here at different scales, but they can of course be drawn on any convenient scale. The United States is drawn on a rectangular projection, as this gives the simplest forms. Using curved parallels would make the drawings more complex.

[1] Raisz, Erwin, Draw Your Own Blackboard Maps! *Jour. Geog.*, Vol. 61, No. 7, pp. 262–264, 1942.

Wright, Helen, Diagrammatic Map Making. *Jour. Geog.*, Vol. 32, pp. 242–244, 1933.

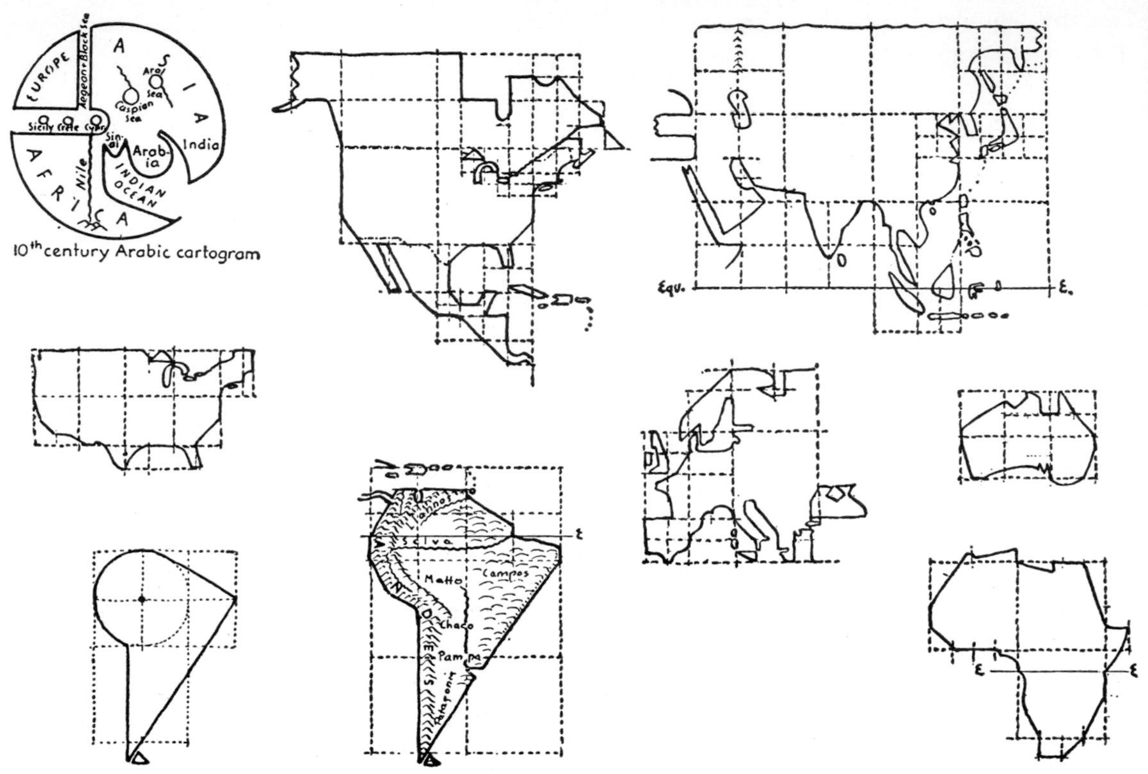


**Fig. 157** Blackboard sketch maps are highly effective tools in teaching. The above outlines are based on a sinusoidal projection. The horizontal lines are parallels, but the vertical lines are not meridians.

All outlines are drawn on a grid of squares divided into half, quarter, or even eighth squares, wherever necessary. The squares do not represent parallels and meridians; they are spaced for convenience in drawing only. Truly the horizontal lines are parallels since they represent the east-west direction, but the vertical lines are not meridians since they are not running north and south, especially in higher latitudes. In filling in the detail, colored chalks will be helpful. Blue wavy lines for rivers, brown for mountains, green for agriculture or forest, red for cities, boundaries, and roads will make not only for more attractive but also for clearer maps.

# CHAPTER 19: *Aerosurveying*

Never in history has the map maker obtained a more powerful tool than the aerial camera. With it the earth can be portrayed with more accuracy, with more detail, and in a fraction of the time that was necessary by the older methods. Aerosurveying, as is any other kind of surveying, is a source rather than a part of cartography. It is discussed here chiefly because of the powerful impact it has on the future of maps.

**History.** It would be very difficult to trace who made the first aerial photograph. As soon as snapshots were invented it was an obvious thought to take a camera up in a balloon or fasten it to a kite. Laussedalt, a Frenchman, is credited with having made the first photographic survey in 1858, and in the war of 1871 the French used aerial photographs for intelligence work. The principles of photomapping were well worked out even before the airplane. The science of photogrammetry was carried to great perfection by the English in the Himalayas and by the Swiss in the Alps, taking pictures from mountain peaks. Only a few years ago the hardy Canadian surveyors still lugged up their panoramic (taking a composite picture of the entire horizon) cameras on the most forbidding peaks of the Rockies. At the beginning of the century, the United States lagged behind the German, Swiss, and English pioneers, but in the 1920's the U.S. Coast and Geodetic Survey mapped the Mississippi delta from the air, the Hydrographic Office surveyed Cuba (1928), and the U.S. Geological Survey began to use photographs for its topographic sheets, especially in Alaska. In 1925, the Hamilton Rice Expedition photographed the impenetrable forest of the Rio Negro and Uraricoera Rivers from the air. The pictures were taken by Captain Stevens who later won fame by his balloon ascent to the stratosphere.

In the last two decades scores of large private companies competed with government agencies in achieving the perfection of aerial photography, and a great national industry was born. Aerial pictures were used in surveying, soil-erosion control, forestry, geology, hydrography, archaeology, exploration, and traffic control, and even photographing golf links from the air became a considerable business. The specialists in airplane photography are numbered by the thousands, and the surveyor, the cartographer, and the geographer fall behind the times if they fail to keep up with the growth of the young giant.

In the midst of this rapid technical development came the Second World War, and airplane photography attained even greater importance. Millions of square miles were surveyed in an incredibly short time, and the slotted templates of radial-line plots literally covered acres at the offices in Washington. For the future plans have been worked out to photograph all the lands of the earth, the greatest cartographic venture of mankind.

**Airplane photographs** are classified as

1. *Verticals*, where the camera is pointed down, usually from a hole in the plane, as exactly vertically as possible.

2. *Obliques*, which can be either high obliques, in which the horizon is visible, or low obliques in which it is not.

There is a great difference between obliques and verticals. The oblique is familiar to us, for there is nothing strange in the view from a high peak or an airplane window. We see a great expanse of land, hills, and mountains, and the various patterns of the earth's carpet will show up

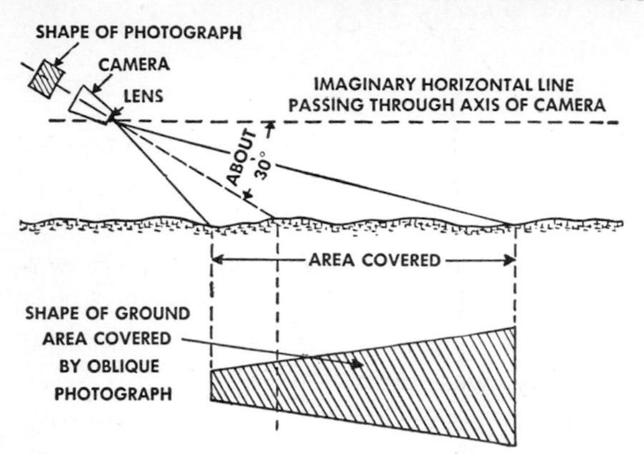


**Fig. 158** Oblique photographs cover large areas, but they have to be put into a transformer in the same relative position as above to produce a picture of uniform scale. (*From FM* 21–26, *United States Army*.)

clearly. The cartographer obtains as great inspiration from this portrait of the earth as the painter does from seeing his model from a new angle. In a vertical photograph, however, we see a strange world; the very place where we live looks unfamiliar. We see the earth as an eagle does, because usually we are unable to look straight down, even from a plane. Mountains and hills are "flattened," river patterns stand out clearly, and variations in the soil and vegetation are most outstanding. The absence of color makes the country even more unfamiliar. The reading of vertical airplane photographs requires special study. Yet it is on the vertical picture that distances and directions appear nearly true, and they can be used more directly for mapping than the obliques.

**Equipment.** Almost any kind of *airplane* can be used for making pictures, but more exacting surveys demand a big, steady plane which has a large fuel capacity and which is able to climb to great heights. The plane should have two holes in the bottom, one for the camera and one for the view finder.

There are a great variety of *cameras*. A typical camera consists of a body, a magazine, and a cone with the lenses. The cone can be exchanged for different focal lengths: 6, 10, 12, and 20 inches or more. The pictures vary from 4 by 5 to 9 by 9 inches. This latter large size is now preferred by most surveys and is demanded by the government. The magazines are loaded with roll film, 100 to 500 exposures, and in better cameras vacuum plates keep the film in exact position during the exposure. The shutters are usually the "between the lens" type, capable of $\frac{1}{200}$ or higher speeds.

**Fig. 159** Aerial camera mounted in the plane. The view finder is at the legs of the operator. (*Aero Service Company*.)

The view finder is mounted alongside and exactly parallel to the camera and on its ground glass the photographer can constantly check the pictures, determine the overlap between successive pictures, measure the "crab" of a wind-driven plane, and identify landmarks. The plane follows planned flight lines. Pictures are usually taken automatically by a clock release or intervalometer at controlled intervals. This instrument also winds the film and releases the shutter. Some cameras are mounted so that they always keep a vertical position; others are leveled by hand. There is usually a round level bubble attached to the camera to check its verticality. Many cameras automatically photograph the position of the level bubble, the hands of a clock, the altimeter, and the date and serial number of the picture; and thus all pertinent data are recorded. During the war, cameras often were placed in a wing or bomb bay, and the pilot needed only to push a button to put in operation an automatic intervalometer and was able to correct for crab by remote control.

Pictures are often made from great altitudes, and at altitudes of more than 12,000 feet oxygen is used. For oblique pictures usually the same camera is used, removed from its mount and aimed by hand, looking through an attached small view finder. Some modern mounts allow for oblique pictures by remote control.

Multilens cameras are really three to nine cameras permanently built together, which make one central vertical picture and a number of wing pictures, thus greatly enlarging the area which can be mapped by a single flight. The Zeiss four-lens camera, the Bagley five-lens camera, the Reading nine-lens camera, and the trimetrogon camera represent highly specialized machinery.

**The Photographic Flight.** The flight itself may take only a few hours but it represents days of planning and weeks of plotting. The season has to be considered. Deciduous forest area is best mapped in spring. Crop areas are shown better at the time of harvest. Snow pictures are usually not favorable for mapping but are very revealing in war. There is a tendency now, however, to use snow pictures for multiplex work. The hours between ten and two are best for uniform lighting and small shadows. The morning and evening hours give highly plastic pictures of a hilly country, but much detail is lost in the large shadows. After the most careful plans are laid, comes the often endless waiting for a clear, cloudless day, and this is the most nerve-wracking part of airplane photography.

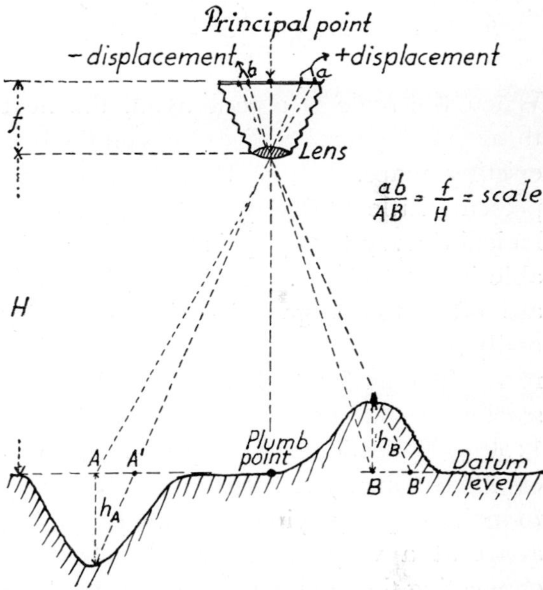


**Fig. 160** Displacement depends on the height or depth of the object and on its distance from the plumb point.

The *scale* of photographs cannot be too small. An auto becomes invisible at about 1:15,000, and a house is indistinguishable under 1:40,000. Major types of regions of land, however, are visible on a scale of 1:100,000 and smaller. From Fig. 160 $ab/AB = f/H$. In other words, the scale of the photograph equals the focal length per altitude. The larger the height of the plane, the smaller the scale; and the larger the focal length, the larger the scale of the picture will be, keeping in mind that a "large-scale" picture shows a small area. The above formula is fundamental in planning operations. For instance, the camera has a focal length of 10 inches; at what height need the camera be to produce pictures at a scale of 1:15,000?

$$\frac{1}{15{,}000} = \frac{10}{X}$$

$$X = 150{,}000 \text{ inches} = 12{,}500 \text{ feet}$$

Or the flight is at 20,000 feet, and the camera has a 6-inch focal length. What is the scale of the print?

$$\text{Scale} = \frac{F}{H} = \frac{6}{20{,}000 \times 12} = \frac{1}{40{,}000}$$

When the scale is agreed upon, the next thing is to lay out the flight lines on the best existing maps. In the United States this presents little difficulty as the U.S. Geological Survey topographic maps are available in most places. These maps, however, are often too large scale, since one may easily fly across one in 6 to 8 minutes. Airmen often prefer to lay out the lines on smaller scale maps, especially on the 1:500,000 Sectional Airway maps. In unexplored country it is sometimes necessary to make maps by flying strips about 20 miles apart at a very great altitude and then connecting them with a few cross strips. The real mapping flight lines are laid out at right angles to the small-scale strips, which will show enough landmarks to go by.

The number of exposures is calculated to allow a generous overlap. Sixty per cent overlap is necessary in the direction of flight to get stereoscopic pairs, and the flight lines are spaced from each other so that there is an overlap of 25 to 30 per cent on the sides. Thus every point on the ground will appear on two or three pictures.

During the flight the pilot keeps the plane on an even level and watches its direction by compass and by the landmarks which appear or which are added to the flight map. The camerman sets the intervalometer in motion and checks the flight line in the view finder. He follows the regression of a landmark in the view finder, and when this line of regression is oblique to the axis of the plane, the angle of crab can be determined and compensated for. At present a special indicator can keep the plane in perfect alignment from two shoran stations. After the flight is completed, the altimeter is checked for changes in barometric pressure, and elaborate records of the flight together with the flight map (with both the originally planned and the actually flown line) is handed in to the laboratory.

**Laboratory Work.** The roll of film 75 to 410 feet long needs a special developing kit in which the film is pulled by an electromotor through the developer, which may be metol hydroquinone or pyrogallic acid to which potassium bromide is added as restrainer and sodium sulphite as preservative and sodium carbonate or some similar salt as accelerator. It is better to develop the roll slowly, taking about 15 minutes. Fixing (sodium thiosulphate plus some preservative and hardener) also takes about the same time. Washing takes about an hour in special tanks with a constant flow of fresh water. The film is dried on a large reel, or drum, that revolves slowly. The dried film is numbered, dated, and coded, usually on the northeast side of the film for easier orientation. The film is preserved in rolled condition.

Contact prints are made by pressing photo paper against the individual pictures in the roll of film using a special frame. Light is passed through. The paper is then developed, fixed, and washed as before. Glossy paper gives more detail, but semi-matte paper is easier to mark. Rectified prints are made through a special projector in which the errors resulting from tip or tilt and varying altitudes are corrected.

Every aerial camera produces four half-arrow-shaped "fiducial" marks on the four sides of the picture. The connection of these marks will give the center of the photograph, which is called its principal point. This point has to be drawn with care and accuracy because it is really the principal point of photogrammetry. In a truly vertical picture the principal point shows the point plumb below the camera; in a tilted picture, however, the plumb point below the camera is off-center.

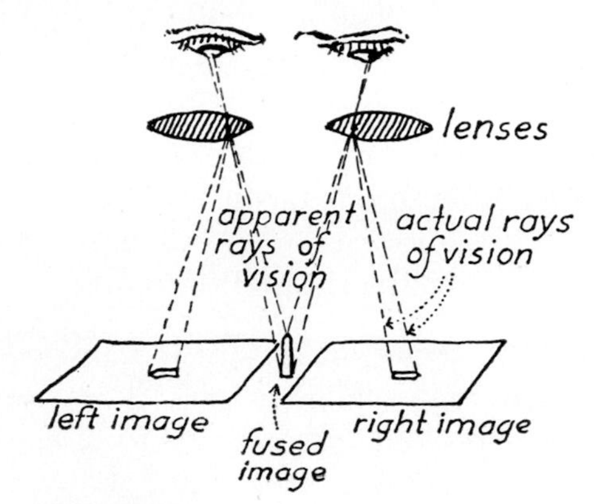


**Fig. 161** In stereoscopic vision we see a fused image standing in high relief.

**Stereovision.** The marvel of airplane photography does not stop by giving rich detail and characteristic geographic patterns in the plane. With the help of stereovision and stereogrammetry it is possible to see the heights as well and to plot contour lines with previously unknown accuracy.

Stereovision is a remarkable mental capacity. Our two eyes are as a rule only about $2\frac{1}{4}$ inches apart; yet the small parallax caused by the slightly different angle of vision enables us to see three-dimensional, plastic images and to judge distances accurately. If one eye is closed, vision flattens into a picture effect. Of course the nearer objects are, the more plastically they are seen, because the parallax of the two images of the two eyes is greater; yet even at 1,000 feet, where the angle between the two vision rays becomes less than a minute of angle, stereovision is still perceptible. The old-fashioned stereoscope in which two pictures are taken by two parallel cameras mounted a few inches apart is familiar to all. When the left picture is seen with the left eye and the right picture with the right eye with a simple stereoscope, the relations of stereovision are restored, and the picture "comes alive" because of mental fusion. Similarly if two subsequent pictures are taken from the flying plane of the landscape miles below, the same small parallax necessary for stereovision is obtained, and with the help of a stereoscope the landscape below is seen, just as a small relief model is seen a few feet below the eyes.

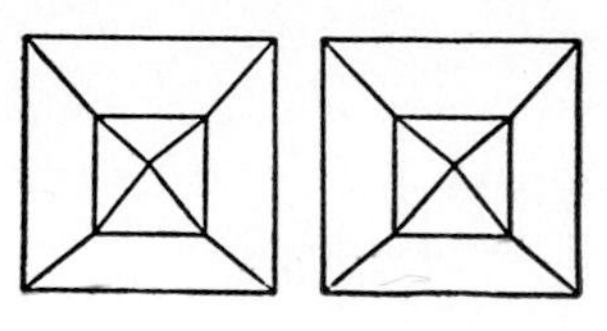

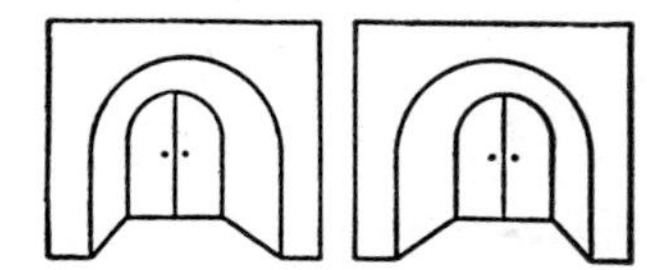

**Fig. 162** Looking through the book, as if it were transparent, fuses the two pictures into a stereoscopic image.

**The Stereoscope.** With some patience it is possible to look at a stereoscopic pair of pictures without any instrument and see a fused image. If a person gazes into the distance and holds a finger before his eyes, but does not focus his vision on the finger but keeps gazing afar, he will perceive two images, if he has two good eyes. If he keeps this distant focus and yet sees the geometric design in Fig. 162, it will dissolve into three figures, the center one showing in high relief. To keep the eyes focused on distance is difficult and requires practice. In viewing a stereo pair of airplane pictures they should not be more than 2 inches apart for unaided view. There is no need, however, to strain the eyes because there are many types of stereoscopes on the market and, in fact, one can be easily prepared from mirrors, prisms, or lenses.

The lens stereoscopes have the additional advantage of magnifying the picture. In

**Fig. 163** A simple device made of two lenses makes a good stereoscope. (*From Abrams, "Essentials of Aerial Surveying."*)

looking at a pair of airplane photographs, it is essential that they should be in the same relative position as the way they were taken; if the order is reversed the picture will show negative relief, the valleys becoming ridges. It is also to be remembered that only the overlapping part which appears in both pictures can be seen in relief. For rapid placing of two pictures under the stereoscope, fingertips may be placed on identical objects on the two photographs and their images brought together until they overlap.

For actual stereoplotting, the photographs are tacked down in the proper position. First a cross is made on the principal points of both photographs and the same points are marked on the other photograph. The line connecting them is the base line. First the left photograph is taped down and the other shifted until the images of the principal points merge. If correctly done, the base lines must be parallel. After some study of the stereoscopic picture it is quite easy to draw—if not exact contours—good horizontal form lines.

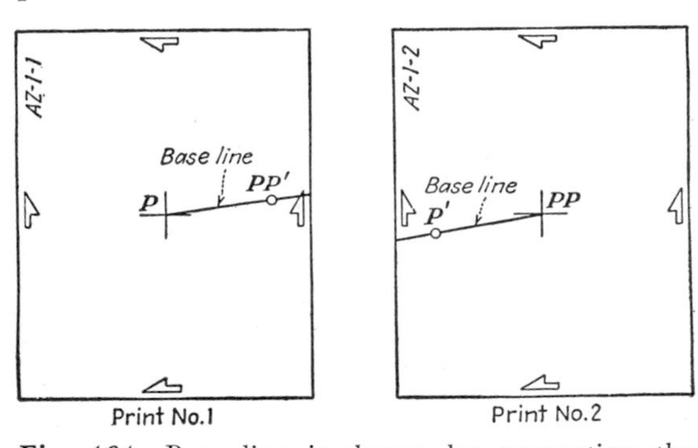


**Fig. 164** Base line is drawn by connecting the principal points of successive photographs. (*From Abrams.*)

**Fig. 165** With a contour finder we can draw contour lines upon a stereographic pair of pictures. (*From Abrams.*)

**Contouring Instruments.** A great variety of instruments appeared on the market almost as early as airplane photography was perfected. The heavy European instruments like the aerocartograph and stereoplanigraph, etc., were later supplemented by much smaller and simpler contour finders, many of which were developed in America. For more accurate work the Multiplex Aeroprojector became the most universally accepted.

*The Multiplex Aeroprojector.* This is a large instrument costing thousands of dollars and requiring 3 to 6 months training for its operation. As most of the new maps of the Army Map Service, U.S. Geological Survey, etc., are made with it, its principle at least is presented here. The fundamental idea of the multiplex is to project a diapositive of each aerial photograph on a table, thus restoring on a small scale the same location, altitude, and tilt in which the plane was when the successive pictures were taken. Each successive picture is projected in red or green color, and by looking at the red picture with a red lens with one eye and looking at the green picture with a green lens with the other eye we see the overlapping part in high relief. This is the principle of the anaglyph, which is used also in three-dimensional motion pictures and in various toys. The first multiplex projectors were made in Germany, but now they are manufactured by Bausch and Lomb in Rochester, N.Y. The photographs for the multiplex are taken with the usual 60 per cent overlap. Shorter focal length cameras are preferred because they make for larger parallax and for more apparent height. For mapping purposes it is important that at least the first and last pair of pictures in the flight should have some ground control, both horizontal and vertical.

The table, the bar, and the projectors of the multiplex can be seen in Fig. 166. The projectors have a focal length corresponding to that of the camera. As many as eight projectors can be used on the bar at the same time. Each projector is provided with a filter slot into which the green or red color filter can be inserted. The tilt, tip, and altitude of the projector are handled with screws. The tracing table has a small adjustable top (Fig. 166) about 6 inches above the main table, and it holds in its center the floating dot that is carried around to draw the contour. A fine vernier screw helps in lifting or lowering the dot.

First, the diapositive has to be put in position so that its center is over the principal-point cross of the glass that represents the focal plane of the projector. Then the "clearing of the model" is done by six adjustments of various screws until the diapositive is in the same relative position to a horizontal plane as the airplane was during the photo flight. This is done by using three control points either established by ground survey or obtained by previous airplane pictures. This is the reason why

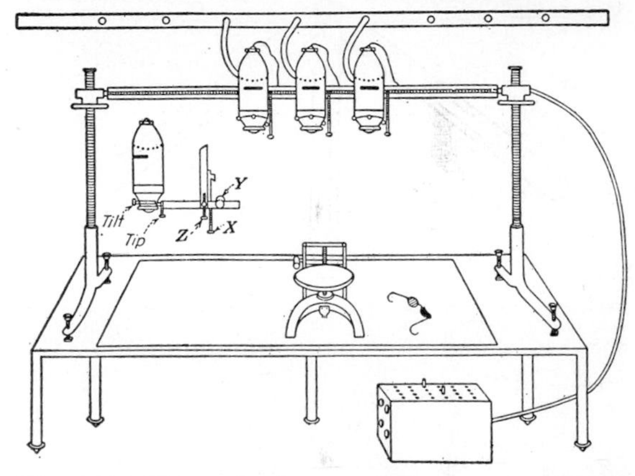


**Fig. 166** The multiplex aeroprojector uses diapositives with red and green filters and corresponding lenses to produce fused images. (*From Abrams.*)

three bench marks in exact locations and height are necessary, if possible, in the first photograph. It is possible to "clear the model" from two ground-controlled points if we know that two of them are at the same elevation, for instance, on a seashore or along a meandering river or railway. After the first pair of photographs is "cleared" by ground control, the other photos are cleared with the first, using the transferred first principal point as it appears on the second picture, etc. The last picture again needs ground control for checking.

**Radial-line Control.** To prepare maps from aerial photographs considerable ground control is needed. When this is not available, it is necessary to provide it by radial-line plotting. Even so there must be some ground control, preferably two fixed points at one end and two points at the other end.

Whatever the location, scale, tilt, or tip of a point may be, the radial direction from the principal point is the same. Thus if a point is fixed from two correctly spaced

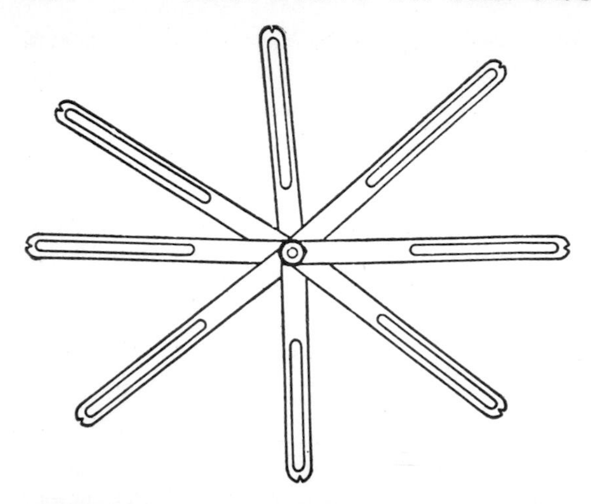

**Fig. 167** Where control points are few, radial-line assemblies serve as a kind of second-order triangulation. (*From Abrams.*)

photographs and radial lines are drawn, a kind of triangulation is performed, and points thus obtained can be used as secondary control points.

There are various methods of setting up a radial-line plot, but nowadays the slotted-arm method is used in most offices. On each photograph the principal point is marked, and the principal points of the adjacent pictures also are marked, which, with 60 per cent overlap, should be visible. In addition at least six other conspicuous points are selected; these points should be well distributed near the margins of the pictures. Into each of these points special pins are pushed. The slotted arms are placed on these pins, arranged radially from the principal point. When the arms are in place, they are tightly screwed fast in the center, and the set is lifted off the pins and preserved. A similar template is prepared for each picture.

Then a base map is prepared on which a map projection is laid down roughly at the scale of the photographs. On this the known ground-control points are laid down, and they will form the starting and end points of the radial-line plot. Then template after template is laid out, according to their principal points, until the whole assembly is ready; it can then be stretched or compressed to fit the end points on the base map. If the assembly is right, each side point should be at the intersection of at least three bars, and thus its actual location can be fixed.

Crude work always produces some inaccuracy. Minute accuracy in the handling of principal points is especially important. The slightest mistake there will be greatly enlarged at the side points. In general, however, radial-line plots are highly accurate, and thousands of square feet of terrain are laid out in photomapping establishments.

**Mosaics.** An airplane photograph rarely covers more than a few square miles, and if we want to see in a single picture a larger area, such as a city, an irrigation project, etc., we paste several pictures together into a mosaic. This assembly of matched pictures can be rephotographed to any desired scale and used as some kind of map without lettering.

Good mosaics are not easy to make. The chief difficulty is the variation in the scale of the pictures. This may be caused by mountainous terrain or by a change in the plane's level, as the barometric altimeter is influenced by changes in weather. Tilt will also change the scale within a single picture.

Displacement due to relief on the sides of the picture changes not only the scale of slopes but also their appearance.

The center portion of photographs is the best. To reduce the accumulation of scale errors, we start with the center picture of the mosaic. We featheredge it all around and paste it down on a board. We place the next picture over the first and trim off the half of the overlap, but do not trim the outer sides. This picture is featheredged in turn, and is pasted down with gum arabic. The excess paste is squeezed out away from the center with a roller, and is sponged. This process is repeated with every picture, proceeding in spirals away from the center and watching out for good color match. Trimming is usually made along edges of fields or woods. Roads are not suitable because they show up mismatches.

*Uncontrolled* mosaics are assembled from pictures as they come from a flight without trying to adjust them to some control. They cannot be too large because the errors accumulate, and it will be increasingly hard to match the pictures. The mosaic maker's chief concern is how to distribute the error. Wet pictures can be stretched a little by strong pull or reduced somewhat by bathing them in alum.

*Straight-line controlled* mosaics are laid out along straight roads or railroads giving them a kind of control.

In *controlled* mosaics a number of secondary control points are needed, at least three in each picture. The pictures are restituted in a rectifying printer for scale and tilt until they match the control. Secondary control can be obtained by radial-line plotting. No stretching or manipulation should be necessary to make perfect mosaics. The photomaps of the Corps of Engineers are photographs of controlled mosaics.

*Flight index assemblies* are made by pinning down each photo into a rough mosaic without trimming the pictures. They are so made that the number of each picture is visible. This is done after pictures of each photo flight are available in order to check coverage and to ascertain whether a reflight is needed.

A cartographer as well as a geographer studies mosaics with deep interest. The basic major patterns of the earth, which may not show well on a single picture, show up well on a mosaic, especially if reduced to smaller scale by rephotographing. Cartographers are looking forward to color mosaics in the near future. It is perhaps from these reduced color mosaics that the true visible line and color pattern of the earth will be disclosed.

**Multilens Aerosurveying.** Almost as soon as aerosurveying came into use, man started to experiment with several cameras permanently hitched together. The coverage of a vertical was small; when flying at a height of 2 miles a single picture covers only about 4 square miles. In contrast, an

**Fig. 168** The Bagley five-lens camera produces picture sets with a wide field and a long base line.

oblique picture covered an immense area. To combine the vertical with oblique and thus extend coverage was an obvious idea. At first one vertical and two side oblique cameras were made. It was soon found, however, that in radial-line plotting the short principal line was not strong enough to project very far sideways, and soon a fourth oblique camera appeared in the direction of flight to make a longer line. This was followed by the Bagley five-lens camera made by Fairchild, which for many years dominated the multilens field. The largest multilens camera is the nine-lens camera of the U.S. Coast and Geodetic Survey. This camera has nine lenses but with the help of mirrors, the nine images register on a single film, 23 inches square, corresponding to a picture with a 130° field. This camera, which weighs more than 300 pounds, and 750 pounds with all equipment, was used for charting coasts of the United States.

In all these systems the negatives of the oblique pictures are placed in a rectifying camera for printing so that the positive pictures are on the same scale with the vertical.

*The Trimetrogon System.* Millions of square miles have been mapped during and after the war with the trimetrogon camera. This camera makes one vertical and two oblique pictures with such a wide angle that the horizon is visible on both sides. The cameras are mounted with axes 60° tilted to each other, and the cameras have a field of somewhat larger angle so that there is some overlap between the vertical and the obliques. The pictures are 9 by 9 inches. If the region is not extremely mountainous and if the flight is high enough, the visible horizons will give the tilt and tip. It is an interesting fact, however, that on most trimetrogon plots the tilt is not taken into consideration. Trimetrogon pictures are used mostly in rapid surveys of large areas since the flight lines can be laid out several times farther apart than by verticals only.

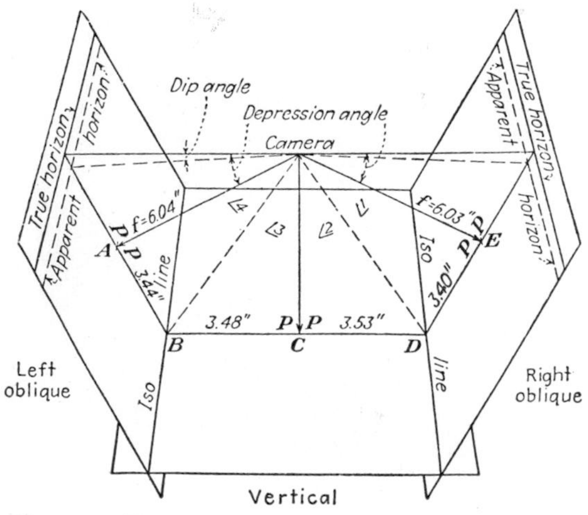


**Fig. 169** The trimetrogon system uses one vertical and two oblique wide-angle cameras, so that the three pictures reach from horizon to horizon.

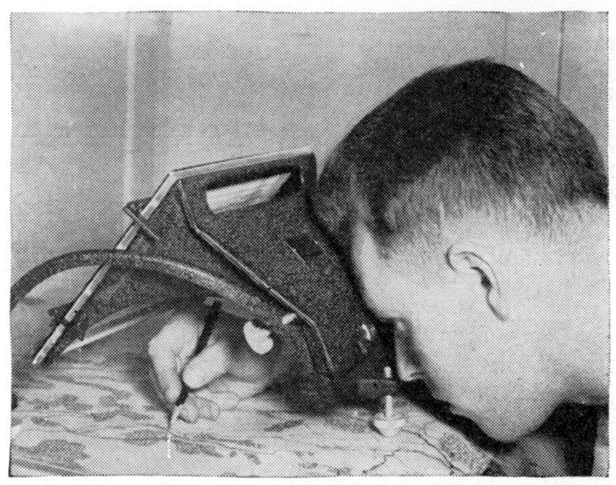

**Fig. 170** Detail from the oblique pictures can be transferred on the map with the help of the oblique sketch master. (*After Abrams.*)

Radial-line plotting of the side pictures does not require rectifying printing as do the usual multilens pictures. Instead, an ingenious instrument, the "rectoblique plotter," is used in plotting the map location of points on the obliques. The radial-line plots are made by slotted templates with much longer arms to include the points of the oblique, the location of which was obtained by the rectoblique plotter. As these points are likely to appear on the next flight strip too, good cross control is possible.

After the secondary control points have been located, the detail of the obliques can be sketched on a map with the help of a half-mirror arrangement with which the operator sees both the map and the oblique simultaneously. The instrument can be adjusted for tilt and scale to the available control points. The vertical pictures are adjusted with the help of the "vertical sketch master."

# CHAPTER 20: *Airplane Photo Interpretation*

A cartographer has to be able to read airplane photographs. Almost all large-scale maps at present are the result of airplane photography. To make a map from photographs requires more than the drawing of roads and houses. A practiced reader of photographs is able to read the vegetation and cultivation types, land-use patterns, and even the social conditions of the inhabitants of the region. Reading photographs is also a great inspiration to the map maker as the true pattern of the earth will guide him in the design of his maps, with better, truer, and more beautiful cartography as a result.

A vertical airplane photograph is a direct map picture of the earth; yet it is surprisingly difficult to read. One of the reasons is the absence of colors. The perfection of color photography will make photoreading considerably easier. More important, however, is the fact that the picture is thoroughly unfamiliar. Ordinarily no human being sees the land looking directly down, not even from a plane where he looks out at an oblique angle. It is no surprise that beginners can read an oblique picture easily while a vertical picture often has no meaning for them. The ability to read vertical pictures, like the ability to read a foreign language, is the result of systematic study.

In the analysis of an airplane photograph we have to follow a systematic set of considerations. This is not the case, however, if we do it all the time because recognition comes with experience. But if a feature is unfamiliar it is advisable to consider the following items step by step:

1. Size
2. Shape
3. Tone
4. Texture
5. Shadow and orientation
6. Approaches
7. Relationships

**1. Size.** To determine the size it is necessary first to establish the scale. This is often indicated on the photo, or it can be easily ascertained if the altitude of the plane and the focal length of the camera are known. If neither is known, the scale has to be found by other means. If there is a football stadium, baseball diamond, or tennis court in the picture, their size can be measured. West of the Alleghenies the section lines help to obtain not only the scale but also the orientation of the picture. The size of roads and houses help to differentiate between the half- and quarter-section lines from the full mile lines. Orchards are of great help if the customary planting distance is known (40 feet in New England apple orchards). If none of these features gives a clue, we have to fall back on smaller features. On railroads the average passenger car will be 80 to 90 feet long while a freight car is 40 feet. The average length of houses is also helpful; if the very large and very small ones are excluded, the length will be somewhere around 50 feet.

Width of roads, railroads, width of power lines (usually 100 feet), circumference of trees vary greatly, and yet they give enough of an allover pattern so that the reader is able, after some experience, to guess within 20 per cent the length of a mile on a photo. The problem, however, becomes increasingly different in foreign or uninhabited countries, and the standards worked out in the United States will not work in the Congo. Once the scale is established, a good look is taken at the size of roads, trees, houses, etc. This will help in the future.

**Fig. 171** Middle Western region with meandering river, dam, small town, farms, woodland, fairgrounds, etc.

**2. Shape.** This is the most obvious feature on a photograph. The ribbon of a road, the square of a house, or the outline of the crown of a tree will not be misread by anybody. Some other shapes, such as the greens and fairways of golf links, the shape of schoolhouses, etc., have to be learned. In general, man-made features have regular geometric shapes, while natural features have irregular shapes. It is the first rule of camouflage to give barracks, hangars, etc., an irregular outline to avoid detection. There are many exceptions. A quarry or dump can be highly irregular, while some clumps of bushes will be undistinguishable from houses.

**3. Tone.** In a photograph, we distinguish various shades of grey, the darkness of which depends solely on the amount of light which the surface will reflect upward at a given position of the sun. The tone may be very different at a different altitude of the sun. What makes photoreading difficult is the fact that this vertical reflection may be very different from the almost horizontal reflection, by which we ordinarily see the landscape. For us, water usually reflects the sun or the sky and is light-colored, usually lighter than land; in vertical photos water appears to be dark, often completely black, and is usually darker than the land (see Fig. 173). Muddy water, however, appears light-colored, and the photograph shows clearly where two kinds of water mix. Grass or grain if standing erect is gray; if, however, grass is trodden down, it will reflect upward and a light streak is clearly visible. It is hard to conceal movements of soldiers in a meadow.

A tarred road appears darker to us than a roadbed of a railroad, yet the loose gravel of the latter will absorb more light and on the photograph will appear darker than the road. Sand usually appears white in airplane photographs. The darkness of various fields differs greatly, depending on the stage of growth and the seasons; usually the higher crops grow the darker they get; yet fully ripened wheat is lighter colored than is half-grown wheat. Winter and spring pictures of deciduous forest are much lighter than in the summer.

The difference in color between wet and dry ground is remarkable, the wet ground being darker. This difference is caused not so much by presence of water as by darker soil and thicker growth on wet places.

**4. Texture.** This means the minor variations in tone and is the most revealing feature for land utilization. In the eastern United States the major land types are

*a.* Forest—appears roughly mottled
*b.* Bush—finely mottled
*c.* Rough pasture—smooth with dots (rocks and trees)
*d.* Hayfields—smooth
*e.* Plowed land—streaked
*f.* Orchards—checkered, regular patterned

*a. Forest* experts can tell from airplane photographs the composition and the age of a stand of timber, but a student does well if he can tell the evergreens from deciduous trees. In winter and spring, the difference, of course, is striking, but even in summer the evergreens appear darker. In winter and spring, if the sun is low, the deciduous forest gets a very streaky effect produced by the shadows of the trees. The even pattern of a planted forest is easy to recognize.

*b. Bush.* There are several kinds of bush. It can be a young forest. Every abandoned field in the East is bound to grow up into bush and later into forest. It depends on the person when to cease to call it bush and begin to call it forest. The bush may consist of some of the natural bushes that never grow into real trees, such as laurel, rhododendron, and juniper. These bushes will appear finely mottled all the year round. In parts of the eastern United States the herbaceous vegetation, such as asters, mulleins, and thistle grow to such proportions in summer and fall that it is impossible to tell them from real woody bushes, but in winter and spring they look like hayfields.

*c. Rough Pasture.* A great part of the country consists of grass or flowering plants mixed with bushes, trees, and rocks. The pictures will appear smooth or very finely mottled and will have darker spots on them, which represent the bushes and their shadows. Cow tracks will often show up in lighter lines. Rough pasture does not mean necessarily that it is always used for actual pasturing, but it is usually kept from growing up into forest by grazing animals. Sometimes, however, the natural combination of heath, moor, and scattered trees produces the same effect.

*d. Hayfields* are meadows where the grass is cut and grazed by animals. It can have a few bushes and trees, but if there are too many they would make it rough pasture. Hayfields look smooth in the photo; the darkness depends on the height of growth and the season. Often, however, hayfields are cut by machine and in this case they will have a very finely streaked appearance. Haystacks will usually be apparent on the side of the field toward the farmhouse.

*e. Plowed land* will have a dark and streaked appearance after plowing, but if grown up into wheat or small grain it is hard to tell it from hayfields. After the wheat is cut, the evenly placed shocks will reveal it. Corn, potatoes, cotton, tobacco, and vegetables have a distinctive pattern, and experts are able even to estimate the crop to be expected.

*f. Orchards* are the most easily identified because of their checkerboard pattern, and the expert can tell the kind of fruit grown from the distance between the individual trees. Vineyards are different according to the type of cultivation. Nurseries will look like miniature orchards.

Arid regions and tropical or arctic lands have different patterns. It would be beyond the limits of this book to give all the land types. The student is referred to the rich collection of airplane photographs of the Army Air Forces; these photographs are available to educational institutions for study.

**5. Shadows.** In a vertical airplane photo the chief indication of altitude of objects is their shadow. Indeed the pattern of shadows often more closely resembles the features as we are accustomed to see them than their shape from above. The shadow of a suspension bridge reveals it much more than its vertical picture does.

It matters a great deal whether the shadow is steep or slanting. Short shadows are preferred for mapping, and pictures are taken in the noon hours, because too much detail may be lost in the shadows. The interpreter, however, will prefer somewhat longer shadows, partly because this brings out the relief of the land, partly because it makes it easier to identify the smaller features.

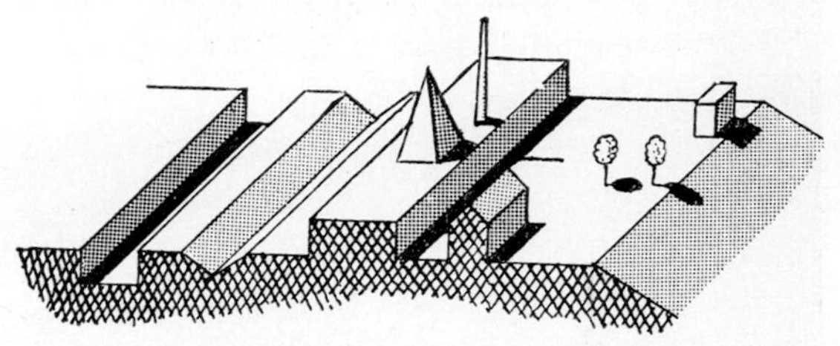

**Fig. 172** The length of shadow depends on the height of the object, the angle of the light, and the slant of the walls and ground.

First of all the angle of the shadows, or in other words the relation between the height of objects and the length of shadow, has to be ascertained. It is easy to see whether an average house or tree is higher or lower than the length of its shadow, but only if we have an object of known height can we be more exact. The height of a railroad car is 15 feet; the height of an office building is about 10 feet per story. Full-grown trees average 50 feet, but almost any other feature varies greatly in height. The best opportunity to obtain the angle of the shadow occurs when the sun is reflected in a body of water, in which case the water appears white instead of the usual black.

If the shadow is outside the object, the object is raised; if it is inside, as in a trench, it is depressed. Only the shadows of nearly vertical objects can be used for altitude determination. Shadows on slopes show false heights, as can be seen in Fig. 172, and only those shadows can be considered which fall on apparently flat ground.

Shadows also help in the orientation of pictures. In middle latitudes, if the shadows

**Fig. 173** Airplane photograph of parts of Framingham and Southborough, Mass.

are short, the sun will be near south. In fall and winter pictures, the shadows can be longer; yet they point north.

If the date, hour, and latitude of the picture are known, the length of the shadow can be determined from a solar ephemeris giving the altitude of the sun.

With a stereoscope and a pair of pictures, the height relationships are obvious and heights can be determined. In most stereoscopes, however, height is exaggerated.

**6. Approaches.** The size of the various features is indicated by the approaches to them. A house or a farm must have a driveway. A house in a forest is often invisible and can be located only by the road leading to it. Abandoned houses can be located by overgrown driveways, etc. The density of the road system is in proportion to the amount of settlement. A railway can often be differentiated from a road, as a road is connected with houses by driveways, while a railroad is not. A plowed or cut field will have a road leading to it, while pastured land needs only a trail. A quarry can be identified as a depression with a road leading into it at its lower end, and a factory usually has a railroad siding. Common sense is the best guide in using the approaches for identification. Camp positions, gun emplacements, etc., are usually well camouflaged in war, and their presence is much more often detected by the trails leading to them than by the sight of the features themselves. It is difficult to conceal approaches especially in snow.

**7. Relationships.** The relationship of buildings, gardens, open spaces, and roads will often enable us to recognize features. For instance, if there is a large building set back from the road, in a light-colored yard with a baseball diamond on it, this is the typical setup of a schoolhouse and it can be recognized. A set of even buildings laid out according to a plan centered on a larger building with a garden in between and a low building with a tall chimney at one side is the typical layout of a hospital. Closely spaced small roads are characteristic of a cemetery. The relation of greens, fairways, and sand traps will reveal golf links. Near reservoirs we look for aqueducts. If a cut in a forest points to a dam it may be assumed that there is a power line. Business sections of a city are characterized by closely parked automobiles. Closely packed small houses indicate second-class residential districts; larger houses farther apart outside the center of smaller cities indicate first-class residential districts. Military barracks, railroad buildings, factories, and colleges all have their characteristic pattern and can be identified by an observant interpreter. It is here that experience combined with intelligence will count most. It was of historical significance when a sharp-eyed interpreter discovered a small black streak beyond an airplanelike structure in Penemünde, Germany, thus giving the British advanced knowledge of the robot bomb.

Unfortunately the half-tone reproduction of the airplane photo shown in Figs. 171 and 173 is far less clear than is the original photograph, and yet the student should try to identify the marked features without looking at the explanation below.

---

*Explanation for Fig. 173:* 1. Railway; 2. Cut (shadow inside); 3. Fill and overpass (shadow outside); 4. Deciduous forest (coarsely mottled); 5. Coniferous forest (much darker than deciduous forest, indicating that picture was taken in spring); 6. Bush (finely mottled); 7. Mixed forest; 8. Rough pasture (smooth with dots); 9. Hayfield (smooth); 10. Plowed land (streaked); 11. Orchard (trees 40 feet apart); 12. Nursery (trees 20 feet apart); 13. Farm buildings; 14. Small farm; 15. Residence with tennis court; 16. Concrete four-lane highway; 17. Asphalt two-lane highway; 18. Dirt road; 19. Red light on main highway; 20. Aqueduct; 21. Dam with spillway; 22. Reservoir; 23. Creek; 24. Swamp; 25. Drainage ditch; 26. Stone fence; 27. Power line; 28. Abandoned gravel pit; N̄. North; $D_1$ and $D_2$ Drumlins.

In this part are discussed the maps that will serve as main reference material for cartographers, such as topographic maps, charts, atlases, and the usual maps prepared by professional cartographic establishments. The maps used by the various branches of the sciences, however, are discussed in a later part of the book.[1]

---

# CHAPTER 21: *Government Maps*

Government mapping started with the great national surveys of the eighteenth century. This was an age of almost continuous warfare on a large scale, and the movements of troops had to be planned ahead and exactly coordinated. This would have been impossible without adequate maps. The Dutch maps of the seventeenth century were not exact enough; the Amsterdam map makers were businessmen—they had to turn out maps cheaply, and the cheapest way to produce maps is to copy or compile them from other maps, with incidental improvements. No actual measurement of land was used in making them.

To measure the land was not a new idea. The principle of triangulation was known in the early sixteenth century; yet the instruments for measuring angles were still imperfect. It was not until the middle of the eighteenth century that the invention of telescopic instruments and the persistent effort and genius of Cesar F. Cassini carried through the first great national survey, resulting in the Carte Géométrique de la France. The story of this great survey has been told in Chap. 4.

To make an exact detailed map of a country it is necessary first to triangulate the outstanding points and then to fill in the detail by plane table. This work is obviously beyond the capacity of the individual, and therefore the organized effort of a group of people is necessary. Since the army was the chief recipient of such maps, it was only natural that the great national surveys should be organized by the general staffs of the various powers. Surveying of the terrain was a most appropriate peacetime occupation for the officers of the army.

By the middle of the nineteenth century every civilized country had its detailed topographic maps, and in the second half of the century the work was carried over into the less civilized parts of the world and into the colonial possessions. At the present time almost the entire world has some kind of survey, even if it cannot be classified with the high-grade surveys of the leading countries. Figure 174 shows the progress of surveys of the various parts of the world.

Although originally topographic maps were made for military purposes, they were

[1] NOTICE TO THE INSTRUCTOR: If the continuity of the laboratory work demands, this part may be taken up later, after the discussion of Statistical Maps and Cartograms in Part Seven.

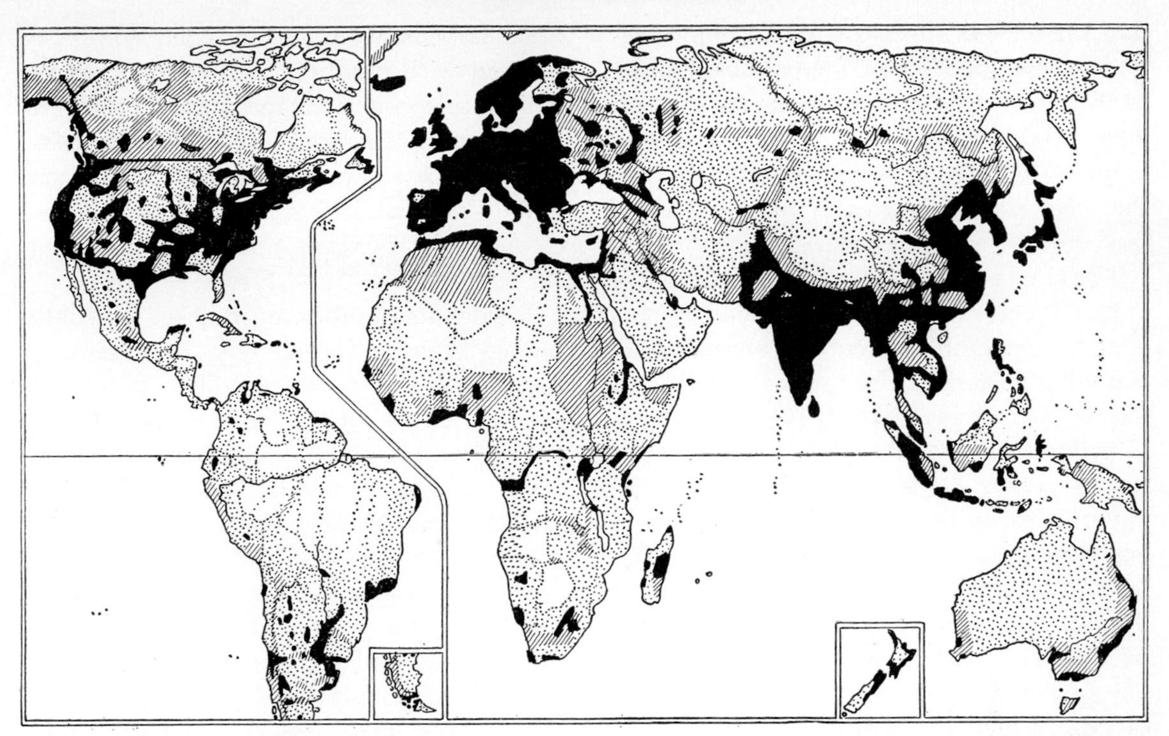

**Fig. 174** Progress of topographic mapping of the world. The darker the shading, the more detailed are the maps. (*Modified after Ray R. Platt.*)

found to have many other uses. Engineers, geologists, foresters, tourists, and others found these maps indispensable; so governments undertook to make them even where the military necessity was less important, as in the United States. With the expansion of the functions of government, many governmental departments found that they could best serve their public by making special surveys, and they now produce climatic, geological, economic, and other such maps. At the present time, the government is the chief producer of maps in almost every country.

## Topographic Sheets

The most important maps of various governments are the large-scale general maps that are published in sections called "topographic sheets."

**Scale.** The scale of these topographic sheets must be large enough so that every hill can be recognized. The land is usually surveyed on plane-table sheets, 1:20,000 or 1:25,000, or photographed on an even larger scale, but the published maps are usually reduced. Most European topographic sheets are on the scale 1:25,000 to 1:100,000; in England the mile-to-an-inch scale (1:63,360) was adopted. The scale of the U.S. Geological Survey topographic sheets is slightly different, 1:62,500 and 1:125,000. Less developed countries use smaller scales. The maps of some parts of Canada have a scale of only 8 miles to the inch. Large tracts of Brazil have maps only on the scale of 1:1,000,000; and even the United States has parts of which topographic maps of no larger scale than 1:500,000 are published. It is important that the scale of sheets should be in proportion to the capacity of the country. Many nations adopted too ambitious scales, and were unable to finish, *i.e.*, the 1:100,000 maps of Mexico. It is much better to vary the scale according to the development of the country, as in Canada.

*Division into Sheets.* The size of the individual sheet varies. With the small presses of the nineteenth century, the sheets rarely exceeded folio size. The German 1:100,000 Reichskarte sheets had only 10½ by 13 inches of printed surface. The present tendency is toward larger sheets. With fast automobiles one may easily cover the width of a sheet in less than a half hour, and a constant changing of sheets is wearisome. The upper limit of sheet size is now determined not so much by the size of the printing presses as by the size of the usual library files, which rarely exceed 42 inches in width.

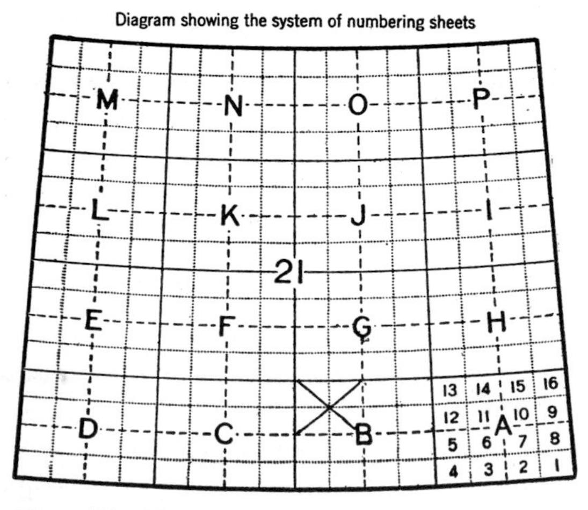


**Fig. 175** Numbering system of the Canadian National Topographic series. The number of the crossed map is 21 $\frac{\text{B}}{\text{NW}}$.

*Numbering of Sheets.* The simplest method of naming sheets is according to their central parallel and meridian. This, however, is rarely done because of the complex figures of degrees, minutes, and seconds. It is much more common to name the sheets after an east-west and a north-south sequence, with numbers and letters. Complications arise when the maps are on different scales, and fractions have to be used. Figure 175 shows the numbering system of the Canadian sheets, in which the marked sheet is numbered "21 $\frac{\text{B}}{\text{NW}}$."

Besides its number, each sheet is usually named after its largest city, mountain, or most characteristic feature. The U.S. Geological Survey sheets have no numbering system, and hence have to be arranged by states alphabetically by name. To have adjacent sheets far apart, sometimes in different folders, is not convenient.

The United States government adopted a general indexing system for all topographic sheets of the world designating the latitude and longitude of the corner nearest the crossing of the equator and the prime meridian, adding the size of the map by degrees and minutes. Thus the U.S. Geological Survey quadrangle sheet of Boston, Mass., is indexed as N 4215-W7100/15′, which locates its lower right-hand corner. In an Australian sheet the upper left-hand corner would be noted.

**Projection.** The problem of projections for topographic sheets is not important, for the small area covered by them differs very little from the plane. Any projection which is true to scale in its central part is good. The most commonly used projections for topographic sheets are the polyconic, the polyhedric, the Bonne, and the various conic projections. Since each topographic sheet has its own central meridian and standard parallel, only a limited number of sheets can be assembled. Small countries use with advantage the conic projection, by which all sheets can be assembled and pasted together. In this case the entire set has one or two standard parallels, and there is a slight variation in scale. The older French

1:80,000 sheets were on a Bonne projection designed for the whole country. This was cut into even rectangles, so that the border of most sheets intersected the parallels and meridians at oblique angles.

**Symbols.** The symbols of topographic sheets were crystallized for centuries and were changed only when new engraving methods allowed greater freedom. For instance, since the introduction of color printing, hachure lines are replaced by contours, and often plastic shading is added to make the maps more easily understood by the public. Especially important is the addition of land use and vegetation symbols on the most modern maps.

The symbol system of each topographic series is usually given on a separate sheet, but since people rarely take the trouble to refer to this sheet, it is more useful to have the unusual symbols indicated in the margin on each map.

**Lettering.** Lettering is a real problem on topographic sheets, for it may obscure important land forms. On modern maps the lettering is simple and is relatively small. The new French 1:50,000 maps have adopted a sans-serif, block lettering. The large lettering may be left off altogether and the names of political divisions can well go on a small inset map, as is done on the 1:1,000,000 map of the world. On the older British Ordnance Survey maps the large letters are often interrupted and crossed by small lettering. The subject of lettering on topographic sheets is analyzed in great detail in Capt. J. G. Withycombe's article, Lettering on Maps, *The Journal of Geography*, 1928, pp. 429–446.

**Marginal Information.** As the entire area inside the borders is occupied on topographic sheets, all titles and explanatory material are outside the borders. Title, number, scale, true and magnetic north, date of survey, name of surveyor, and index

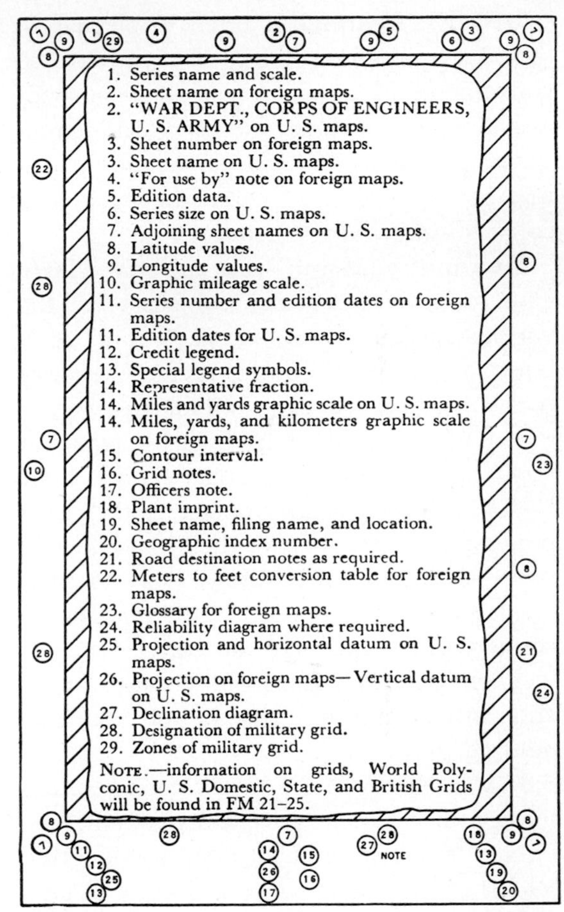


**Fig. 176** Marginal information gives useful data for the use of the maps. (*From TM* 21-30, *United States Army*.)

to adjacent sheets are the most important trimmings. The tendency is for more and more marginal information, and a key to symbols, a glossary, and grid information are usually added on modern maps.

It adds greatly to the educational value of topographic sheets if their reverse side is utilized for descriptive material. A short geographic summary, supplemented by a small geological map, sections, block diagrams, and pictures, are very helpful in understanding the nature of the land, even for those who are less versatile in reading contour lines. This is used to great advantage on some of the topographic sheets of the national parks. This supplementary, descriptive material is often published in separate pamphlets, but this is not so convenient. The surveying party spent considerable time in the area and could easily provide a description including human occupation that would be most welcome to everybody.

**Extranational and International Maps.** The topographic sheets published by the various nations often extend beyond their boundaries. Any country prefers to carry the war outside its own boundaries; hence, it is more interested in maps of the adjacent territory than of its own. Indeed, some Near East countries seriously object to the mapping of their domains, for their chief defense is the difficult terrain known only to their own men. It has been said that every country is mapped for the convenience of its enemies. In all European countries forts and other military works are carefully omitted from maps.

It was chiefly the military consideration that prompted some governments to include foreign territories in their topographic series. Such famous sets of maps are those of central Europe and the Balkans (1:200,000), published by both Germany and Austria, and those of the Balkans and the Near East (1:250,000), published by Great Britain.

The British Geographical Section of the General Staff and L'Institute Géographique National (Paris) are especially active in publishing international maps. The new airway maps of our Army Map Service cover the whole world.

Truly international are the maps prepared by the cooperation of different countries. The most important international map is the "International Map of the World, 1:1,000,000" which was discussed in Chap. 3.

**Military Grid System.** During the First World War it was found that reference to locations and directions was too complex in our usual system of parallels and meridians, recorded in degrees, minutes, and seconds of unequal lengths. For this reason the French overprinted a network of even kilometer squares upon their maps, in which quadrillage each line was numbered from a zero point in the southwest of the war zone.

Such a system apparently has many disadvantages. First of all, the so-called "grid north" may be many degrees off from the true north. Then, too, the grid coordinates of a certain locality are true only on one set of maps and are not true on another set on another projection. It must be kept in mind, also, that the squares of the grid are not exactly square on the earth's surface, and their actual shape and size are different and dependent upon the projection system of the map.

Against these serious objections stands the advantage of easy reckoning. Each point can be exactly located by the use of a printed celluloid sheet that can be placed on any of the squares. For instance, in the French kilometric quadrillage a certain point can be marked as "142.23/231.86"; this means that it is 142.23 kilometers east and 231.86 kilometers north of the zero point—not in actual distance and direction but in the grid system of the map. In actual use they drop the hundreds and hundredths of the kilometers, so that the foregoing location symbol reads as "422-318," which determines the location within a hundred meters.

The U.S. Coast and Geodetic Survey, together with the Corps of Engineers, developed a grid system for the United States. Since the country is too large for a single grid system, it was divided into seven zones, as shown in Fig. 177. Each zone includes 9° of longitude of which 1° on each side overlaps the adjacent zones. In these overlapping sections it must be definitely indicated whether the zone east or west thereof is used for the location of points. The grid system is based upon a quadrillage of 1,000 yards. This system is described in *U.S. Coast and Geodetic Survey Special Publication* 59. For each grid zone a polyconic projection was drawn with a maximum scale error of only ½ per cent. The 1,000-yard squares were laid out starting at the intersection of the central meridian with parallel 40°30′. To avoid negative coordinates, in actual reckoning a point 2,000,000 yards south and 1,000,000 yards west was chosen as the origin of the "false" coordinates. Thus a point referred to as 865.925-2172.142 Zone B will be somewhere near Detroit. (Such detailed reference is rare. Actually in a given area 65.9-72.1 will fix the location of point *D* within a hundred yards.) The grid north may deviate from true north about 3° at most. These grid squares are marked on the margins on all new topographic sheets.

Several states have their own grid systems; thus on many maps we have four coordinate systems, the parallels and meridians, the United States grid, the state grid, and the sections and townships of the Public Land Survey, which is also a kind of grid system. The great extension of grid systems all the world over is described in Chap. 24.

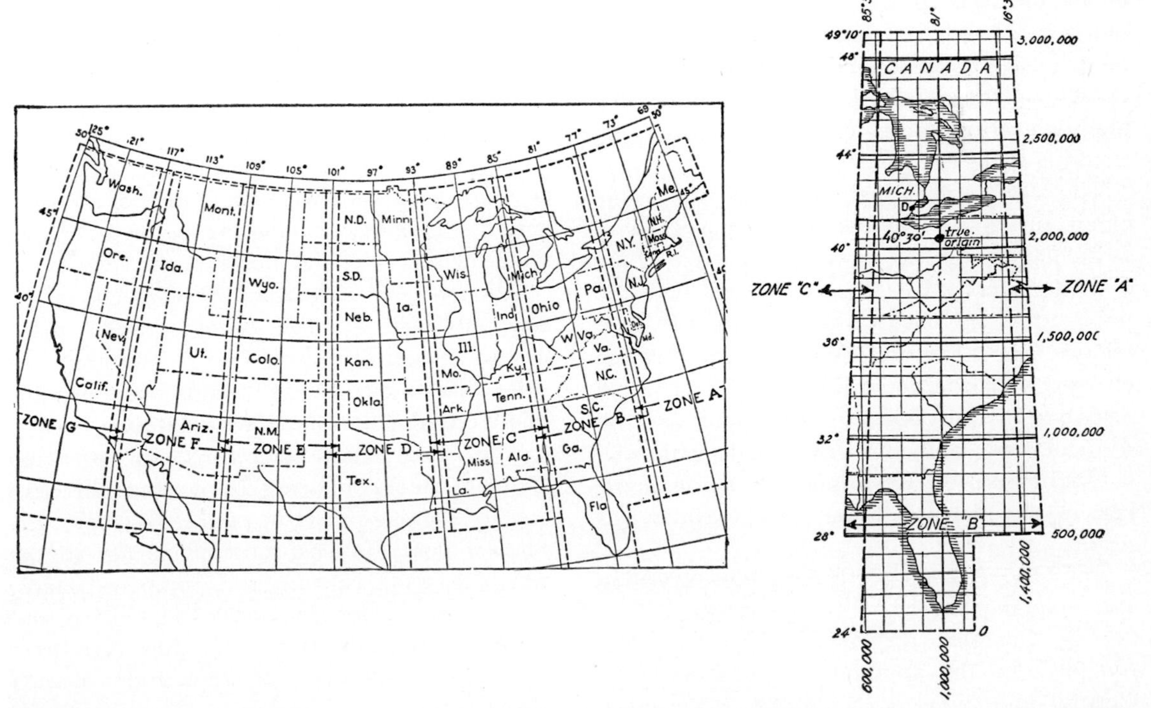


**Fig. 177** Progressive military grid of the United States. In Zone B (right) the coordinates of point *D* 865.9-2172.1 fix it within 100 yards.

## Other Government Maps

Even before the war, in the United States no less than 24 Federal offices, belonging to every branch of the administration, published maps regularly. The Map Information Office of the U.S. Geological Survey can be consulted about government maps. When the enormous production of the Army Map Service, the Office of Strategic Services, the Navy, and Air Forces, and other war agencies is added to this, the output of government maps runs into unprecedented figures.

The most important government mapping agencies are listed below as quoted from a statement of the Map Information Office:

The *Geological Survey* is the most productive of the mapping organizations, for it is engaged in making the basic topographic map of the entire area of the United States. It is also engaged in making a geologic map of the United States and Alaska, involving both topographic and geologic surveys. In conducting investigations relating to surface and underground waters, classifying the public lands, and supervising the engineering phases of mineral leasing, the resulting maps are incidental.

The *Coast and Geodetic Survey* is one of the oldest surveying bureaus of the government. It is charged with the survey of the coasts of the United States and its possessions and with the publication of navigational charts of these regions. The Coast and Geodetic Survey is also charged with the determination of geographic positions by astronomic observations and by triangulation and traverse, and with the determination of elevations by spirit leveling, in the interior of the United States and Alaska.

The *General Land Office* is the oldest surveying and mapping bureau of the government. The act of Congress approved May 18, 1796, provided for the appointment of a Surveyor General and directed the survey of the lands northwest of the Ohio River. A subsequent act of Congress, approved April 25, 1812, provided for the establishment of a General Land Office under the direction of a commissioner. This bureau makes rectangular surveys of the public lands. These are published in the form of township plats. The bureau issues annually a wall map of the United States, showing the extent of the public surveys; national parks; national monuments; national forests; Indian, military, bird, and game reservations; and other useful information. It also issues maps of the 29 public-land states, Alaska, and Hawaii.

The *Hydrographic Office* is charged with topographic and hydrographic surveys in foreign waters and on the high seas, and in the preparation and printing of maps and charts required in navigation on those waters.

The *Corps of Engineers* makes special topographic maps of areas of military importance, and has made topographic maps of a few quadrangles not surveyed by the Geological Survey, besides revising some of the older topographic maps of the Geological Survey.

The *Forest Service* publishes general geographic maps of national forests and topographic maps of portions of them.

The *Bureau of Reclamation* publishes topographic maps of many of the federal irrigation projects.

The *Office of Indian Affairs* has mapped portions of the Indian reservations.

The *Mississippi River Commission* has published a series of maps showing the profile of the river and the topography along the shores, extending from the source to the mouth of the river.

The *International (Canada) Boundary Commission* has published a series of topographic maps extending approximately 1 to 10 miles on each side of the United States-Canada boundary line and along the east boundary of Alaska.

The *Lake Survey* publishes hydrographic charts of the Great Lakes for navigational uses.

The *Topography Branch* of the *Post Office Department* compiles post-route maps for all the states, Alaska, Hawaii, the Samoan Islands, Guam, Canal Zone (Panama), Puerto Rico, and the Virgin Islands. It also compiles rural-free-delivery maps of many of the counties in each of the states.

The *Bureau of Chemistry and Soils* publishes maps which show the character of the soils in the areas covered. A single soil map will usually cover the area of a county.

The *Bureau of Public Roads* publishes maps of the United States, showing the Federal aid system of highways, and also maps of some of the states, carrying more detailed information of the same character.

The *Soil Conservation Service* is engaged in the production of planimetric maps compiled from aerial photographs.

The *Tennessee Valley Authority* prepares maps of the Tennessee watershed.

*National Resources Committee* sponsors various regional and state planning organizations the publications of which contain important map material.

If we add to the maps described on the previous pages the multitude of maps published by states, counties, and cities, and by semiofficial bodies, such as the National Geographic Society, the American Geographical Society, the Pan American Highway Commission, and Carnegie Institution, we can appreciate the magnitude of official cartography of a single country. Since a proportionate amount of official maps are published by other countries, we can assume that official cartography is producing more and more important maps at the present time than private industry. The changes brought forth by the Second World War are discussed in Chap. 24.

## Important Topographic Maps of the World

The list of important topographical maps of the various countries that was published in the first edition of this book is now omitted for two reasons. (1) The postwar reorganization of the topographic surveys and the new sets of airphoto-based maps did not crystallize enough so that a new list could be made. (2) The Army Map Service and other government agencies supply a rich coverage of foreign countries, which satisfies the map demands of American colleges, and therefore it is seldom necessary to go to the original sources.

# CHAPTER 22: *Charts*

The history of charts is as old as the history of land maps. Lists and descriptions of ports (which may originally have been accompanied by charts) have come down to us from as early as the fifth century B.C. The charts of the great Phoenician navigator, Marinus of Tyre, of about A.D. 100, were frequently quoted by Ptolemy. The magnificent portolan charts of the fourteenth century were based on compass surveys, as described in detail in Chap. 1. The first important atlas of charts, Waghenaer's "Spiegel der Zeevaerdt," was published in 1584. In the seventeenth and eighteenth centuries, chart making was a lucrative business—first centered in Amsterdam and later in Paris and London. The Hydrographical Office of the British Admiralty was established in 1795; and similar offices were established by other maritime nations. The U.S. Coast Survey was founded in 1807, but its first charts did not appear until 1844. The U.S. [Navy] Hydrographic Office dates from 1866, and it provides charts of foreign coasts.

At the present time most of the world's coasts are sufficiently surveyed for the publication of some kind of charts, but only a comparatively small part of the world's coast has been surveyed in detail. The most complete and up-to-date sets of charts are published by the British Admiralty and by the U.S. Hydrographic Office.

**Surveys.** Enormous advancements in marine surveys are at the disposal of the chart maker at the present time. The 60° astrolabe makes it possible to fix the latitude and longitude of a location within a few hundred feet. Triangulation and leveling, using the old principles but with better instruments, measure positions along the coast, and airplane photographs help in filling in detail. The greatest advancements, however, are in submarine topography. It is no longer necessary to lower heavy weights on piano wire, taking hours for each sounding, for the fathometer records the depth of the deepest ocean in a few seconds with great accuracy. This is a sonic or supersonic device; a "ping" is echoed from the sea bottom, and the interval of time is measured. The exact distance can be calculated by considering the density of sea water and the corresponding velocity of sound. There are fathometers that draw a continuous profile of the bottom as the ship moves along. In the case of a steeply sloping bottom, the sound will reflect somewhat sideways, and in narrow straits the device may not work at all and it may then be necessary to resort to the weighted wire; but under normal circumstances the fathometer will give the skipper a very accurate idea of his location on a known course, as he can recognize "landmarks" at the sea bottom.

The fathometer is not sufficiently reliable in harbors, as it may miss a boulder or submarine pinnacle, which can rip open the bottom of vessels. Here the old wire drag is still the safest and most reliable method; this is greatly aided, however, by airplane photography. Airplane photographs penetrate clear water to about 100 feet, and an expert can read a great amount of detail. The depth of the water can be judged by the darkness and the type of vegetation or coral growth, and also by the displacement of shadow of wave crests. There are great expectations for the use of color photography in marine surveys. The color will not only give better indications of depth but will help in marine biological surveys and in determining the type of bottom, sand.

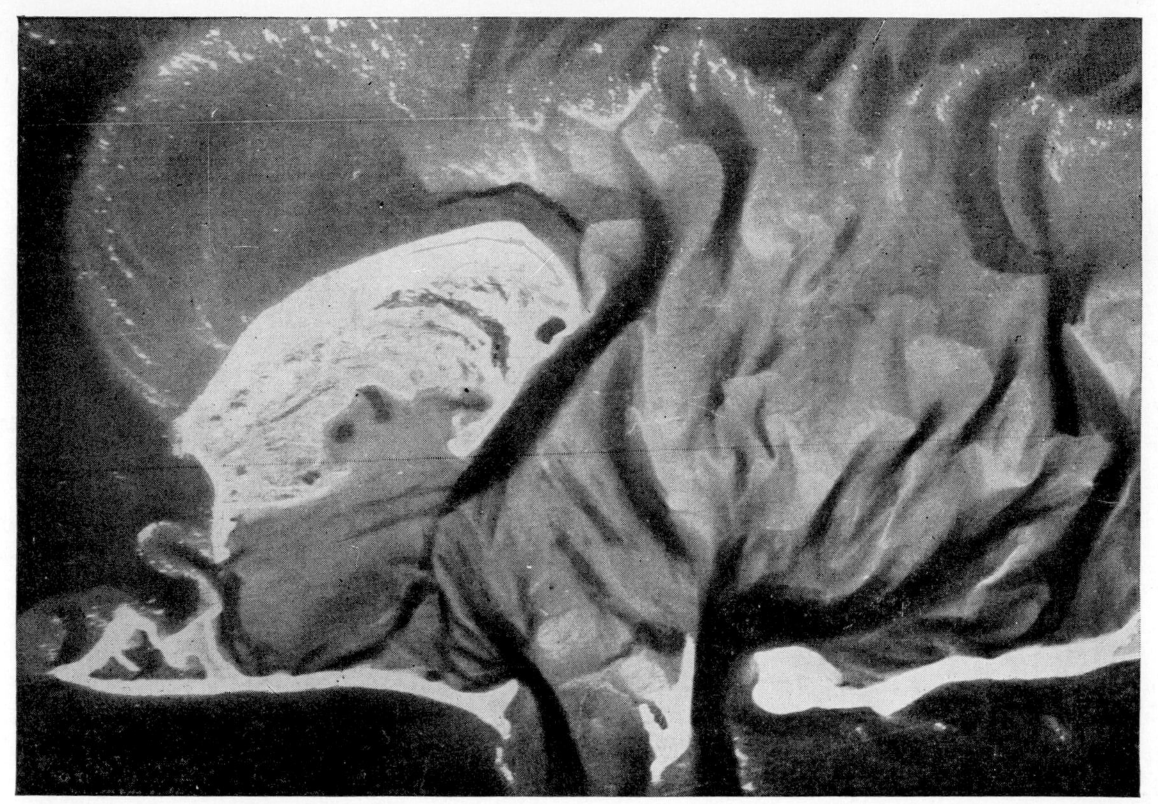

**Fig. 178** Submarine sand formations at Tuckernuck Island, Mass.

mud, gravel, rock, coral, seaweed, etc. Airplane photos have revealed rich patterns of types of sea bottom, many of which were hitherto unknown.

It is not enough for the surveying vessel to ascertain the depth; it has to know the exact location of the sounding. As long as charted points on the shore are visible, there is no difficulty. The ship measures the angle between three points and gets its own location by "resection." If the ship proceeds on a known course, the angle between the true course and a single point will give the location.

If the ship is out of sight of land, some special equipment has to be used. In coastal waters *radioacoustic* charting can be used. Sono-radio buoys are located along the shore at known and fixed intervals. The surveying ship throws a bomb into the sea. The sound travels to the shore and is picked up by the sono-radio buoys and is radioed back automatically to the ship. When the velocity of sound in water and the exact location of the buoys is known, a fix can be made.

Excellent results were obtained by using *shoran*, an all-radio instrument. The survey ship sends out short-wave signals that act as a key to release bursts of radio impulses from intermeasured and fixed shoran receiver-transmitter stations. The time lag of the return signal gives the distance, and direction can be obtained by intersection to another shoran station. As the short-wave signals do not follow the earth's curvature, shoran can be used for coastal surveys only. Airplanes, however, have used it up to 500 miles. It is the fastest method of getting a fix. The U.S. Coast and Geodetic Survey ship "Explorer" was able to get her position in 15 seconds.

Out in the open sea far from land the *loran* is the newest and most generally used device to establish the location of the ship. Loran stations are established all along the important coasts of the world, usually in the combination of one master station and one or two slave stations. The master station gives out an extremely short (40 microseconds) radio signal, which is followed by a signal from the slave station; both signals are picked up by the vessel. The time difference of the signals indicates that the ship must be along a parabolic line, which is indicated on a "loran chart." Another reading is taken from a second loran station, and the intersection of the two lines gives the fix. Positions obtained by loran in a few minutes time compare favorably with astronomical observations taken much more laboriously under average conditions.

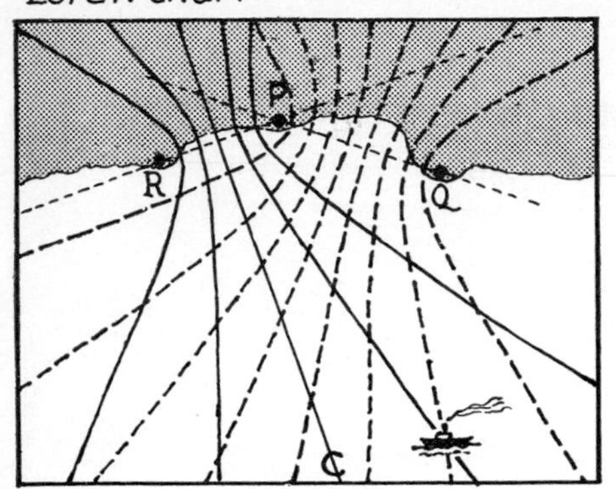


**Fig. 179** Loran charts give the location of a vessel by the time difference of radio signals from two pairs of stations. *P* is a double-pulsed master station. *R* and *Q* are slave stations.

Loran stations and loran charts now cover two-thirds of all oceans. An interesting development that has been made by the U.S. Coast and Geodetic Survey is the printing of the loran curves on the reverse side of the chart in mirrorlike fashion; the position is obtained by pricking through the paper to the regular chart.

**Scales and Projections.** Contrary to the uniform scale and size of topographic sheets, charts vary widely in both respects. Harbors and channels may be shown on a scale of 1:5,000 to 1:60,000; for well-frequented coasts 1:80,000 is the most common scale, and there are smaller scale charts in great variety. Most charts are in the Mercator projection because this is the only projection that shows rhumb lines (compass directions) as straight lines. Such charts are often not provided with graphic scales owing to the great variation in scale with the latitude. Degrees and minutes are recorded on the sides of the chart, and this can be used for scale by considering that 1 minute of latitude averages 1 nautical mile.

Gnomonic charts for plotting the great-circle routes of transoceanic travel are published for each ocean. As constant changing of the compass direction would be impractical for actual navigation with a ship's compass, these great-circle lines are transferred to a Mercator chart. The original plane-table surveys are usually plotted on polyconic base sheets. The U.S. Coast and Geodetic Survey often used the polyconic projection until recent years, when it partly changed to the Mercator projection in order to comply with the practice of other nations.

**Symbolism.** On many charts the land is left blank; only information pertaining to navigation (such as lighthouses, landmarks, and fresh water) are marked. Soundings are shown by numbers and by submarine contour lines. The 6-, 12-, and 18-foot contours are usually shaded. Contour intervals increase with depth, and contours are rarely shown below 100 fathoms. A recent tendency in charting is to show the configuration of the deep ocean bottom with greater detail, for this helps vessels to determine their locations with the help of echo-sounding instruments.

Much confusion is caused by the various units of depths. Greater depths are shown in fathoms, lesser depths in feet; it is important to note carefully which unit is used. Most non-English countries use the metric system. Uniformity of symbols and of units of length and the use of the same prime meridian on the various charts are highly desirable.

**Plane of Reference.** On the Atlantic and Gulf charts, depths are reckoned from the mean low-tide level. Pacific, Alaskan, and Philippine waters have a larger and smaller tide daily and the soundings are measured from the mean of lower low waters. In Puget Sound a plane 2 feet lower still has been adopted, because of the variability of low tide in the Sound. Usually the datum plane is chosen so that it lies from 1 to 2 feet above extreme low water. Strong offshore winds and unusually high barometric pressure may cause still lower levels. In the Atlantic, even unusually low tides rarely fall below 1 foot of the reference plane.

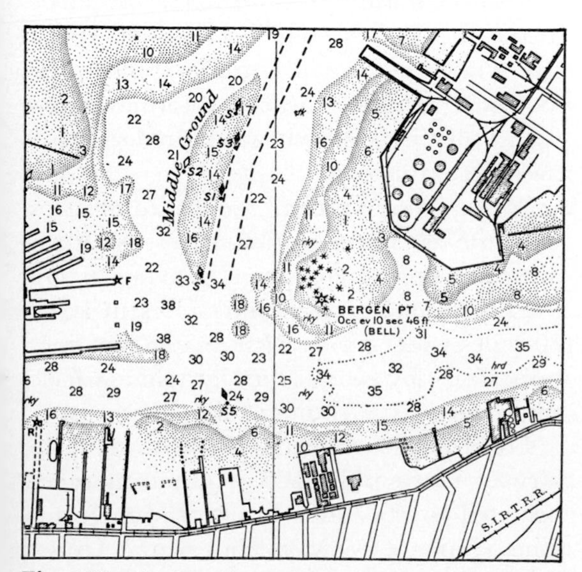


**Fig. 180** Section of a marine chart. (*After Deetz.*)

Heights on land are generally reckoned from mean high-water level, because usually this line is clearly visible on the shore; sometimes, however, the mean tide level is used in accordance with the topographic sheets.

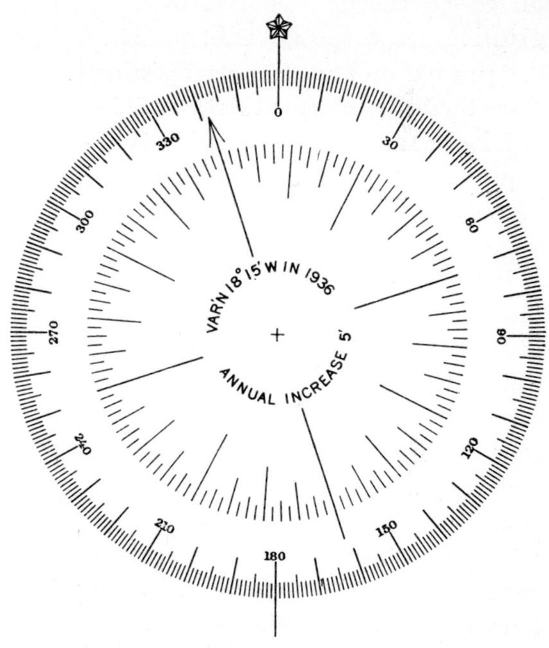


**Fig. 181** Compass roses on charts usually have two dials. The outer dial has north at 0 and is divided into degrees. The inner dial, starting with compass north, is divided into quarters of points (1 point = 11°15′).

Charts as a rule contain information as to the nature of the tides and currents. Usually several compass roses are printed on charts. The compass roses have two dials; the outer dial is reckoned from the true north and is divided into degrees; the inner dial shows magnetic north and is divided into points (11°15′). In recent navy charts they are also in degrees. Isogonic lines which show the variation of magnetic north are also recorded on charts, so that the navigator should have no difficulty in finding his true bearings.

The life of a chart is short. The rapidly expanding aerial surveys, the multitude of echo soundings, the installation of new aids to navigation, the constant dredging of harbors, and natural changes in sandy shores soon make a chart obsolete and require new editions. For this reason, charts are rendered in a simpler manner than topographic sheets. Colors are rarely used on charts except as flat tints or for overprinting some special information. Charts are printed on heavy, water-resisting paper; thus they are more expensive. The sheets are large, averaging 2 by 3 feet, for convenience in plotting. Large steamers contain separate chartrooms for the storing of a full set of charts for every eventuality.

**Pilot Charts.** The monthly Pilot Charts published by the Hydrographic Office in cooperation with the Weather Bureau contain a wealth of information. Winds, currents, magnetic lines, storm trails, radio stations, fog conditions, floating derelicts, icebergs, etc., are recorded on a separate chart for each ocean. On the reverse of these charts scientific essays of interest to navigators provide profitable reading during the long hours at sea. Pilot charts that show conditions of the upper air are helpful in long-range weather forecasting.

**Lake and River Surveys.** The United States Survey of the Northern and Northwestern Lakes was inaugurated in 1841, at a time when steamers and schooners on the Great Lakes carried thousands of settlers into the new northwestern territory. At present about 125 charts of the Great Lakes, Lake Champlain, the New York canals, and the Lake of the Woods are published by the Corps of Engineers in polyconic projection, and are obtainable from the U.S. Lake Survey Office (Detroit, Mich.). These charts are prepared in the same manner as the Coast Survey charts.

**Mississippi River Survey.** The survey of this great, ever-changing river is a problem that requires constant attention. Since the Young Survey in 1821, the river has repeatedly been mapped in detail. Especially famous is the "Delta Survey," completed in 1861. In 1870, several survey parties of Army Engineers, of the Coast Survey, and of the Lake Survey worked on the river simultaneously. Their efforts were unified by the creation of the Mississippi River Commission in 1870, with a central office in Vicksburg, Miss. This commission's 1:20,000 map of the river was completed in 1894. Since then the constantly changing river has been resurveyed repeatedly, with resultant overprints to the map. In 1928, in connection with the flood-control project, a new set of maps of the entire valley was issued. These were similar in style and system to the topographic sheets of the U.S. Geological Survey. The commission has a large, functional relief model of the Mississippi River at Vicksburg.

**Air-navigation Charts or Airway Maps.** In the last decades a very important group of maps has appeared—those to serve air traffic. Most airway maps are 1:500,000 in scale and are drawn on the Lambert conformal, conic projection, which combines straight azimuths with small scale error. These maps show roads, railroads, rivers, cities, landmarks, and altitudes, with 1,000-foot contour intervals. All information for flying, airports, radio beacons, and signals is overprinted in red.

Some airway maps are published in strips, with the air route in the center, whatever direction that may be. These strips are usually 10 inches wide and represent a belt 80 miles wide. Strips without contour lines, published by the Hydrographic Office, show the coastal routes of the Americas.

From a geographer's point of view the airway maps published in uniform sheets oriented to the north are more important. The Sectional Airway Map of the United States (1:500,000), published by the U.S.

Department of Commerce, is one of the most important modern maps of the country. It is only to be regretted that the wide contour interval of 1,000 feet makes this map less useful for geographical purposes.

During the Second World War the use of aeronautical charts rose to previously unheard-of proportions. Airmen had to fly over the Sahara and the Chinese-Tibetan borderland and air maps were lacking. The U.S. Army and Navy, and the British offices, set to work to produce these charts in the shortest possible time. There was not much time for experimenting to find the best type of chart. The only major change in the prewar type of cartography was the adoption of an odd-looking color scheme for night flying and the use of luminescent paper or of fluorescent paints.

Long-range charts for celestial navigation prepared by the Aeronautical Chart Service of the Army Air Forces cover the earth on 1:3,000,000 on Mercator projection. Pilotage charts to be used on the planes for contact flying are 1:1,000,000 on the Lambert conformal conic projection, except for an 8° belt around the equator, which is in Mercator, and the polar regions N or 72°, which are on the stereographic projection. The lands of the earth are covered by 1,172 charts. Europe, North America, and Eastern Asia have 1:500,000 maps too, and a 1:250,000 Approach Chart is well advanced. Add to this the 1:125,000 and larger target charts, loran charts, "low-visibility" charts, radar charts, etc., and we gain an idea of the enormous magnitude of aeronautical charting in recent years. Strikingly successful are the 1:1,000,000 radar navigation charts in gray or sepia half-tone shaded relief.

As time goes on, more and more pilots and navigators feel that the usual type of pilotage chart could be improved. The main problem is that the colors for altitude tints are not easily discerned in variable lighting conditions, and some think that many crashes could have been avoided if the pilot had read the tints correctly. It is also felt that the color scheme of charts has little relationship to the landscape below, and typical landmarks, such as cliffs, hollows, buttes, etc., are not sufficiently shown. It is possible to conceive a chart where the heights of peaks are indicated by bold numbers to the next hundred feet. A peak 6,252 feet high would be marked as 63. Colors could indicate field, forest, pasture, desert, etc. Relief could be indicated by plastic shading and landmarks by landform symbols. Interesting experiments have been made by all the large mapping agencies, and it is hoped that a better type of aeronautical chart will create an entirely new style in cartography.

# CHAPTER 23: *Private Maps*

In this chapter we deal with maps that are produced for profit by private concerns. To be profitable such maps must be produced cheaply and satisfy a widespread demand. A map publisher naturally prefers not to engage in expensive land surveys or researches, but to get his material by compilation from existing maps. A commercial map must be attractive in appearance and easily understandable, and is likely to be decorative.

**Atlases.** Official topographic surveys are published by the various governments on different scales, in different projections, with different symbols, and in different languages, and are generally on too large a scale for general demand. A collection of maps, usually bound together, published in one language, with uniform symbols and projections but not necessarily in uniform scale, is called an "atlas." The name is derived from the mythical Greek god who holds the Earth upon his shoulders, a picture of whom often decorated the title pages of Renaissance atlases. The first known atlas was the 28-page work of Ptolemy. No real atlases were made in the Middle Ages. The fifteenth-century editions of Ptolemy with their "Tabulae Modernae" were the forerunners of modern atlases, which perhaps start with the Theatrum Orbis Terrarum of Ortelius, 1570. The following century was the golden age of grand atlases. Beautifully arrayed, embossed, parchment-bound folios containing hundreds of ornate maps augmented with historico-geographical text were the pride of every respectable library of Europe. The 11-volume Blaeu atlas of 1662 is perhaps the culmination of this ornamental style.

The eighteenth-century French atlases were less pretentious, but no less rich in content, and were excelled only by the exceptionally fine English volumes at the end of the century.

In the nineteenth century, with the growth of government mapping, the importance of the grand atlases diminished; they became smaller in size, unadorned; and the geographical text was often omitted. Germany was the leading producer, closely followed by other nations.

The *scale* of maps in a general atlas varies with the importance of the country; the tendency is to use only a limited number of scales. Large-scale city maps are usually added as insets. The projections also vary; those generally used have been discussed in Chap. 5. Maps showing sections of a larger unit are usually drawn in a conic projection because any meridian can be chosen as central.

Since atlases are printed in 5 to 10 colors, the *symbol system* is rich but far from uniform throughout the various countries. In German, French, and Italian atlases, mountains are usually shown by hachuring; the English use altitude tints; American atlases usually do not show mountains at all. A very important part of a modern atlas is a voluminous pronouncing index of all geographic names contained in the atlas, each place located by page and by coordinates.

American atlases are somewhat cruder than are the best European products. On the other hand, they are very rich in names and new editions are published yearly. The last typical general, or "grand," atlas was that of the Touring Club of Milano, published in 1929. The more recent "Columbus Weltatlas" of Debes uses chiefly old plates. The general atlas, as developed in past centuries, was primarily a reference for location, but with the growth of geographic knowledge it does not quite satisfy present needs. The public now demands more diversified information than mere location. The grand atlas of the future should contain not only topographic maps, but climatic, vegetation, geologic, economic, and population maps as well, with text material and statistical data added. Nothing would be more helpful as a reference for students of geography than such an atlas, but the work involved is so enormous and the atlas would so soon be out of date that probably no commercial company would dare to undertake it on a large scale. The nearest present attempt is the "Grand Soviet World Atlas," which is now issued at the expense of the government.

**National Atlases.** If the ideal grand atlas of the world is still a project of the future, the various national atlases are pointing out how it should be done. Several governments and private concerns have published national atlases, and although these are not always private undertakings, they are discussed here.

Such atlases usually contain, besides the topographical pages, such a rich assortment of special maps that almost all informative or statistical data concerning the country can be conveniently obtained. Such atlases are published by Finland, Scotland, Sweden, Norway, Denmark, Czechoslovakia, Poland, Canada, Mexico, Cuba, Yugoslavia, Algiers, French Colonies, France (in preparation), Egypt, Katanga, U.S.S.R., China, etc., and by various German states. The United States issued a statistical atlas after each census, but the material grew to such proportions that it was divided into various special publications. The "Atlas of American Agriculture" and the various recent reports of state planning boards contain good basic material for the compilation of an atlas of the United States. A new national atlas is planned by a special committee of the American Society of Professional Geographers. National atlases are of very different size and quality, nor is it always the great nations which produce the best atlases.

The chief difficulty with national atlases seems to be that the richness of statistical material calls for new editions every few years. Another difficulty is the language. Thus, the "Grand Soviet Atlas" is published in Russian only, and thus its use outside the country is restricted. Many national atlases are published with the text in two or three languages.

## List of the Most Important Atlases of the World

The largest American atlas is the Rand McNally "Commercial Atlas," which reached its 77th edition in 1946. It weighs 20 pounds, is 21 by 15½ inches, and is sold by subscription. It is primarily a reference atlas for businessmen of the United States with lesser emphasis on foreign countries of the world. Rand McNally publishes a number of smaller atlases for the general public in the same style but with some noteworthy addition of pages that are doubtlessly composed by geographers. A widespread publication of the firm is the "Goode School Atlas."

Hammond's "Loose Leaf Atlas" has somewhat more foreign pages and inset maps and maps with altitude tints. Hammond also published the "Encyclopaedia Britannica World Atlas" by G. Donald Hudson, edited by Walter Yust, which has a remarkable statistical summary of all countries. Hammond's 50-cent small hand atlas shows what mass production can do in popular editions.

Among the British grand atlases, the largest is the "Times Survey Atlas" published by Bartholomew in Edinburgh in 1922. This is the first atlas that made a brave attempt to show relief all over the world by altitude tints. It has a valuable index. The "Citizen's Atlas" put out by the same firm is a popular medium-sized atlas, and new editions of it appear almost every year. The "Oxford Advanced Atlas" is an excellent small atlas on the college level.

The "Royal Atlas" and the "International Atlas" published by George Philip & Son, Ltd., are good reference atlases. Philip and Darby also publish the "University Atlas," an excellent work on the college level. The "commercial development" maps of the Putnam atlas are perhaps the greatest step in modern cartography toward a land-use map of the world.

The most famous German atlas is Stieler's "Handatlas" published by Justus Perthes in Gotha since 1825. Its "International" edition was interrupted by the war in 1939. It is a locational atlas, and yet it has a rich symbol system and fine hachuring. The maps look overcrowded for our taste. Its index is one of the richest in the world. Andrée's "Allgemeiner Handatlas," Velhagen und Klasing, Bielefeld, is more modern and somewhat more pleasing then Stieler's, and it has more special maps of climate, vegetation, geology, etc. Debes's, "Columbus Weltatlas," published shortly before the war, goes even farther in special maps than Andrée's.

The Italian "Touring Club Atlas," which reached its fifth edition in 1938, is perhaps the most up-to-date reference atlas of the world. It closely resembles Andrée's with its buff hachures, and its altitude tint maps of the continents are among the best. The Agostini atlases made in Novarra are also of the highest standards.

The "Atlas Universel de Géographie" by Vivien de Saint-Martin and F. Schrader (Librairie Hachette) is the best known French grand atlas. It is remarkable for its extremely fine hachuring and delicate lettering, and it ranks with the others in excellence.

The "Grand Soviet Atlas" (first volume 1937, second 1939) is really a national atlas but with enough special world maps to rank among the best world reference atlases. Volume One is divided between world maps and maps of the U.S.S.R. as a whole. Volume Two contains detailed maps of the country. The special pages show climate, geology, frozen soil, agriculture, manufacturing, etc., and represent a geographical research project of unusual magnitude.

A remarkable small "Atlas of World Maps" was published by the Army Special Training Program;[1] this was compiled chiefly by the geographers of the O.S.S. and the U.S. Department of State. All phases of world problems from economics to religions are portrayed by small sinusoidal world maps with accompanying text.

It would be beyond the scope of this book to list the excellent Swedish, Dutch, and Swiss atlases of the world, and the student is referred to W. W. Ristow's "World Reference Atlases," New York Public Library.

**School Atlases.** Since the time of the Arabic school atlases of the twelfth century, these small atlases have always been profitable undertakings for map publishers. The scope of these atlases has varied greatly with the centuries; the present tendencies in modern school atlases are most encouraging.

Older school atlases were simply small editions of a grand atlas, but in recent years climatic, economic, and special regional maps are added in great diversity. Because of the large and ever-changing market, new editions can be issued easily, and keen competition eliminates the inferior and antiquated products. School atlases are not common in the United States, since the textbooks of geography contain all the map material necessary, but in Europe such atlases are generally used even in the lower grades.

The school atlas has a threefold function:

1. *Source of Information.* The atlas should contain enough detailed maps showing environmental conditions, such as relief, climate, soil, vegetation, and an equal number of maps of human relationships,

[1] Army Special Training Program, *Man.* 101.

such as political maps and maps of density of population, railroads, roads, crops, manufactures, etc., to provide reference material for the students.

2. *To Give Clear-cut and Memorable Pictures of Geographic Patterns.* For this purpose the map should not be too complex. If a map shows several sets of lines overprinted (*e.g.*, rainfall and temperature on the same map), it is useful as a source of information but fails to give an easily remembered mental picture of such distributions. All unessentials should be omitted. It is useful to have one general map that gives the aggregate pattern of all mountains, cities, railroads, etc., and smaller special maps showing landforms, rainfall, vegetation, crops, natural resources, languages, administrative districts, etc.

3. *To Stimulate Interest.* Particularly useful for this purpose are large-scale maps of cities and of places of scenic or historic interest. Large-scale representation makes it easier for the student to perceive the connection between the map and the land it represents, particularly if accompanied by pictures. To make the map alive should be the aim of a good school atlas. Distant places have a lure for most of us. We all want to travel, if in no other way than on the map. An interesting map can go far in stimulating geographic thinking. Statistical material and cartograms can be made interesting by using pictograms. Even pictorial maps of the kind popular in advertising may be useful.

Most school atlases use in their general maps altitude tints, the disadvantages of which have already been discussed. Bright green on desert lowlands is likely to give rise to false inferences. Alfred Söderlund in his "Folkskolans Kartbook" uses a gray plastic shading for relief, overprinted with colored land-use tints, as yellow for farmland, green for forest, and white for pasture or waste land. In his latest maps he uses the physiographic method for representing mountains. This work represents the most advanced method at the present time.

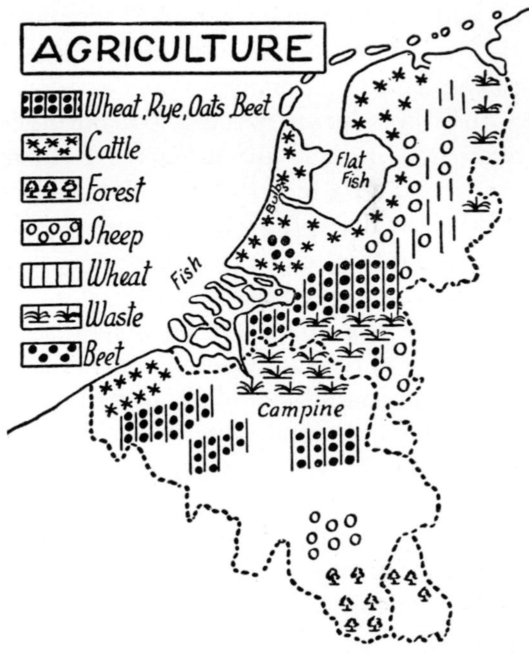


**Fig. 182** Informal, simple cartograms are better understood by children than very complex, formal maps. (*Birkett-Lewis Atlases, Evans Bros., London.*)

**Wall Maps.** Classroom instruction in geography is incomprehensible without good wall maps. The first wall maps especially for schools were introduced by Sydow and Petermann in Germany about a hundred years ago. A good wall map is so drawn that its major features can be seen across a classroom, although not all the lettering can be made that large.

Most of our wall maps are nothing more than enlarged atlas maps, although the function of wall maps is different. While an atlas map is partly for study and information, the wall map, as used in classroom instruction, forms the background for the teacher's explanations just as the scenery is the background for the actor in a play.

An atlas map differs from a wall map in the same way that a picture differs from a poster. The rules of poster design are the rules for making wall maps, too. The colors are bolder, the lines are heavy, and detail is omitted. Mountains shown in plastic shading with deep shadows are particularly effective. Names of cities and rivers cannot be expected to be seen across the classroom; yet they are shown, perhaps for no other reason than to help the teacher. As colors carry across a room better than lines, colors should show the various land types, such as forest, mountain, cultivated land, etc., and not the traditional altitude tints.

Effective wall maps can be obtained by lantern slides, the slight cost of which allows for a greater number of maps, offsetting the disadvantage of certain difficulties in coloring. Black outline wall maps, which can be filled in by the teacher and washed off again, are particularly useful teaching tools.

**Textbook Maps.** Almost every textbook, whether it deals with history, science, geography, or economics, is supplemented by maps and diagrams—a growing tendency in modern books. As such maps are printed together with the text their size is limited to the printed page size, which rarely exceeds $4\frac{1}{2}$ by $7\frac{1}{2}$ inches. Of necessity such small maps must be kept simple. Parallels and meridians are usually shown in the margin only. As colors cannot be used, the representation of mountains by hachures or contours is not easy; here the physiographic method may be advantageously employed.

Books of travel should always be accompanied by maps; it is to be regretted that some of the cheaper publishing houses issue travel books without them. Such maps are best placed on the cover lining (end papers) of the book, which not only makes them readily accessible but, by doubling the size and omitting margins, permits a larger map (in average 12 by 9 inches). Owing to the crease in the center, the map must be interrupted and pulled apart in the middle, leaving an empty strip of about $\frac{3}{8}$ inch. Both end papers of the book should have the same map; thus, when a library card is pasted over one, the other can be used. As cover linings are printed separately, there is longer time available for their preparation than for the other maps. On the other hand, library books have to be rebound every few years, and the map is lost altogether unless some extra copies are supplied to libraries.

## City Maps

City maps comprise an important part of a map maker's job. The chief aim of these is to help us find our way in a large city's labyrinth of streets. The scale of a city map is determined by lettering. Since each street must be labeled, the scale can seldom be smaller than 2 inches to the mile. Even on this scale the names of the narrower streets could not be lettered within the width of the street, and it is quite customary to exaggerate the width of streets at the expense of the blocks.

City maps are usually in the rectangular projection, but meridians and parallels are rarely shown. It is common, however, to have a grid system of mile squares, numbered and lettered on the sides so that each street or building can be determined by its coordinates. An index of streets is usually added to city maps.

European city maps usually show the built-up areas by different shades or colors. American city maps show the street system as laid out by the city engineers, whether built up or not. It is not an unusual experience to arrive at a swamp or forest where the map indicates a dense network of streets.

City maps rarely indicate mountains, chiefly because of the lack of a suitable system. Contour lines or hachure lines would confuse the map. The best method is plastic shading with oblique illumination, but the necessary half-tone overprint would increase the price of the map and an ordinary city map must be inexpensive.

More accurate maps on larger scales, showing exact width of streets, property lines, etc., are prepared and used by the city engineers. Functional city maps showing zones and the development of cities are described in Chap. 30.

## Communication Maps

All forms of transportation, railways, roads, steamers, and airways, need maps to show their routes to the public.

**Railroad Maps.** The usual railroad maps, printed in timetables, are quite diagrammatic. Their only purpose is to show the system of lines and sequence of stations. The lines are straightened and

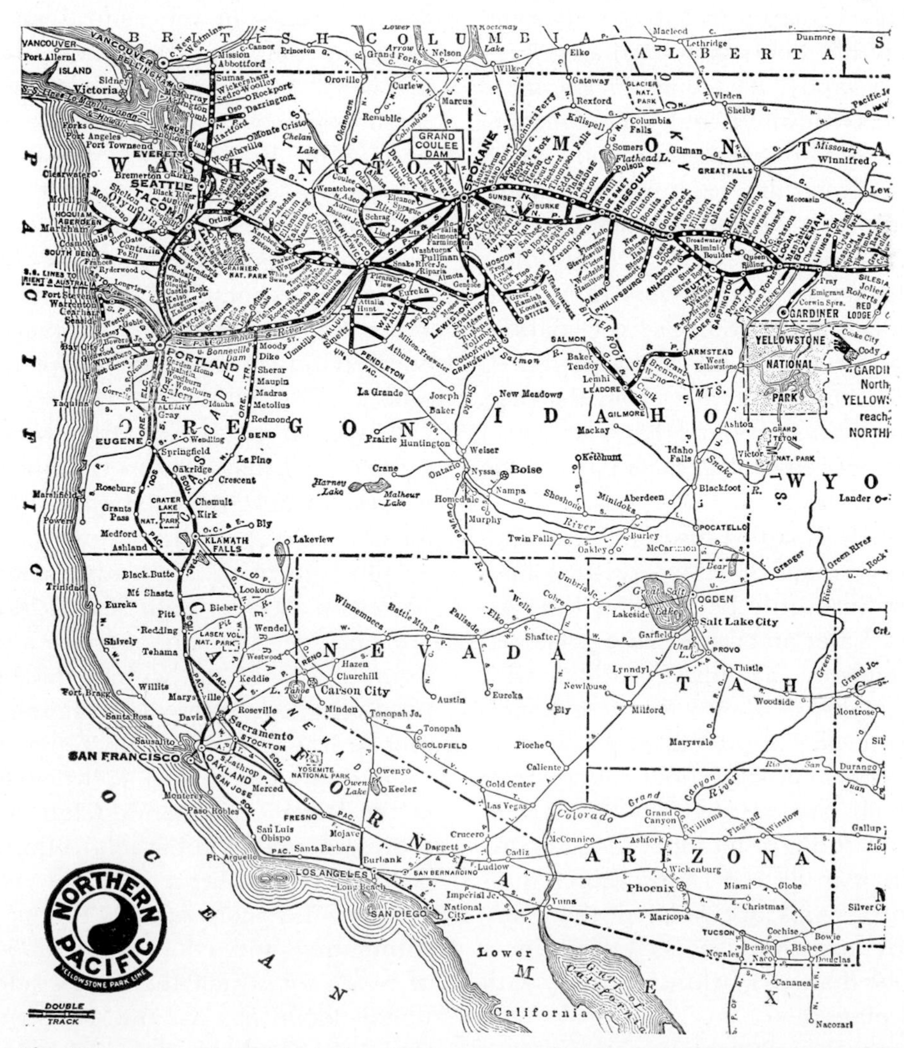


**Fig. 183** Railroad maps are often diagrammatic. Note how the southern states are reduced in size.

simplified; the stations are laid out like beads on a string with little respect for exact location. It is also customary to show in large scale the region served by the company and compress the rest of the map. The term "cartogram" for such design is more correct than map.

Although these totally utilitarian maps serve their purpose well, it is somewhat unfortunate that a great educational opportunity is neglected. Attractive railroad maps showing the nature of the country, its geology, products, and interesting features, would awaken interest in travel and would make the weary hours in a train an adventure in geography. The magnificent maps of the Swiss railroads and the charming and enlightening pamphlets of some English railroads are worthy of imitation. Some of the scenic western lines are described by the U.S. Geological Survey, but these guidebooks are too voluminous to be read by a wide public. Some lines publish road strips in which the railroad line is straightened out and centered on the page and information is printed left and right; an idea introduced by Matthew Paris in the thirteenth century.

**Automobile Road Maps.** The first automobile road maps sold by private map companies were little better than the railroad maps. Later an oil company presented the customers of its filling stations with automobile maps. Competing companies followed suit, and at present every large oil company seeks to produce better automobile maps, which are printed in millions of copies, constituting a national industry. At present in America perhaps more automobile road maps are printed than any other kind; and certainly they acquaint a wider public than ever before in history with the use of maps.

The amount of information supplied by a good automobile road map is remarkable. With filling stations all over the country, the oil companies can gather local information from everywhere, and for some places this is the best and most recent information available as new editions are published yearly. Besides road conditions, these maps show cities, state parks, interesting places, elevations, etc. No successful attempt has yet been made to show land forms on automobile road maps. Here the physiographic method would be of great advantage.

The usual scale of automobile road maps is 4 to 8 miles to the inch in the East, and 8 to 16 miles in the central and western parts of the country. They are usually arranged by states; this causes much duplication of marginal areas. Sectional automobile road maps of even size would not only facilitate country-wide travel, but could be handily folded accordion-wise and put into convenient folders like some European automobile road maps. Many European automobile road maps are intricately folded and can be opened at any place.

The great popularity of the present automobile road maps makes us hope that they will be further improved and will be transformed into powerful conveyers of geographic education. Indication of land forms, places of scenic and historical interest, great engineering structures, even geological formations, are all within the bounds of possibility; and increased interest in automobile travel would amply repay the cost of preparing such maps. The little folder maps of the Royal Automobile Club of England represent a good approach to this problem.

**Air-travel Maps.** Airway companies seem to be more aware of the interest-stimulating and educational opportunities of travel for which the planes offer exceptional facilities. As the country unfolds under the observer, his interest is awakened if he can follow his route on a map. For this, a map has to be about 1:500,000. On a millionth map, a mile is $\frac{1}{16}$ inch, and this is hard to translate into the visible reality by an untrained observer. The map has to resemble the country and here is a great challenge for a good "landscape" map. The possibilities of air-travel maps are like those of the ideal automobile road maps, except that patterns of vegetation, geology, and types of farming show up very well from the air and should be pointed out. At present, air-travel maps are published in the form of strips on a scale too small for use.

Actual strips of airplane photographs, colored and lettered, would make good air-travel maps, but their large scale would render them too bulky and expensive.

**Maps in Newspapers and Periodicals.** Most newspapers illustrate current events with small simple maps. These maps contain important reference material for recent changes in the world's map and should be carefully filed by cartographers and geographers.

Perhaps the most important cartographic reference material for current developments is contained in geographical periodicals. The maps of the *Geographical Review* excel with their fineness and accuracy, strictly adhering to their principle that no unnecessary line should appear on their maps. The maps of the *National Geographic Magazine* are also fine and well proportioned and present a remarkable amount of information with little overcrowding. Their large colored maps of the various countries, continents, and oceans have set a standard for private cartography in the United States. The artistic maps of The Royal Geographical Society in London have also created a style which is now widely imitated in England. Among American periodicals the colorful and original maps of R. E. Harrison in *Fortune* and the dynamic maps of R. M. Chapin in *Time* deserve mention.

**Artistic Maps and Maps for Advertisement.** Such maps are fairly common in newspapers and periodicals and in the pamphlets of travel agencies. Unfortunately, they are made by artists and not by cartographers, and by their single desire to appeal to the eye they often violate every rule of good cartography. Most of these maps are decorated with pictures or, more correctly, consist of a set of small pictures placed according to their location on a very generalized map, the pictures being often more important than the map.

The *decoration of maps with pictures* is an age-old custom, and the medieval maps especially were full of them. This custom gradually died out in the eighteenth and nineteenth centuries and only recently has it been revived in artistic maps. The most serious objection to pictures on maps is that they are out of scale and dwarf the other symbols of the map. Where, according to the scale of the map, a 10-mile-long man is catching a mile-long fish, even Lake Michigan will look like a pond. Especially where mountains are shown, the discrepancy between the size of a mountain and, for instance, an approaching covered wagon may be ridiculous. Therefore, it is important to relegate the pictures to empty parts of the map, and to set them more or less apart from natural features. Another method is to set the little pictures in a frame so that they will not be regarded as part of the main map.

A good cartographer either makes an honest *picto-map*, where an outline map serves merely as a framework for the rough location of pictures, or he makes a real map with cartographic detail, in which case he will decorate only the border, the sea, and the empty places of the map. Among the first category, the richly illustrated and minutely detailed maps of Ernest Dudley Chase of Winchester, Mass., deserve mention.

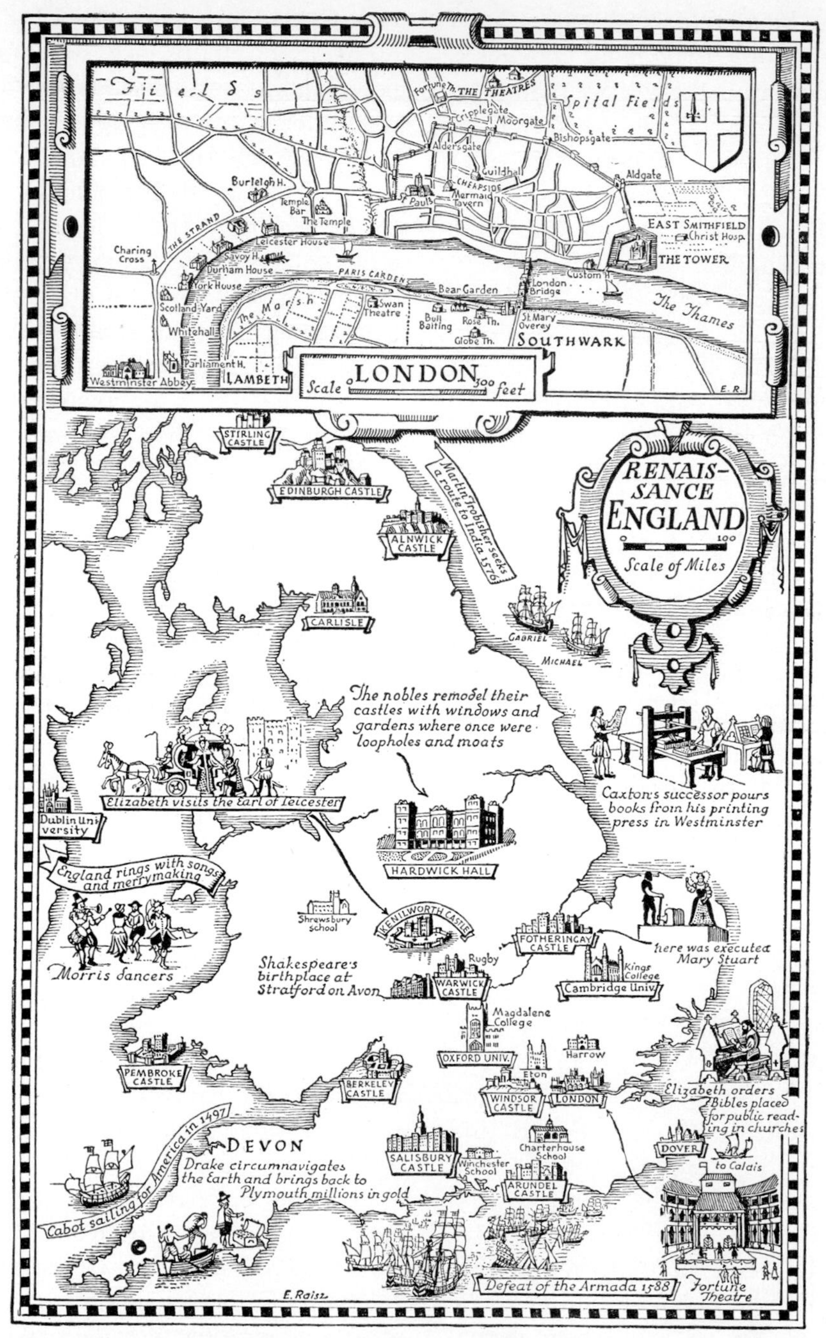


**Fig. 184** In this type of pictorial map the outline of the land forms only the background for the pictures. (*Charles Scribner's Sons.*)

A charming type of artistic map is coming into fashion nowadays, which shows the roads leading to suburban homes. As these maps rarely show anything other than roads and landmarks, they may well be decorated with characteristic pictures and still serve their purpose. The preparation of this kind of map is a welcome play for the cartographer's imagination between long hours of dry and precise work.

# CHAPTER 24: *Cartography in War*

It may not be true that more maps have been printed during the Second World War than in all times previously, but the fact remains that no greater advancement has been made since the time of Columbus. The progress was not so much in design—the war maps are not very different in appearance from the prewar types—but in (1) the enormous coverage, (2) the intensive use of airplane in mapping, and (3) the world-wide interest in maps.

**British Maps.** Both Great Britain and America reorganized their mapping program. Of these two the British were the more active. There the entire mapping program was centralized under the Directorate of Military Survey. This included the immense establishment of the War Office, the Ordnance Survey, the various surveys of the Empire, and close cooperation with the Admiralty was established. The directorate had much more to go on at the outbreak of the war than its American counterparts had. The excellent India Survey maps of Southern Asia were at their disposal and the various dominion and colonial surveys had ready material. Early in the war British and American mapping was coordinated, with Britain concentrating on Europe, the Near East, and India, and the United States on the Pacific. Free access to each other's material was agreed upon to the great benefit of both. Most of the maps used in the North African campaign were reprinted from L'Institut Géographique National sheets in the original French language with the addition of a grid system.

At the beginning of the war, the United States was ill-prepared for the task ahead. Approximately half a million different maps were in the collection of the Army War College in Washington, and several important maps, especially modern city plans, were missing.

**Army Map Service.** With the imperative demand for fast production of maps the Army Map Service was organized in 1942. An enormous plant covering several acres was built in record time. The building had no windows and it was so effectively camouflaged that there was little suggestion outside of the spacious drafting rooms, map collections, and engraving and printing establishments inside.

All the major map collections of the country were combed for every bit of geographic information, maps, and pictures, and soon more than 2,000,000 maps were collected, exceeding any other map collection in the hemisphere. The country was combed for cartographers in a similar manner. Here the inadequacy of cartographic education in America was most keenly felt, and the inexperienced personnel produced maps much below standard. The young cartographers, however, soon learned, and the fast improvement was striking. Courses in cartography were organized in the colleges all over the country, and hundreds of college girls entered the A.M.S., which employed several thousand people. Tons of maps were shipped in a single day for the urgent calls from the army, and many of the maps were produced under stress and strain on a three-shift day.

A statement of the A.M.S. is quoted here verbatim:

> Approximately 30,000 different maps were prepared, and 500,000,000 individual sheets were reproduced by the Army Map Service or its affiliated organizations. Some 22,000 tons of maps were shipped to the various theaters,

120,000 gazetteers to supplement the maps were prepared and reproduced.

To accomplish this huge task an organization was built up both in Washington and in field offices located strategically throughout the eastern and central United States. At its peak the Army Map Service employed over 3,500 people. In addition, they made use of practically all the commercial cartographers in the United States and over 90 commercial lithographers. As an example of the quantity of maps needed by an operational theater, for the Normandy invasion 70,000,000 sheets of 3,000 different maps were supplied by the Army Map Service alone. This figure does not include the large contribution made by the British as well as by the Army topographic field organizations in England.

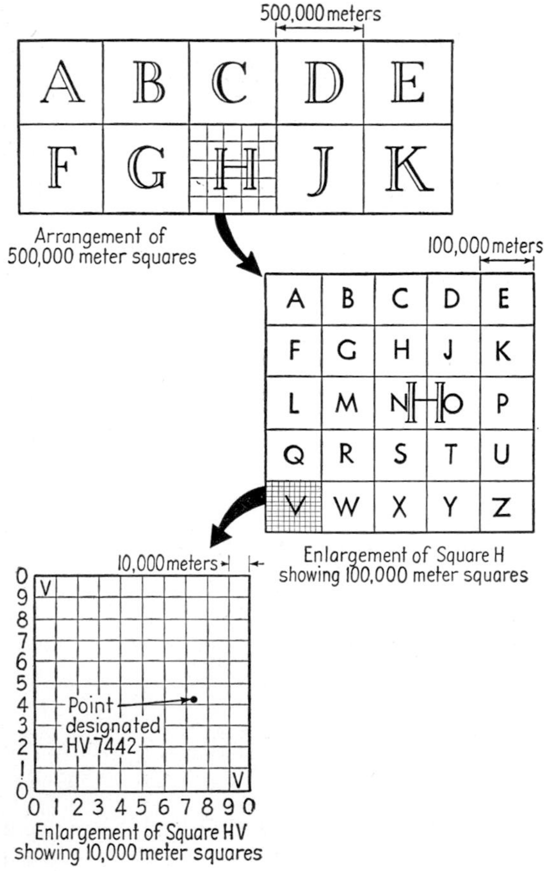


**Fig. 185** The British and most other grid systems use a 25-letter system for 500- and 100-kilometer squares; within the 100-kilometer square the position is given by numbers.

Increasing amounts of information came in from the aerial—mostly trimetrogon—surveys of the Army and Navy Air Forces, and as the war went on compilation gave way to radial-line plotting. Slotted templates covered the spacious floors of the building and long rows of multiplex projectors added contours to the more important areas. Airplane photographs are necessarily of large scale, and the demand on floor space was so great that another even larger building was erected.

The program of the A.M.S. was varied. Small-scale planning charts were prepared for the entire world; the millionth map was recompiled and its coverage extended. The 1:500,000 map of the western Pacific area and the 1:250,000 China, Korea, and Japan contain a great amount of new material. The maps of North Africa and the European theater were mostly recompilations, but proved so untrustworthy that a completely new set on 1$50,000 was prepared by multiplex—one of the greatest mapping undertakings of all times.

The coming of peace did not slacken the activities of the A.M.S. Indeed the program for many years ahead is laid out; it will lead ultimately to a multiplex or trimetrogon survey of the entire world.

**Grid Systems.** Military grid systems were greatly expanded in this war and they were generally used in all operations. There was a great amount of confusion, however. The British, French, Dutch, Norwegians, Russians, etc., all had their own grid systems, and sometimes different grid systems were used in older or newer sets of maps on different projections. Sometimes yards were used, sometimes the metric system. To bring order to the chaos was the unenviable task of war cartographers.

The maps of Europe, Asia, Africa, and

Australia were grided by the British. As the map sets used were on different projections, no uniform system of grids could be used. Thus the Old World was divided into a patchwork of zones or belts. Each zone had its own grid system overprinted in its own specified color. For most zones, the metric system was used. Each zone, or belt, is first divided into 500-kilometer squares each designated with a letter of the alphabet from which the letter *I* is omitted. Each of these squares is similarly divided into 2,500-kilometer squares and designated by two letters. On large-scale maps these 100-kilometer squares are further divided into single kilometers or even 100-meter squares and are recorded from the lower left corner, reading right and up. No hyphens are used in reference. In smaller zones, such as Egypt and Malta, no letter reference need be used. India, South Africa, Australia, Malaya, and other British territories use yards instead of meters, but the system is the same.

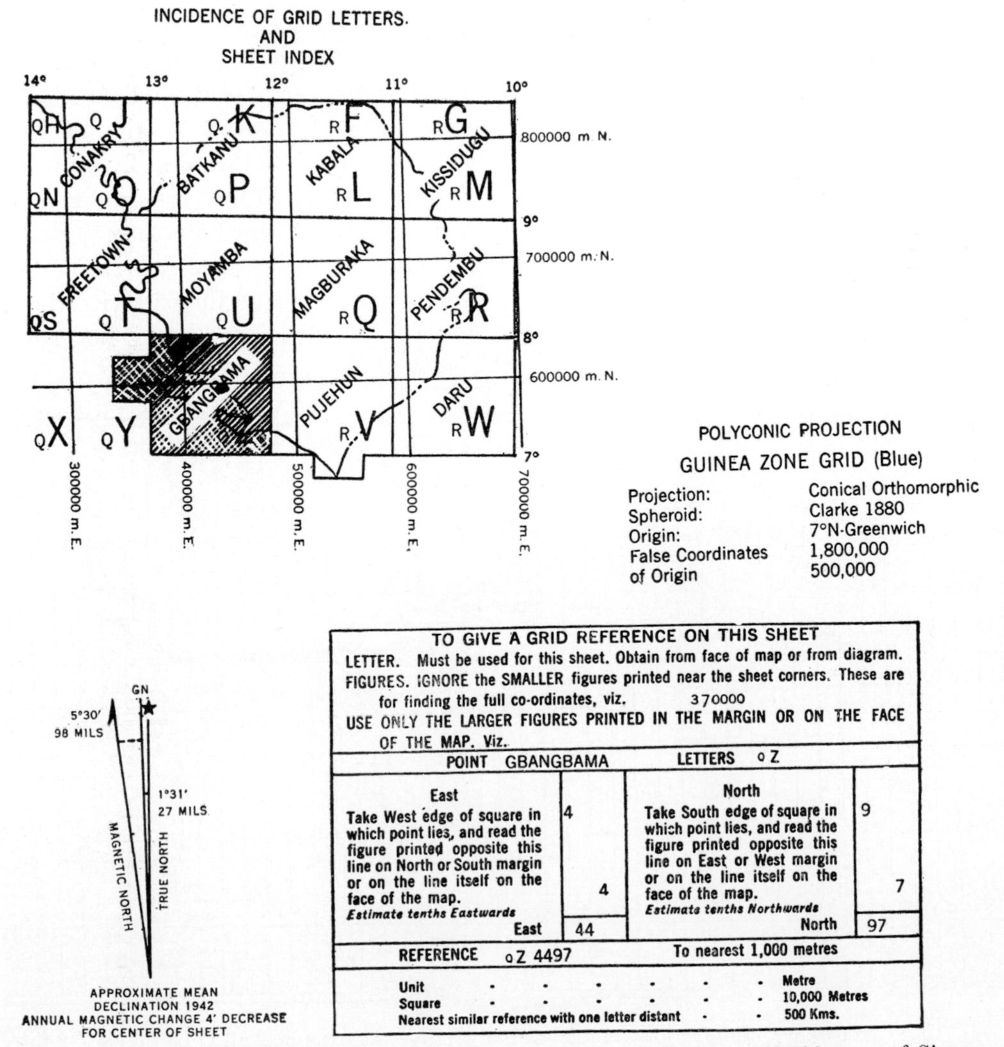


**Fig. 186** War maps supply elaborate grid information, as on this 1:50,000 map of Sierra Leone. The full meter reading of Gbangbama would be 444000–597000.

All the British maps have on their margin an elaborate Grid Reference Box printed in the color of the grid; a sample of such a box is given in Fig. 186. A Standard Grid Note describing the nature of the grid is added on many maps. Three-pronged declination diagrams are given usually in the color of the grid.

The U.S. Military Grid has been described already on page 206. Similar single-zone polyconic grids have been prepared for Hawaii, Panama, and the Philippine Islands. The World Polyconic Grid system is an extension of the domestic grid to cover all areas not covered by the British. This, however, leaves only the Americas, Eastern Asia, and the oceans to be grided by this system. It could be applied, however, to any part of the world except the polar region north and south of 72° latitude.

The world in this system is divided into five north-south bands, each 73° longitude wide, with 1° overlap. Band I is over the United States, and Band II is west of it. Each band is divided into nine north-south segments called "zones," each 9° wide with 1° overlap, as in the domestic system. They are marked from east to west *A, B, C, D, E, F, G, J*. A polyconic projection was drawn for each of these zones and upon this was placed a 1,000-yard grid. The origin of the grid of the part of the zone north of 28°N is on the central meridian at 40°30′ to agree with the domestic system. For the rest of the zone, however, the origin is at the intersection of the equator and the central meridian. To avoid negative values the actually used origin in the northern belt is 1,000,000 yards grid-west and 2,000,000 yards south of the true origin. Between the equator and 28°N the actually used origin is on the equator 1,000,000 yards grid-west from its intersection with the central meridian. Grid references are expressed the same way as on the domestic grid with the exception that, if full reference is necessary, the

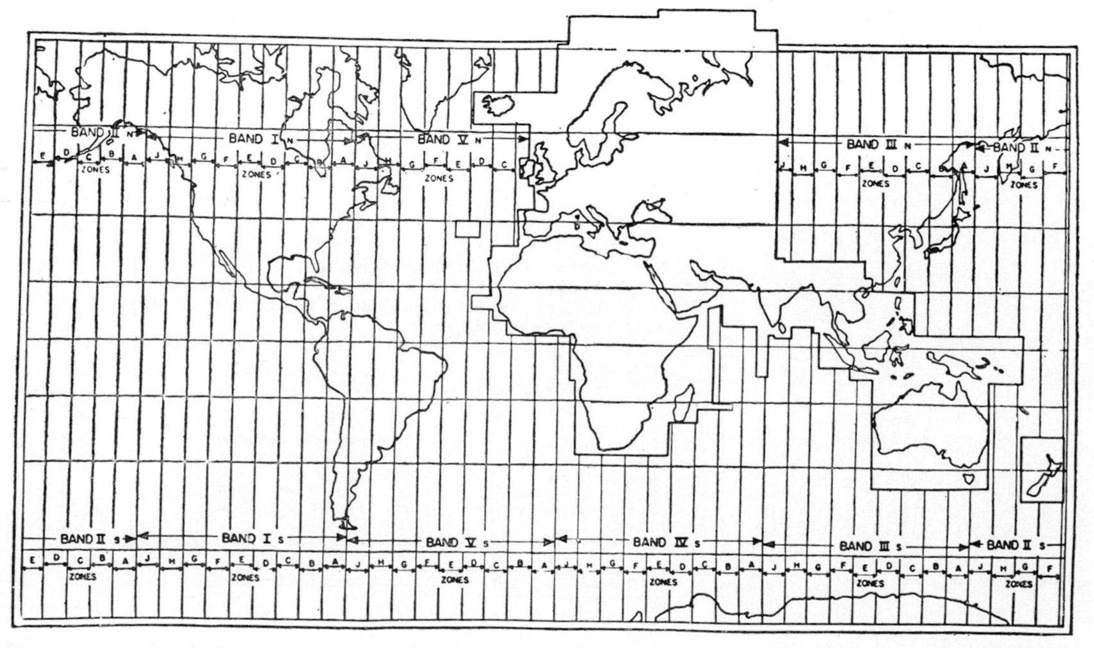


**Fig. 187** The progressive military grid of the United States was extended all over the world during the war, except on those parts where the British and other foreign grids were used. (*From United States Army Manual.*)

band, zone, and hemisphere have to be given. Thus a full reference may read IIIBN1,329,-200-2,625,400. On large-scale maps however, where the approximate location is known 29,2-25,4 would be enough to locate the point with 100 yards.

**The Universal Transverse Mercator Grid.** The many overlapping grid systems caused endless confusion during the war. One does not change horses midstream, but as soon as the fighting was over the Universal Transverse Mercator Grid was introduced.

Since it is a conformal grid all computations are simpler. The world is divided in 6° N.-S. belts reaching from 80° N. to 80° S.; zones begin at 180°, numbered eastward. The origin is the central meridian of each zone at the equator. False origin is 500,000 miles west on the equator (for the southern hemisphere 10,000,000 miles south). Twenty-five miles of overlap is provided but never used for reference. Scale error of the projection is less than 1:2,500. For North America the Clarke Spheroid 1866 is used, others elsewhere. The new tables are in A.M.S. Tech. Manuals No. 7 and No. 19.

Most large-scale maps of the A.M.S. are now on the transverse Mercator projection, including the new 1:25,000 and 1:50,000 topographic sheets of the U.S.

**The Office of Strategic Services.** While the A.M.S. prepared maps mostly for tactical use, the O.S.S. collected material for more general strategic purposes. The maps are of the greatest variety, ranging from mineral maps of Alaska to an ecclesiastical map of Hungary. The various field units of the O.S.S. were instructed to bring in any map that they could obtain, and the O.S.S. map collection exceeds a half-million different maps. Much of the O.S.S. map work was illustrative, added to the reports on the geography of many regions. Much of this rich mine of geographic research is now available to colleges.

The immense production of the O.S.S. was made possible by its unique organization under the direction of Dr. A. H. Robinson. The work of the compiler was strictly separated from the work of the

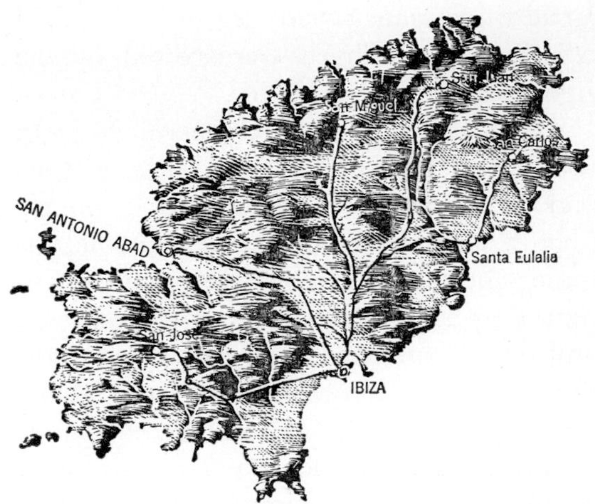


**Fig. 188** Scratchboard map of Ibiza in the Balearic Islands, prepared at the O.S.S.

draftsman; they were often in different buildings. The compiler had a sample book containing all types of lettering symbols and a complete color chart, and from these he drew up his specifications or marked a sketch map, carefully selecting the thickness of the boundary lines, the type of lettering, etc. This method gave the geographer-compiler a great responsibility, while the actual drafting could be done by artists and draftsmen. Indeed some of the most advanced type of maps came from the O.S.S. Although under ordinary circumstances the work of a cartographer combining the artist and the geographer is preferable, under the given conditions Robinson's method gave good results.

**Aeronautical Charts.** The greatest demand for new maps came from the Air Forces for more and better flying charts. The activities of the various map-making agencies were coordinated by the Aeronautical Chart Service of the Army Air Forces. The charts range from 1:250,000

(Philippines and Indo China) to 500,000 in general maps, and 1:1,000,000 or 1:3,000,000, for air plotting charts. Much of the work was given out to A.M.S., to the Coast and Geodetic Survey, and to private firms. In addition, charts were drawn in five field offices, and all charts were edited by the Aeronautical Chart Service.

The charts do not differ essentially from the prewar style. They show altitude tints and air information overprinted in purple upon a Lambert conformal projection. On some charts the colors were chosen so that they should be discernible under an amber-red or ultraviolet light during night flying. Purples, browns, and orange colors were used, giving an odd impression; greens were added for daylight use only. Many charts were printed on fluorescent paper or with fluorescent paints.

The charts were not altogether satisfactory. Vegetation patterns, landmarks, and land types were not differentiated, not because their necessity could not have been recognized but because it would have been difficult to change the system under the stress of war. Later charts are greatly improved by adding plastic shading.

**Target Charts.** This new type of chart was introduced during the war and it soon became one of the most important items of war cartography. At first these charts were prepared by the A.M.S. but later the U.S. Coast and Geodetic Survey was the most important producer.

These charts encompassed a single city, factory, bridge, or any other important object. As the bomber flew over the target in a few minutes, there could not be too much detail on them. They showed rivers, railroads, primary highways, and the features that would help locate the target. The target itself is indicated by concentric circles 4 miles apart. The usual scale was 1:75,000, but later a combination of 1:180,000 on one side and 1:36,000 on the other side proved more useful. Simplified perspective views of the targets were added to help quick identification. The greatest difficulty in the production of these charts was the lack of reliable up-to-date city maps, and many of the charts had to be remade from flight information.

**Photomaps.** Intensive use was made in the last years of the war of photomaps. These are reduced half-tone reproductions of controlled mosaics made possible by an extremely fine half-tone screen of about 350 lines per inch. Over the mosaic a grid was drawn and white or black lettering was added by cellophane stick-up. Many of the 1:50,000 maps of Europe and Eastern Asia had this photomap printed on their back on the same scale. This is an important step in cartography, as it provides a comparison between a map and a picture and the combined effect of the two gives a better understanding of both.

**Relief Models.** Never before were relief models used to such an extent as during the

**Fig. 189** Model prepared for landing in Algiers (Bains Romains) on 1:2,000 scale. Note the naturalistic handling of the terrain. (*Courtesy of H. P. Reed in Geog. Rev.*)

war. All theaters of operation were portrayed by small-scale strategic models, and thousands of large-scale models of Pacific islands, landing beaches, etc., were distributed among the field commanders.

Many new materials were used. Plaster models were made stronger yet lighter with an ingenious rib system. Their plastic effect was enhanced greatly by the use of a sidewise spray of dark color with an airbrush intensifying the shadows. The rubber models that could be rolled up and shipped and used under battle conditions proved to be surprisingly serviceable. A thin layer of liquid rubber was spread into a hard plaster negative and was backed with sponge rubber. Plastics sucked into a mold by vacuum made good transparent models. Steel deposited in an electrolytic bath into a mold made a strong model that could be magnetized to hold little iron ships, troop symbols, etc., instead of the usual colored pins. Professor Cook of Princeton developed a method by which stereoscopic images of contour maps projected on a block of soft plaster indicated the depth to which the plaster had to be whittled down. "Egg crate" models were made rapidly in the field by cutting out parallel profiles from planks and stretching canvas over them. Rough painting, sanding, sponge trees, etc., gave a natural finish to the work. Much of the relief map work was done by the O.S.S. under Maj. W. W. Atwood, but notable models were made by other departments too.

**Fig. 190** Reflection of continuous short-wave impulses presents an ever-changing chart on the screen, not influenced by darkness, rain, or fog. Note Manhattan, the Hudson River, and Central Park on the above radar chart. Position of plane is shown by central ring.

**Radar Charts.** This is also a completely new development of the war. The echoes of directional short-wave impulses are received on a sensitive plate, and the places which have reflective power, such as built-in areas, industrial establishments, ships, etc., will show up white, while water, which does not reflect radar waves, will be black. Land in general is gray, but slopes facing the receiver give lighter reflection producing an effect of plastic shading with the light in the center. As clouds and weather do not obstruct radar waves much, this chart is used in cloudy weather or at night. The charts are prepared from an interpretation of radar pictures, and are still in the experimental stage.

**Port Shipping Plots.** By frequent photographing of the enemy harbors, close surveillance was kept of the whereabouts of every known vessel. These were recorded on an ingenious set of charts, which helped a great deal in the crippling of enemy shipping.

**City Maps.** In the Second World War, more than in any other war before, fighting was concentrated in cities, and large-scale maps were produced in enormous quantities. They were used partly as a complement to target charts, but their chief use was by the invading infantry and artillery. At present they help civil administration. Never before were so many cities mapped by uniform symbols and language, and these maps will be of great use for urban geography. The maps are of 1:10,000 to 1:25,000 scale and are the result of both aerial photographs and compilation, plus local information.

**Road Maps.** Mechanized warfare is dependent on roads, and 1:500,000 maps were prepared for all theaters of war with roads classified as to width, surface, bridge capacities, etc.; steep slopes and sharp curves were shown by special symbols.

**Landing Maps.** Landing operations are planned with exact correlation of activities, and they require the most detailed charts and maps. These were drawn in all scales, sometimes as large as 1:1,000, showing the types of bottom, beach features, tide levels, and the inland topography. They were oriented so that the sea was on the bottom and the land on top, a departure from the almost universal north orientation.

**Charts.** The war production of the Hydrographic Office of the Navy skyrocketed to 45 million charts a year. A great number of captured Japanese charts were translated, revised, and printed. The polyconic 1:72,000 Approach Charts, and the 1:36,000 Bombardment Charts have a 1,000-yard grid, and are used both on sea and on land. Several sets of air-navigation charts were specially designed for navy fliers. Loran charts were published for all major shipping lanes. The monthly Pilot Charts were printed on "wet-strength" paper and were tucked away in lifeboats and rafts. This paper is impregnated with a plastic and gets stronger when wet. Submarine warfare was aided by the Current and Temperature Charts and Bottom Sediment Charts. Sea and Swell Charts aided the fliers of the Navy. Special charts were developed for the polar regions where usual methods of navigation fail. The "Ice Atlas" of the Northern Hemisphere gives the greatest collection of ice data of the world, a truly satisfying contribution.

The above-related activities can be repeated for the Coast and Geodetic Survey. The usual sets of nautical charts, tide and current charts, geomagnetic surveys, aeronautical charts, coast pilots, and seismographic and gravity surveys were carried on with many improvements. Nautical charts are now printed with brown altitude tints, another example of close approach of map and chart.

**Escape Maps.** Prize souvenirs of this war are the 1:1,000,000 maps of the Pacific Theater printed on nylon. These maps stood up after prolonged immersion in salt water. They could be laundered and faded only slightly in sunlight. They were part of the equipment of the inflatable rubber rafts used on airplanes.

**Special Publications.** *Gazetteers, etc.* Volumes of gazetteers giving latitude, longitude, various spellings, and grid references of hundreds of thousands of places were published by the A.M.S. These were made in cooperation with the Board on Geographical Names of the U.S. Department of the Interior. The "Glossary of Geographic Names" was particularly useful in using Japanese, Italian, and German maps. Giving small glossaries on every topographic sheet was a welcome addition for the soldiers fighting in Tunisia with maps reprinted directly from the French. *Symbols of foreign maps* were published in several booklets. The A.M.S. often took over the symbols of foreign maps if they were better adapted to showing the local conditions than the American symbols. For instance, the Japanese symbols for shrines, temples, etc., are used since we have no symbols of our own.

*Topographic Battalions.* Each army corps had a topographic battalion in the field, which consisted of a photographic, drafting, and printing unit, turning out maps in the field for local operations. The outfit of these battalions was compact, mobile, and amazingly efficient. Unhampered by conventions and under the direct pressure of the demands of a new type of warfare, they turned out the most original maps, and many of their innovations were later picked up in Washington. The use of vegetation patterns in the Pacific area was in response to an environment where the knowledge of the type of forest or savanna was vital. They also used a great deal of plastic shading and landform method in their maps. Their offset presses produced sheets 19 by 21 inches and were carried in trucks.

*Newsmaps.* A novel feature of this war were the poster-sized "newsmaps" published by both the U.S. Army and Navy. These boldly designed displays of maps, pictures, text, and diagrams kept the man in the field informed about the salient facts of war better than any newspaper. Both used photographs of relief models for the base of their maps, an easily attained and effective method of plastic shading. Private newsmaps were published for the general public in response to the new interest and understanding of maps by everybody.

*The United States Department of State.* Remarkable progress in cartography was made in the geographic section of the U.S. Department of State under Dr. S. W. Boggs. Maps and globes were prepared of the greatest variety, showing the factors affecting the peace treaty. Much of this material was published in the "Atlas of World Maps," showing such items as climate, soil, languages, religions, economic factors, communications, etc. This approach to a general world atlas filled a gap in American cartography. The maps consisted mostly of an assemblage of continents on a sinusoidal projection.

*Private Atlases.* In 1944 in short succession three small atlases were published indicating recent trends in cartography. "A War Atlas for Americans," although published by a private firm, was prepared with the assistance of the O.W.I. It showed the history and strategic problems of war. R. E. Harrison's "Look at the Earth" was mostly a collection of his maps in *Fortune.* This atlas was also mostly concerned with geographical and strategic problems of the war and as one of his reviewer's remarked his "handling of relief represents a cartographic triumph." "The Atlas of Global Geography" by Erwin Raisz was a more general geographical atlas with some special pages on the geography of disease, poverty, illiteracy, etc. All three atlases had a great amount of text, a quarter to a half of the space of maps; all three used a number of orthographic projections or photographs of globes at various angles. They represented

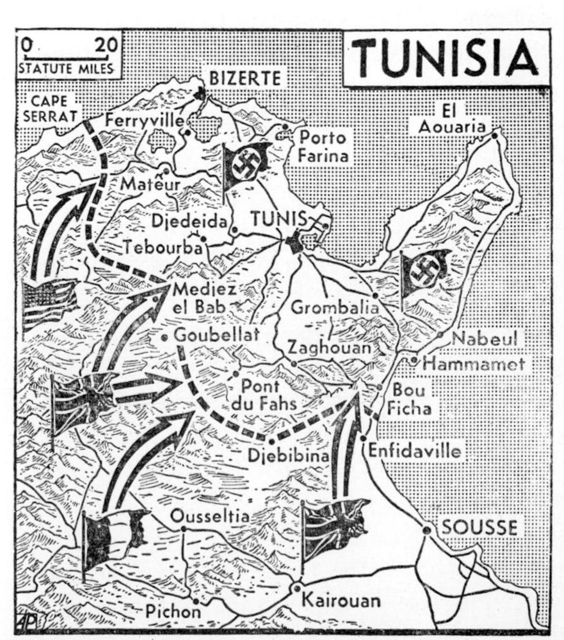


**GERMANS RETIRE—Map locates the approximate battle line in Tunisia, where late dispatches reported an Axis retreat from high ground which had been bitterly defended. Flags show sections of Allied line held by various nations, and arrows indicate direction of principal drives. (AP Map)**

**Fig. 191** Newspaper maps showed great improvement during the war.

an attempt at the dynamic handling of the world in motion.

*Newspaper Maps.* Never before were newspapers so copiously endowed with maps as during this war. These maps, which illustrated situations which were changing hourly and which were often changed in the last minutes before going to print, gave a real understanding of far-off battles to our news-hungry public. The maps of the Associated Press were relayed to the subscribing newspapers by wirephoto. Among the independent papers the maps of *The New York Times*, *PM*, and the *Christian Science Monitor* deserve mention. On these maps mountains were represented by a crude trachographic method, which, although a great improvement over the older maps, could be easily improved by adopting a more scientific symbol system.

**Summary.** The greatest progress in wartime mapping was not so much in new systems of cartography—there was hardly time to develop that under the urgent pressure of military demand—but rather in an enormous new coverage. Whole countries have been mapped anew and the area of large-scale mapping almost doubled. This new coverage could not have been accomplished without the use of airplane photography. With the exception perhaps of the trimetrogon process, here also the progress was not so much in new methods but in the extensive use of what has been worked out before. Air power produced airway maps also on a world-wide spread and developed such new features as target maps, radar maps, and fluorescent maps for night flying.

The social and economic mapping of the world was a part of political, psychological, and economic warfare and here we encounter new symbolism and new methods.

Adding to all the awakened interest of the public, which stimulated the production of newsmaps, models, atlases, etc., and all the elements are here which may produce a progress in cartography which is unprecedented in history.

## PART SEVEN: CARTOGRAPHIC SPECIALTIES

Modern geography is becoming more and more an exact science and there is a noticeable tendency among geographers to use quantitative methods in regional analysis. The increasing use of diagrams, statistical maps, and cartograms in the more recent volumes of geographical periodicals is especially noticeable. The graphics of these representations have been worked out more often by statisticians and economists than by geographers. It is important, however, for every geographer to be familiar with these methods.

---

# CHAPTER 25: *Diagrams*

Modern science could hardly have been developed and certainly it could not have been transmitted without the use of diagrams. They represent a second language for scientists and engineers and are exactly in line with the work of the cartographer. Strictly speaking, diagrams are not part of the system of cartography, but since they are used on statistical maps and form a substantial part of geographic illustrations, their inclusion seems to be justified. The terms "graphs" or "diagrams" are used here interchangeably. Economists call them "charts," for example, "pie charts" or "bar charts," but as the term "chart" in cartography means a mariner's map this term is not used here.

**Bar Graphs.** Bar graphs are the simplest type of diagrams used for simple comparison of quantities. The quantities involved are represented by bars of equal width and of length proportionate to the quantity on a chosen scale. They can be used horizontally or vertically, as the case demands. Horizontal bars have the advantage over vertical bars in that their labels are somewhat more easily read. On the other hand, according to classroom experiments, vertical bars are somewhat more easily evaluated. Bar graphs offer easy comparison but are not satisfactory where one quantity may be several hundred times larger than the other, since some bars would be so short as to become barely visible. Bar graphs can be subdivided, and lettering can readily be placed on them.

There are many different types of bar graphs. In Fig. 194 is shown a series of closely set bars representing the variation in time. This type of graph is sometimes called a "staircase graph"; if the sub-

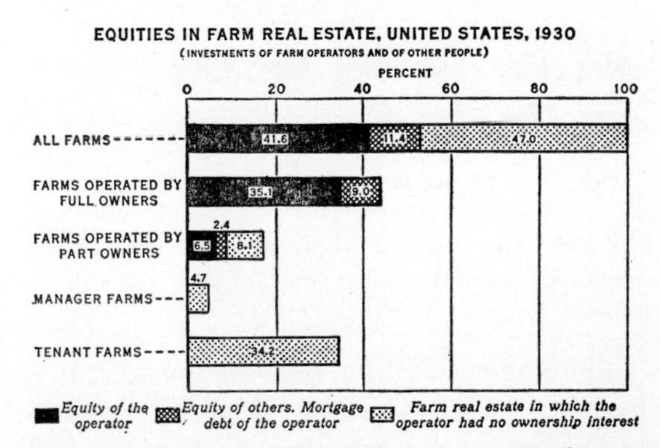


**Fig. 192** Bar graph. Horizontal bar graphs are easier to label but more difficult to compare than vertical sets of bars. (*Courtesy of U.S. Department of Agriculture.*)

divisions are labeled in one-hundredths, they are called "percentage bar graphs." Bars are sometimes shown on both sides of a vertical zero line. It is a fact proved by classroom experiments that these *mirrored bar graphs* make a better impression on the memory than the usual one-sided graphs.

**Unit Graphs.** Bars are often broken up into countable units, such as rows of even circles or rectangles, or rows of small pictures—each circle, rectangle, or figurette representing a certain quantity. These unit graphs are used not only to enliven the pages of our popular magazines, but form a standard method in state and national planning-board reports. They became exceedingly popular under the name of "pictographs," and whole establishments of artists are engaged in their design. Fractions can easily be represented if circles or squares are used, but the pictorial unit graphs have the disadvantage that it is difficult to show half a cow or quarter of a telephone. Vertical piles of coins are shown in Fig. 193.

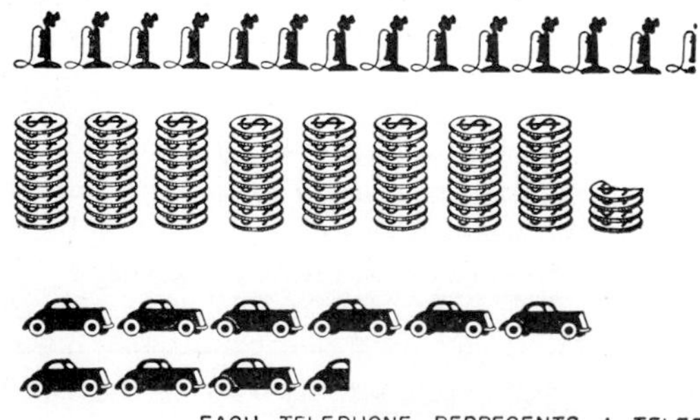


**Fig. 193** Pictorial unit graphs are used generally for simple comparison of quantities. (*From "Our Cities," National Resources Committee*, 1937.)

The value of either kind of bar graph is greatly increased if the quantities represented are also given in exact numerical figures.

**Line Graphs.** This type of diagram is used to show the change of one variable

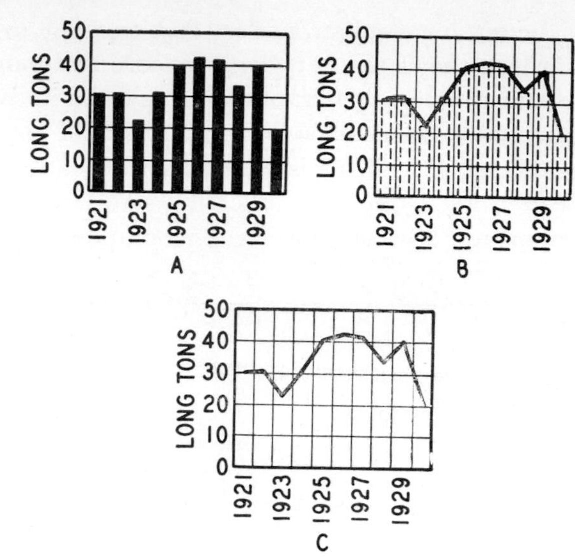


**Fig. 194** Time relationship can be shown by both bar and line graphs. (*From Riggleman, "Graphic Methods."*)

in reference to another. One of the variables is usually time, but this is not necessarily so. It is customary to show time on the horizontal line. The variation is shown by a curve, each point of which is determined by two coordinates.

Fine horizontal and vertical lines marking units of measurement are convenient for evaluation of the curve. The lines should not be very close; $\frac{1}{2}$ to 1 inch is a reasonable distance.

Although the principle of line graphs is extremely simple, there are several mistakes to guard against. First, the variable has to be marked off at the proper time coordinate. If *average* values are shown as, for example, yearly temperatures, the average for each month is marked off at the middle of the month, and the points so marked are connected with a continuous curve. The names of the years or months should be directly under the marked points. If *aggregate* values are represented (as, for instance, production of motor cars), the value for any given year is obtained only at the end of the year and should be marked there. In both cases it is better to avoid misunderstanding, and to mark the years between the vertical lines and not directly under them.

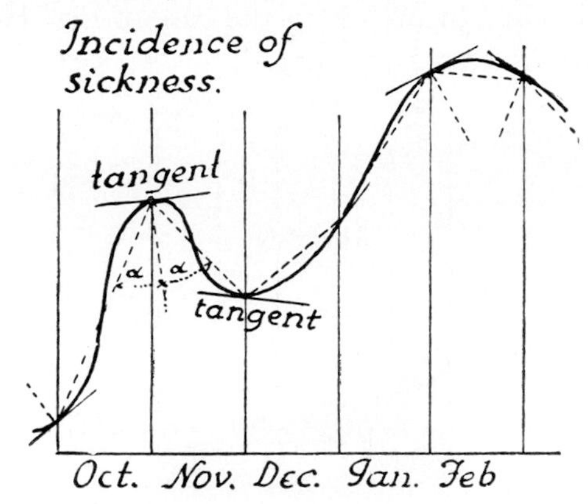


**Fig. 195** If the variation is continuous, we are nearer the truth if we make a continuous curve.

When the line graph shows a *continuous* variation, the error is less if the known points are connected with a continuous curve rather than with straight lines. In the case of a noncontinuous variation, as, for instance, the price curve of steel, a jagged line is justified.

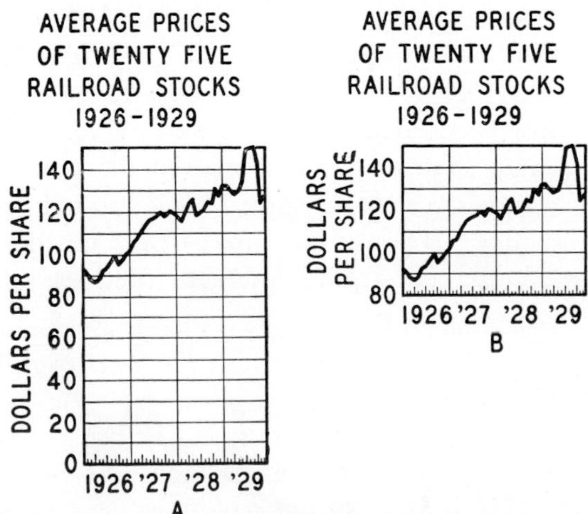


**Fig. 196** The incomplete vertical scale on time curve *B* may give a false impression of great variability. (*From Riggleman, "Graphic Methods."*)

The choice of the vertical scale should be such that the curve will not show too sharp a vertical variation. Line graphs that resemble the oscillations of a seismogram are not easy to read. It is also important that the whole value should be represented from the zero figure; in other words, the chart should not be "amputated" at the bottom, since an excessive variability may thus be indicated where there is actually but little. If it is necessary to save on space, a horizontal break near the bottom of the graph will call attention to the fact that the whole vertical scale is not included. On every line graph the zero line should be made heavy.

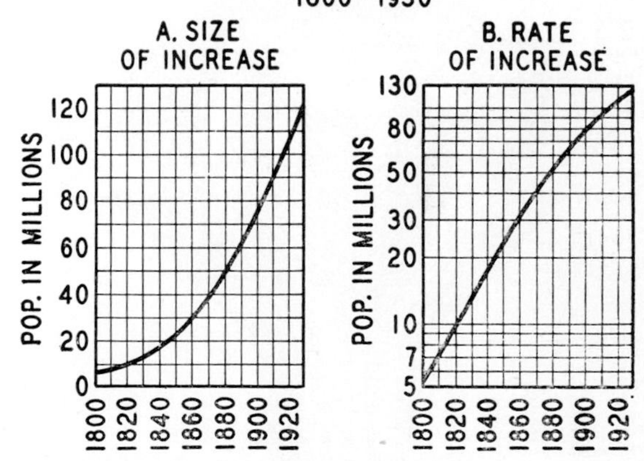


**Fig. 197** The arithmetic graph shows only that the population is still increasing, while the logarithmic graph reveals the fact that the rate of increase is declining. (*From Riggleman, "Graphic Methods."*)

**Logarithmic Line Graphs.** If we are not interested in the actual amount of change, but are interested in the *rate of change*, of certain variables, we use a logarithmic vertical scale. Figure 197 illustrates this method. The graph on the left shows the *size of increase* of the population of the United States on an arithmetic scale. A greater number of individuals are added to the population of the country in every successive decade. Yet, when this increase is compared with the total population, we find that the *rate of increase* is constantly diminishing. This is clearly shown on the logarithmic graph on the right. Logarithmic graphs are generally used to show variability in stock and bond quotations.

Paper lined in logarithmic scale can be purchased at engineering-supply stores. Ruled paper on which the horizontal time scale is even and only the vertical scale is logarithmic, is sometimes called "semilogarithmic." This is the usual type of paper used in geographic work.

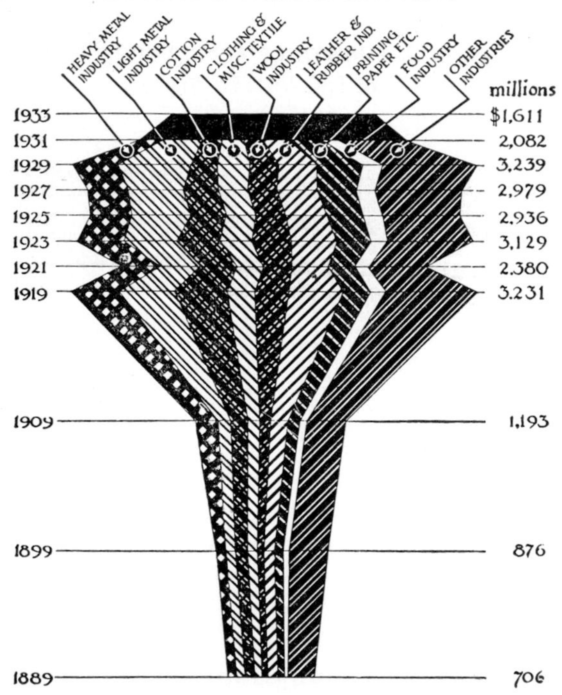


**Fig. 198** Band graph in symmetrical arrangement with vertical time scale. (*Courtesy of National Resources Committee*, 1936.)

**Band Graphs.** If a line graph is subdivided and the bands formed by subdivisions are tinted differently, it is called a "band graph," as shown in Fig. 198. This diagram also shows that the time element can be fully as well indicated along the vertical coordinate as along the horizontal. Band graphs are not easily read, especially if the quantities are quite variable. In some cases it will be found advisable to replace them by several single graphs. A band graph showing the variation of percentages in time is shown in Fig. 199. If it is possible, the smallest and least variable bands should be in the bottom or, in the case of Fig. 198, in the center.

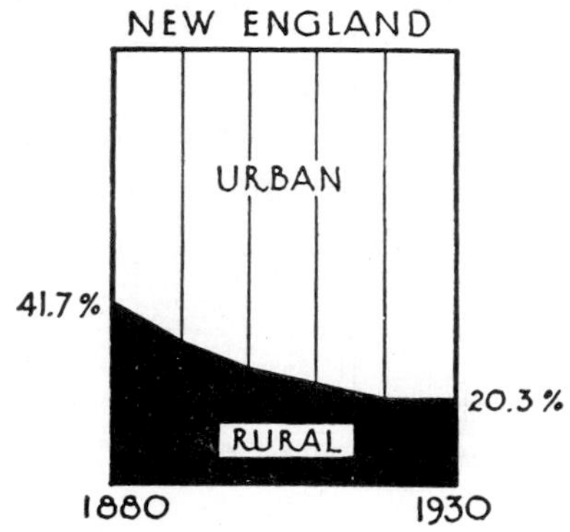


**Fig. 199** Percentage graph. (*Courtesy of National Resources Committee.*)

**Averaging of Line Graphs.** Line graphs are often composed by averaging several single observations, as, for instance, temperature readings. For each observation a dot is marked by its coordinates. The curve is drawn either as a median or as a central (mean) line. In every narrow vertical strip the *median* line has an equal number of dots above and below. The *central line* is placed so that the momentum of the dots above and below is equal; *i.e.*, in each narrow vertical strip the sum of the distances of the points from the curve is the same above and below the line. The most rapid, but mathematically not quite perfect, method of

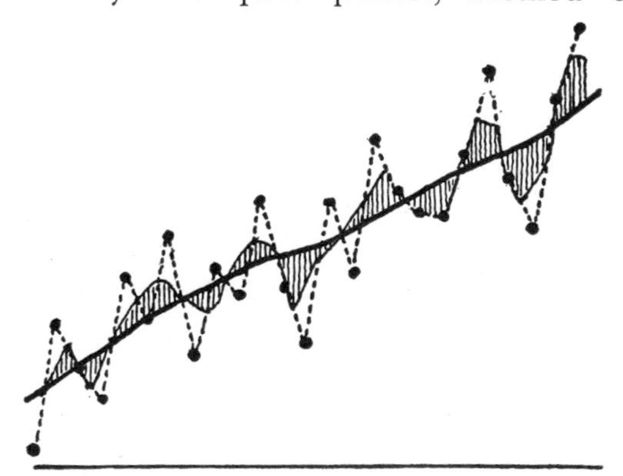

**Fig. 200** Averaging line graph from scattered information.

obtaining this line is to take two succeeding points and replace them with a point in the middle. If the line thus obtained is still too up and down, the process may be repeated with the succeeding new sets of points until the line is smooth. It is obvious that the median and the central lines are not the same. The median line is not changed if a number of dots above it are placed still higher, but such change greatly affects the central line.

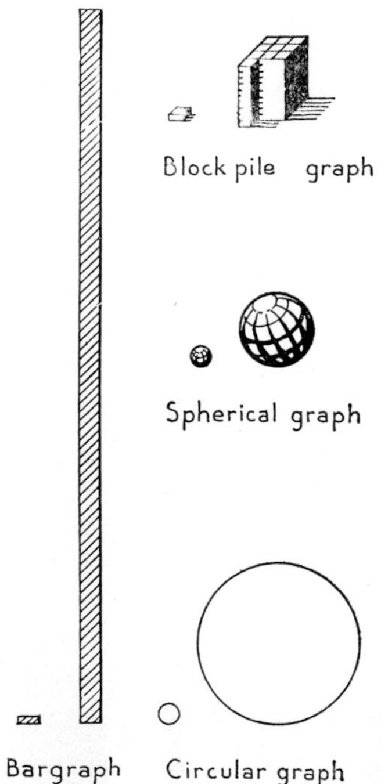


**Fig. 201** Different types of graphs showing the comparison of two quantities related at 1 to 100.

**Two-dimensional, or Areal, Graphs.** In this type of graph the *area* of a circle, square, or of any other shape is made proportionate to the quantity represented. If several pie graphs are to be compared, we take the square root of each quantity involved and measure it off on the diameters of the circles or the sides of the squares or any similar lines in similar figures.

*Circular (pie, coin) graphs* are the most common areal graphs. They are often used for simple comparison of quantities instead of bar graphs, but much more often they are subdivided to show percentages. This division may be made by drawing a circle on transparent paper or on a celluloid sheet and dividing it with 100 equidistant radial lines; this sheet is then placed over the pie graph, center over center, and the percentages can be pricked through. Pie graphs are not easy to compare, and are difficult to label. Areal graphs are not so easily commensurable as bar graphs and cannot be lettered so well. Their advantages are that they can be packed closer on a map and that they need less space to show the difference between very large and very small quantities.

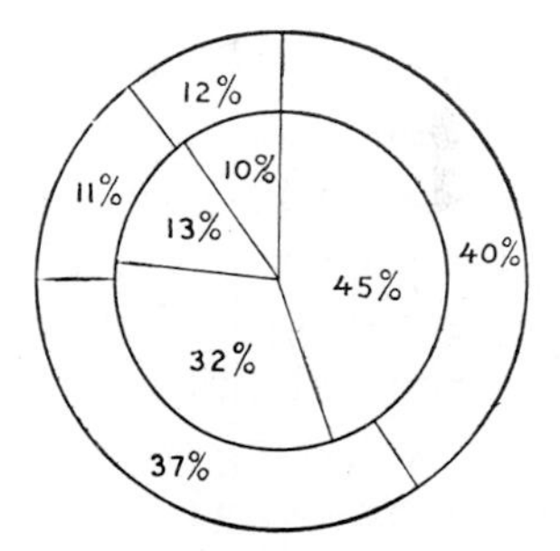


**Fig. 202** Ring diagrams are used for subdivision of divisions. Quantities are not easy to compare by this method.

*Ring diagrams* are used if further division of the subdivisions of a pie graph are necessary. In this case the radius of the whole quantity is calculated, and the large circle is drawn first. Next the inner ring is drawn proportional in area to the subdivisions. In spite of the fact that it is very difficult to compare the subdivisions, ring diagrams are often used in European statistical atlases.

*Square graphs* are more easily labeled than circular graphs and are also more easily subdivided.

*Rectangular and Other Two-dimensional Graphs.* On these graphs the area of a rectangle or square, or any other figure of

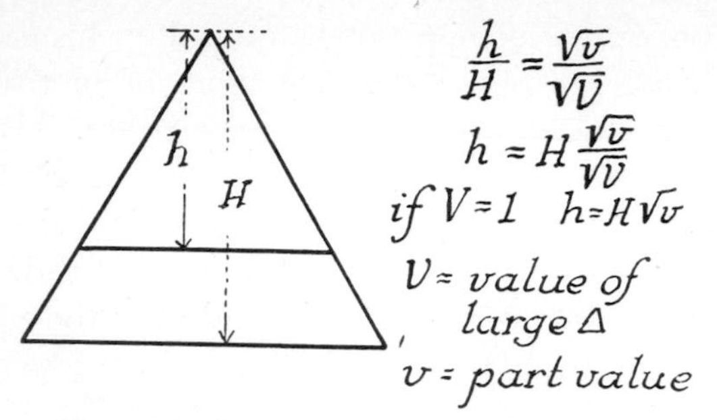


**Fig. 203** Triangular diagrams are good when one value is very large in comparison to the others.

plane geometry is made proportionate to the quantities represented. The various geometrical forms may be used to differentiate various products. Rectangular graphs are particularly useful when subdivisions are further subdivided. The layout of such subdivisions is shown in Fig. 230.

*Two-dimensional Unit Graphs.* Instead of a single large circle or square it is often preferable to draw a group of even-sized small circles, squares, or triangles. Thus the quantity represented can be appraised by counting. This method is shown in Fig. 269.

**Three-dimensional Graphs.** These graphs consist of pictures of blocks, cylinders, or spheres, or any other forms of solid geometry, and here the *volume* of the graph is proportionate to the quantities to be represented. The volume of cylinders is calculated by the formula

$$V = r^2\pi h$$

where $h$ is the height of the cylinder. The volume of a sphere is $\frac{4}{3}r^3\pi$. In the case of spheres or cubes, the *cube roots* of the quantities are proportionate to the diameters of the spheres or the sides of the cubes. Blocks are drawn isometrically; spheres and cylinders are usually heavily shaded to give a three-dimensional effect. These graphs lend themselves well to comparison of quantities of very different amounts. Their disadvantage is that it is extremely difficult to evaluate the volume of geometrical solids by simple appraisal. For instance, two spheres related in volume 1 to 100 were shown to the class. The average estimate was that they were related 1 to 20.

Instead of cubes, rectangular blocks can be used. An interesting experiment was made to make the shape of the block express variation in the volume. For instance, the income of cities from (1) manufacturing, (2) commerce, and (3) other sources is laid out along the three coordinates on a cube-root scale. Thus not only the total income but also the type of income is visible at a glance.

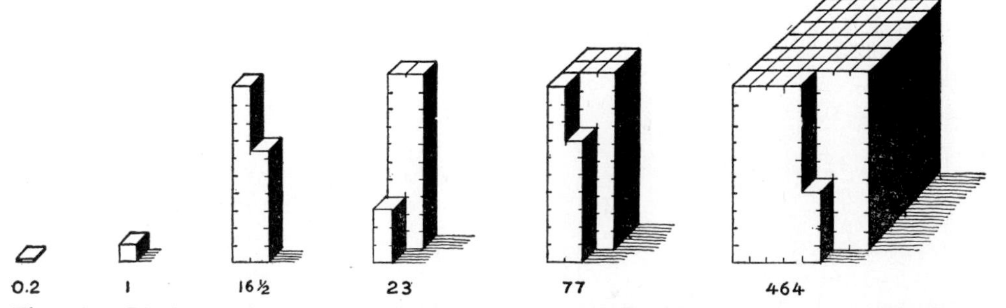


**Fig. 204** Block-pile system of comparison of quantities. The blocks are 10 units high. Fractional pillars are always in the foreground.

**Block-pillar System.** To overcome the difficulty of the appraisal of three-dimensional graphs, an attempt has been made to devise a system in which the geometrical solids are divided into countable units. The basic element of this system is a small isometric cube corresponding to a certain unit quantity. Larger quantities are shown

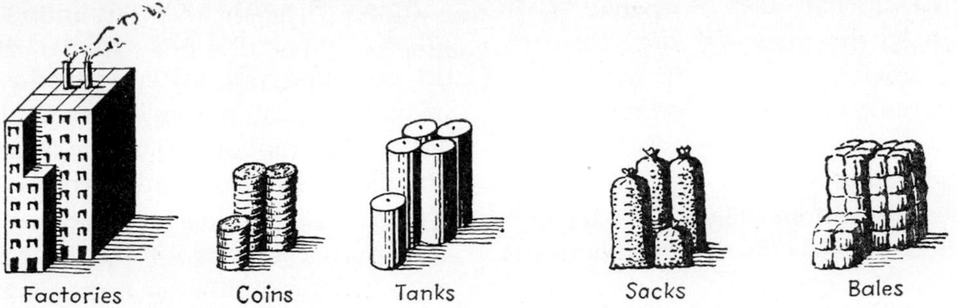


**Fig. 205** Pictorial symbols can be substituted for block pillars.

by piling the cubes over each other up to 5 or 10. Over ten, the cubes are grouped as shown in Fig. 205. In this grouping, the fractional blocks should always be in the foreground so as to be easily countable.

The advantages of this system are that (1) blocks can be counted and are easily commensurable, (2) blocks can be subdivided, and (3) lettering can be applied directly on the blocks. The three-dimensional effect of blocks is also better than that of spheres, especially when shadows are added. A convenient size for the basic cube is $\frac{1}{16}$ inch. If the subject demands, piles can be replaced by pictorial symbols.

**Pictorial Graphs.** Diagrams have little appeal to the average man, but his interest is immediately aroused by pictorial or semi-pictorial representation. Almost every type of graph can be drawn pictorially.

Bar graphs and block piles can be formed into bales or boxes of even base. Circular graphs are often pictured as coins, showing how the "dollar is split." Cylindrical graphs can be replaced by piles of coins, groups of tanks, sacks, or barrels.

Caution should be used in pictorial graphs, where the quantities are represented by single human figures or animals of proportionate sizes, instead of by rows of figures of even sizes, because, in order to make such figures accurately, their height must be proportionate mathematically to the cubic root of the quantities and psycho-visually at least to the square root—a rule that is often violated. Moreover, the sizes of the figures are not easy to compare.

The *pictorial unit graphs*, already mentioned, are better. These came into fashion in the last decade, introduced chiefly by the

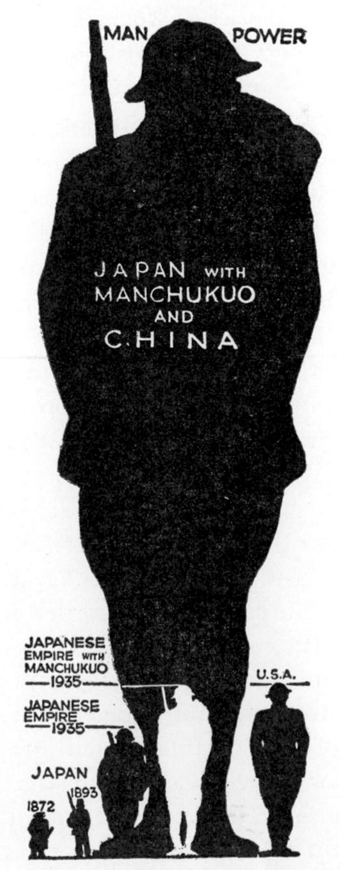


**Fig. 206** Misleading use of pictorial graphs. The height of the silhouettes should be proportionate at least to the square root of the quantities.

atlas, "Gesellschaft und Wirtschaft."[1] In these graphs the quantities are shown by rows of small, simplified pictures, each figure corresponding to a certain quantity. Since these figures can be easily counted and remembered, these pictorial unit graphs have great educational value. They actually represent bar graphs divided into countable units.

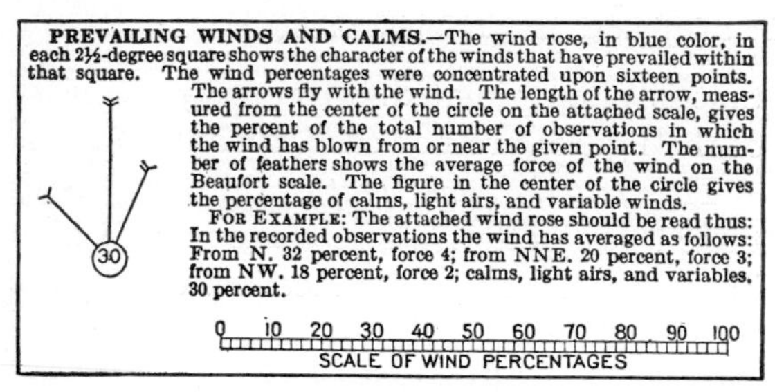


**Fig. 207** Wind roses on the United States pilot charts.

**Star Graphs, or Direction Graphs.** These graphs are used to express relationships in which direction is involved. One common type of star graph is the *wind rose* found on pilot charts and climatological maps. These wind roses show by a line of proportionate length the number of hours that the wind blows from a certain direction. The number of barbs is proportionate to the average velocity of the wind. While in wind roses the arrows fly toward the center, in current roses the directions are away from the center. As further illustration, the trend of railways or of auto roads in a certain area may be recorded in similar fashion. Instructive star graphs can be worked out to show trends in population of a city from decade to decade. The usual method of construction of such graphs is to draw 16 or 32 evenly spaced, radiating lines and to mark on each line the quantity which falls within its own segment. For easier comparison the end points of lines are often connected to form a starlike figure.

[1] "Gesellschaft und Wirtschaft," Bibliographisches Institut, Leipzig, 1930.

**Spoke Graphs.** These are similar to star graphs except that the radial coordinates do not represent actual directions; they merely represent a number of variables laid out on lines radiating from the center. Such are the *econographs* introduced by Griffith Taylor.[2] Taylor analyzed the habitability of various countries for white people and expressed the results on a graph, the construction of which is apparent from Fig. 209. The obvious shortcoming of this method is that it does not take into account some very important factors of habitability. Thus Southern California, with the help of irrigation and oil production, proved to be much more habitable than would appear

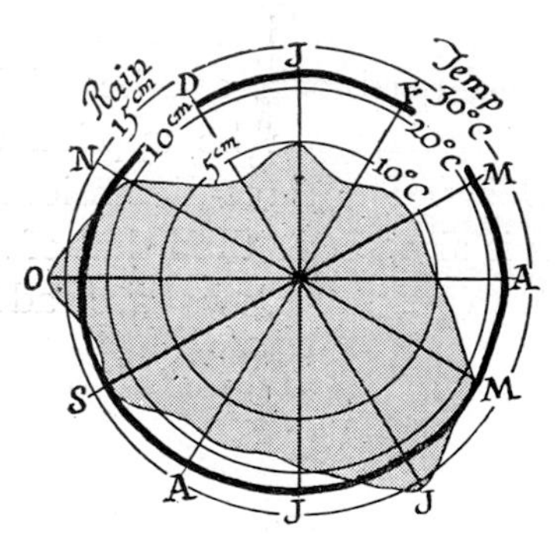


**Fig. 208** The heavy line represents mean monthly temperatures, the shaded area the mean rainfall, for Havana. The divisions on the spokes correspond to square roots of values.

from the diagram. Still, the idea of the econograph is sound and, by using eight coordinates instead of four, for the eight most important geographic factors, interesting comparisons can be made of different regions. Spoke graphs are very good to show "cyclic" variables that repeat themselves time after time. For instance, yearly rainfall and temperature can be shown excellently by this method. The character-

[2] TAYLOR, GRIFFITH, The Distribution of Future White Settlement, *Geog. Rev.*, Vol. 12, pp. 375–402, 1922.

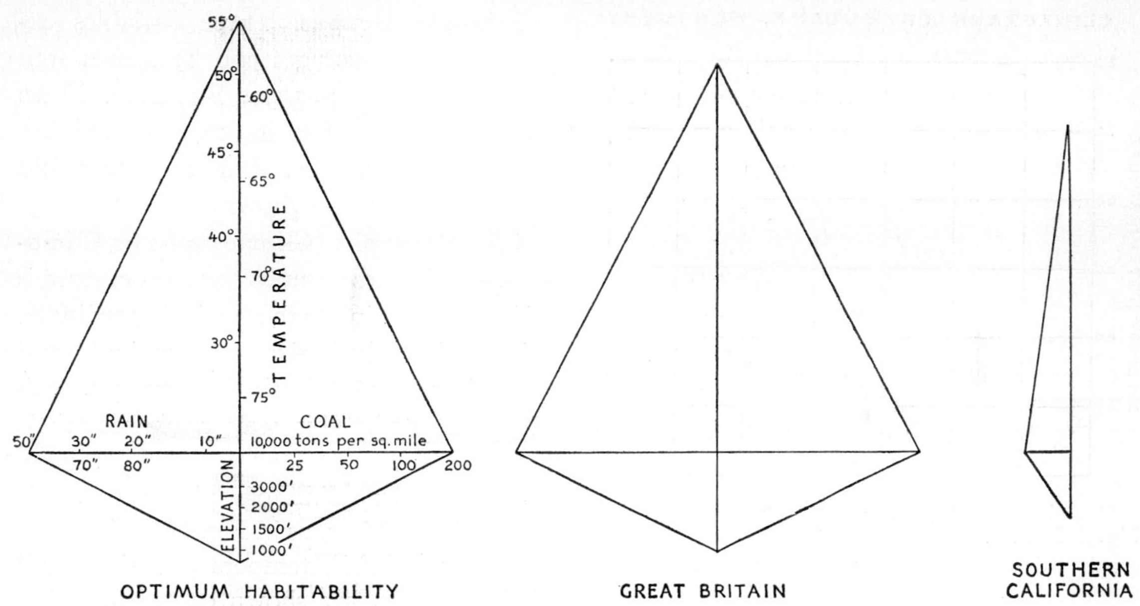


**Figs. 209 and 210** Econographs devised by Griffith Taylor. (*Courtesy of Geog. Rev.*, 1922.)

istic shapes of the curves are easy to remember (see Fig. 210). The spokes are graduated as 1, $\sqrt{2}$, $\sqrt{3}$, $\sqrt{4}$, etc., so that each ring is the same area as the other. This will make the area of one shape representing rainfall comparable with other shapes.

**Volumetric Diagrams.** These are three-dimensional diagrams, either built up into actual relief models or drawn isometrically, which serve for comparison of three variables. The method of isometric construction is described in Chap. 31. The name is derived from the fact that when such a model is divided into small vertical prismatic sections, the volume of each section will be proportionate to the product of the three variables. Volumetric diagrams are often used in meteorology and climatology. The variation of sunlight with the season

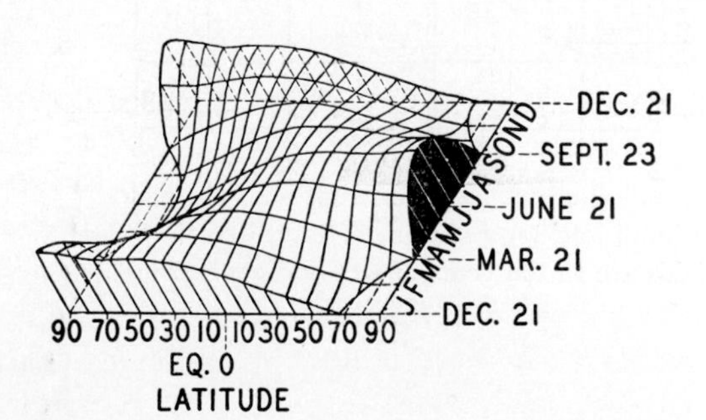


**Fig. 211** Volumetric diagram showing the relation of three variables, sunlight varying with latitude and seasons. (*Modified after William M. Davis.*)

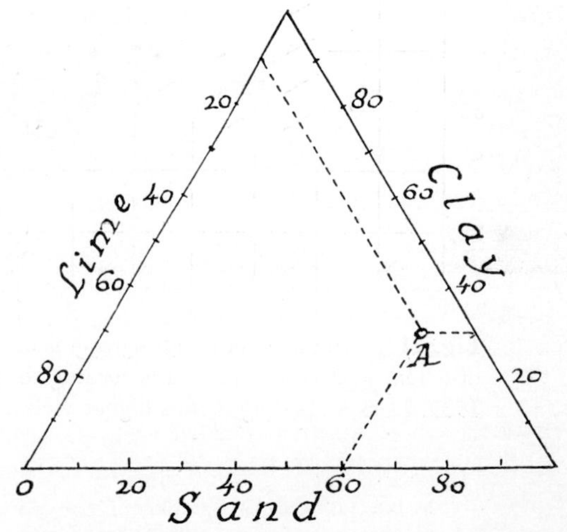


**Fig. 212** Three variables expressed in percentages are best shown on triangular graphs. The earth sample *A* is of 60 per cent sand, 30 per cent clay, and 10 per cent lime.

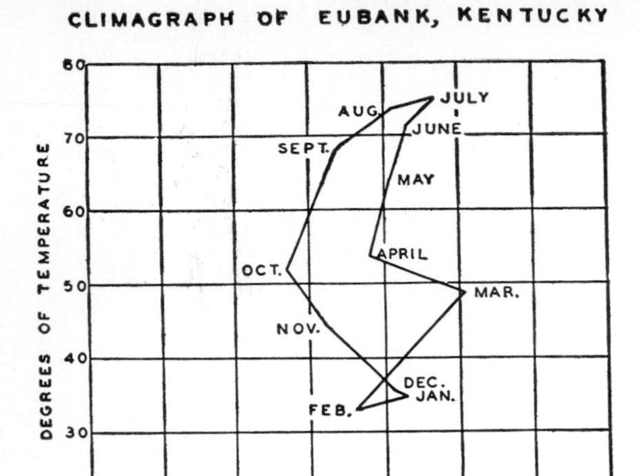


**Fig. 213** A monthly rainfall-temperature climatograph will have a characteristic shape for every locality.

and with latitude, is usually shown by such a diagram.

**Triangle Graphs.** Three variables expressed in percentages can be shown well on triangular graphs (see Fig. 212). These diagrams are used to indicate composition of rocks, soils, etc., but any threefold division can be thus shown.

**Climatographs (Climagraphs or Climographs).** In these graphs the temperature is laid out according to the vertical coordinate, rainfall along the horizontal coordinate, and the points thus established for every month are connected. This way a characteristic figure can be obtained for every region. More complex climatographs were made by Stephen Visher, as in Fig. 214. Here four variables (rainfall, temperature, time, and yield of grain) are shown on a single diagram, giving a most useful method of prognosticating crops.

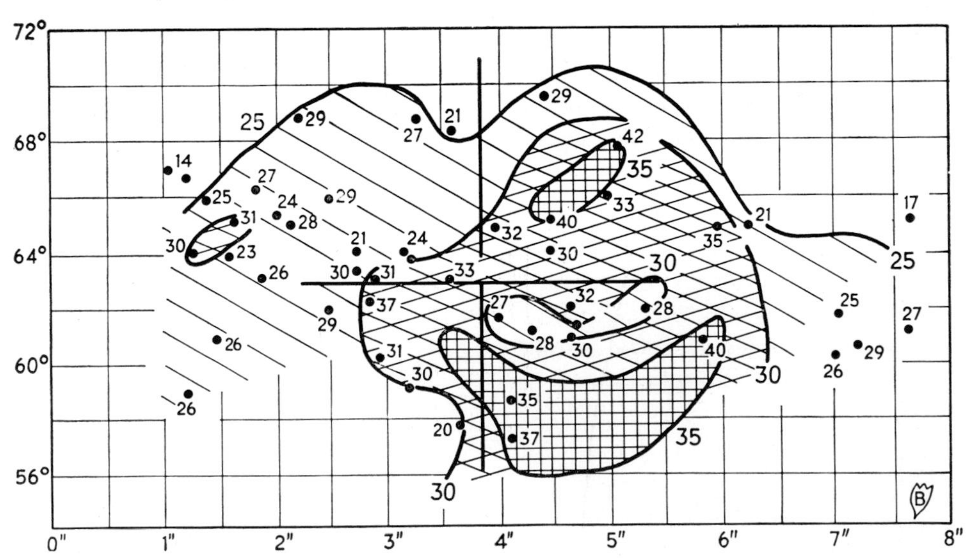

**Fig. 214** This kind of climatograph is used in forecasting crops. Numbers represent the yield of wheat in Indiana, placed according to spring rainfall and temperature of each year 1887–1939. Darker shading means higher yields. Best yields are in the years of wet and cool spring.

# CHAPTER 26: *Statistical Maps*

To put life into these inert masses of figures, to bring out their hidden meaning and expose the comparative significance of factors in area, either individually or fused in index combinations to admit valid comparison, they must be visualized with the area from which they came. This can only be done graphically through symbolized representation. (F. J. Marschner.)

## Maps of Nonquantitative Areal Distribution

In this group are included the maps that show the areal distribution of a certain element without taking into account the density of distribution. For instance, a map may show by color, pattern, or tint the distribution of forest in the United States. Some other maps show how the land is divided according to the various types or subdivisions of a certain element, for instance, soil maps, geological maps, or maps showing various forms of government. Maps of dominant areal distribution show how the land is divided in the case of a mixed distribution, as, for instance, vegetation, language, or religion, showing only the dominant type. A map showing agricultural regions of the United States belongs to this group.

The cartography of qualitative areal distribution is relatively simple. The most common is the *color-patch* (chorochromatic) method by which the area of distribution is distinctly colored or tinted. This method is applied to most geological, soil, or political maps. The colors or tints are either sharply outlined or, in the case of transitional distribution, they may merge into each other. Such are the technical difficulties, however, in reproducing merged tints that they are rarely used even in the case of such transitional distributions as maps of religions or races.

In chorochromatic maps it is important that the colors of similar distributions should be related. In early geological maps it was customary to differentiate adjacent formations with widely different colors to make the distinction very apparent. The result, however, was so confusing that a conventional color scheme was adopted in which the formations of various geologic areas are colored in a sequence that more or less follows the chromatic scale of yellow, green, blue, violet, red; individual formations may be differentiated by various hues or overprinted patterns.

Another method of drawing maps of areal distribution is to cover the area with *small semipictorial symbols* (choroschematic maps). This method is used chiefly for land utilization and vegetation maps (see Fig. 291).

Still another method of showing areal distribution is used where the various distributions, such as geological formations

**Fig. 215** Interdigitation is a common but somewhat misleading way to show mixed or transitional values.

or land-use types, are sharply outlined and marked with *index figures and letters*. This method is used mostly in combination with the previous methods. The weather maps showing air masses (Fig. 289) belong to this type.

Difficulties may arise in the case of mixed or transitional distribution. In the color-patch maps the most common is the interdigitation method, according to Fig. 215. This is at best a poor substitute, and if the colors are not contained in each other, as for instance yellow in green, they may become confusing by disregistration. Better results are obtained by the choroschematic method, where the symbols can actually be mixed on border areas. For instance, dotting and hachuring can well blend into each other (see the geological column in Fig. 272).

The various methods of qualitative maps will be discussed in more detail in Part Seven in connection with maps of the various sciences.

## Statistical Maps

In this group belong the maps that show the variation in the value, amount, or density of various distributions, such as rainfall maps, population maps, and other statistical maps. The variation in quantity is expressed by various devices, such as isopleths, dots, choropleths, and small diagrams placed over the map.

**Isopleths.** Isopleths are lines on a map which connect places of equal density or value of distribution of any certain element. If such lines connect places of equal tem-

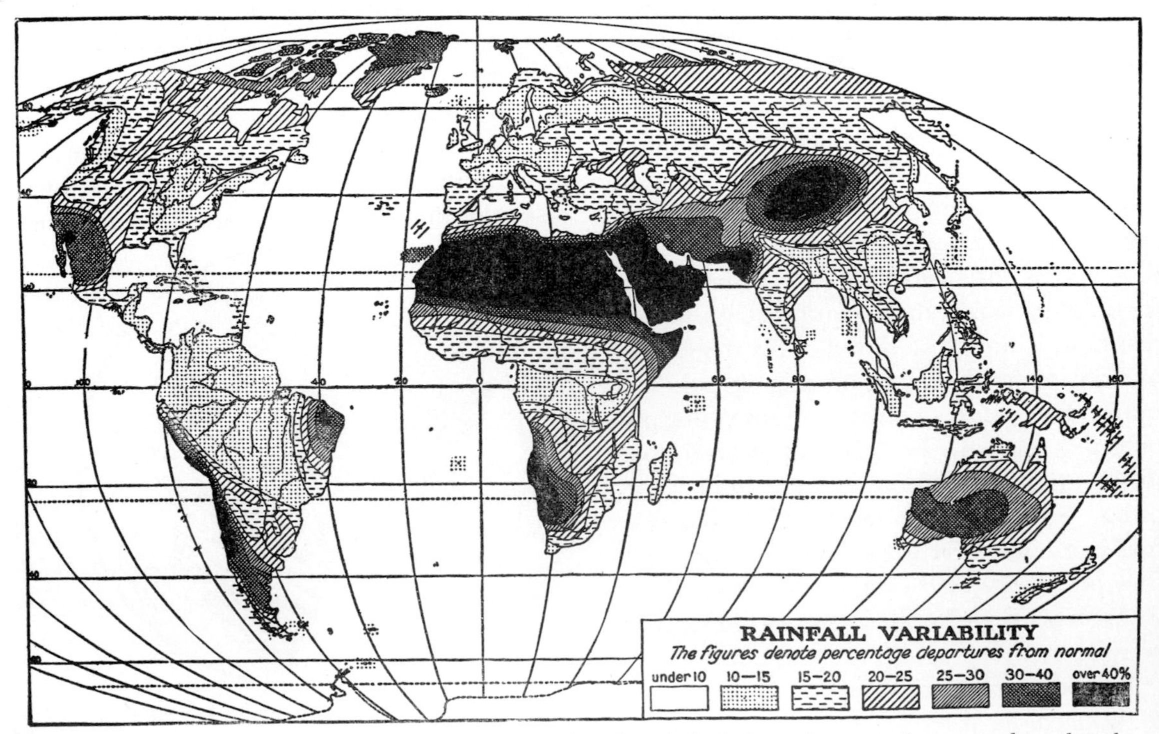


**Fig. 216** Isopleth map, with tints which are selected so that their darkness is proportionate to the value they represent. (*From Trewartha, "An Introduction to Weather and Climate."*)

perature, they are called "isotherms"; places of equal rainfall are connected with "isohyets"; barometric pressure is shown by "isobars"; magnetic variation, by "isogones"; and places of equal elevation are expressed with "isohypses," commonly called contour lines.

The term "isopleth" (*isos* = same; *plethron* = measure) is by no means generally accepted. Some authors use the term "isarithm" (*arithmos* = number) or "isogram." Others restrict the use of the term "isopleth" to lines showing density of population only. Most European authors call them "isarithms." John K. Wright makes a differentiation between isarithms and isopleths. If the lines represent a continuous value, such as temperature or elevation, they are called isarithms; if the lines indicate an average number of individual units, as density of population or acreage of agricultural products, they are called "isopleths." The two types of lines are drawn in the same manner, but the mathematical concept differs. Between the 40- and the 60-foot contour lines the elevation is everywhere between 40 and 60 feet, but it is not true that the density of population at any point between the 40 and 60 isopleths corresponds to 40 to 60 people per square mile. For instance, if the maps were made on such a large scale that every individual man would be visible, there would be extreme concentration at every man, and empty spaces between. The isopleth map in this case would be the same as a map in the dot system.

However important this difference is mathematically, from the point of view of the practical cartographer, the two types of lines serve the same purpose and in the discussions which follow, the term "isopleth" is adopted for both generic types. The question of terminology, however, is still open.[1]

In a more recent article, J. K. Wright proposed the term "isogram" for these lines. As the term "gram" means rather a complete design, as diagram or econogram, than only a line in it, this term seems to be less expressive.

[1] See Isopleth as a Generic Term, *Geog. Rev.*, Vol. 20, p. 341, 1930.

The nature of isopleths has already been discussed in connection with contour lines. They are reckoned from a datum plane or zero isopleth and drawn at certain selected intervals, and the density of distribution at any one place can be determined within the isopleth interval. Where isopleths are close the variation is sharp. The exactness of the map depends on the isopleth interval, which is selected in accordance with the scale of the map and the available data. Isopleths are usually marked with numbers as are contour lines.

Isopleths share not only the advantages but also the deficiencies of contour lines. They give and demand exact information, and where this is not available they cannot be used. Isopleths can be used only where the distribution is fairly transitional; they are not adapted to show greatly variable elements, such as density of population.

**Tints.** To make contour lines more expressive, altitude tints are used; in the same way, the belts between isopleths are often colored or tinted in a graduated color scheme. If the map is reproduced in colors, a fine graduation of a great number of tints is easily possible, but on a black-and-white map the number of tints is limited. Mechanical patterns of variable darkness, ranging from dotted, ruled, and cross-ruled patterns to solid black, can produce from 5 to 10 shades, but the general effect is often confusing, for lettering must be placed in frames in the darker portions. It is important that the degree of darkness of the tints should be in proportion to the value represented. This can be controlled by measuring with a magnifying glass the proportion of the black and white areas. Some recent experiments show that even the exact proportions of black and white areas will not produce the correct impression.[1] It has been found that to produce even gradations, the lighter tints should be made of closely set fine lines, and the darker tints of widely set heavy lines. If mechanical tints (Zip-a-tone,

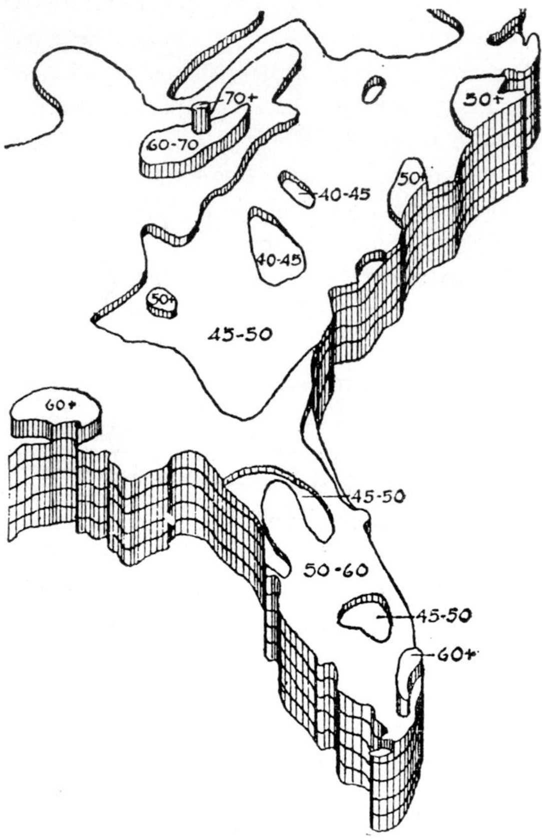


**Fig. 217** Part of a built-up isopleth map, showing the annual rainfall of the United States. (*Courtesy of National Resources Committee.*)

Craftint, etc.) are used, better results are achieved by choosing quiet dotted or lined patterns than the more fancy ones.

If the map can be reproduced in half tone, various shades of wash can be applied. The darkness of hue of the tints should be proportionate to the amount represented. This can be accomplished by making a large amount of the darkest tint and diluting it with a proportionate amount of water for every gradation. Wash is likely to be patchy, however, if painted by unskilled hands. More foolproof are the gray poster colors that can be purchased in five or six even gradations of darkness. It should be borne in mind that half-tone reproduction causes white surfaces to appear light gray. The tints can be made exactly proportionate to the value only if no extreme values are present. For example, on a rainfall map of the United States, if the area of 200 inches of rainfall is represented by black, most of the United States, if exactly proportioned, would have its rainfall represented in too light a shade. It is better to have the area of more than a 100-inch rainfall all black.

**Isopleth Maps Showing Percentages.** An important use of isopleths is in the "ratio" or "percentage" maps. In these maps not the actual quantities but the ratios of certain quantities to others are shown. From the geographer's point of view it is often more important to know what percentage of all land is cultivated in cotton than to know the absolute amount of cotton land in a certain territory. Cartographically the ratio maps do not present special difficulties, since they are drawn in the same manner as the simple isopleth maps. Ratio maps are discussed in detail in "Ratios and Isopleth Maps . . . ," by Wellington D. Jones, *Annals of the Association of American Geographers*, Vol. 20, pp. 177–195, 1930.

*Built-up Isopleth Models.* If each isopleth is cut out from cardboard, and these cardboards are built up on each other, the result is a statistical relief model of distribution. Such a model gives a vivid visual impression. To locate places on such models it is simple to cut the base map into belts along each isopleth and to paste these belts on top of the cardboards. An effect similar to that of a model can be obtained on a flat map by

[1] JONES, LLOYD A., and LEONARD STONE, "Graded Shadings on Statistical Maps," American Geographical Society and Population Association of America, 1938.

vertically offsetting each isopleth to the height that its value represents, as shown in Fig. 217. Cities, rivers, and boundaries must also be vertically offset to a corresponding degree.

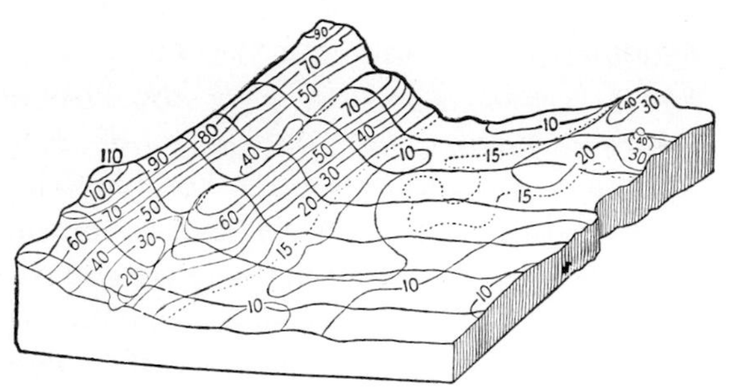

**Fig. 218** Isometric diagram of the rainfall of Oregon.

For better visualization of distribution, an isopleth map may be transformed into an isometric block diagram in the same way that a contour-line map is transformed. The various methods of transformation are discussed in Chap. 24. Such an isometric distribution map is shown in Fig. 220.

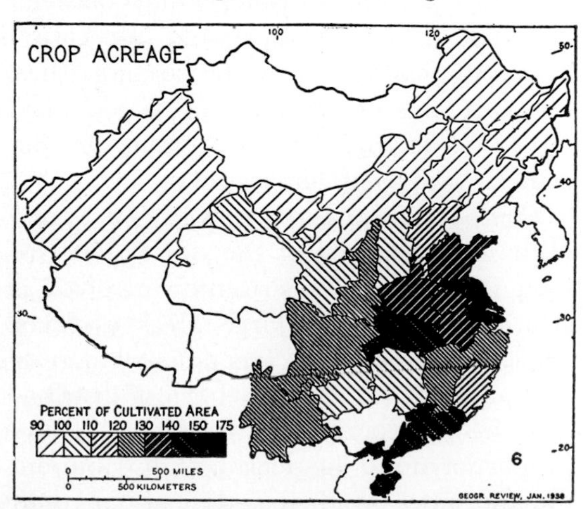


**Fig. 219** A choropleth map by Glenn T. Trewartha. (*Courtesy of Geog. Rev.*, 1938.)

**Choropleth Maps of Distribution.** Statistical data are usually available by counties, townships, or other civil divisions. The simplest way to show these data on a map is to tint the civil divisions with

AVERAGE ASSESSED VALUE OF LOTS IN DENVER, 1931

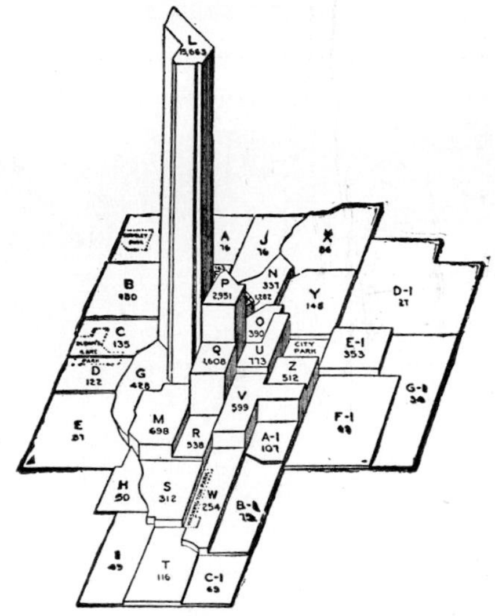

**Fig. 220** Isometric choropleth map. (*From University of Denver, Bureau of Business Research.*)

graduated lines or with colors, the degree of darkness of which is proportionate to the value represented.[1]

Generally such a map will not give a true picture of distribution, because in most cases it is not at the county or township line where the value changes. In every book or atlas of the United States there are many maps that show statistical distribution by states only. Since American state boundaries are singularly deficient in their line-up with natural boundaries, such choropleth maps by states will give a particularly false picture of distribution. For instance, on certain statistical maps Indiana and Illinois will appear very different, owing to the fact that Chicago is situated in one extremity of the latter state. Whenever possible, a geographer will strive to transform a choropleth map into an isopleth or dotted map, but he will often be prevented by the

[1] The term "choropleth" (quantity in area) is not necessarily limited to civil divisions. If the area were divided into squares and tinted proportionately, this would also make a choropleth map.

lack of detail in the available statistical data. Choropleth maps can be easily transformed into isometric diagrams which give a vivid portrayal of distribution.

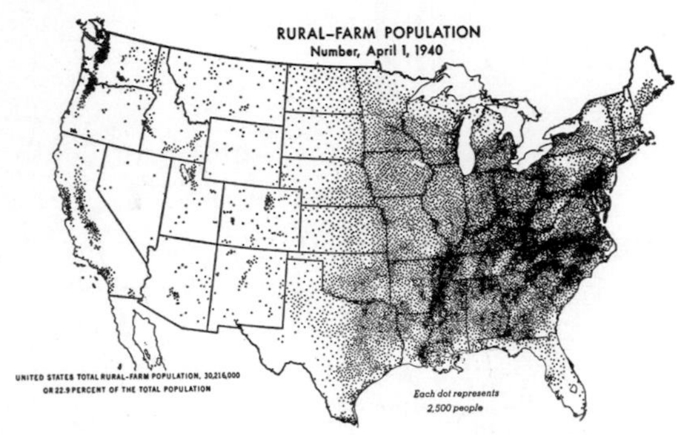


**Fig. 221** Dot map. (*Courtesy of U.S. Department of Agriculture.*)

**Dot Maps.** In this system the density of distribution is represented by dots of uniform size. Each dot represents a given quantity, perhaps 5,000 people or 1,000 acres of farm land. The size of the dots and the value for which they stand should be fixed so that the dots just coalesce in a solid mass at the place of greatest density and in other places be proportionately distributed. Uniformity in the size of the dots can be obtained by the use of various ball-point, Payzant, LeRoy, or similar pens. It is well to remember that the dots tend to clog together in reproduction if they are spaced too closely in drafting. In many maps the dots appear too large or too close, simply because the effect of the engraving processes was not taken into account.

The placing of dots must be done with an understanding of the distribution. As a general rule, every dot should be in the center of gravity of distribution in the region it represents. For instance, if we have, in a distribution-of-population map, a single dot representing a certain number of people in a township, the dot will be placed in the part of the township that is the "center of population."[1] Practically, dot maps are on such small scale that the exact centers are not calculated; their exact location depends on the sense of proportion and on the geographic knowledge of the cartographer. If the statistical data are available by counties, the dots should be agglomerated in that part of the county which is most likely to have the largest quantity. Hence, the knowledge of geographic conditions is essential. For example, in Arizona, alfalfa will be shown in the irrigated valleys and not in the arid uplands. If a county lies between a heavily dotted and an almost empty region, and if the value to be shown is intermediate, the dots are likely to be concentrated in that part of the county which is nearest its heavily dotted neighbor, assuming that the distribution is transitional.

As a rule, only one variable is shown on a dot map. It is possible to show two widely separated distributions on the same map, as, for instance, sugar cane and sugar beets. It is also possible to differentiate between varieties, as between dairy and beef cattle. This differentiation can be accomplished by using dots of different shape—circular, square, triangular, full or empty in the center—or dots of various colors.

**Comparison of Isopleth and Dot Maps.** Both the isopleth and the dot system are used wherever the distribution involved is relatively even over large areas and not concentrated in cities. The dot system gives a clearer picture of the pattern of distribution, for the darkness of the map is always proportionate to the density of distribution. On the other hand, it is difficult to count the dots where they are close together and not supplemented by exact figures that may be used for reference. Isopleths do not show the variations so vividly as does the dot system, but at every place the actual density can be read by figures. This comparison recalls to mind the difference between

[1] See "Centrograms" in Chap. 27.

hachure lines and contour lines in depicting topography. The choice of system depends on the problem. Isopleths are used almost exclusively to show ratios or percentages and gradations of a condition that can be measured by instruments or by money, as temperature, rainfall, land values, etc. The dot system is used chiefly where the quantity of individual units is involved, such as number of cattle or acreage of corn. Often, however, either method is equally satisfactory. In scientific papers the tendency is to favor isopleths; in educational maps the dot system is often preferred on account of its illustrative quality. A combination of isopleths and dot system is sometimes recommended.

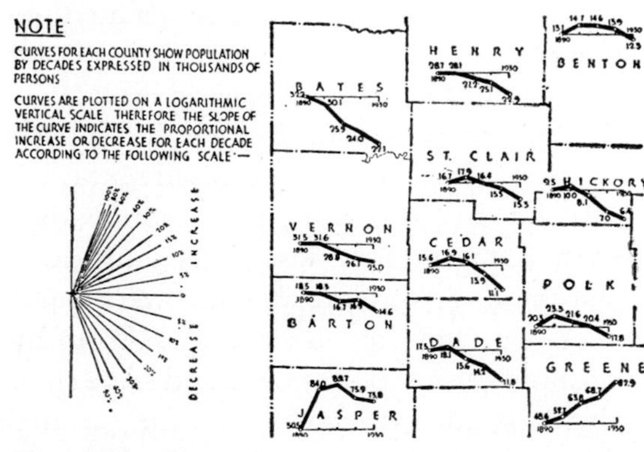


**Fig. 222** Statistical map with logarithmic line graphs showing the rate of change in the population of Missouri. (*Courtesy of Missouri State Planning Board Report*, 1937.)

**Statistical Maps with Individual Diagrams.** A large group of statistical maps consist of a number of small diagrams distributed all over the map. This method is used (1) when there are not sufficiently detailed data to prepare an isopleth or dotted map, as in presenting the value of mineral production by states; (2) when it is desired to show variation within the distribution, as in placing line graphs all over the map; (3) when the variable is subdivided; (4) when there are several variables; (5) when there is extremely variable or very concentrated distribution, as in a map of manufacturing.

Almost every kind of diagram can be placed upon a map. Only the most important types are described in the following sections.

*Bar-graph Maps.* In bar-graph maps all bars are vertical and have the same width, and their length is proportionate to the quantity represented. The bottom of the bars points to the exact location. Bar-graph maps are easily commensurable and are recommended if they do not involve the use of inconveniently long bars. Bars can be subdivided, and the subdivisions marked by different tints. If two or more different but related distributions are shown, two or more differently tinted bars can be placed next to each other. For instance, the birth rate and the death rate can be shown by this method.

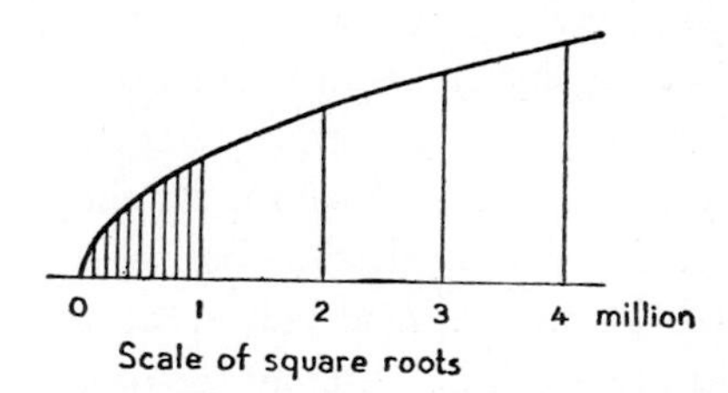


**Fig. 223** This type of scale is used for finding the radii of pie graphs.

*Pie-graph Maps.* In this system the distribution is shown on the map by circles of different sizes, the area of each circle being proportionate to the amount to be represented. Thus, the radii of the circles will be proportionate to the square roots of the quantities. The quickest way to obtain square roots is with a slide rule. It is a simple matter to prepare a scale for these circles, as shown in Fig. 223. The scale of the circles should be as large as possible without overcrowding in the dense places. It is permissible for circles to cut into each other if this does not make the map confusing. A circle may also be subdivided, and the sub-

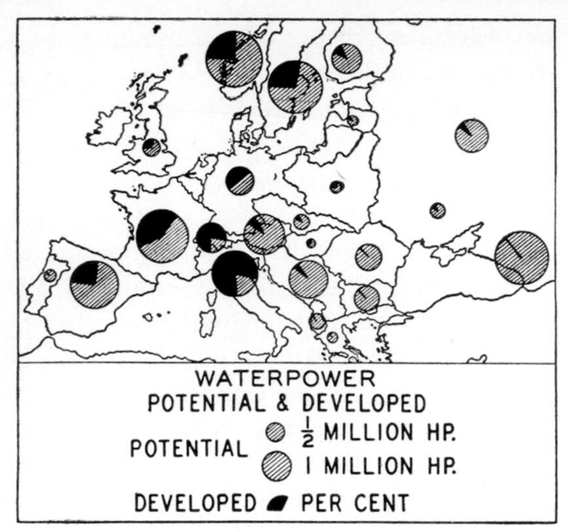


**Fig. 224** Pie graphs are often used on statistical maps. (*From Whitbeck and Finch, "Economic Geography."*)

divisions marked by various tints and colors. It adds greatly to the value of a pie-graph map, if each graph is labeled with its exact numerical value. Pie-graph maps are often used in books and atlases. Although they are not so easily commensurable as bar-graph maps, they are more likely to show a highly variable distribution, for they can be smaller in size and can be more closely packed on maps. The center of the circle should always be at the center of gravity of the distribution. For instance, in a map of manufacturing shown by states, the circle for Illinois should be in the northern part of the state.

*Square-graph Maps and Other Two-dimensional Graphs.* These are used chiefly in combination with the circle system to differentiate between various crops or other distributions on the same map. Any regular figure of plane geometry, such as triangles or rhombs, can be used as needed. The areas of the figures are proportionate to the quantities represented.

Different-sized squares, circles, and other shapes are not easily commensurable. Better results are obtained if they are arranged in countable units, such as rows or groups of squares, circles, triangles, or pictorial figures which can be counted. Each unit then represents a certain quantity. The groups should be within their political boundaries, but there is usually a greater freedom of spacing than in the previous groups (see Figs. 269 and 292).

*Sphere-graph Maps.* This method is used when the variation in the distribution is extreme, as in maps of distribution of manufacturing since this activity is concentrated in relatively few cities. The radius of each sphere is proportionate to the cube root of the quantity. A graphic scale can also be easily constructed. The center of the sphere marks the exact location of the city, or the center of gravity of a larger area. Usually the various-sized spheres are printed on gummed paper and pasted in their proper places (see Fig. 227). The advantage of using spheres instead of circles is that spheres can be packed closer. The disadvantage is that the spheres cannot be subdivided. When they are too close, it is difficult to label them. Sphere-graph maps were introduced by Sten de Geer in 1917 in his population maps of Sweden, and have since gained great popularity in the United States.

*Block-pile Maps.* To avoid the many disadvantages of the sphere system, we may use block piles or similarly grouped small cylinders, or piles of coins. Block piles can be just as closely packed as spheres, and the advantage of having countable units gives them a great superiority over the other method. Block piles can also be more easily labeled on maps. Block-pile maps can be used with advantage for maps of manufacturing, mining production, etc., wherever the distribution is highly concentrated (see Fig. 267). The possibilities of this method have yet to be explored.

*Other Diagrammatic Maps.* In his "China's Geographic Foundations" George B. Cressey[1] uses a map wherein mineral production in China is shown by letters of various sizes (Fig. 266). The height of the letter is roughly proportionate to the square root of the production. The disadvantage of this system is that the letter *I* will look smaller than the letter *C* of the same height. The method is justified in this case, however, because many different minerals are shown on one small map, and the quantities indicated are approximations.

*Pictorial Statistical Maps.* Since almost every diagram can be substituted by pictorial graphs, statistical maps are often rendered more vivid by their use. Even dots on a map can be transformed into minute pictures of sheep, houses, or whatever they may represent. The obvious difficulty in this rendering is that even very small pictures take up more space than dots, and thus each little sheep symbol has to represent a larger number of sheep.

*Pictograms.* Statistical maps upon which the distribution is expressed by means of bar graphs, unit graphs, grouped graphs, or block piles lend themselves particularly well to pictorial representation. Little houses, men, tanks, bales, or piles of coins on a map given an impression of distribution that is easily grasped and remembered by children and the public in general. Even in the various reports of national and state planning boards such maps are used in great variety. The chief objection to this pictorial presentation is that the pictures are exceedingly out of scale as compared with the scale of the map. If, however, the map is shown only by outlines, more or less as the background for the statistics, such an arrangement is permissible.

Less satisfactory are the pictorial statistical maps on which the distribution is represented by pictorial figures, the sizes of which are proportionate to the quantities. For instance, the distribution of horses throughout the various countries of the world may be represented by figures of horses of different sizes. Correct proportions are obtained if the height of each symbol is proportionate to the cube root of the number of horses in each country. This rule is often violated. The disadvantage of this method is that the pictures are not easily comparable.

**Fig. 225** Pictorial map of Northern Argentina showing distribution of crops with different-sized pictorial symbols. (*From "Serial Maps."*)

**Density-of-population Maps.** For the geographer the most important distribution on the earth is its population. Density-of-population maps constitute one of the most debated problems of cartography. The essential difficulty in preparing these maps lies in the very unequal distribution of population due to urban centers. Density of urban population may reach 100,000 people per square mile, whereas rural population is considered to be very dense with only 100 people per square mile. One-third of the earth's land has less than

[1] Cressey, G. B., "China's Geographic Foundations," McGraw-Hill Book Company, Inc., New York, 1933.

two persons per square mile. Such inequalities cannot be expressed by either a dot system or by isopleths unless the map is drawn on a very large scale.

Several methods have been proposed to overcome this difficulty. In one method the whole population is shown by a dot system, and where the dots run together into a solid mass the urban population is shown separately by circles. The size of the dots and the number of people represented by each depends on the scale of the map and the density involved. The area of the circles is proportionate to the population of the cities. The center of the circles is at the exact location of the cities, and their area is in proportion to the size of the dots. For example, if a dot $\frac{1}{50}$ inch in diameter represents 100 people, a city with 10,000 population will have a circle 10 times the diameter, or $\frac{1}{5}$ inch, because

$$\frac{\sqrt{10,000}}{\sqrt{100}} = \frac{100}{10} = 10$$

A circle of this size will cover a considerable rural area; hence it must be transparent, so that the dots underneath may be visible. The usual method of making it transparent is by the application of a color or a fine tint. Where cities are close together,

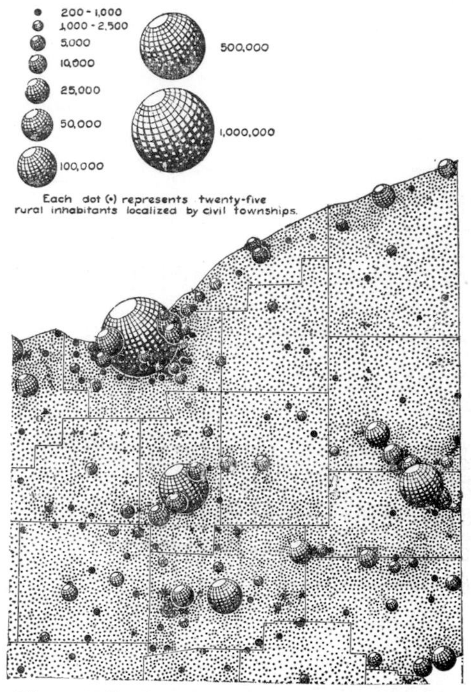


**Fig. 227** Density of population map. Spherical symbols stand out clearly, but they are not easily commensurable. (*Map by Guy-Harold Smith, Geog. Rev.*, 1928.)

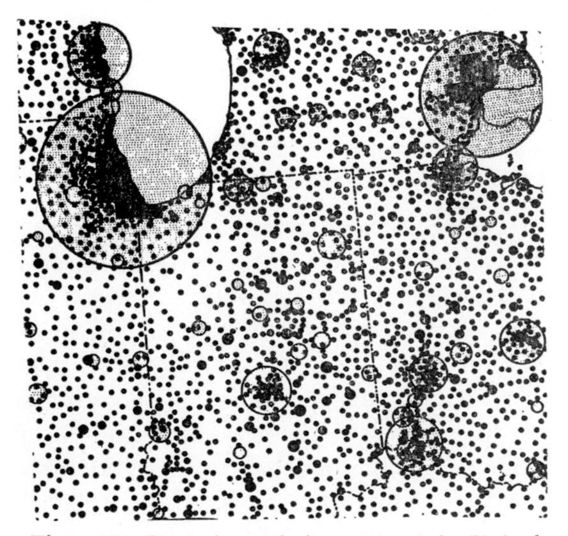

**Fig. 226** Part of population map of the United States by F. D. Stilgenbauer. Transparent circles show urban population. (*Rand McNally & Company*, 1932.)

the circles will overlap. It is easier to show the large population of metropolitan districts by means of a single circle than to show each suburb separately.[1] Stilgenbauer's map (Fig. 226) is a good example of this type.

Another method of showing density of population was presented by Sten de Geer in 1917.[2] A grouped dot system was used for rural population, and small spheres for urban population; the cubic root of the

[1] STILGENBAUER, FLOYD D., "A New Population Map of the United States," Rand McNally & Company, Chicago, 1932.

[2] STEN DE GEER, A Map of the Distribution of Population in Sweden, *Geog. Rev.*, Vol. 12, pp. 72–83, 1922.

spheres was proportionate to the population. These spheres occupy much less space than circles of corresponding size. Thus, in the previous case, a city with a population of 10,000 would be represented by a sphere

$$\frac{\sqrt[3]{10,000}}{\sqrt[3]{100}} = \frac{21.54}{4.46} = 4.64$$

less than 5 times the diameter of the dot. If one dot of $\frac{1}{50}$ inch in diameter represents 100 people, the city is represented by a sphere of $\frac{1}{10}$ inch in diameter. This sphere occupies one-fourth as much space as the corresponding circle, as calculated in the previous paragraph. A sphere of such small size on a reasonably large-scale map covers not much more than the actual location of the city. Nevertheless, it is often necessary to move some dots or smaller spheres in order to avoid crowding.

In comparing the two methods, it is evident that the spheres will give a more vivid picture of distribution but are not so easily commensurable as the circles. Furthermore, circles can be subdivided to show, for instance, white and colored population, whereas spheres are not so divisible. It is also less difficult to draw overlapping circles than overlapping spheres, but in the case of spheres there is less need for overlapping.

Neither type of map can have lettering, for the bulk of the letters would ruin the dot effect. Boundary lines and rivers are shown only when they are necessary for location. They are then drawn with very fine lines or in different colors.

Successful experiments were made to use the block-pile system instead of spheres. They can be more easily compared and labeled, and the blocks are somewhat more indicative of a city than spheres.

More generalized small-scale density of population maps are often made by using isopleths. The obvious advantage of this method is that the figures of density can be directly read within the limits of the isopleth interval, but the picture seldom indicates adequately the enormous difference of density. It is possible, however, to show rural density with isopleths and urban density with spheres or blocks.

# CHAPTER 27: *Cartograms*

The term "cartogram" is subject to many interpretations and definitions. Every map departs to a certain degree from the original conception—a picture of the earth's pattern—in abstraction, conventionalization, and selective use of its elements. How "diagrammatic" a map must be in order to be called a cartogram depends largely on individual judgment. Some authors, especially in Europe, call every statistical map a cartogram, because it shows the pattern of distribution of a single element. This idea, however justified, is somewhat contrary to American usage, since it is customary to speak of rainfall "maps," dot "maps," etc. In the following discussions the term is restricted to any highly abstracted, simplified map, the purpose of which is to demonstrate a single idea in a diagrammatic way.

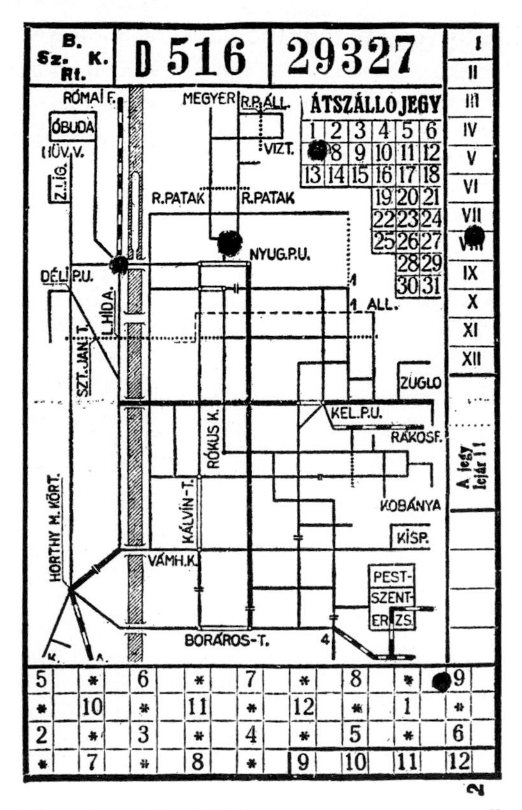


**Fig. 228** Simplified cartograms are well understood by the trolley conductors of Budapest.

The most conservative use of the term is for those maps in which even the outlines of the land or the exact locations of other features are altered. In accordance with this latter definition, the railroad map shown in Fig. 183 is a good example of a cartogram. Here the southern part is constricted, the lines are straightened and simplified, and only general directions are retained. Even more abstracted cartograms are used to show electric power, telegraph, and postal systems in a diagrammatic way. The Roman Peutinger Tables are typical cartograms; and so are the T-in-O maps of the Middle Ages. The Hereford map, however, with its enormous Holy Land, cannot properly be called a "cartogram," since it is an imaginary conception of the world rather than a purposeful distortion.

Cartograms are useful tools of modern geography, and their possibilities are not yet fully explored. The invention of new designs is a fruitful field for cartographers. Only a few types are discussed here.

**Diagrammatic Maps in Teaching.** The teacher of geography or of history—even if he has only moderate drawing ability—can stimulate the interest of his students by drawing on the blackboard simple diagrammatic maps on which all detail is omitted, lines are straightened and simplified, and only those places are shown that have a direct bearing on the subject.[1] By so doing the teacher is no more lax than the textbook which omits much detail and emphasizes only the important points.

[1] See White, Helen M., Diagrammatic Map Making, *Jour. Geog.*, Vol. 32, pp. 242–244, 1933.

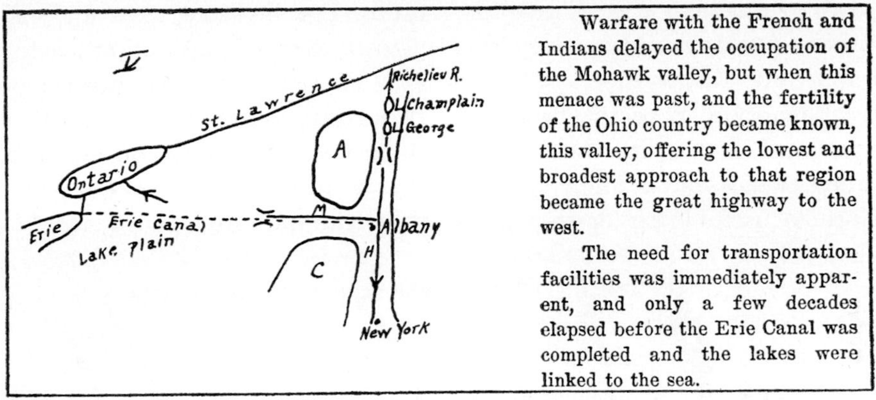


**Fig. 229** Diagrammatic map for teaching, by Helen M. White. (*Courtesy of Jour. Geog.* 1938.)

Figure 229 is a good example of how to draw simple diagrammatic maps. Equally simple methods for freehand drawing of diagrammatic maps of the various continents is demonstrated in Fig. 157.

**Value-area Cartograms.** In these cartograms a region, country, or continent is subdivided into small regions, each of which is represented by a rectangle. This rectangle is proportionate in area to the value which it represents in certain statistical distributions. The regions are grouped in approximately the same positions as they are on the map. For comparison of different distributions, it is important that the same arrangement be followed whatever may be the distribution represented. It is advisable to begin with the larger divisions and arrive at the smaller ones by "proportionate halving," as shown in Fig. 230. Calculation can be made readily with a slide rule, and the cartogram can be drawn on checkered paper. It is convenient to select a scale so that one small square of the checkered paper corresponds to a round number of units, such as 100,000 people or 1,000,000 dollars, but this is by no means necessary.[1]

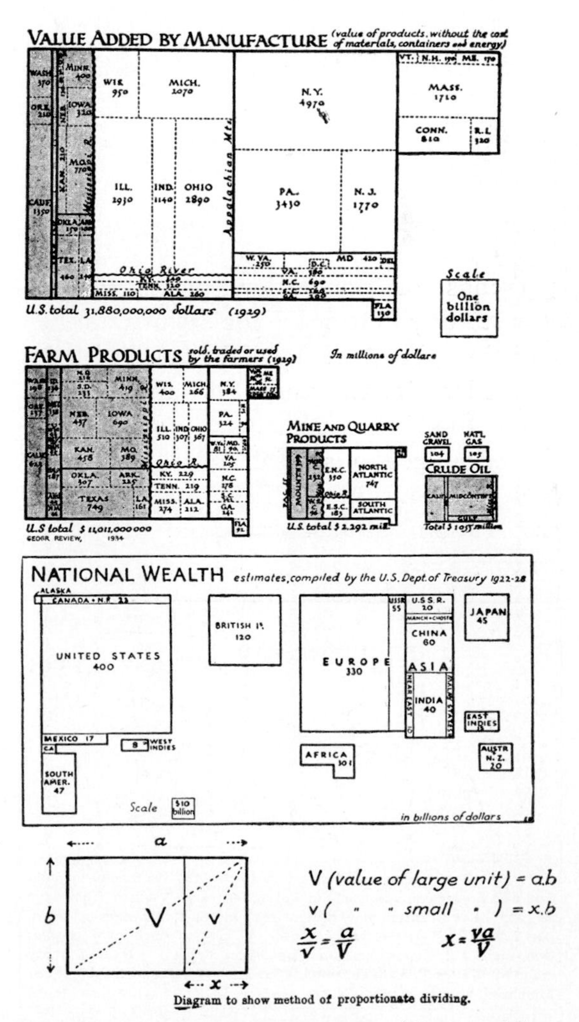


**Fig. 230** Value = area cartograms. (*Courtesy of Geog. Rev.*, 1934; *Jour. Geog.* 1936.)

[1] For further details of this method see Erwin Raisz, The Rectangular Statistical Cartogram, *Geog. Rev.*, Vol. 24, pp. 292–296, 1934; and Rectangular Statistical Cartograms of the World, *Jour. Geog.*, Vol. 35, pp. 8–10, 1936.

Value-area cartograms help a great deal in our geographic thinking. Almost every humanly important distribution in the United States resembles more the proportions shown in Fig. 230 than the usual map to which we are accustomed. These cartograms also form a useful base for showing ratios. For instance, dots for wage earners placed over a population cartogram will show the real picture of industrial population. In no way is it necessary to use rectangles; rhomboids, triangles, or any other shapes can be used so long as the area is proportionate to the value, as in Figs. 231 and 293.

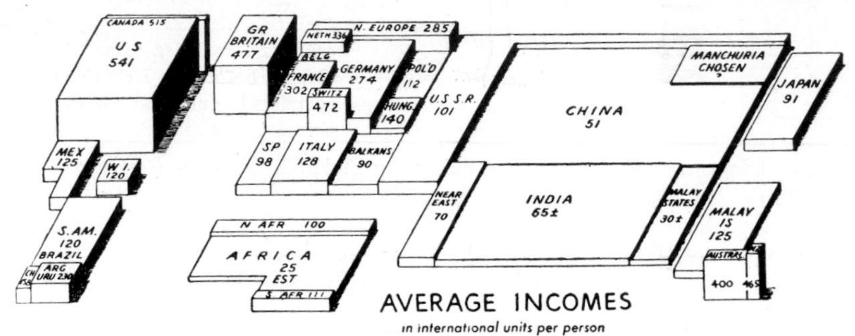


**Fig. 231** The area of the bases of the various countries is proportionate to their population; height represents per capita incomes.

## Centrograms

Trends of population, industry, and almost any element for which ample statistical data are available can well be shown by a centrogram. So important has this method become lately that the U.S.S.R. has organized a special office, the Mendelyeev Institute at Leningrad, for the preparation of centrographic maps or centrograms.

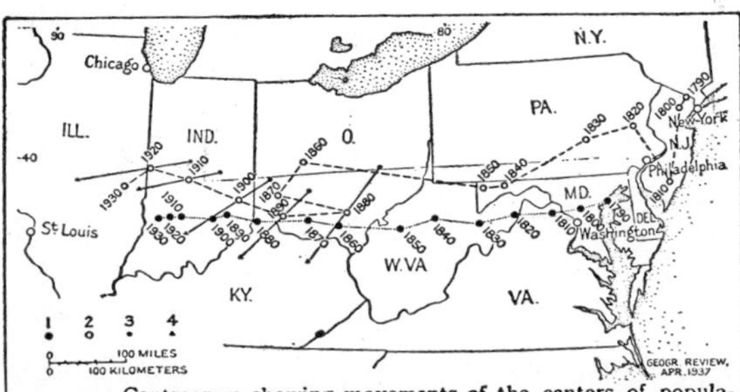


Centrogram showing movements of the centers of population and higher education in the United States of America from 1790 to 1930 Key: centers of 1, general population; 2, higher educational population (universities and colleges); 3, higher educational population, men; 4, higher educational population, women. (From a study made by Walter C. Eells for publication in the forthcoming Mendeleev Memorial Volume of the Centrographical Laboratory in Leningrad.)

**Fig. 232** Centrogram. (*Courtesy of Geog. Rev., April,* 1937.)

As early as 1874, the "Statistical Atlas of the United States," compiled by Francis A. Walker, presented a map showing the center of population of the country for each census year since 1790. J. E. Hilgard of the Coast Survey made an earlier and similar computation which included definitions and computations for centrograms.[1]

There are several kinds of possible centers. The center of population is defined as "a point upon which the United States would balance if it were a rigid plane without weight, and the population were distributed thereon, each individual being assumed to have equal weight and to exert an influence on the central point proportionate to his distance from the point." This point is also called the *center of gravity* or *pivotal point*.

[1] SLOANE, CHARLES S., "Center of Population and Median Lines, and Centers of Area, Agriculture, Manufactures and Cotton, Etc.," Fourteenth Census of the United States (1920), Washington, D. C., pp. 12–41, 1923.

The actual construction of this point requires considerable work. First, it is assumed that the center is at a certain point, and through this point a parallel and a meridian are drawn. The country is then divided into small areas, perhaps square degrees, and the population of each such area is multiplied by its distance from the assumed parallel, thus giving its north or south movement. In a similar manner the east and west movement can be calculated. If the sum of the opposite movements does not balance, the assumed parallel and meridian have to be shifted until it does balance. Greater accuracy can be attained if, instead of a parallel, a great circle running east-west is used. Theoretically an oblique azimuthal equidistant projection should be constructed centered on the assumed center point, and if the assumption proved to be far wrong a new projection should be constructed. It is also possible to calculate the pivotal point of each state and work with the states as units of area.

*Median Point.* Sometimes, since its computation is simpler, the so-called "median point" is used instead of the center point. This median point may be described as the numerical center of population irrespective of the distances of the units from the center. Usually a parallel and a meridian are figured, which bisect the population of the country. The intersection of the lines is the median point.

The median point is different from the center-of-gravity point. For instance, the entire population of Minnesota might move to Oregon without affecting the median point; but this movement would considerably affect the center point of gravity.

For regional analysis the first type, the center of gravity, is the most significant, and is worked out for many countries. Not only the centers of population but also the centers of agriculture, manufacturing, schools, and other distributions can be expressed by centrograms. A center of the *area* of the United States could be found by constructing a map on an oblique, azimuthal, equidistant projection centered on an assumed center point. This map, if cut from cardboard, will balance on the center point.

All problems of centrography get a new meaning if applied to the entire spherical surface of the earth. The center of the earth's land surface was obtained[1] by taking a light globe and covering all lands with an even sheet of lead. Immersing this globe in water, it came to rest with a point at the bottom upon which all lands balance. This center is near the Rumanian-Bulgarian boundary where it reaches the Black Sea, not far from Varna (see Fig. 72). The median point of the earth's population, using parallels and meridians, was found to be near Lahore, India. The median points of wealth, foreign trade, land centers of the land, and people's hemispheres all clustered in or around France.

*Quartilides and Decilides.* The evenness of distribution of certain elements can well be shown by quartilides or decilides.[2] These points are constructed in the same way as the median point, except that they are not derived from the bisection of the population with a single parallel and meridian. Instead, the population is divided by 3, 4, 10, or any desired number of parallels and meridians, each spaced according to the corresponding fraction of the population.

The chief purpose of all centrograms is to discover the trends of population and its distribution, primarily for regional planning. Their preparation is even recom-

[1] Raisz, Erwin, Our Lopsided Earth, *Jour. Geog.*, Vol. 43, pp. 88–91, 1944.

[2] See Sviatlosky, E. E., and W. C. Eells, The Centrographical Method and Regional Analysis, *Geog. Rev.*, Vol. 27, pp. 240–254, 1937.

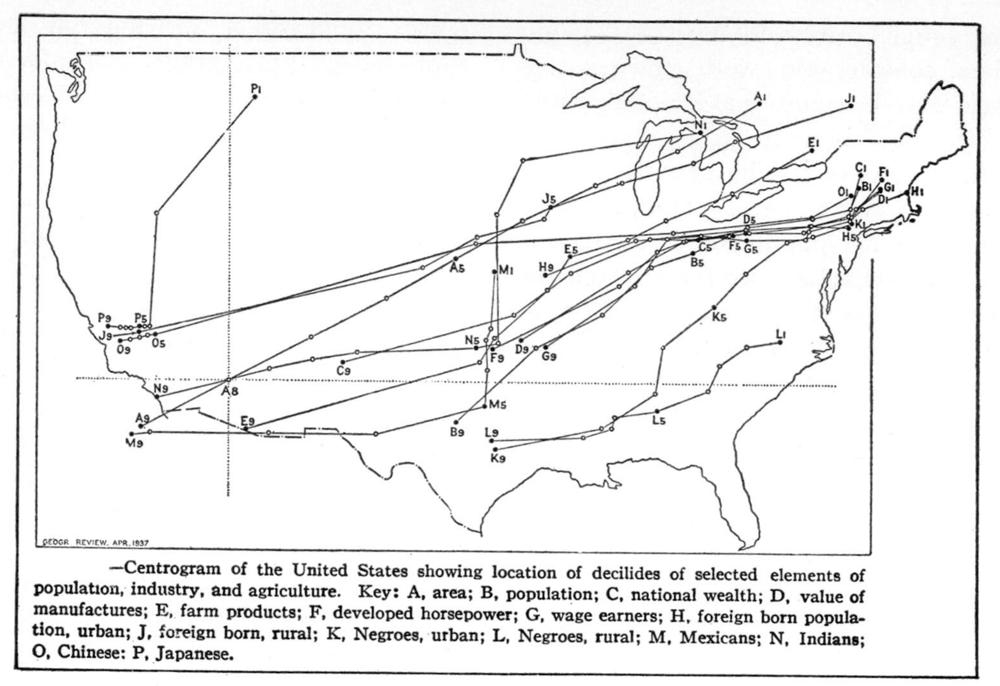


—Centrogram of the United States showing location of decilides of selected elements of population, industry, and agriculture. Key: A, area; B, population; C, national wealth; D, value of manufactures; E, farm products; F, developed horsepower; G, wage earners; H, foreign born population, urban; J, foreign born, rural; K, Negroes, urban; L, Negroes, rural; M, Mexicans; N, Indians; O, Chinese: P, Japanese.

**Fig. 233** Decilides. (*Courtesy of Geog. Rev.*, 1937.)

mended for small units, such as states or cities. The greatest hindrance in their preparation is the lack of sufficiently detailed statistical data.

## Dynamic Maps

In contrast to those maps which express static conditions are dynamic maps, which present *movement*. This movement may be transportation, migration, military maneuvers, or even the spread of ideas. Many historical and political maps are of dynamic character. The symbols of dynamic maps are flow lines and arrows. Sometimes the amount of change is expressed by isopleths or choropleths. In the case of very complex changes we often find it preferable to show a set of successive static maps. Many dynamic maps can be classified as cartograms.

**Traffic-flow Maps.** In these maps or cartograms the lanes of transportation are drawn proportionately thicker with the amount of traffic they carry. Such transportation lines as those shown in Fig. 234 resemble the organic-circulation system of veins and arteries in the human body, and give a vivid picture of the flow of traffic. The lines are usually straightened and simplified.

It is difficult to measure the thickness of lines. Therefore, if space permits, the lines may be composed of several thin parallel lines, the counting of which renders their value everywhere apparent. Lines are likely to be too crowded around traffic centers, and it is therefore customary to show such centers separately on larger scale inset maps. If lines are of very unequal thickness, as, for instance, when one line represents 50 or 100 times as much as another, it is sometimes necessary to use a diminishing scale for their width and to mark their real value with index numbers. One may reduce the thickness of lines to one-quarter if the thinnest line is not solid but dotted, and the next thinnest is short-dashed, the next long-dashed, and only the four-unit line is solid. Another way to handle this is by picturing round or square pipes (Fig. 235).

Maps showing the flow of traffic on the Great Lakes are familiar to every geographer; they show vividly the interrelation of coal and iron-ore transport. Several state-planning-board maps show density of automobile traffic, from which conclusions can be reached regarding future road-building programs. Maps showing the shipping lanes of the world, with lines indicating the tonnage of international trade, are common in atlases.

Singularly lacking are maps that show the *railroad traffic density* of the United States. The few local maps that are published show the number of passenger or freight trains, but since these trains vary in length and load, the information thus given is of limited value. The difficulty in constructing such maps lies in the lack of information. Data are often available for tons of freight carried, but they are likewise not very significant, since a ton of silk is of very different value from a ton of gravel. A good base for a railroad traffic-flow map of the United States would be freight revenue; but, since charges are paid at certain stations, and since not all lines can or will disclose the distribution of this revenue, this important map is not yet available for the United States.[1]

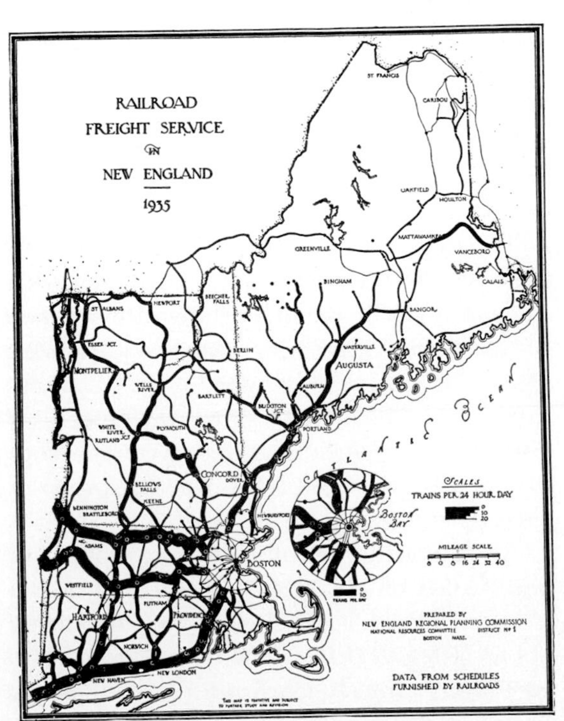


**Fig. 234** Traffic-flow map. The thickness of the lines is proportionate to the number of freight trains per day. (*Courtesy of National Resources Committee*. 1936.)

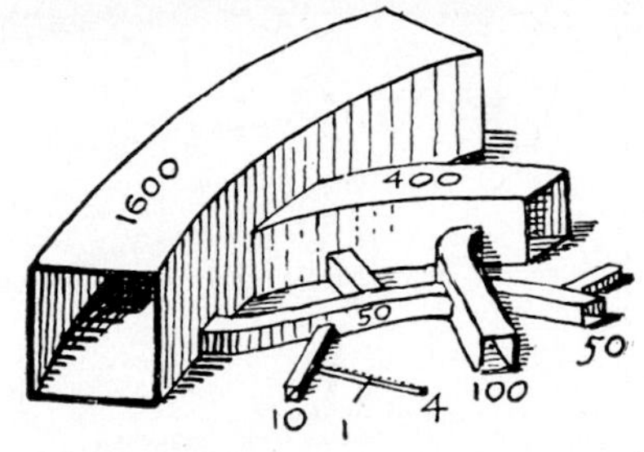


**Fig. 235** The carrying capacity of the largest pipe is 1,600 times larger than the smallest.

**Maps of Migrations.** In these maps the migration of men or of animals is shown by arrows, the thickness of which is proportionate to the number of migrants. The exact route of migration is not always followed. C. W. Thornthwaite's maps of the "Internal Migration in the United States" are good examples of this type. In these maps even the general route taken is disregarded, and only the states of birth and of present residence of the migrants are connected by arrows of varying width. Maps showing migration to or from a single location are called maps of "simple migrations" in contrast to maps of "compound migrations," in which the migration to and from several locations is considered. Figure 236 is a com-

[1] A yet unpublished map of railroad tonnage was prepared in 1947 by Edward Ullman at Harvard University.

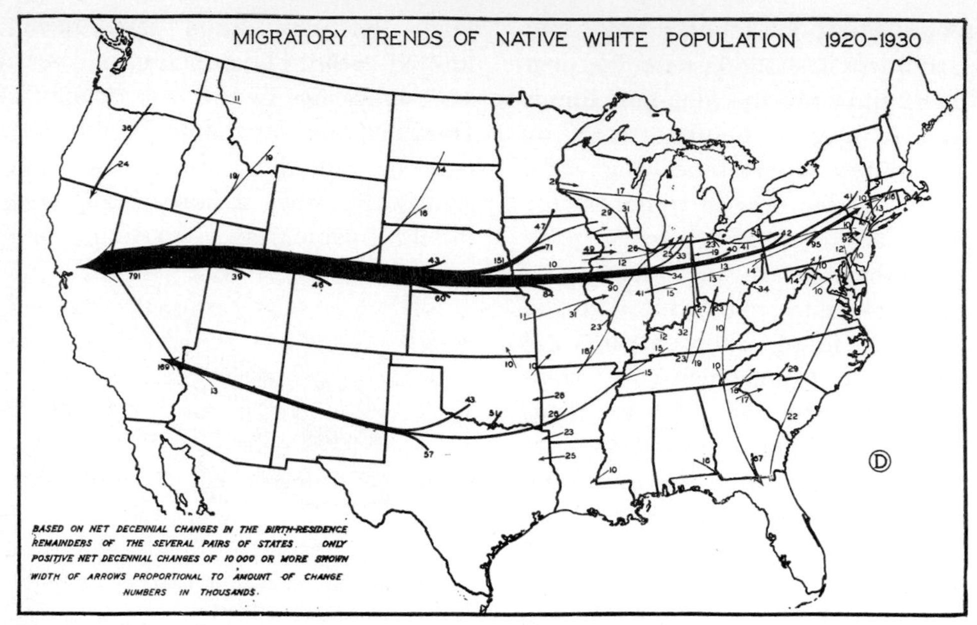


**Fig. 236** Migration map. The thickness of lines is proportionate to the number of migrants. (*From C. W. Thornwaite, Internal Migration in United States*, 1934.)

pound migration map; in such a map the arrows will cross each other.

**Isochronic Maps.** These maps show the possible progress of travel in all directions from a given center in certain specified time intervals. A century ago the distances that could be reached in a day, week, or month were much closer than at present. This "shrinkage" of the world is one of the most significant facts of modern history; it is a phenomenon that even today is actively changing the pattern of our life, and for this reason the study of isochronic maps is important (Fig. 238).

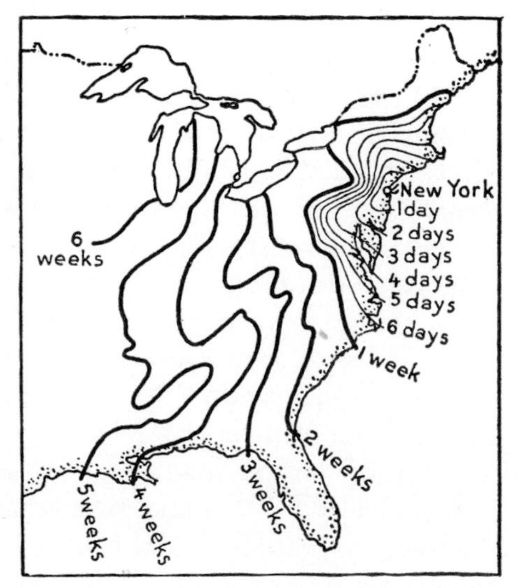


**Fig. 237** Isochronic map showing the rates of travel from New York City in 1800. (*Paullin and Wright, Atlas of Historical Geography of the United States.*)

The most common type of isochronic map connects points of equal time-distance with *isochrones*. Isochrones may show rate of speed of passenger travel, or time required for mail, freight, or any other type of transportation; they may show the speed of earthquake vibrations in seconds, the progress of tidal waves in hours, or the spread of the gypsy moth in years.

An interesting set of isochronic maps is in the "Atlas of Historical Geography of the United States." It shows the increasing speed of travel during the period from 1800 to 1930. Formerly isochrones were more or less concentric lines but recently airplane travel has introduced such saving in time that exact isochrones are highly irregular lines, since it often takes longer to reach a rural house from an airport than to travel by air hundreds of miles. The lines will also become disconnected because while it is true that Chungking can be reached from India in a day, a point in the mountains in between would take weeks to reach.

In isochronic world maps the matter of *projection* is essential. Theoretically, the best projection is the oblique, azimuthal, equidistant projection centered on the zero point of the isochrones. This is the only projection in which both directions and distances are correct.

Another type of isochronic map graphically shows how the world became smaller. Although such maps powerfully convey the underlying idea, their use should be restricted on account of their inherent inaccuracy.

Maps similar to isochronic maps may present cost of transportation instead of time. These *isephodic* maps (equal cost of travel) are important for both passenger travel and freight shipments. Places of equal freight rates are connected by isephodes similar to isochrones. Isephodic lines, placed on a regular map, are very complex and irregular; hence it is not inconceivable to prepare another type of isephodic cartogram on which concentric circles are drawn around the central city at even intervals,

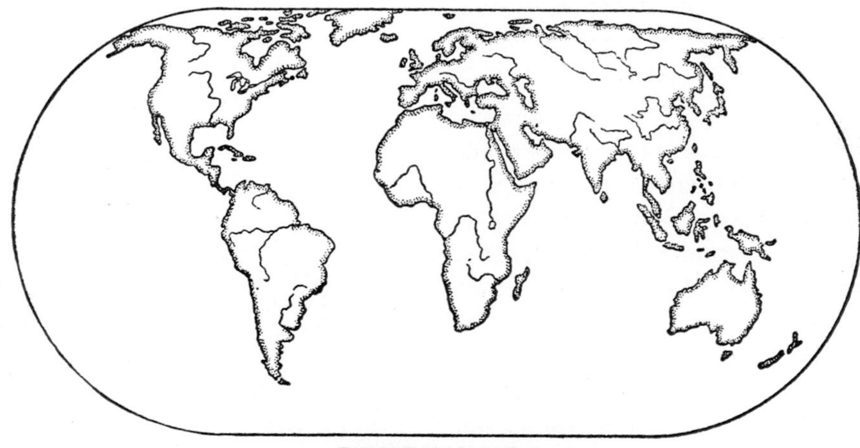

EOTECHNICS
(to 1830's and 40's)
Best regular speed on land and sea 10 m.p.h.

PALEOTECHNICS
(late 19th, early 20th centuries)
Best regular land speed 65 m.p.h. best regular sea speed 36 m.p.h.

NEOTECHNICS
(present era)
Best regular speed in air 200 m.p.h.

**Fig. 238** "Shrinkage maps" of the world. (*From E. Staley, "This Shrinking World."*)

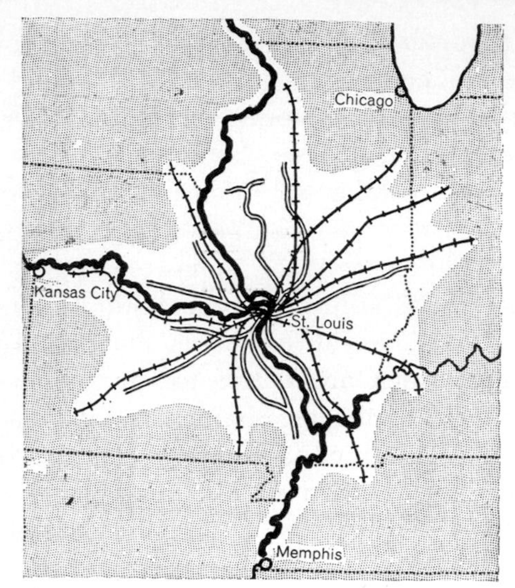


**Fig. 239** Isephodic or equal-coast distance map shows how far you can carry goods from a point for the same money. (*By S. W. Boggs.*)

each circle representing a proportionately higher freight rate. All other important cities are arranged in their proper direction but at distances proportionate to freight rates. Such a cartogram will at a glance show the freight-rate category of the various shipping points.

**Isotachic Maps.** These maps show the best speed of carriers in any area (in contrast to the isochronic map which shows the best speed from a certain point). Airplanes are excluded because air cargoes are used only under special conditions; it would also be extremely difficult to construct an isotachic map including air travel.

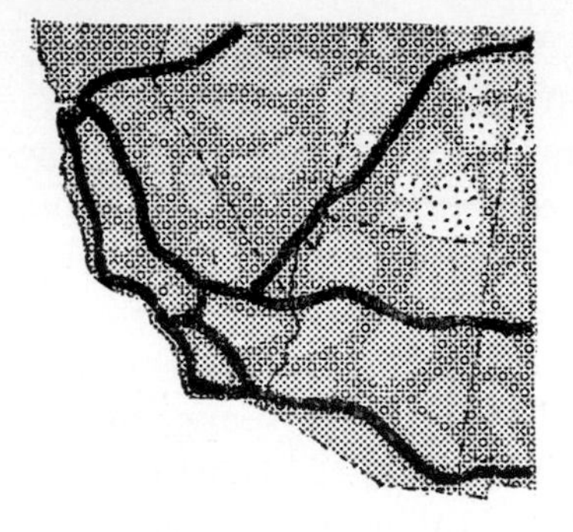

**Fig. 240** Isotachic map dividing the Earth into freight-speed areas. (*After S. W. Boggs.*)

Transportation is speediest along railroads, less so on trucks or steamers, and is slowest with wagons, pack animals, and back packing. The higher the speed, the darker the tint; thus the railroad system will be black, roads dark gray, sea and waterways lighter gray, etc. An isotachic map of the United States was prepared by S. W. Boggs.[1] He also prepared a similar map, tinting areas of different cost of transportation, and called it an "isotimal" map.[2]

[1] Boggs, S. W., Mapping the Changing World, *Assoc. Am. Geographers Annals*, June, 1941.

[2] Boggs, S. W., Mapping Some Effects of Science on Human Relations, *Sci. Monthly*, Vol. 61, pp. 45–50, July, 1945.

# CHAPTER 28: *Globes and Models*

Maps are not the only subjects of cartography. Three-dimensional representations, such as globes and models, are becoming more and more generally used in portraying the earth. The solution of their many technical problems progressed greatly in recent years.

## Globes

The spherical form of the earth was recognized by the ancient Greeks, and this conception was followed by attempts to prepare a globe. The size of the earth was known and the size of the "habitable world" was also fairly well estimated. It was found, however, that the known world hardly filled a quadrant of the earth, the size of which was calculated by Eratosthenes; and speculation was rife about the other quadrants. Crates, about 150 B.C., prepared a globe with three other balancing continents, thus anticipating the discovery of the Americas and Australia. This is the first terrestrial globe of which there is a record. Celestial globes involved fewer problems, and several such globes made by the Romans, and later by the medieval Arabs, have survived.

The first terrestrial globe that has survived was made by Martin Behaim in Nuremberg, in 1492. This globe is based entirely on the Ptolemaic concept of the earth, and, of course, America does not appear on it (Fig. 17). When the great discoveries of the fifteenth and sixteenth centuries brought a new conception of the earth, there was no better method to demonstrate the new geography than by globes. The early Renaissance is the golden age of globes. In 1507 printed globe gores were introduced by Waldseemüller, thus making possible the manufacture of globes in quantities. Almost every Renaissance cartographer was also a producer of globes. The most famous early globe maker was Johannes Schöner of Nuremberg. His globe of 1515 showed the Strait of Magellan before it was discovered. Perhaps the finest ones were made by Coronelli in Venice at the end of the seventeenth century. He made a globe for Louis XIV, which was 12 feet in diameter; it was a terrestrial globe outside and celestial inside, and it moved by a clock mechanism that turned it around every 24 hours. The Renaissance was the time of large ornate globes, in some cases more famous for their decorative quality and scientific air than for their practical value. After the Renaissance the use of globes declined, but recently it has been revived, with increased recognition of their educational value.

**Uses of Globes.** A globe is the most correct representation of the earth and the only representation in which the scale is true everywhere. Great-circle distances can be scaled off directly with a narrow ribbon scale, which is a very common task in this air-age world. We will see, however, that there is an inherent inaccuracy in the usual construction of globes and the distances measured may be off a few per cent. They will be more accurate than on any map where the projection method introduces a sizable error. Globes are good for planning long air or sea routes, because the actual distances and directions can be seen undistorted by map projections. Propagation of earthquake, tidal, and radio waves can best be followed on a good globe.

The globe is the highest achievement of

cartography. It enables man to step outside his planet and see its wonderful pattern as from the heavens. We can see the relationship of oceans, of continents, and of the polar regions; we can see unusual views and unusual relationships. It is with good reason that in the most progressive schools they use globes in the very earliest stages of geographical education. It is on a globe that such fundamental concepts as day and night, summer and winter, planetary winds, time zones, tides, etc., can best be understood.

Globes are no less important in higher education. Mathematical geography, geodesy, climatology, oceanography, seismology, geotectonics, earth magnetism, radio, etc., are obviously globe subjects. Never before have we realized how "global" our conceptions of geography, geopolitics, world communication, aviation, and economics should be in order to understand our place on this limited planet. At the very beginning of the Second World War a 5-foot globe was prepared for the use of the President of the United States.

Every classroom and every home should have a globe. Yet classrooms and homes with globes are the exception rather than the rule. It may be that the reason for this is that globes are bulky, difficult to store, and somewhat expensive as a whole atlas can be bought for the price of a globe. It is also true that globes show less than half of the surface at a time, and thus some world relationships are not as clear as on a map. Yet the chief reason that globes are not used more is probably the fact that the common type of globe is not good enough. It does not suggest a mighty sphere whirling through space, but rather a set of political reference maps pasted on a ball.

First of all, a globe, really to portray the earth, has to be large. The 12- or 16-inch balls in our schoolrooms do not suggest in any way the immensity of our planet; even a 2-foot globe does not come near the effect of a globe that is larger than the person who looks at it. A large globe, in spite of its size, has to be fine in detail. In the actual picture of the earth on a 4-foot globe (about 1:10,000,000) even the highest mountains would be only $\frac{1}{30}$ inch high and the largest rivers only microscopic lines. Obviously these features have to be exaggerated to be visible but not to lose the impression of extreme smoothness or delicacy of detail that the actual earth would give us if viewed from a rocket ship a few thousand miles away. This space traveler would be impressed by the green of forests, the dark blue of the oceans, the vivid green of the prairies, the somber gray of the barrens, the glittering of ice and snow, and the brilliant reddish colors of deserts, etc. This view would be different in summer from winter, and paired summer and winter globes are most instructive. Obviously on an ideal globe the lettering should be as small and unobtrusive as possible so as not to spoil the over-all picture.

**Construction of Globes.** Globes are usually made from ready-printed globe gores, which are pasted on a suitable base. This base may be made from cardboard, pressed metal, or plastics. Globes, in the past, were usually constructed on a wooden frame upon which were applied layers of a mixture of paper pulp and plaster of paris, strengthened with hair and glue. Some globe makers applied this mixture to the inside of a hemispherical mold. After this had hardened, it was taken out of the mold, and the halves were glued together at the equator. This method is still applied to some large globes, but for the present mass-production methods, the metal, plastic, or mesh has to be pressed into molds.

**Globe Gores.** Smaller globes usually have 12 gores, each of which represents 30°

of longitude. The Arctic and Antarctic regions are frequently pasted on separately in round pieces.

Globe gores are usually drawn in a modified sinusoidal projection. The central meridian and the equator are divided truly. Flat sine curves through the poles and the divisions of the equator determine the meridians, which can be drawn by simply measuring off true distances from the central meridian. Thus far it is exactly the central portion of a sinusoidal projection. The difference comes in the parallels which are not horizontal but slightly arcuate, and which are derived by the even division of each meridian.

Obviously the central meridian is shorter than the meridians on the sides of the gores, and yet on the globe they should be equal. The difference is taken care of by proper wetting of the paper—more in the center and less on the sides. The same holds true for the polar pieces that are drawn in a polar azimuthal equidistant projection. The amount of reduction in scale must be found by experimentation, for it varies with the type of paper.

More exact globes can be made by the 24-gore method, in which the gores are arranged as in Fig. 242, separated at the equator. This method saves the separate round pieces at the poles and gives in general much better fit. The parallels are circular arcs at true distances; the meridians are derived by true division of each parallel left and right of the straight, radial central meridian of each gore. The side meridians are slightly longer than the central one, but the difference is much less than in the previous method. All gores for a hemisphere are printed together, mounted flat on cardboard or metal. The space between the gores is cut out but 10 to 15° around the poles are kept together. Each hemisphere is pressed in a hemispherical mold, reinforced inside, and the two halves are pasted together at the equator. A narrow tape at the equator hides the possible little discrepancies between the meridians in the two halves.

**Accessories.** Globes usually have a steel or wooden *axis*, around which they can be turned. On larger globes this may be an elaborate, two-piece axis with a spring to ensure even pressure; ferrules and ball bearings permit even turning. Smaller globes may have no axis but, instead, turn in a socket. The axis or sockets are usually attached to a full- or half-meridian ring.

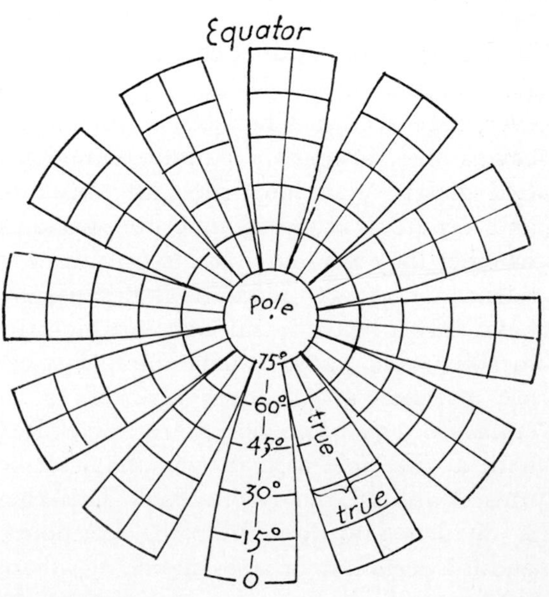


**Fig. 242** Globes are often made from 24 zones arranged radially from the poles. The two hemispheres are joined together later.

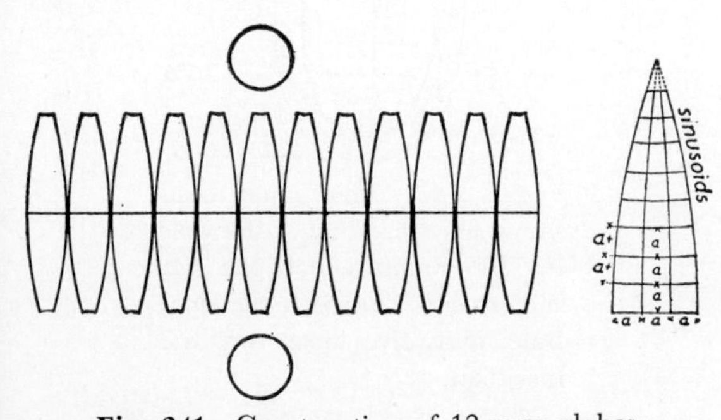


**Fig. 241** Construction of 12-gore globes.

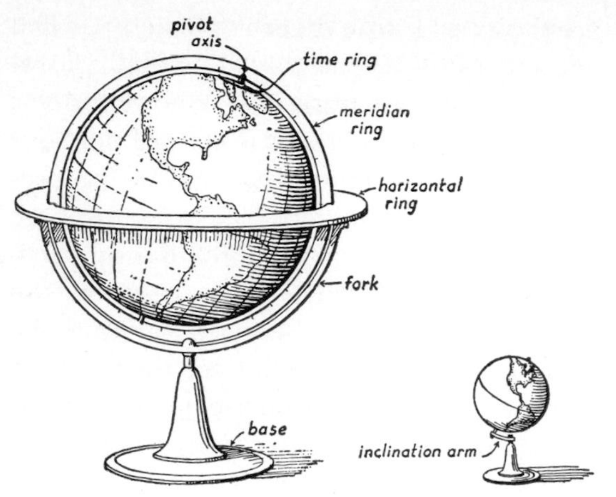


**Fig. 243** Parts of globes.

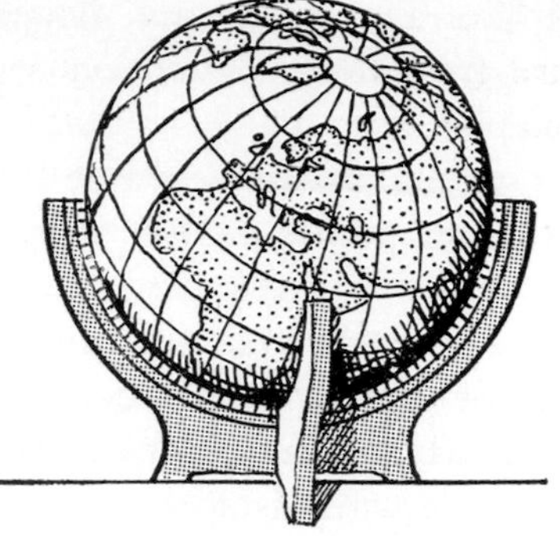

**Fig. 244** Globes are often placed in a cradle from which they can be lifted and replaced in any position.

This *meridian ring* can be supported at the bottom, attached to a fork, or suspended from above. In any case, both the ring and the globe are generally movable, so that the axis of the globe can be made either vertical or inclined 23.5°, to show the inclination of the earth's axis to the plane of the ecliptic. This latter position is preferable for showing planetary relationships and explaining seasons. Some globes mounted in this ecliptical position are equipped with a *horizontal ring* that represents the plane of the ecliptic. The ring is sometimes decorated with the signs of the zodiac. Modern globes, however, rarely have a horizontal ring, for it covers and darkens the equatorial regions. Old globes often have such an elaborate and ornate framework that one wonders whether they were intended to be a work of science or of art. Modern globes usually have only a heavy metal base to which the meridian ring is attached. The simple globes are attached at an angle of 23.5° to an *inclination arm*. Most globes are augmented with a *time dial*—a small ring that can be turned around the North Pole. This ring is divided into twenty-fourths for hours, and if a certain hour is set on one meridian, the local time on any other meridian can be told. Nowadays globes often come in a cradle without any attachment whatever. The globe can be placed in any odd way and unusual settings often show some startling relationships.

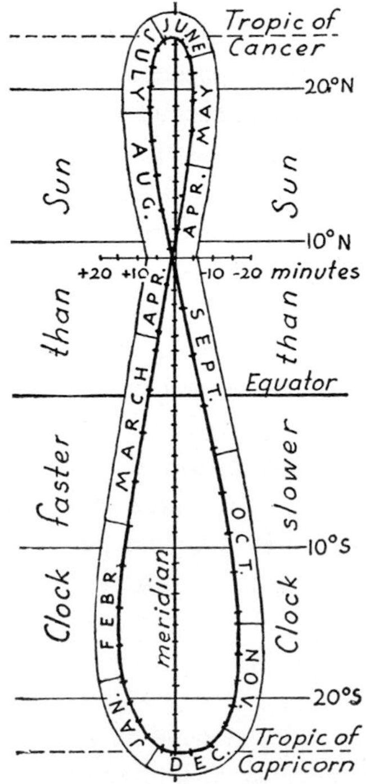


**Fig. 245** The analemma shows for every day of the year the spot upon which the sun shines vertically when the local time is twelve noon on the meridian.

**The Analemma.** Many globes have a curious figure-of-eight-shaped diagram over the blue of the Pacific Ocean, which is called the "analemma." This is a line which connects the points on the earth's surface where the sun is directly overhead throughout the year when it is twelve o'clock local time on the meridian upon which the analemma is centered. Identical analemmas can be drawn on any meridian.

The analemma is shaped by two factors. The north-south component is caused by the declination of the sun. The sun is overhead at 23°27′N on June 21, is at 23°27′S on Dec. 21, and is over the equator at the equinoxes. The up-and-down migration of the vertical rays of the noonday sun is faster near the equator than it is near the tropics.[1]

The east-west component of the analemma is due to the equation of time. Due to the unequal speed of the earth's revolution (Kepler's law) and also to the inclination of the earth's axis, one day is not so long as the other. Although the difference between two sequent noons is rarely more than a few seconds, these differences accumulate so that on Nov. 2 the sun is the highest at $11^h43^m$ local time, while on Feb. 10 it will be highest at $12^h15^m$. As a minute of time represents 15 minutes of arc, these differences can be laid out left and right of the meridian and combined with the declination of time and we get the familiar 8-shaped figure. It should be noted that on most globes the analemma is incorrect. If drawn right, it is not symmetrical, nor does the crossing of the 8 come on the meridian. The analemma is useful to figure out the angle of the sun at any time and any place. It is also used in the construction of sundials.

**Types of Globes.** Most globes on the market are *political* in emphasis, and show the various countries in vivid colors. These, as a rule, stress communication lines, such as railroads, air lines, and steamship routes. Better representation of the earth's pattern is given on the *physical* globes that use conventional altitude tints, sometimes combined with hachuring. Such globes usually show ocean depths and currents, and perhaps vegetation belts and magnetic isogones. The general criticism of the conventional altitude tints, that they overemphasize elevation above sea level, is especially apparent on globes.

*Special globes* are on the market for showing climatological elements, temperature, rainfall, and pressure for the different seasons. Such globes give a better idea of the earth's climate than do maps.

There have been various attempts to prepare *relief globes* in which the mountains protrude and the oceans are depressed. Since, on a 2-foot globe of about 1:20,000,000 scale, the highest mountain would not rise more than the thickness of the paper, enormous vertical exaggeration is necessary to show relief, with the result that these relief globes are more caricatures than true likenesses of the earth.

Washable *outline globes*, with black land and dark-blue sea, are useful aids for teachers to draw upon with chalk. Plain black globes, without continents but with parallels and meridians, are useful for teaching mathematical geography.

In recent years various materials for making globes have been tried. Glass globes are also very common; patents for globe lamps, illuminated from the inside and rotated by clockwork, showing day and night, are registered at the U.S. Patent Office. Transparent globes from plastics are used to show the relationship of continents. Photographic reproduction of transparent globes by sensitizing the surface is a promising pos-

[1] Raisz, Erwin, The Analemma, *Jour. Geog.*, Vol. 40, pp. 90–97, 1941.

**Fig. 246** Mapparium in the Christian Science Building in Boston. The photograph is taken from one of the entrances and thus shows the globe in stereographic projection. (*Christian Science Publishing Co.*)

sibility, especially if the colors will be well reproduced by photography. A large transparent globe was prepared by impregnating printed gores with a plastic acetate in a hemispherical mold. Inflated rubber, cloth, and silk globes are also on the market. Some of them are good, but more often they are very crude and cannot be regarded as anything but scientific toys.

For the illustration of the motions of the Earth, Moon, and planets, schools are often equipped with a mechanical device called a planetarium, or *orrery* (named after Charles Boyle, Earl of Orrery). Some of the eighteenth- and nineteenth-century orreries were extremely elaborate, with complicated clockwork to put the mechanism in motion. They now have become valuable museum pieces, but their educational value was rarely proportionate to their cost.

**Celestial Globes.** Celestial globes are constructed similarly to terrestrial globes. They have a movable meridian ring, and most of them are equipped with a horizontal ring to present celestial coordinates. If the axis of the globe is tilted to the degree of our latitude and pointed to the celestial pole, the globe can be turned so that every radius passing through a star points to the same star in the sky. Older celestial globes bristled with masterfully arrayed mythological figures of the constellations and were more or less pseudoscientific pieces of decorative art. Modern celestial globes are used for instruction in astronomy, and they show the visible stars according to their magnitudes, clouds, clusters, the Galaxy, etc.

**Large Globes.** Many notable, large globes are in existence. In the lobby of the News Building in New York is a large rotating globe, 12 feet in diameter, made with excellent craftsmanship. A similar globe rotates in the hall of the Pan American Airways in Miami. A glass georama (where one looks from the inside upon the walls of the globe), 30 feet in diameter, is in the Christian Science Building in Boston, Mass. It is interesting to note that west is on the left, while, seen from the earth's center, it should be on the right.

Reclus, the great French geographer, proposed that a large globe, on a scale of 1:1,000,000, be constructed from international funds and kept up to date as the most modern image of the world. The diameter of such a globe would be nearly 42 feet. This great man's dream is now to be realized at the Babson Institute, Wellesley, Mass., using the sheets of the Millionth Map of the World, but coloring them according to natural colors, rather than according to altitude tints. This globe will be located near the Babson model of the United States, 1:250,000, which is really a part of a globe and is described in the next chapter. The American Geographical Society also has a map of Latin America, 1:1,000,000, on a globular surface.

## Topographic Relief Models

To make a relief model is the most obvious way to portray a region. As the history of sculpture is older than that of painting, so the history of topographic models is as old as, or even older than, that of maps. The remarkable ability of primitive peoples to make relief models was mentioned in Chap. 1. In the early ages of scientific cartography, however, good topographic models were very rare, because little was known of the height and configuration of mountains. Two remarkable topographic models of central Switzerland date from the eighteenth century; one made of wax by R. L. Pfyffer, is in Lucerne, and the other, made of paper pulp by Meyer and Müller, is in Zürich. When accurate, detailed, contour-line maps became available in the middle of the nineteenth century, the art of model making was carried to great perfection. The models of J. Albert Heim of various parts of the Alps are perhaps the most famous.

A topographic model is the most perfect representation of a small region. It is recommended that every thesis which analyzes a small region be accompanied by a relief model. Certainly, every student of geography should be able to prepare one. Many geographic relationships appear very obvious when viewed on a model. Models are used also for engineering problems, landscape architecture, demonstration of interesting geological structures, and for the planning of military operations. They have a great appeal for the public because they have a sense of reality that is often lost on maps.

**Vertical Exaggeration.** If a 2-foot relief model were made of Mt. Rainier, it would look perfectly well without vertical exaggeration. On a 2-foot wide model of the United States, however, Mt. Rainier would stand only $\frac{1}{50}$ inch high over Puget Sound, if the vertical scale were the same as the horizontal. For mountains to resemble on this small scale the usual conception of mountains, the vertical scale has to be exaggerated. This vertical exaggeration cannot be too large, because if it is exaggerated, 40 times, for instance, Mr. Rainier would look like a needle.

How much vertical exaggeration to use is the first question in making a relief model. No definite rule can be given. It depends on the scale, on the map, on the roughness of the relief, and the amount of

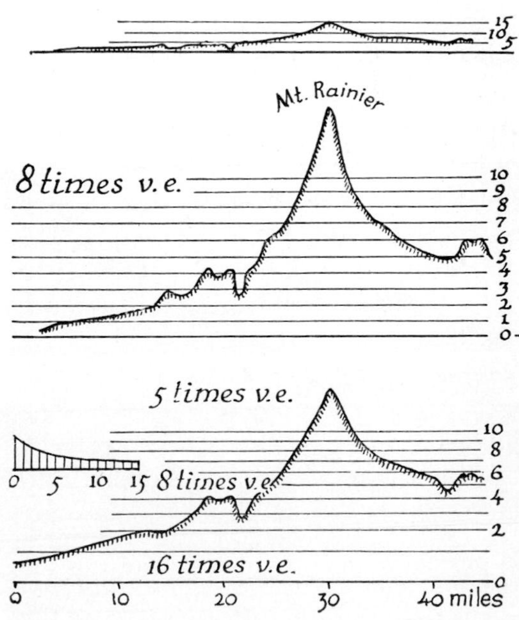


**Fig. 247** In small-scale models of high mountains, the vertical exaggeration has to be reduced at higher elevations.

generalization, scale being the most important factor. As a rough empirical formula, the best exaggeration on a model of a low or gentle hilly region executed with medium detail would be

$$\text{Vertical exaggeration} = 2\sqrt{m}$$

where $m$ is the number of miles represented by 1 inch. Thus the average vertical exaggeration for 1-inch-to-mile models is twice; 4-inch-to-mile models is four times; 16-inch-to-mile models is eight times; 64-inch-to-mile models is sixteen times.

If the region is mountainous, the exaggeration is less; if it is very flat, the exaggeration may be slightly increased. If a small-scale model is of very fine detail, the vertical exaggeration may be less.

In small-scale models (even in large-scale ones if the relief is very great) the best result is obtained if the vertical exaggeration scale is variable, more in the plains and less in the mountains. For instance, in a 1:4,000,000 map, while the exaggeration in low parts may be 16 times, this can be gradually reduced to 8 or even 5 times at higher elevations. It is advisable to draw a profile with the planned exaggerations and to see how it looks.

When we use cardboards to cut out contour lines, we are working with only certain available thicknesses, and the calculated vertical exaggeration can only be approximated. In the calculation we compare inches on the model with feet in nature. For instance, we want to find out the vertical exaggeration of a 1-inch-to-the-mile model, where every 20-foot contour is cut from a $\frac{1}{40}$ inch-thick cardboard:

Horizontally 1 inch corresponds to 5,280 feet
Vertically 1 inch corresponds to 800 feet
Vertical exaggeration = 6.6 times

which is too much. Thus we do better to use only every second contour line, which will bring the vertical exaggeration to 3.3 times, which is not too much in a low region.

**Cardboard Cutting.** If a contour-line map is available, the model is usually cut from cardboards. The cardboards should be thin; if they are less than $\frac{1}{20}$ inch thick they can easily be cut with a knife. If $\frac{1}{15}$ inch thick they can be cut with a round-blade jig saw. Thicker cardboard requires flat-blade jig-sawing, which is difficult because it requires the constant turning of the cardboard in the direction of intricate contour lines. Special oil-soaked cardboard is easier to cut. If still thicker cardboards are required, beaver board, plywood, Celotex, etc., can be used. The author tried rolling out plastiline into sheets for rapid modeling with good results.

**Positive Method.** After the cardboards are chosen, the map, or a photostat of it, is carefully squared. A carbon paper is pasted on the back of the map and the lowermost contour is traced on the cardboard. A few corners of the next higher contour are also marked for proper spacing. Then on another cardboard the next higher contour is traced, and so on until all contours are cut

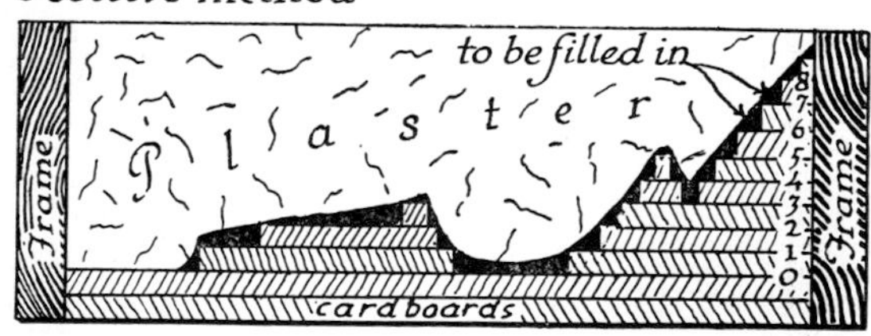


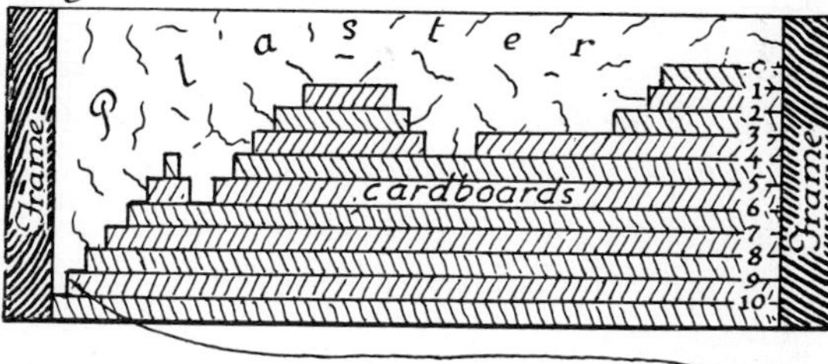

**Fig. 248** Simple large-scale models are made by the positive method; the negative method is used for small-scale models with fine detail.

and laid. Only the lower cardboards have to be cut to a full-size square. The tops of mountains can be traced close to each other to save cardboard. Each tracing is marked with the contour line it represents. The boards are now ready for cutting.

Cutting out cardboard exactly along contour lines is a matter of practice. If there are deep, narrow embayments, it is better to leave them until later and cut them out from both sides. The cutting begins in the lowermost contour line. Then each successive contour is cut, and the pieces are built upon each other to make a positive model. The cardboards are pasted down with thinly applied rubber cement. The marked corners will help to determine exactly the placing of the next cardboard.

The rough cardboard base is now smoothed with plastiline, an oily clay, and the finer topographic features, such as cliffs and river channels, are worked in by hand until a perfect positive model of the region is achieved. Care must be taken to leave no extra plastiline, especially in the valleys. The contour lines should be barely visible. Then a wooden frame, not much higher than the highest peak, is built around the model. This frame is then oiled and tightened on the sides with plastiline, and the model is ready for casting the negative.

**The Negative Method.** Another method of constructing relief models reverses the foregoing process. First, the highest contour is cut out, and the remaining cardboard is laid upside down. The next contour is then cut out and laid on top, and so on, until the entire *negative* is built up from cardboard. From this negative a positive is cast. For high-grade work this positive will be modeled with tools so as to give finer detail, and a new negative and then a new positive cast. The advantages of this method are that it saves the copying of contour lines, for the same map can be attached to the successive cardboards as the successive contour lines are cut out, and that it involves no danger of loss of some of the minor peaks. On the other hand, there is great danger that the cardboard will be soaked from the wet plaster and will consequently bulge out of position. It is therefore advisable to soak the cardboard with oil before casting. In general, the negative method is better for small-scale models with fine detail, while the positive method is better for large-scale models.

**Casting.** By measuring the sides and average depth, the number of cubic inches to be filled in can be estimated, 30 cubic inches making roughly a pint. We fill a pail with the required pints of water and measure out about 1.5 pounds of plaster to every pint of water. Then we slowly fill in the plaster by hand, casting it all over the water surface and letting it sink. Plaster should not be thrown in from a great height as this will cause air bubbles. Slowly the water will fill with plaster, and if the powder does not sink any more we know that it is full. The level of water will rise about one-fourth. We disturb the plaster as little as possible, but it is advisable to loosen the clumps with the fingers. A layer of plaster is gently brushed into the model, progressing from a corner and slowly advancing to avoid air bubbles. More plaster is added with a ladle, always gently letting it down toward the wooden frame, not throwing it in and forming air bubbles. The plaster will not harden for at least 10 or 15 minutes, and hurry will spoil the model. On large models, two or three people can work from different corners. The frame is filled completely, and when the plaster begins to harden the top is smoothed with a board. The plaster will harden in a few hours, but it is safer to separate the mold the next day. This is done by driving wooden chisels preferably on a flat part of the model (showing sea or lake). This will leave a scar that has to be fixed with half-wet plaster.

**Finishing.** The best time for finishing is while the plaster is still soft. Air bubbles are filled in, rivers and creeks are carved, and cliffs are sharpened. Fields and plowed lands can be shown by grooving parallel lines in the plaster with a broken jig saw. Forest can be shown by roughening the surface of the plaster with a hard wire brush. A "vibrotool" is excellent to work the plaster. The model is then shellacked and painted with oil colors. Forests can also be shown by salting the wet paint with sand. Lettering can be applied with India ink directly on the dry oil paint, or by pasting thereon ready-stenciled paper letters. Lettering can also be carved into the negative and will appear raised in the positive. Vivid models can be made by cleaning the plaster with sandpaper and then painting it with ordinary water colors instead of oil. The sides of the model are the natural places for showing the geologic structure. If this is not required, it is better to keep the model in the frame.

**Pasting of Maps on Models.** By this method the map is printed on thin tissue paper, wetted, and pasted on top of a model made of plaster of paris. One of the notable exhibits of the 1931 Geographic Congress in Paris was the enormous relief model of northern France, on a scale of 1:20,000, with a 1:2 vertical exaggeration, the topographic maps being pasted on top. This method was perfected by Wentschow of Munich whose models of various parts of Germany are famous.

**Special Materials.** Various attempts have been made to mount a map on cardboard, heat it in steam, and press it into a steel mold, which consists of a negative and positive model of the area. Such an early attempt, the Royal Relief Atlas (G. P. Bevan, London, 1884), caused considerable attention, but the great expense of the steel molds deterred imitation. The Denoyer-Geppert Company came out recently with a wall map of this kind.

Great advancement has been made in *rubber models.* These can be cast in hard plaster molds; thus they are much cheaper than the hot-pressed or plastic models. First a thin sheet of rubber is placed in the mold, then it is backed by sponge rubber with a spray gun. The map can be photographed on sensitized rubber. Airbrushing sideways with dark gray, something like an artificial shadow, makes the relief stand out boldly. Durability and ease of packing made rubber models very popular during the Second World War. The U.S. Army, Navy, and Air Forces all produced excellent models both in the office and in the field, and a large outfit of the O.S.S., under the direction of Maj. Wallace W. Atwood, Jr., prepared models of every theater of war and of every invasion coast. These models proved their worth in the field.

*Plastics* are excellent for models. Although light and unbreakable, they are not much in use as yet because of the high cost of the steel molds into which the model has to be pressed. But one steel mold can produce thousands of models, and we may expect cheap, yet very good, models produced in quantities in the future. Transparent plastics are good for certain purposes, particularly for geologic structures, mines, and ore bodies, but surface relief shows up poorly in transparent material.

A hot sheet of vinylite can be sucked by vacuum into a plaster mold, and when it hardens it can be lifted off, and a light strong replica can be made from it. The map can be printed or photographed on the vinylite sheet.

*Metals* are also used for models. Zinc, tin, or copper can be sprayed from a gun into a graphite-covered mold, and thus a light, strong model is prepared. Models can also be prepared by electroplating a negative. Steel models thus prepared can be made magnetic and are used for placing little airplanes, cannons, troop symbols, etc., on them in war games.

**Hammered Models.** The map is photographed on a sensitized copper, aluminum, or other metallic plate, and electric hammers raise the thin plate to the desired elevation. This method is better for large-scale than for fine small-scale models. The "third-dimensional maps" of J. J. Bround are of this kind.

as the map and are numbered in the same manner. Over this frame is placed a rod, in the center of which is a peg that can be moved up and down. This peg is graduated according to the contour interval and must be large enough to be numbered. The rod has the same divisions as the map, lettered in reverse, as shown in Fig. 249. The position for each spot height can be determined by its coordinates, *i.e.*, by moving the rod up and down according to the side coordinates, and left and right according to the figures on the rod as read on the inner side of the frame. The peg is let down so deep

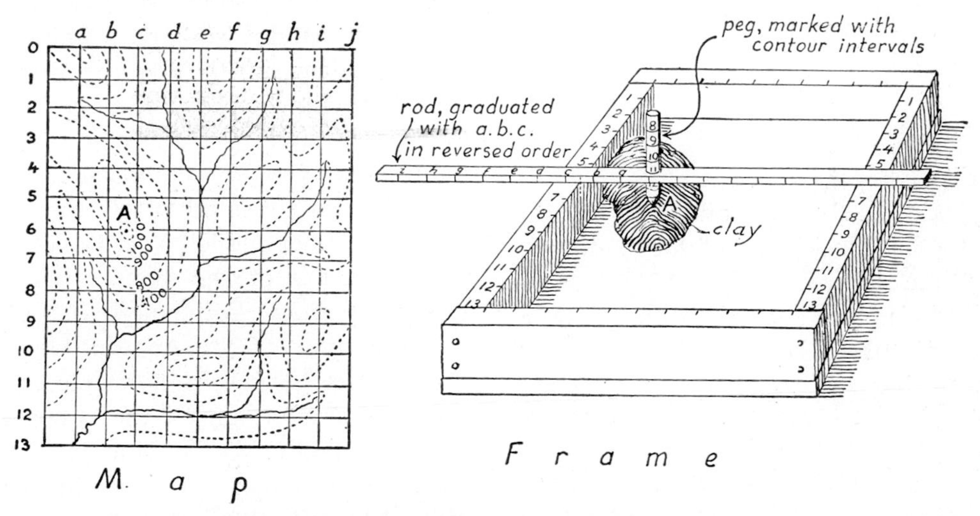


**Fig. 249** Spot-height method of making models.

**Spot-height Method.** If no detailed topographic sheets are available but the nature of the country and the heights of several places are known, a topographic relief model can be built by the spot-height method. By this method a network of squares about $\frac{1}{2}$ inch in size is drawn over the map and numbered on the sides. Then a wooden frame is built, somewhat higher than the highest peak on the map. This frame does not have to be the same size as the map; it can be proportionately larger or smaller. Two sides of the frame are divided into the same number of divisions

that its point reaches the top of the peak. The clay or plastiline is built up to the spot height at every point of known elevation; the remainder of the topography has to be modeled by hand with tools made of wood or wire.

If a good suspension pantograph is available, the marker of the pantograph can be transformed into a spot-height peg and, while the pointer is placed over a peak on the map, the marker will locate the peak on the model, which can be made larger or smaller than the map.

The spot-height method is especially useful for making quickly a less exact model for temporary use.

**Rough Models.** The above types of models apply to geographic models of some accuracy. Very often, however, the demand is for a speedily built large-scale model of the sand-table type for demonstration or teaching purposes. Any available material can be used. Plastiline is good, but it does not harden. The U.S. Navy recommends, in its pamphlet "How to Build Terrain Models," a mixture of

1 pint of sawdust
$\frac{3}{4}$ pint of plaster
$\frac{1}{2}$ pint of library paste
3 drops of glue

They dissolve paste in water and thin it slightly, add glue, plaster, and sawdust, and knead to the consistency of tough dough. Setting time is 8 hours.

The map is placed at the bottom of a box and the mixture is built up to the desired height, testing its height with a marked toothpick. For the surface, precolored sand, chalk powder, sawdust, and farina are used.

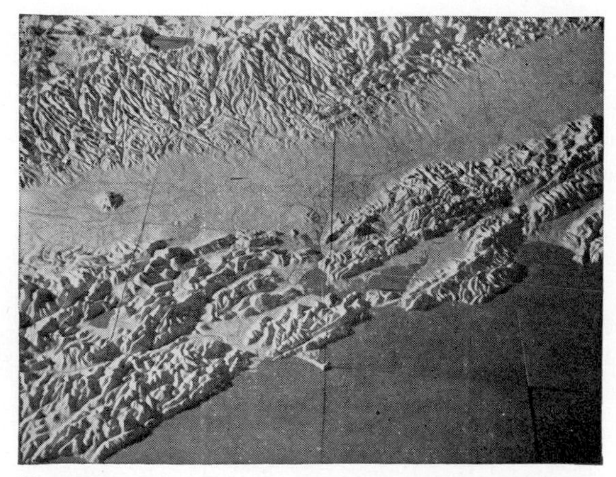

**Fig. 250** The Babson model of the United States is really part of a huge globe 170 feet in diameter. The United States is 64 feet wide.

Cities can be imitated with chopped red eraser, roads, and railways by colored strings, and water with shiny blue enamel. Very large-scale "egg-crate" models have been made by sawing out contours from wood and stretching canvas over them, nailing it down. During the war, the author made a large model of Germany in 5 days, by building up a base from pearl barley mixed with rubber cement to the base level of the rivers. Over this was placed a $\frac{1}{4}$-inch layer of rolled-out plastiline, upon which the rivers were marked from a map. All that had to be done was to build up the interstream areas, and the model was ready for finishing.

**Notable Model Makers.** Notable among model makers in the United States was E. E. Howell, who prepared several hundred topographic models of various parts of the United States, always emphasizing the geological structures. One of the greatest artists in relief models was G. C. Curtis, whose models of the Boston region, the Island of Bora Bora, and the Kilauea Volcano, now at the Agassiz Museum of Cambridge, Mass., are masterpieces.

Curtis also organized the work for the big relief model of the United States, located at the Babson Institute in Wellesley Hills, Mass. This is made on a scale of 4 miles to the inch, with a vertical exaggeration of 12 times. It covers a round steel frame 64 feet in diameter, and conforms to the curvature of the earth. Its progress was slow because no topographic sheets were available for more than half of the country. The model was finished before the Second World War under the direction of Maj. W. W. Atwood, Jr. Large parts of the model had to be remade because the vertical exaggeration in the western part of the country was too great. It is now 6 times exaggerated above the 6,000-foot level. To view the relief pattern of the country on such a large scale is a thrilling sight.

## PART EIGHT: SCIENCE MAPS

This part of this book carries us to the frontiers of cartography. Each science requires some special kind of maps and diagrams, and each presents problems. Solving these problems gives us new approaches of presentation, thus enriching the language of cartography. This part also includes land-slope analysis, which constitutes a science in itself, and presents the "land-type" maps, which are the most promising maps of the future.

---

# CHAPTER 29: *Land-slope Analysis*

If we describe a piece of land, the first question is whether the land is flat, hilly, or mountainous, or, in other words, the lay of the land. Within the same climatic region the use of the land depends mostly on its slope. To express slope conditions quantitatively has been the aim of many geographers, and various methods are in use. The most obvious method is to express slope on some kind of map, but it is possible to express the slope conditions of certain areas by diagrams, curves, or coefficients. Five different methods are in use to express the steepness of a single slope:

1. With topographic sheets the easiest method is to work with *feet per mile*, as for instance 400 feet per mile.

2. The engineer may prefer to express slope in *percentage*, as in this case

$$\frac{x}{100} = \frac{400}{5{,}280} = 7.6 \text{ per cent}$$

3. The army likes to express angles in *mils*, which is roughly (taking the true mil, extending 1 foot in a 1,000-foot distance) 10 times the percentage, in this case 76 mils. Taking the exact military value of the mil, 6,400 in a circle (in which case 1 foot will be extended in 6,400/6,280 = 1,018 foot distance), the angle will be $x/1{,}018 = 400/5{,}280$, $x = 77$ mils.

4. For many computations the *gradient* expressed by a fraction, or in decimals, will be the simplest; in this case

$$\frac{400}{5{,}280} = \frac{1}{13.2} = 0.076$$

5. The Abney level expresses slope in *degrees*. One degree is about 1 unit high in 57.3 units of horizontal distance as long as the angle is flat, as in our case $x/57.3 = 400/5{,}280$, $x = 4°20'$. For rapid calculations it is best to keep in mind that 100 feet per mile is about $1°5'$.

**Land-slope Maps.** One might expect that the usual relief methods would give all the answers for the student of land slopes. This, however, is only true in the case of *large-scale maps*, where contour lines can be drawn with fair accuracy and close intervals. The ruggedness of land can be read anywhere by measuring the distance of the contour lines—the closer they are, the steeper the land. One may miss some rugged moraine land or sand dunes, which may be partly lost in a 50-foot contour interval, but on an average there is no better way of representing slope conditions. In hachured maps the thickness of the lines, and with it the darkness of the tone, should indicate ruggedness, but this method depends too much on the individual. The same holds true for plastic shading. Both methods fail completely in lowlands.

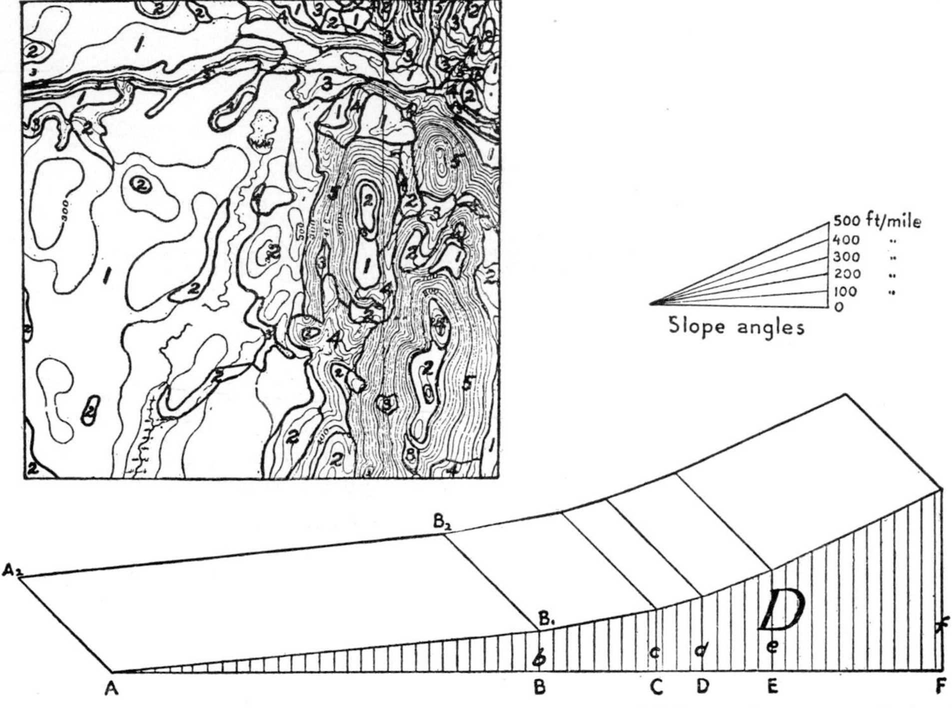


**Fig. 251** Calculation of the coefficient of slope. The areas of different slope were calculated on the map with a planimeter, and the figures so obtained were laid out from *A* to *F*.

**Average-slope Maps.** In *medium-scale maps*, 1:500,000 to 1:1,000,000, the contour interval may be 500 to 1,000 feet, too great to tell us much about slope conditions. For instance one thinks of the very rugged Middlesex Fells near Boston that is missed completely on such a map, since the relief is nowhere more than 300 feet. The best answer to the problem on medium-scale maps is a *slope-category map*. The large-scale topographic sheets of the same area are divided into 5 to 10 slope categories, as in Fig. 251. This is done with the help of an indicator that shows how dense the contour lines are on a certain scale at certain contour intervals, for 100-, 200-, 300-feet-per-mile slopes, etc. Holding the indicator against the various parts of the map, it can be divided easily into the required categories. The patches thus obtained are numbered and preferably painted in different colors. These patches are now transferred to the medium-scale map either by a grid system or by photography or by an optical projector. Pantographs can also be

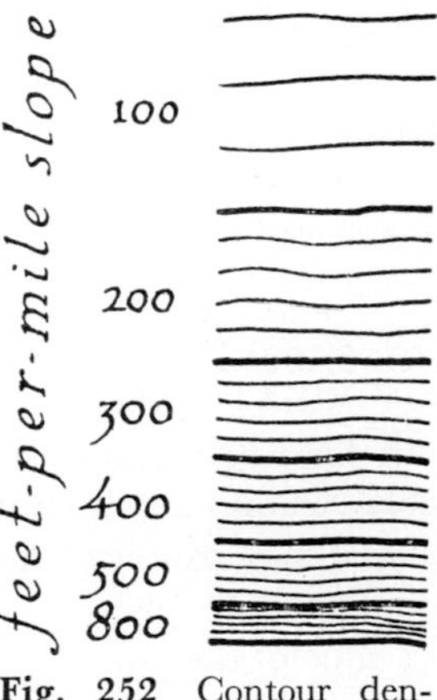


**Fig. 252** Contour density indicator.

used but only by very skilled operators. The 4-inch grid on a 1:62,500 map makes only about $\frac{1}{4}$-inch mesh on a 1:1,000,000 map.

The slope categories are tinted in 5 to 10 shades, the steeper the slope, the darker the shade, and a vivid picture of the slope conditions will result (Fig. 253). It is obvious that no category smaller than a square mile can be shown, as it would be less then $\frac{1}{16}$ inch on the millionth map. It is not good to use a very heavy black border line between patches if small categories are used, because the darkness of dividing lines may influence the allover impression of the map.

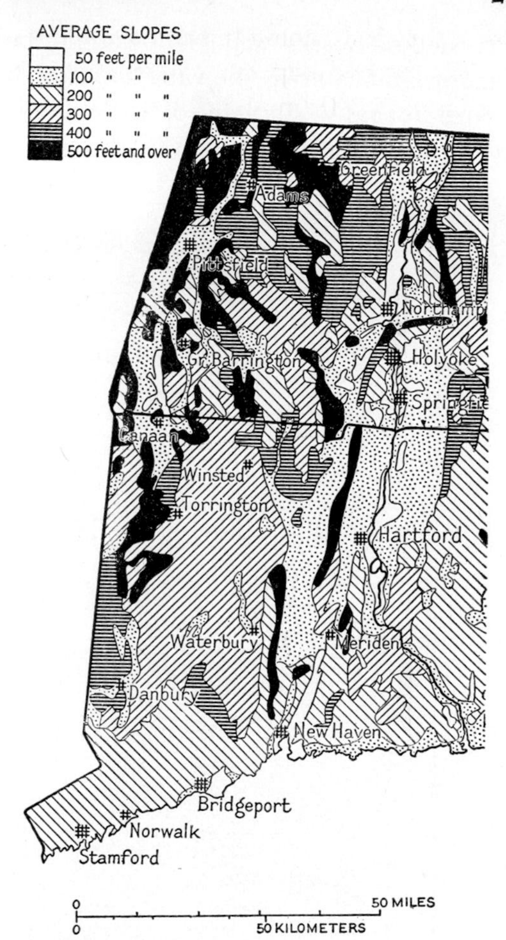


**Fig. 253** For medium-scale maps, slope conditions are best shown by the slope-category method. (*Courtesy of Geog. Rev.*, 1937.)

**Wentworth Method.** In laying out slope categories, much depends on individual judgment, and it takes some experience to judge where one category ends and the other begins. A more laborious but more impersonal method has been designed by C. K. Wentworth.[1] The contour-line map is divided into small squares, and an index figure is obtained by counting the number of contour lines along the two diagonals. Since the density of contour lines is in direct relationship to the steepness of the slopes, this method gives a fair indication of ruggedness. It was found that in some complex New England regions the squares had to be made $\frac{1}{2}$ inch wide, while in the central plains 1-mile squares were sufficient.

**Small-scale Land-slope Maps.** The slope category method can still be used in maps smaller than 1:1,000,000, but the categories have to be broader and the generalization has to be carried further. For instance, on a 1:4,000,000 map a single 1-inch-to-mile sheet would be $\frac{1}{4}$ inch high and it obviously cannot be divided into many categories.

**Flatland Ratio Maps.** The practical use of land-slope analysis is primarily for agriculture, and the farmer is best served in *flatland ratio maps*. These maps have only two categories: (1) lands flat enough for plowing and (2) slope lands. All the flatlands are outlined on topographic sheets from which they are transferred to medium-scale maps. The white of the flatlands will still show up well against the black of the slope lands.

For small-scale flatland ratio maps we calculate for each (or part of each) topographic sheet the percentage of flatland and connect places of equal ratio with isopleths.

[1] WENTWORTH, C. K., A Simplified Method of Determining the Average Slope of Land Surfaces, *Am. Jour. Sci.*, Ser. 5, Vol. 20, pp. 184–194, 1930.

This method works well for lowlands, but in mountainous areas the variation may be so extreme that the drawing of isopleths with any degree of accuracy may be impossible. It is possible, however, to tint the little rectangles representing each topographic sheet differently, and thus make a kind of choropleth map.

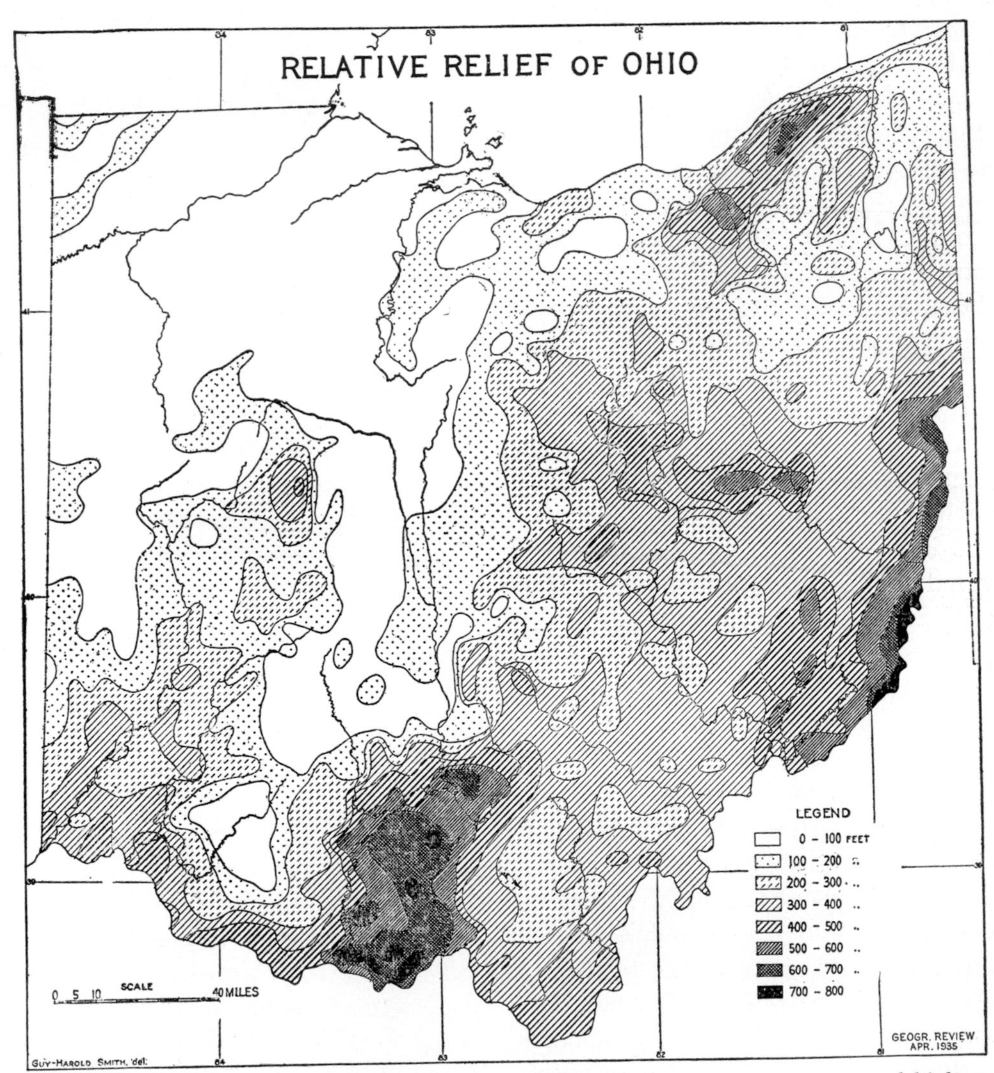


**Fig. 254** This map was constructed by marking the difference between lowest and highest elevations in every 5-minute rectangle. (*By Guy-Harold Smith.*)

**Relative Relief Maps.** The history and principles of this delineation are available in an article by Guy Harold Smith, "The Relative Relief of Ohio."[1] The process originated in Germany and Poland, where this type of study has received attention for a long time.

In the method adopted by Smith each topographic sheet was divided into rectangles of 5 minutes of longitude and latitude. In each rectangle the difference between the highest and the lowest points

[1] SMITH, G. H., The Relative Relief of Ohio, *Geog. Rev.*, Vol. 25, pp. 272–284, 1935.

was noted and plotted on a small-scale base map. Places of even differences were connected with isopleths[1] for each 100 feet of relative relief. Smith's map gives a vivid picture of the relative relief of Ohio. His method works well in maturely dissected plains and plateaus but does not give satisfactory results in complex, glaciated regions.

**Trachographic Maps.** This kind of map can be much more easily understood than any of the previous kinds, but it needs a certain amount of skill for its preparation. It shows both the average slope and the relative relief. The method is described in Chap. 11, and it is particularly adapted to small-scale maps.

**Superimposed Curves.** Slope conditions can be better understood and visualized from some kind of slope profile. These curves can be placed upon the map, for instance, for every county, and will give a good idea about the prevailing slope conditions there. Several kinds of curves are in use and the more important ones are described in the following.

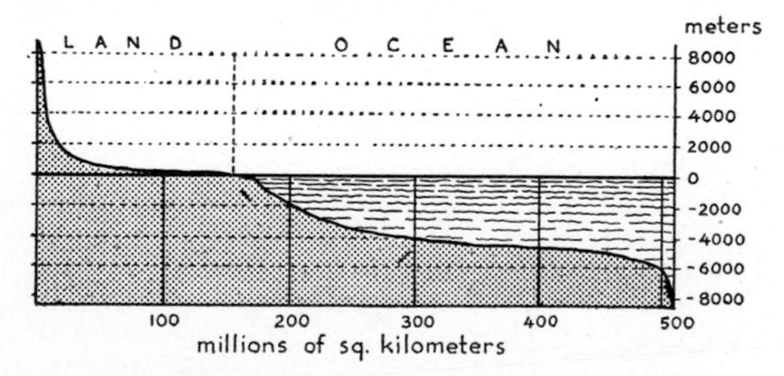


**Fig. 255** Hypsographic curve showing the distribution of the earth's surface according to altitude.

*Hypsographic Curve.* The idea of the hypsographic curve dates back to de Lapparent (1883), and since that time it has been often used by geographers to express the amount of land surface that occurs at various elevations in a given area.

The curve is constructed by calculating the area of land between each two contour lines. The area enclosed by the first contour line is represented by $A_1$, and that enclosed by the next higher contour line is represented by $A_2$. $A_1 - A_2$ is marked off according to a chosen scale for the horizontal component of the curve, and the vertical component is the corresponding contour interval (Fig. 255), usually with some vertical exaggeration. The areas can be conveniently measured with a planimeter. This curve will show how much land there is at various elevations, but it will not be the same as the general profile of the land, as shown in Fig. 94, where the hypsographic curves of various solids are shown by dotted lines. The hypsographic curve of a cone is very pointed; only a paraboloid has a straight one.

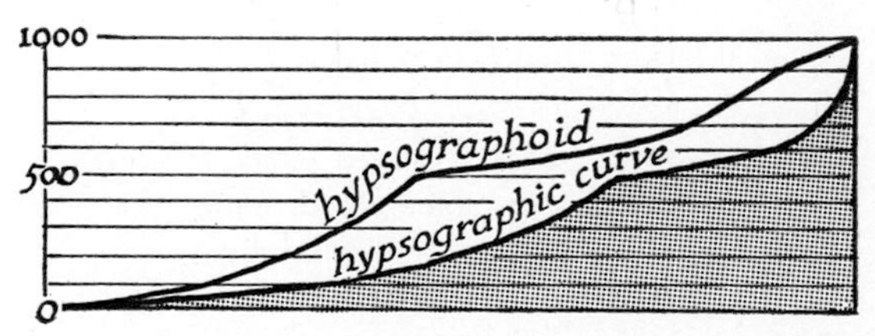


**Fig. 256** The hypsographic curve shows the amounts of land at each elevation. The hypsographoid curve shows the radii of circles representing the amount of land at each elevation. The two curves are in quadratic relationship.

To show the actual generalized profile of the land, F. Uhorczak[2] of Lemberg drew a *hypsographoid* where the land within each contour interval is represented by truncated cones built one upon another. A side view of this rotational solid gives a curve that shows the actual, general profile of the land on an exaggerated, vertical scale. The construction of the hypsographoid is as follows: The area enclosed by the lowest contour line is $A_1$, and the area inside the next con-

[1] Isopleths that show equal slope or relief conditions may be called "isotrachonic (equal ruggedness) lines."

[2] See ROMER, EUGENE, Une Nouvelle Représentation Graphique de l'Hypsométrie, *Comptes-Rend. Internat. Cong. Géog.*, Vol. 1, pp. 328–340, Paris, 1931.

tour line is $A_2$, etc. These areas are replaced by circles of equal area, from which $R_1$ and $R_2$ can be calculated. By marking off to scale the distances $R_1$, $R_2$, etc., as horizontal components, and by using the corresponding contour intervals as vertical components, a continuous curve can be drawn. Obviously, $R_1$, $R_2$, etc., are proportionate to the square roots of $A_1$, $A_2$, etc., and the hypsographic curve and the hypsographoids are in quadratic relationship. The hypsographoid helps to discover breaks in the general profile of the land, and indicates the plateaus and peneplains.

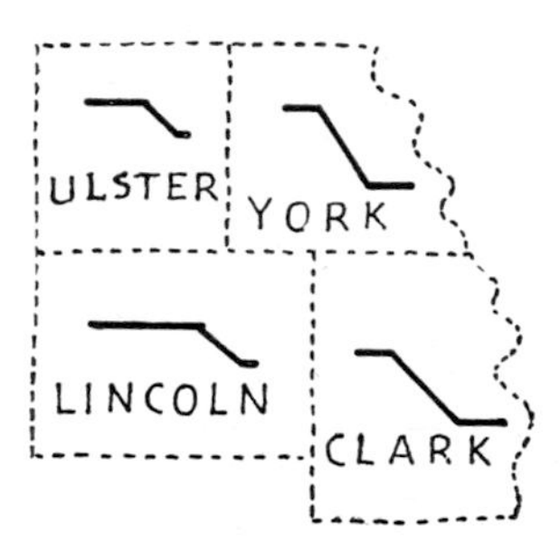


**Fig. 257** Flatland ratio maps show flat upland, flat lowland, and slopeland by superimposed diagrams.

*Flatland Ratio Curve*. Even more than in the general profile, the agriculturist is interested in the amount of flat, cultivable land in his region. Veatch[1] divides the land in three categories: flat upland, sloping land, and flat lowland, which classification applies well in the Appalachian Plateau and the central states. The areas of each kind are measured on topographic sheets with a planimeter and expressed by a curve, as in Fig. 257. Several such curves placed on a map, for instance for each county, will give a good idea about the cultivable land of each region.

*General Land-slope Curve*. The obvious shortcoming of the flatland ratio curve is that it does not give much information about the land in slope. Yet the slopes are used for orchards, vineyards, hayfields, rough pasture, or terrace cultivation, each type best suited to a particular slope. Before we can draw a general slope curve, we have to prepare a slope category map, as explained before. Then we measure all the land belonging to each category with a planimeter, and add up. We draw a horizontal line, and lay out these values—first the flatland, then the next steeper category, and so on. Then we draw sloping lines, steeper for each slope category, as shown in Fig. 251, and then we can draw a continuous curve. If we wish to express the slope of a region with a coefficient, the area of $D$ will give a characteristic value. In the case of perfectly flat land $D$ is zero.

[1] VEATCH, J. O., Graphic and Quantitative Comparisons of Land Types, *Jour. Am. Soc. Agronomy*, Vol. 27, pp. 505–510, 1935.

# CHAPTER 30: *Land-use and Economic Maps*

Mankind occupies this earth in hundreds of different ways and wrings a livelihood from its resources. The patterns of this use of land and its economic results are the subject of this chapter. The cartography of land-use and economic maps is far from being crystallized. The pattern is complex and the points of view are many. As these maps bear heavily on economic decisions, considerable funds are available for their preparation and reproduction, and many new richer techniques have been developed.

## Land-use Maps

In this group belong the maps that show the actual and possible uses of the land, including both agricultural and nonagricultural (industrial, urban, recreational, mining, and lumbering) uses. The importance and possibilities of such maps are great, and for a geographer they are more useful than topographic sheets. The preparation of good land-utilization maps is a difficult cartographical problem.

A successful land-use map of a well-cultivated country requires a rather large scale. "The Land Utilization Survey of Great Britain," uses the 6-inches-to-the-mile Ordnance Survey maps as a base showing each field separately. The surveyor places an index letter upon each field for the following divisions:

*F* for forest and woodland
*M* for meadowland and permanent grass
*A* for arable or tilled land, fallow, and rotation grass
*H* for heathland, moorland, commons, and rough hill pasture
*G* for gardens, allotments, orchards, nurseries, etc.
*W* for land agriculturally unproductive, including wasteland, buildings, yards, mines, etc.
*P* for water (lakes, streams, etc.)

From these marked sheets, colored reductions are made by the Ordnance Survey on a scale of 1 : 63,360. These reductions vividly portray the intricate pattern of land use in the British Isles. The land was surveyed by volunteers organized by Dudley Stamp, the noted geographer. Groups of students, teachers, scouts, and interested citizens

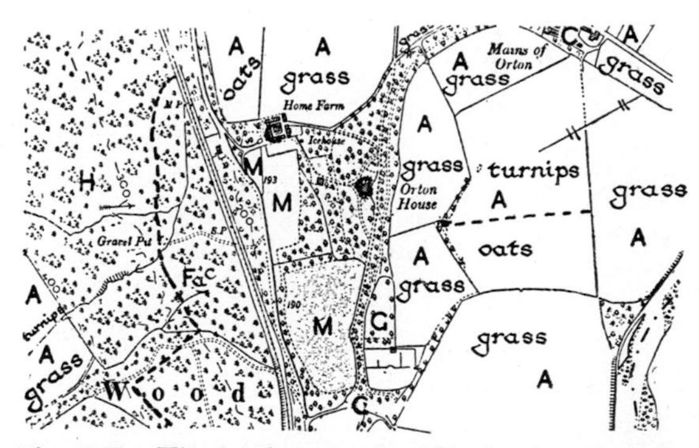


**Fig. 258** The land-use map of England was made by volunteer workers, who marked every field in the 6-inches-to-the-mile map of Great Britain with one of six letters.

found this survey very interesting and of great educational value. It is hoped that this healthy plan will be followed in all civilized countries.

In the United States, where no 6-inches-to-the-mile maps are available, the best approach to the problem is to mark airplane photographs. It is true that it is not easy to mark on photographs, but a matte surface, or a glossy surface if rubbed with any home abrasive, takes the ink of a fountain pen well. Photographs can be obtained from

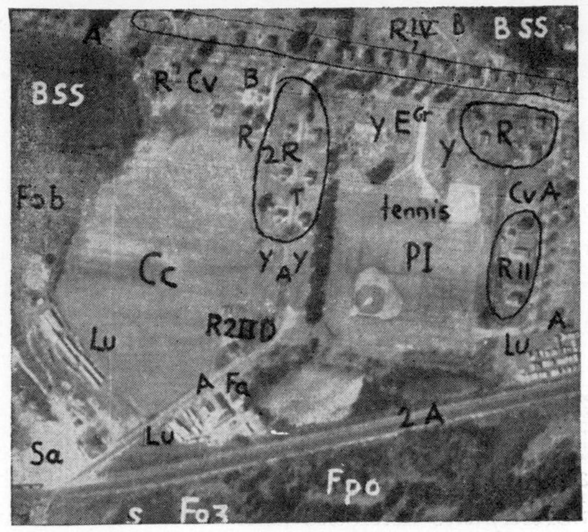


**Fig. 259** Large-scale land-use maps are best made by marking airplane photographs in the field.

the U.S. Department of Agriculture. In many parts of the United States, with so much idle land, the British system with its extreme simplicity would not give enough information in addition to the amount that could be read from the photograph anyway.

**Code Index Methods.** For any part of the world a simple code index can be worked out that gives a great deal of information about the land. As an example, the index used by the author's class is here reproduced. The fundamental idea is that the most common condition is not marked, only the unusual condition. This makes the index figures small, but even so 1:10,000, or larger, photographs had to be used.

## Fractional Code Index for a Land-utilization Survey in Southern New England

GENERAL ARRANGEMENT

type, composition, age, upkeep
―――――――――――――――
slope, drainage, soil, stoniness

Except for "type" all other factors have to be recorded only if significant or when they depart from normal.

*Types*

| | |
|---|---|
| Forest | *F* |
| Bush | *B* |
| Pasture | *P* |
| Hayfield | *H* |
| Cropland | *C* |
| Orchard | *O* |
| Nursery | *N* |
| Gardens | *G* |
| Lawns | *L* |
| Yards | *Y* |
| Cemetery | † |
| Golf links | *Go* |
| Playgrounds | *Pl* |
| Airport | *X* |
| Sand or gravel pits | *S* or *Gr* |
| Quarries | *Q* |
| Lumber yards | *Ly* |

*Composition in Forests*

| | |
|---|---|
| Oak | *o* |
| Pine | *p* |

*Composition in Forests (Con't.)*

| | |
|---|---|
| Birch | *b* |
| Beech | *be* |
| Hickory | *h* |
| Cedar | *c* |

*Composition in Cropland*

| | |
|---|---|
| Corn | *c* |
| Wheat | *w* |
| Oats | *o* |
| Alfalfa or clover | *a* |
| Potatoes | *p* |
| Vegetables | *v* |
| Beets, turnips | *t* |
| Pumpkin and squash | *s* |

*Age*

| | |
|---|---|
| Old | 1 |
| Medium | |
| Young | 3 |

*Upkeep in General*

| | |
|---|---|
| Excellent | *A* |
| Medium | |
| Poor | *C* |
| Abandoned | *D* |

*Upkeep in Forest*

| | |
|---|---|
| Excellent | *A* |
| Good | *B* |
| Unkept | |
| Heavy hurricane damage | *H* |

Thus a young unkept pine-oak-birch forest will be marked *Fpob*3. A cornfield with interspaced squash in bad shape will be marked *C c*+*s C*. A newly laid out cemetery in excellent upkeep is marked †3*A*

DENOMINATOR

*Slope*

| | |
|---|---|
| Show down-dip with arrows | |
| Level, less than 100 feet per mile | |
| Gentle or undulating—less than 200 feet per mile | 2 |
| Moderately hilly—300 feet per mile | 3 |
| Hilly—400 feet per mile | 4 |
| Steep, 500 feet per mile | 5 |
| etc., | |

*Drainage*

| | |
|---|---|
| Good, no problems | |
| Swampy in wet season | *S* |
| Swamp | *SS* |

*Soil*

| | |
|---|---|
| Black or brown soil | *b* |
| Yellow-gray soil | |
| Sand | *s* |
| Gravel | *gr* |

*Stoniness* (mark only in pasture or hayfields)

| | |
|---|---|
| Plowable | |
| Plowable but stony | 0 |
| Very stony, precluding cultivation | 00 |
| Bare rock in 50 per cent of area | 000 |

**Buildings.** In more detailed surveys, it is just as important to mark the buildings, roads, etc., as the fields. They can also be marked on the photographs with an arrow pointing to the particular building or road. A row of similar buildings can be bunched together. For city surveys, however, a still larger scale photograph, around 1:2,000, will be necessary. We mark the type starting with a capital letter, and size, material, age, original quality, and upkeep. Again the most common kind of buildings are not marked at all, only the significant departures from normal. Individual farm buildings are marked in very detailed surveys only, or if it is a specialized form, for instance, a poultry farm. The same holds true for garages and cottages.

*Buildings* (mark *type*, *size*, *material*, *age*, *quality*, *and upkeep;* omit if visible from photograph)

*Type*

| | |
|---|---|
| One-family house | *R* |
| Two-family house | 2*R* |
| Three-family house | 3*R* |
| Four-family house | 4R |
| Apartment house | *Ap* |
| Barn | *B* |
| Silo | *SI* |
| Horse stable | *HO* |
| Poultry house | *PO* |
| Pig sties | *PI* |
| Greenhouse | *GR* |
| Garage | *Ga* |
| Cottage | *Co* |
| Church | *Ch* |
| School | *Sc* |
| Library | *Li* |
| Theater | *Th* |
| Club | *Cl* |
| Fire station | *Fst* |
| Railroad depot | *Rd* |
| Factory (note type) | *Fa* |
| Workshop (note type) | *Wo* |
| Powerhouse (note type) | *Po* |
| Storage house (note type) | *St* |
| Wholesale store | *Wh* |
| Retail store | *Rt* |
| Bank | *Bk* |
| Restaurant | *Rest* |
| Hotel | *Ho* |
| Old car yard | *Oldc* |
| Filling station | *Fi* |

*Size*

Large . . . . . . . . I
Medium . . . . . . . .
Small . . . . . . . . III
Very small . . . . . . . . IV

*Material*

Stone . . . . . . . . *St*
Brick . . . . . . . . *Br*
Frame . . . . . . . .
Stucco . . . . . . . . *Stu*

*Age*

Early nineteenth century . . . . . . . . 1
Late nineteenth century . . . . . . . . 2
Pre-1930 . . . . . . . .
Post-1930 . . . . . . . . 4

*Original Quality*

Palatial . . . . . . . . I
High grade . . . . . . . . II
Medium . . . . . . . .
Low grade . . . . . . . . IV

*Upkeep*

High grade . . . . . . . . *A*
Medium . . . . . . . .
Dilapidated . . . . . . . . *C*
Abandoned . . . . . . . . *D*

LINES OF COMMUNICATION

*Railroads*

Railroads, one track . . . . . . . . 1
two tracks . . . . . . . . 2
three tracks . . . . . . . . 3
Electric . . . . . . . . E

*Railroad Maintenance*

Trunk line . . . . . . . . *A*
Secondary line . . . . . . . .
Rarely used . . . . . . . . *C*
Abandoned . . . . . . . . *D*
Rails removed . . . . . . . . *E*

*Roads*

Concrete . . . . . . . . *C*
Stone—asphalt . . . . . . . . *SA*

*Roads*

Asphalt . . . . . . . . *A*
Tar . . . . . . . . *T*
Gravel maintained . . . . . . . . *Gr*
Dirt . . . . . . . . *D*
Footpaths . . . . . . . . *F*

*Road Upkeep*

Excellent shape . . . . . . . . *A*
Medium . . . . . . . .
Maintained . . . . . . . . *C*
Abandoned . . . . . . . . *D*

*Fences*

Stone . . . . . . . . *St*
Hedge . . . . . . . . *H*
Barbed wire . . . . . . . . xxx
Ditch . . . . . . . . *Di*

Thus a large, stone late-nineteenth-century railroad depot which was originally high grade but which is now delapidated will be *RdSt*211*D*, while a one-family frame house of medium size, built before 1930, and of medium quality and medium upkeep is simply *R*.

It is recommended that each class in cartography work out a similar index adapted to local conditions and try it out in the field. This may not be true for all parts of the country, but in New England it is seldom necessary to leave the car to mark the photographs.

**The Preparation of Large-scale Land-use Maps.** For classroom work the roads, rivers, houses, fences, edges of fields, etc., are copied from the photograph over the light-table upon one-ply drawing paper and inked in. The fields are marked with their index numbers and the major features are emphasized by coloring. The following color scheme is recommended for the Eastern United States:

| | |
|---|---|
| Coniferous forest . . . . . . | Dark green |
| Deciduous forest . . . . . . | Medium green |
| Bush . . . . . . . . | Light green with dark-green irregular dotting |
| Rough pasture, heather | Yellow-green |

| | |
|---|---|
| Hayfield | Yellow |
| Plowed land | Brown |
| Orchard | Black symbol pattern over yellow |
| Vineyard | Black symbol pattern over brown |
| Swamp | Blue horizontal lines over the forest, bush, or grass symbol |
| Yards, gardens | Pink |
| Houses | Red |
| Industrial areas, railroad yards, docks | Purple |

Within a field there may be variation of land types, for instance, the rough pasture often goes over into forest. In this case we change in color without a black boundary line.

If no colors can be used, black-on-white mechanical patterns may help. The Zip-a-tone pattern sheet gives patterns that are designed exactly for this purpose.

**Soil Conservation Maps.** The nearest approach in the United States to a real land-use map is produced by the Soil Conservation Service, although the emphasis is more on soil erosion than land use. Only a small part of the country is yet covered. Airplane photographs are composed into mosaics from which planimetric maps are prepared, mostly on a 4-inches-to-the-mile scale. The major land-use categories are differentiated by green symbol patterns, such as

1. Cultivated or urban land—colorless
2. Idle land—crosslined
3. Pasture—grass symbols
4. Woodland—tree symbols

The land is divided into tracts. Each tract has an index number of three figures, the first of which represents the type and amount of erosion; the second, the amount of slope; and the third, the type of soil. Ownership of land is disregarded. These maps not only show the present utilization, but also give a clue to possible future uses. Their primary purpose is to aid in the battle of preserving the country's rapidly waning soil.

The U.S. Department of the Interior, in cooperation with the U.S. Department of Agriculture, has made land-classification maps of much of the Great Plains. These do not include soil-erosion or related data. The most elaborate fractional code index is that of the Tennessee Valley Authority, which uses as many as 18 figures to designate a patch of land.

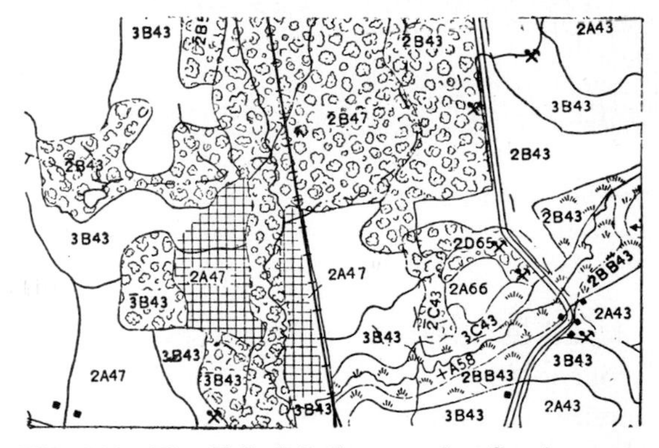

**Fig. 260** The U.S. Soil Conservation Service maps show land-use patterns and indicate erosion, slope, and soil types by index letters and numbers. The originals are in three colors.

**Foreign Maps.** In the 1860's, several great map sets appeared that combined a land-use and a topographic map. The 1:50,000 Spanish maps used a combination of contour lines with hand-drawn patterns of vineyards, olive orchards, pastures, etc., in vivid colors. Even better were the 1:100,000 Residency maps of Java with an elaborate system of land-use patterns and colors combined with plastic shading for relief. Similar excellent maps were produced by the French in Algiers. One cannot help feeling that cartography lost a great deal when this colorful and realistic method was abandoned in favor of the purely contour-lined map. Now that airplane photography reveals the true pattern of the earth's surface, we find that the old land-use type of map was much closer to this reality. At present, many colonial surveys (East Indies, Katanga, etc.) produce land-use maps; many other surveys at least add to their topographic sheets a green overprint for forest, and many show special forms of cultivation, such as vineyards, orchards, etc.

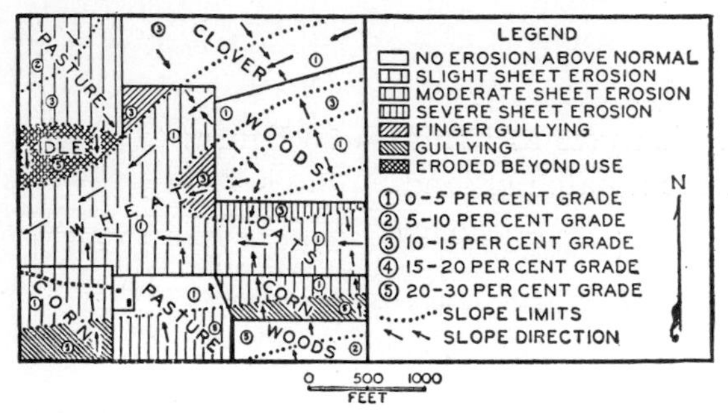


**Fig. 261** Slope, slope direction, land use, and erosion shown in a single map. (*R. M. Glendinning, Michigan Univ. Papers in Geography, Ann Arbor, Mich.*, 1937.)

**Land-use Maps in Geographic Papers.** Geographic essays on regional analysis are usually accompanied by land-use maps. The geographer will often find that the standard symbols do not fit his requirements, and he will have to design his own symbols. In so doing he will find naturalistic patterns more satisfactory than mechanical rulings.

Robert M. Glendinning[1] proposes a method for large-scale maps, in which slope categories are shown by dotted outlines and index figures, slope direction by arrows, land use by labeled outlines of lots, and erosion by tints. If erosion is not important, the slope categories are tinted. Whether it is practically possible to show all these elements on a single black-and-white map remains to be proved, but the method is stimulating for further experimentation.

**Land-use Profiles.** Profiles always help to understand land problems and they are particularly useful in showing how land-use depends on slope, altitude, soil, and geology. Some vertical exaggeration will be necessary; otherwise these profiles do not present problems. They can be made more vivid by adding a narrow strip of surface in the same way as in the animated profiles in geology (see Chap. 31).

**Block Diagrams.** These are used more and more in expressing the connection between geology, relief, and land use. The construction is described in Chap. 31.

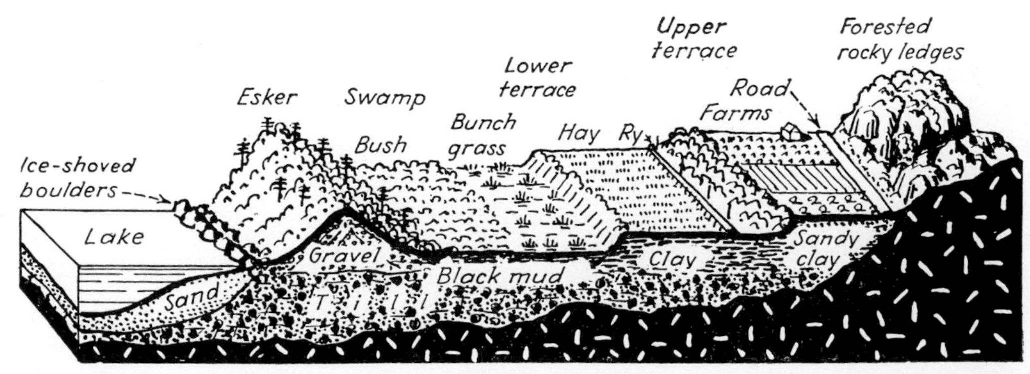


**Fig. 262** Land-use profiles are most useful tools in understanding the geography of a region.

**Maps of Urban Geography.** Maps of urban geography present many cartographic problems. Large-scale (1:5,000 to 1:10,000) urban maps can show every building separately and denote its function by tints and indexes, making such distinctions as first-, second-, and third-class family

[1] Glendinning, Robert M., The Slope and Slope-direction Map, *Michigan Univ. Papers in Geography*, Ann Arbor, Mich., Vol. VII, pp. 359–364, 1937.

houses, tenements, or apartment houses; business, industrial, or recreational buildings, schools, churches, hospitals, barracks; and open places such as parks, gardens, truck gardens, cemeteries, fields; railroad yards, airports, harbor facilities, and undeveloped lots. If airplane photographs are available, they will help to a great extent in the construction of such a map. Airplane photographs may even be used directly, instead of maps, with an overlay of transparent color tints and the addition of index numbers.

Small-scale maps of urban geography rarely show more than the various functional zones of a city by the use of tints. It is good cartographic practice to have the darker tints indicate areas of densest population. Black is usually reserved for public buildings.

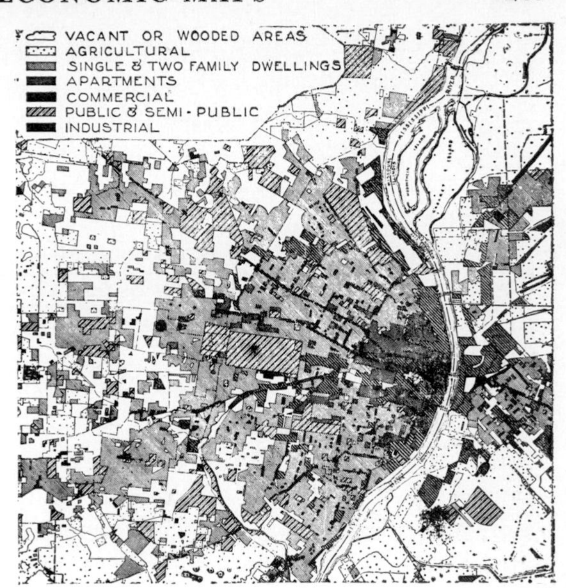


**Fig. 263** Small-scale functional map of a city. (*From St. Louis Region, National Resources Committee,* 1936.)

Besides the horizontal pattern, the vertical differentiation of city buildings is also significant. The first floors may be used for business, the second for offices, and the upper floors for residence. To indicate ver-

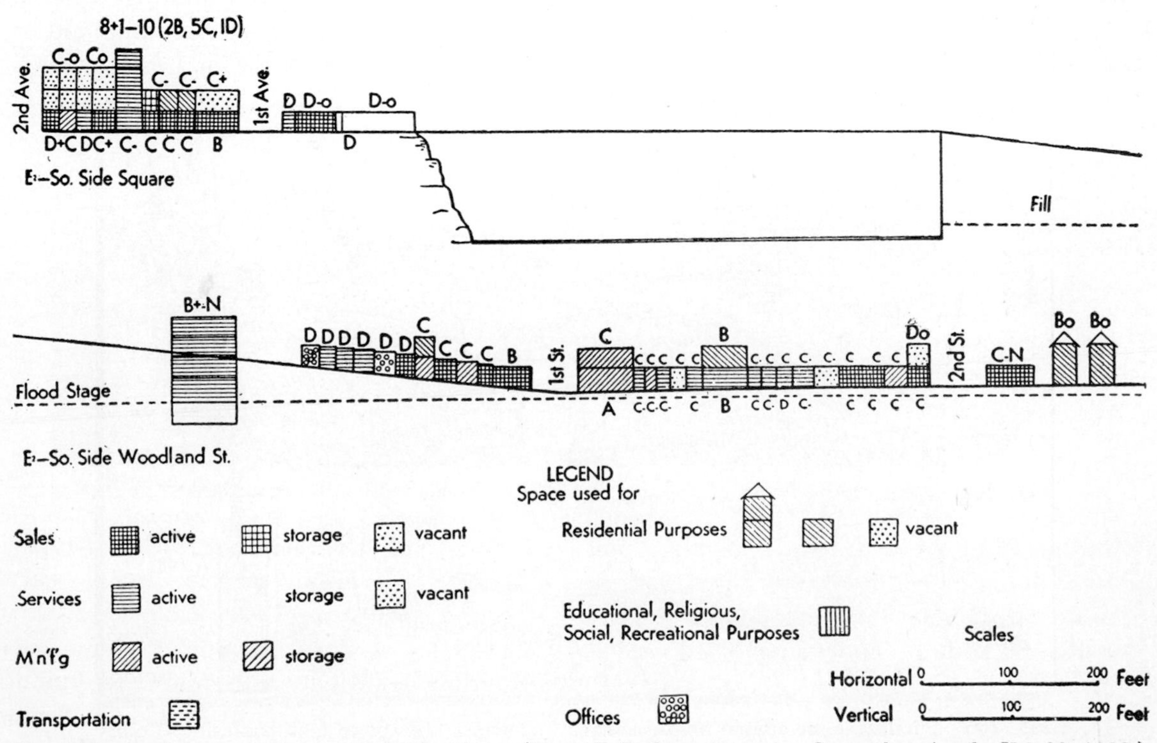


**Fig. 264** Profile of a section in Nashville, Tenn. (*By A. E. Parkins, Assoc. Am. Geographers Annals, Vol.* 20, 1930.)

tical differentiations, city profiles may be added, as shown in Fig. 264.

The urban geographer works with a great number of maps to solve the many perplexing problems of a growing city. Automobile traffic density maps are made by sets of airplane photographs taken hourly. Surveys of day and night density of population maps show how many people have to be moved around nine and five. Diagrammatic maps showing the number of people on each bus or trolley at each hour will help to plan the economical use of these conveyances. Gas, electricity, telephone, sewer, water, and all other public utilities require maps. The social conditions, income groups, languages, races, churches, recreational facilities, and health conditions all present many challenges to cartographers. Wholesale and retail business and deliveries, milk, newspaper, and mail distribution, garbage disposal, etc., can be worked out on large-scale city maps. Most cities have cadastral maps showing home ownership which are most valuable for other purposes also. The cost of the preparation of a detailed exact city map is usually amply repaid by the resulting economies. Some cities even prepare relief models showing each house for more effective planning. No field in cartography offers such variety and so much challenge to the cartographer's ingenuity as the great complexity of a large city. The Sanborn Fire Insurance maps of Pelham, N.Y., which cover almost every house in the country on large scale and great detail, offer a most valuable aid in city surveys.

**Medium- and Small-scale Land-use Maps.** In the foregoing discussion, we considered land-use maps where practically every house and field can be shown separately. It is not easy to generalize the variegated pattern of land use into small-scale maps. It can be done only by omitting all detail and by color-patching 5 to 10 main types of land use, such as two or three forest types, bush, grazing lands, cultivated lands, desert, etc. Most difficult to show is scattered cultivation such as that of New England or the Piedmont. Here little squares of yellow-

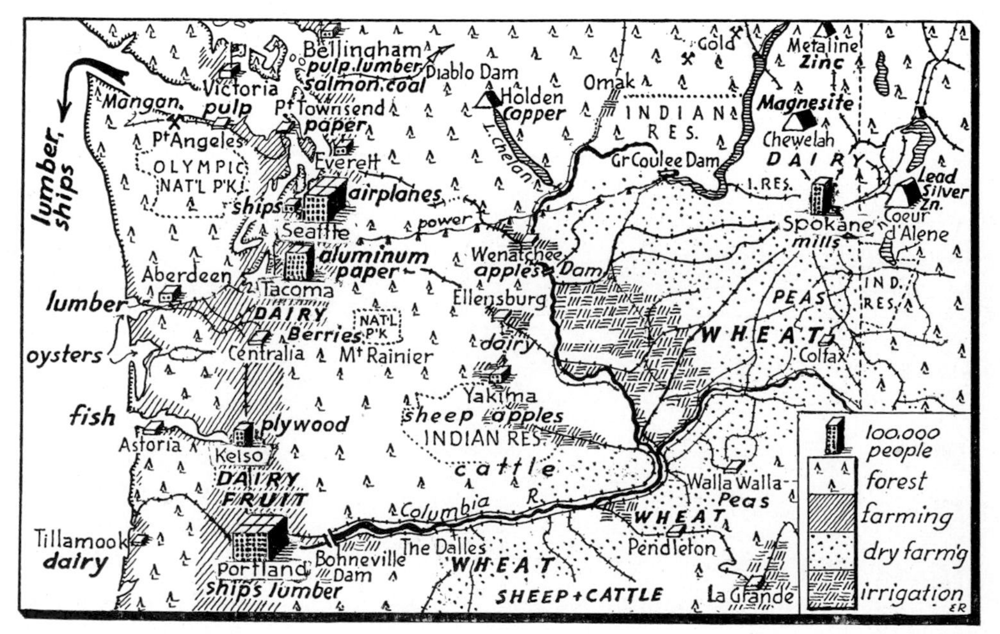


**Fig. 265** Small-scale economic maps in black and white are apt to look confusing. Colors help much in clarifying land-use symbols.

green in the dark green of the forest, occupying about the true proportion of the area, may help. The dominant types of crops can be indicated by naming them, or by index letters. Small-scale land-use maps approach economic maps. They show roads, railroads, and waterways, manufacturing and mining centers, emphasized in excess of their actual area. Small-scale and medium-scale land-use maps can be made in black and white only, with the land types patterned, but a black-red key plate showing urban centers, railways and roads, and manufacturing and mining overprinted with 5 to 10 flat colors for land types will be far more effective. The Economic Development maps of Philip are good but far from satisfactory examples. The possibilities of small-scale land-use maps are not fully explored, and they have to be compiled from large-scale maps that are not yet available for most of the world.

## Economic Maps

The maps of this group are concerned with the production, transportation, and distribution of goods. These are broad relationships involving large areas—often the whole world—and the maps are necessarily small-scale maps. Economic maps are likely to pattern a single or a group of products. If the total economic picture is shown, they become land-use maps. Most economic maps are statistical in nature.

**Maps of Agriculture.** Maps of the various phases of agriculture are published by all important nations; the national atlases especially contain many agricultural maps. The U.S. Department of Agriculture has excellent cartographers, and their maps fill many volumes.

The distribution of crops and animal products is usually shown by the dot system. The dots may indicate either acreage or quantity by weight—rarely value of production. The most reliable and checkable figures are available for *acreage*. The *quantity of production* in bushels, bales, or tons is usually obtained by taking into consideration the yield per acre in different localities. Since yields per acre may differ considerably, maps showing production by quantities are more significant than those showing acreage. Maps that show the *value of products* are still more significant because they take into consideration the difference between high-grade and low-grade products. Furthermore, money value is a common denominator by which maps of various products are comparable. If, however, the products of several years are compared, any change in the value of the currency must also be taken into consideration. These value maps, likewise, are of more permanent nature than the quantity maps, because in times of poor crops higher prices partly offset the difference. For certain studies, agricultural *ratio maps*, which show by isopleths or choropleths such relationships as yield per acre or percentage of one crop to all crops, are prepared.

In addition to products, many other important items are recorded on agricultural maps, such as value of farm equipment, number of trucks or horses, farm tenancy, farm mortgages, value of farm property, average cash expenditure for labor, taxes, marketing methods, irrigated areas, drained land, marginal lands, and many others. All kinds of statistical mapping methods are employed in these maps—dots, isopleths, choropleths, and various types of diagrams, as the subject requires. It was, indeed, in connection with agricultural maps that most statistical map methods developed.

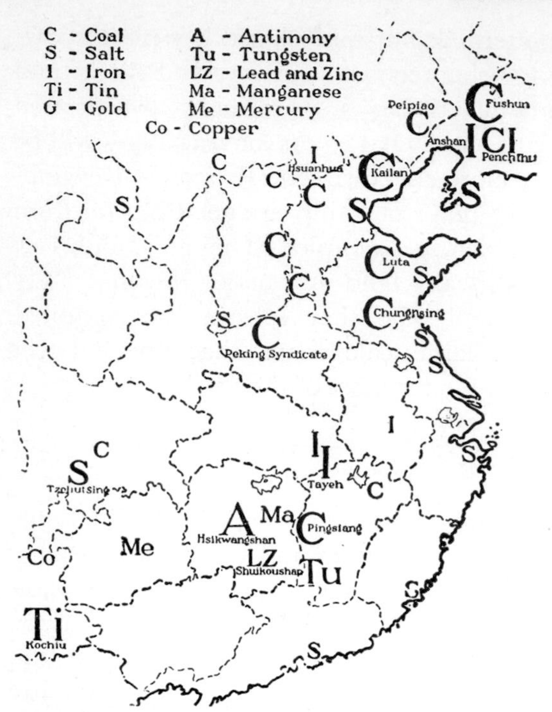


**Fig. 266** A simple type of mineral map shows the importance of the mine by differently sized letters. (*From George B. Cressey, "China's Geographic Foundations."*)

**Maps of Mineral Products.** These maps, which record the occurrence of coal, oil, metals, and other mineral products, are common in atlases and geographies. They more often record the occurrence of certain minerals than the quantity or value of production. Maps of coal basins and reserves are more common than maps that show production in each coal field. The same is true for oil and metals. The letters and symbols, which are undifferentiated in size, not only make them confusing but also fail to give the true pattern of mineral production.

Mineral production is usually highly concentrated in few localities and the map has to be quantitative to have any value, even if the yearly output may be quite variable. The simplest method is that used by Cressey—using initial letters of different sizes—which is an excellent method where the quantities and their value are not well known. For more detailed maps, the block-pile system is recommended. By this method it is possible to have some mines show 10,000 times more than others. It is often necessary to show some small-value mines because their potentialities are specially important, as in the case of the cryolite mine in Greenland, the only one of its kind.

In the author's set of mineral maps of the United States[1] crude petroleum is recorded by value at wells, coal by tons with prices indicated, metallic minerals by value of recovered metals, referred to the mine, even if smelted elsewhere. In the case of nonmetallic minerals, the value at mine is recorded. The "U.S. Minerals Yearbook" is an excellent source book for data.

**Maps of Manufacturing.** Manufacturing produces by far the greatest part of the national income of the United States; yet only very generalized maps are available showing the geographic distribution of this industry. Maps of manufacturing can be based on available data of various kinds, such as number of wage earners, value of wages, value of products, and value added by manufacturing. From the economist's point of view, value added by manufacturing is the most important. The geographer who is interested in social problems would use a map showing the number of workers as the measure of the industrialization of a region. R. Hartshorne[2] shows in his maps the number of wage earners by the sphere system. The maps of A. J. Wright,[3] on the other hand, are based on

[1] RAISZ, ERWIN, Geographical Distribution of the Mineral Industry of the United States, *Mining and Metallurgy*, March, 1941, pp. 158–166.

[2] HARTSHORNE, R., A New Map of the Manufacturing Belt of North America, *Econ. Geog.*, Vol. 12, pp. 45–53, 1936.

[3] WRIGHT, A. J., Manufacturing Districts of the United States, *Econ. Geog.*, Vol. 14, pp. 195–200, 1938.

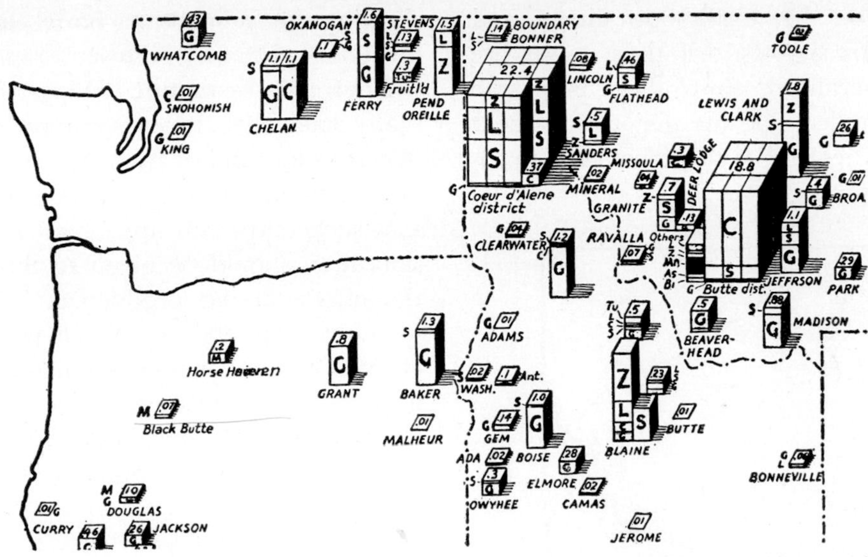


**Fig. 267** Metallic mineral production in the Northwest in 1938. (*From Mining and Metallurgy.*)

value added by manufacturing, also in the sphere system. Manufacturing maps can well be drawn in the block-pile system as shown in Fig. 268. Enormous amounts of data are available in the publications of the U.S. Census of Manufactures.

Special manufacturing maps, such as those for the steel industry, may show in a dynamic way the motion of the various raw materials and semimanufactured products, in addition to the manufacturing centers indicated by one of the methods mentioned before. The preparation of such maps requires a thorough knowledge of the industry and makes an interesting cartographic problem. To date not enough has been done in this field.

**Maps of Commodity Movements.** Maps showing production, transportation, and marketing of certain commodities, such as rubber, oil, and cotton, which are subject to considerable international trade, are often found in modern books or atlases on economics.[1] These maps are usually on a small scale, partly because detailed data are not easily available. More detailed maps, such as those showing the marketing of wheat and cotton in the United States, are available in books on economics. Data for imports and exports of each country can be found in the Commerce Yearbooks of the U.S. Department of Commerce. Production is shown by grouped circles or squares,

[1] See Atlas of World Maps, Army Service Forces, 1943, for iron and steel.

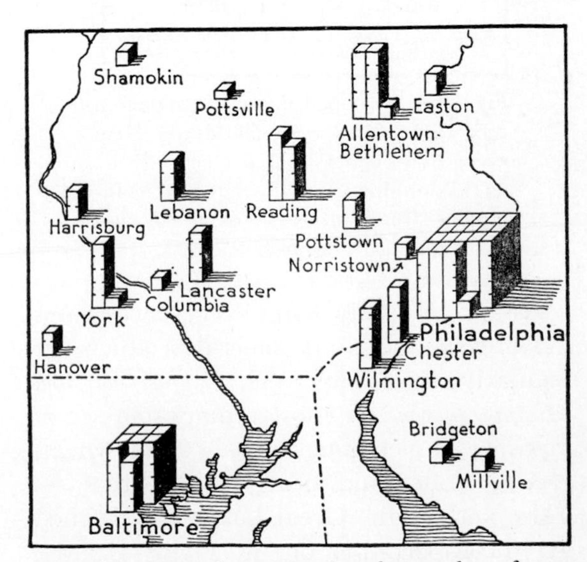


**Fig. 268** Part of map showing the number of wage earners in manufacturing. Block-pile maps are compact and easily commensurable.

transportation by traffic-flow lines, and marketing by arrows. All these maps are highly generalized, but they help the student to understand the major movement of commodities and the international problems arising therefrom.

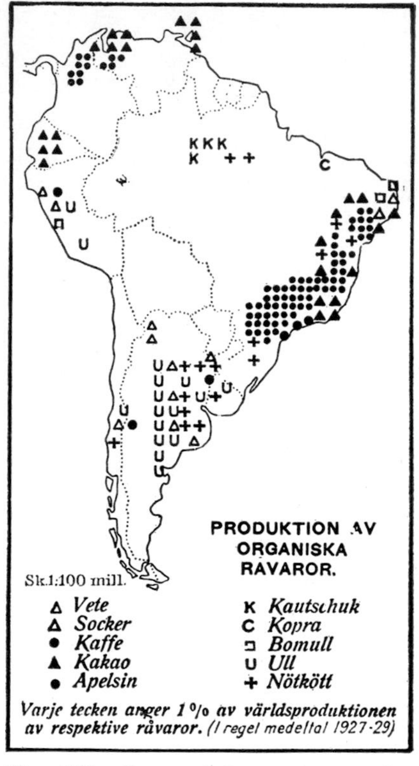


**Fig. 269** Grouped dot maps are often used for regional economic maps. Here every unit represents 1 per cent of the world's production of the respective commodity. (*From colored original in Ahlmann and Samuelsson, Geografisk Atlas.*)

As for domestic commerce, cartograms showing the motion of mineral products are regularly issued by the *Engineering and Mining Journal*. A most remarkable set of maps of movements of coal, iron, wheat, grains, stone, and other commodities to, from, and on the Great Lakes is published in "Transportation on the Great Lakes," Corps of Engineers, U.S. Army, Washington. This publication has also a cartogram showing the freight rates on wheat from all important shipping points.

**Regional Economic Maps.** These are really small-scale land-use maps. The products may be marked by name, by figurettes, or by letters; but there is always the danger that such maps will appear crowded. Consideration should be given to the fact that the characteristic product of a region is sometimes not the one which produces the greatest income or is economically the most important. For instance, watches are very characteristic of Switzerland; yet her income from their manufacture is smaller than that from textiles.

Such maps are likely to give a false picture of the economic pattern, if labels or symbols for oil, gold, furs, and other products are distributed all over the map, regardless of whether the production is large or small. Thus, for instance, if the word "Furs" is written several times on a map over the vast expanses of Northern Canada, the student may get an exaggerated impression of the importance of this product which accounts for less than 1 per cent of the national income. Therefore, such maps, although they have certain informative value, are suitable only for elementary schoolbooks and tourist folders.

Maps on which the economic pattern of production is shown by small diagrams are better, for they designate not only the kind of product but also the quantity. Several methods of making such maps have been attempted. Figure 269 shows a grouped dot system in which the dots take the distinctive forms of squares, circles, triangles, and letters. Every symbol stands for 1 per cent of the world's total production of this commodity. There are two dangers in this method: (1) in the case of concentrated production, the symbols will crowd each other out; (2) 1 per cent of the world's cacao is hardly comparable with 1 per cent of the world's wheat. A more characteristic picture of the world's economic pattern would be obtained if each symbol showed the money value of the product.

An atlas of maps, diagrams, and cartograms showing the entire economic pattern of each major commodity would be a distinct gain to our equipment in geography. At present the rapidly changing economic pattern does not encourage the investment of work and expense in this undertaking. Putnam's "Economic Atlas of the World" is a somewhat overgeneralized approach to the problem.

## Landform, Landscape, Land-use, and Land-type Maps[1]

The above terms are used by geographers, with considerable variation as to their meaning. To clarify these terms is important, because they represent the most meaningful conceptions that whirl around in the minds of map makers thinking of the fundamentals of their profession. These four terms represent the four basic approaches to making a map.

1. *Landform* maps show the plains, plateaus, mountains, etc., and also the rivers, lakes, and seas that helped to shape them; with one word, the geomorphology of the region, including its hydrography. Map publishers call these "physical" maps, not such a bad term if it would not be contrasted with "political" maps, which is a remainder of the days when the description of boundaries was regarded as one of the most essential parts of geography.

The cartography of landform maps is relatively simple. For large-scale landform maps we may use contour lines, hachures, plastic shading, or horizontal form lines, depending on the available surveys. For medium-scale maps (1:250,000–1:1,000,000) contour lines with altitude tints give the best results. For small-scale land-form maps, we may think of morphographic or trachographic maps (see Fig. 110); or we may use a photograph of a good, uncolored relief model or imitate the result of this with plastic shading. If we use altitude tints only, as many textbooks do, the result is likely to be misleading. Landform maps will often form the bases of the other types of maps.

2. The *landscape* approach shows the "looks" of the earth's surface. If we photograph the earth from a plane vertically on color film and add some lettering to the picture, we have essentially a very large-scale landscape map. This is the most objective method of cartography. Field, forest, roads, and cities are all there. The cartographer did not interpret anything, he only added names to the features, and the map has to be interpreted by the reader without the help of the cartographer. The cartographer, however, should do some interpretation for medium- and small-scale landscape maps. It would not do at all to make a huge mosaic of colored photographs and reduce it a hundred times (for instance, from 1:10,000 to 1:1,000,000). Roads and small rivers would be so microscopic as not to show at all; fields and even cities would be small blurs on the picture. The cartographer has to design suitable symbols for field, forest, road, and stream, etc., similar in shape, texture, and color to their appearance on the large-scale photograph. His desire to make features distinctive will induce him to standardize some symbols and use more contrasting colors. For instance, he will paint a rather yellowish lake in blue, and he will differentiate between green wheat fields and green grasslands, but generally he will try to be as objective as possible. This map will be appreciated by airplane travelers and also by the ground traveler who is usually baffled by how differently the map shows the actual landscape, especially in color.

In very small-scale maps the cartographer should select the orthographic projection, or a photograph of a globe, as this is how the earth would *look* to him if he saw it from the heavens. The landscape map will be different for the seasons. There is nothing wrong with this idea; for certain parts of the world the comparison of

[1] Reprinted largely from the author's paper of same title, *Jour. Geog.*, Vol. 45, No. 3, 1946.

paired summer and winter maps would be most instructive. If the cartographer is limited to a single map, he should select the most representative season for each symbol. One's usual conception is for rather green cornfields, golden wheat fields, etc.

It is not likely that pure landscape maps will be used in the future to a great extent, but any real cartographer should study the problem and should try to prepare to cross-fertilize his convention-bound methods with the actual truth, revealed so conveniently by the airplane.

3. *Land-use* maps emphasize the relation of man to the landscape. On large-scale maps the maker of a land-use map should show the various kinds of fields, meadows, pasture land, and forest with highly contrasted colors or patterns. He should emphasize roads, railways; in cities he should differentiate between the functional belts, such as residential, manufacturing, etc. In small-scale maps he should show the "dominant" pattern (wheat belt, corn belt) and emphasize manufacturing and mining, which, though highly important, do not show well on a landscape map. He is likely to add symbols, labels, and letters to show the types of products, and he should indicate shipping routes, and likely add statistical insets. Mountains and relief will interest him only insofar as they influence farming or communications, and sometimes he will omit them altogether. The presence of mountains can be interpreted from the type of culture rather than the other way around (see Fig. 265).

Land-use maps are highly important, for geographers even more so than topographic sheets, and a complete set of land-use maps of all parts of the world is highly desirable.

4. *Land-type* maps. Each of the foregoing types of maps represents an approach to the representation of the earth. The landform map shows the configuration of land, mountains, and waters; the landscape map shows chiefly vegetation and cultivation in an objective manner; the land-use map approaches the problem from the human view. Is there a chance to combine these approaches into a harmonious unit to express the all-round geographic type of the region? It is not an easy task. For instance, in the Rocky Mountains the land forms will predominate; in the agricultural Middle West the cultivation pattern of a landscape map or airplane photograph will give most of the answers, while in the urbanized East the economic land-use approach will be the most important. The variety of the features is endless. The cartographer, however, has to use a limited number of symbols to be understood. He should select his symbols so that (1) they show the land and water forms, (2) they resemble the features in line and color, and (3) they emphasize the human importance of the features. No satisfactory map has yet been designed that would be harmonious yet distinctive, rich in detail yet not overcrowded, and simple enough to be understood. The old 1:100,000 Dutch maps of Java, and even the old Spanish maps of 1:50,000, come remarkably close to the ideal.

The coming of the land-type map is inevitable. More and more people travel by air, and they cannot fail to observe the immense reality of land types. They complain that our present maps do not express the "looks" of the earth well. Colored airplane photographs point the way that cartography must travel in order to keep up with the demands of the Air Age.

# CHAPTER 31: *Geological Maps and Block Diagrams*

Among the various branches of science, the earth sciences, especially geology, are most dependent on maps. In America, a closer relationship exists between geology and geography than in most other countries, and from this relationship cartography has received much stimulus. The development of geomorphology in particular gave rise to new, illustrative methods, such as block diagrams, physiographic maps, multiple profiles, and some processes of landslope analysis. For this reason a special chapter is here devoted to geological maps and to graphic methods in geomorphology.

*History.* A small but creditable geological map of the United States was published by William Maclure in 1809, antedating the famous geological maps of England by William Smith of 1824. In the nineteenth century, geological mapping of the leading nations was carried on with great vigor, paralleling and sometimes even preceding topographic mapping. By the second half of the century most European nations had detailed geological maps. At the end of the century these surveys were brought together in the "Carte Géologique Internationale d' Europe" (1:1,500,000), which was one of the first important international maps made with the cooperation of various governments. For this map an international color scheme was adopted to replace the arbitrary colors of earlier maps.

The United States did not lag behind the European countries in geological mapping. As early as 1830 to 1840, most of the eastern states were geologically mapped by such brilliant men as W. B. Rogers of Virginia and Edward Hitchcock of Massachusetts. For the history of geological survey in the United States the student is referred to the famous book of G. P. Merrill.[1]

[1] MERRILL, GEORGE P., Contributions to a History of American State Geological and Natural History Surveys, *U.S. Nat. Mus. Bull.* 109, Smithsonian Institution, Washington, D.C., 1920.

*Geological Maps of the World.* At the present time only the most remote parts of the earth are completely unsurveyed by geologists, and even the less advanced countries have good, general geological maps.

The detailed geology of the United States is contained in the U.S. Geological Survey Atlas folios. These show the various phases of geology, such as historical, structural, economic, and surface geology on separate maps, supplemented by sections and columns and a prodigious text. Only a small part of the United States is covered by these folios. Most of the states have geological maps on the average scale of 1:500,000. In 1930 a good, general geologic map of the whole United States was published on a scale of 1:2,500,000 followed by a "tectonic map" on the same scale in 1944.

The geological maps of England and Scotland are highly commendable. The sheets show, in addition to colors for the various formations, such geologic forms as dikes, fault and joint systems, lines of schistosity in metamorphic rocks, dips, and strikes. Contact metamorphism is shown by fading out the red color of the intrusives. Even more detailed are the geologic maps of Switzerland, which are augmented by successive profiles of the extremely complex Alpine structures. Almost all European countries and Japan have complete detailed geological maps and special large-scale maps of their mineral regions. Large-scale geological mapping is in progress in Alaska, Canada, Mexico, several South American countries, in most members of the British Empire, in the French, Dutch, and Belgian colonies, and in China. The U.S.S.R., China, India, South Africa, Australia, Brazil, and several other countries have published good, general geologic maps.

*Tints and Colors.* Most geological maps are "chorochromatic," that is, the areas which are underlain by the same formation have the same color or pattern. Geologic maps

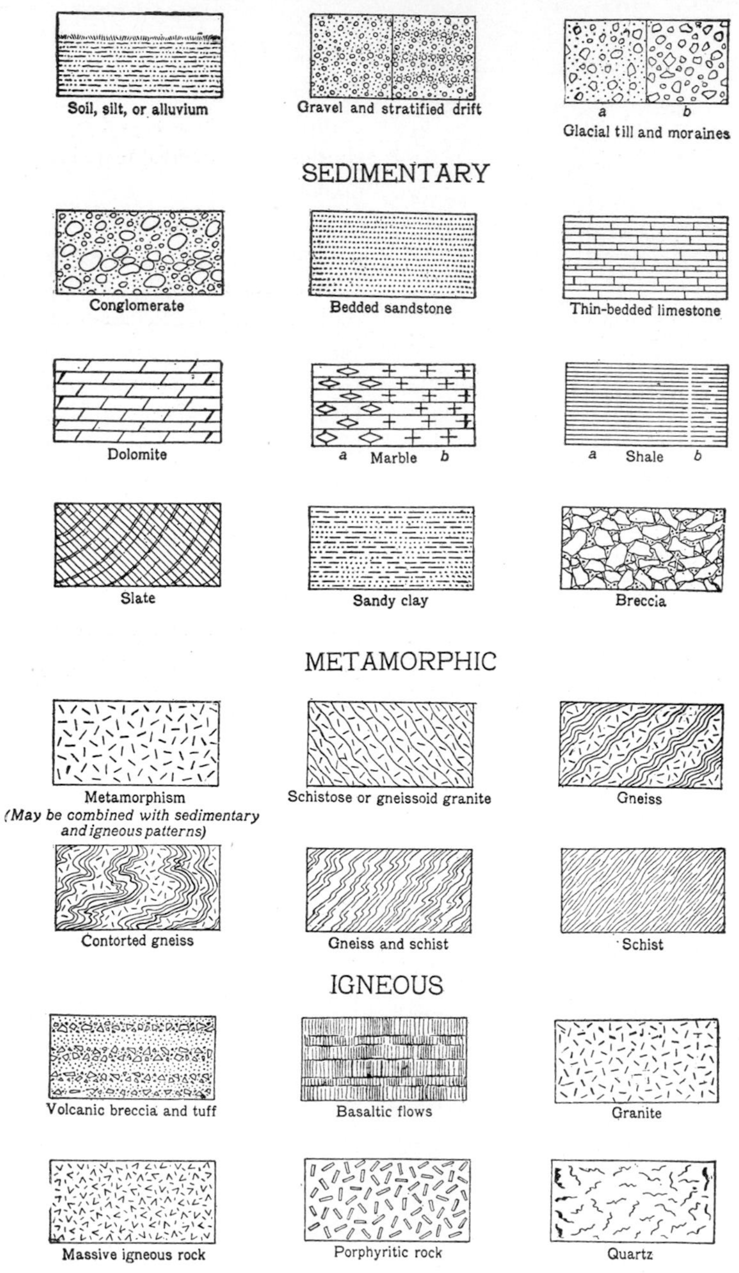


**Fig. 270** Some geological symbols of the U.S. Geological Survey to be used on columnar sections. (*From J. R. Ridgway, "Preparation of Illustrations," U.S. Geol. Survey.*)

**Fig. 271** Animated profile. (*From Preston E. James, "Outline of Geography."*)

can be successfully made in black-and-white patterns, if judgment is used in their selection. The pamphlet, "Preparation of Illustrations" for the U.S. Geological Survey, by John L. Ridgway (1920) is a good guide in this matter. The addition of structural symbols for dips, faults, joints, etc., adds greatly to the value of a geologic map.

*Geologic Sections, or Profiles.* Geologic structures are much better understood from profiles than from maps. The profiles should be perpendicular to the trend of the structure. A detailed, large-scale geological section does not allow vertical exaggeration, since it would show false dips. Generalized small-scale sections, however, have to be exaggerated, because otherwise the formations would not be thick enough to be seen. In this case, we have to exaggerate the thicknesses more than the dip, and the structure has to be simplified. The various rock types are drawn according to certain conventional patterns. Some of the patterns of the U.S. Geological Survey are here reproduced.

If a narrow strip of landscape is added to the profile, so as to form a long, narrow block diagram, it "comes to life" and is sometimes referred to as "animated" profile. The construction of block diagrams is described in the second part of this chapter.

*Geologic Columns.* The thickness, age sequence, and rock types of the formations of a region are shown in geologic columns (see Fig. 272). The oldest formation is at the bottom, and each formation occupies as much space as its average thickness in the

| SYSTEM | SERIES | FORMATION | SYMBOL | COLUMNAR SECTION | THICKNESS |
|---|---|---|---|---|---|
| QUATERNARY | Recent / Pleistocene | Surficial deposits | | | Feet 0-200+ |
| | | UNCONFORMITY | | | (40?) |
| DEVONIAN OR CARBONIFEROUS | Boston Bay group | Cambridge slate | Cc | | 2000 to 3500 |
| | | Roxbury conglomerate | Cr | | 1500 to 3000 |
| | | UNCONFORMITY | | lmv | |
| CAMBRIAN | Middle Cambrian | Braintree slate | Ꞓb | gd | 1000± |
| | Lower Camb. | Weymouth formation | Ꞓw | | 300-600 |
| | | RELATION UNKNOWN | | | |
| PRE-CAMBRIAN | | Woburn formation | wb | | 500± |
| | | Marlboro formation | mb | epi | 1500± |
| | | Westboro quartzite | wt | | 500± |
| | | RELATION UNKNOWN | | | |
| | | Waltham gneiss | wh | | ? |

**Fig. 272** Geologic columnar section. Note the wavy lines for unconformities and the various intrusives.

locality. Note the handling of disconformities and unconformities where the new formation was laid down upon an eroded surface. Intrusives that penetrate older formations are shown as coming from below.

have been intricate. It is therefore better to represent an old shore line of submergence with a lobate outline even if we do not know the exact location of every lobe.

It may be supposed that the geomor-

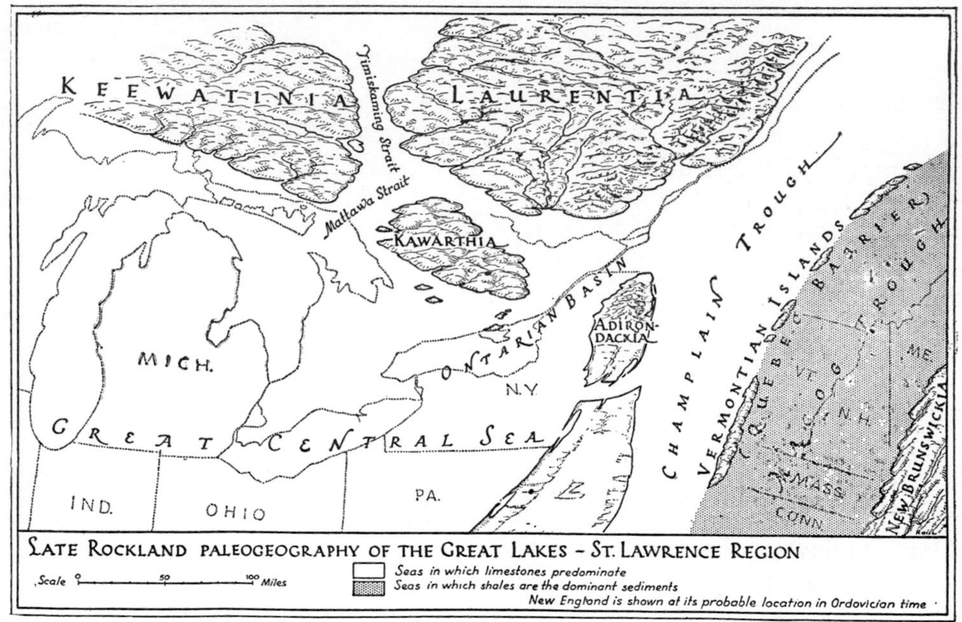


**Fig. 273** Paleogeographic map. Note the difference between the shore lines of emergence and the shore lines of submergence. The dotted outlines, modern states, are pulled apart along the line of the future Green Mountains. (*After G. Marshall Kay, Geol. Soc. America Bull.*, *Vol.* 48.)

*Paleogeographic Maps.* These maps picture the earth's pattern in past geological ages. Some of the greatest geologists attempted to prepare such maps, but our present knowledge of the conditions of the remote past hardly warrant more than small-scale maps of Europe and some parts of America. Yet paleogeographic maps are highly stimulating and tend to indicate the places toward which future investigation should be directed.

Many of the existing paleogeographic maps are deficient from a cartographic point of view. For instance, on most of these maps the shore lines are represented by smooth curves. The outline of the land is not a smooth line now and never was. Shore lines of submergence, in particular, must

phologic types in the past were largely the same as they are at present. Past topography can best be presented by the physiographic method, for this method shows landform types, the nature of which may be assumed, but does not show exact elevations which are not known. In pre-Devonian maps it may be assumed that erosion was more rapid on land unprotected by forests, and that most of the hills were cut into badlands. On paleogeographic maps, the present outlines are indicated by dotted lines for identification of localities. It is a common mistake to show the present outlines more prominently than those of the past age that the map represents.

Figure 273 shows a paleogeographic map that involves a peculiar problem. Since the earth's surface was pushed together for tens of miles to form the Green Mountains, this same region had to be extended on the map so as to fit past conditions. Since paleogeographic maps represent geomorphic rather than geographic conditions, the name "paleogeomorphic" would be more accurate.

*Maps of Geomorphology*. The various features of geomorphology, such as peneplains, erosion levels, terraces, and moraines, can be shown with flat tints and colors. This type of map is shown in Fig. 274. If the same land forms were expressed by physiographic symbols, as discussed in Chap. 11, the map would require a much larger scale.

The Glacial Map of North America, issued by the Geological Society of America in 1945, the cooperative effort of all outstanding glacialogists, is an outstanding work in this line.

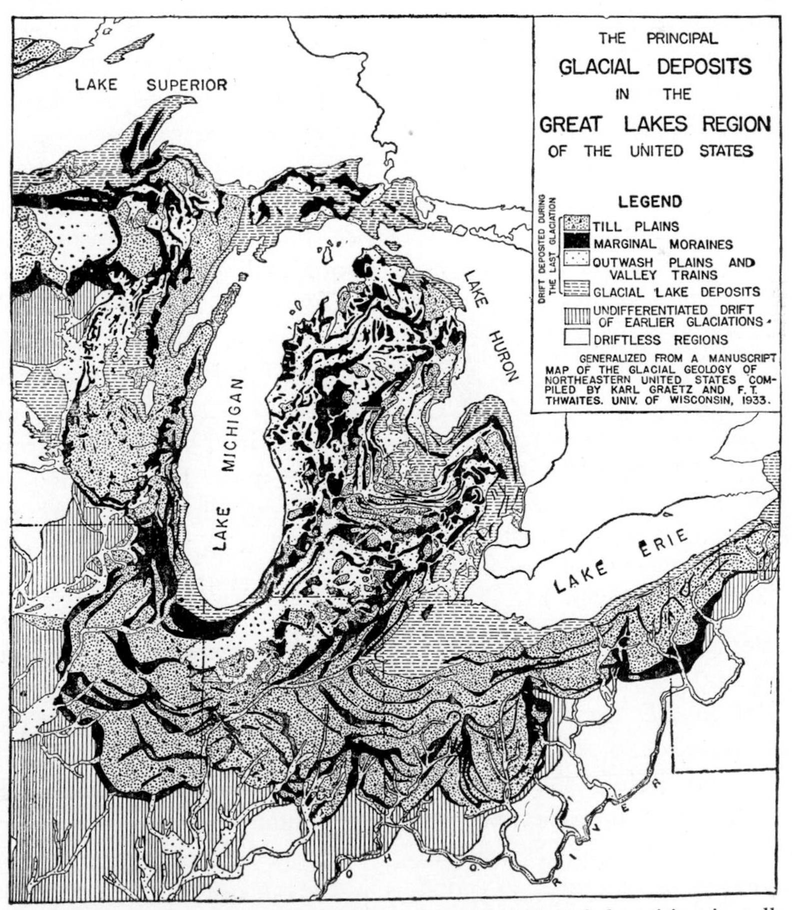


**Fig. 274** Geomorphologic map. The pattern of glacial deposition is well emphasized by using solid black for marginal moraines. (*From Finch and Trewartha, "Elements of Geography."*)

## Block Diagrams

Block diagrams are widely used to represent the geomorphology of small regions. They were introduced by Grove Karl Gilbert and perfected by William M. Davis in the late nineteenth century. The original conception of a block diagram was to cut out an imaginary block from the earth's crust and show it in perspective as seen from far above. On the sides, the geological sections are visible; the surface presents the landscape of the region. Practically, they conform to a perspective view of a small relief model rather than to the actual picture of the earth with all its complexities. Very often block diagrams do not show any actual landscape but illustrate geomorphologic principles. They can also be used to show geography, especially if it is conditioned by geology or soil.

The block can be drawn in regular two-point perspective, but often it is sufficient to use a simplified construction which is not a true perspective but which gives an acceptable approximation.

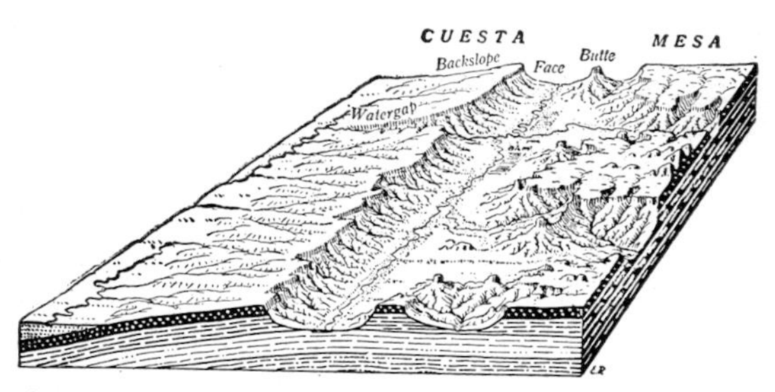


**Fig. 275** Block diagram showing the relation between geologic structure and land forms. (*From Preston E. James, "Outline of Geography."*)

**One-point Perspective.** This construction can best be understood from Fig. 276. All lines parallel to *AD* are shown horizontal; all lines parallel to *AB* are shown converging into one point, the *vanishing point*, which may be far off the paper. Several arrangements of the block are possible but not all are equally satisfactory. A good average block has *AB* at an angle of 45° and *CD* at an angle of about 55° if a small area is shown, or at about 60° if the area is large. To locate *BC* a horizontal ruler is moved up and down until the surface appears to the eye as a perfect square. This is an approximation, but, since the whole method is but approximative, no better rule can be given. The eye is usually keen in locating the exact upper horizontal line of the block to form a square. In the above arrangement a good impression of a square is usually obtained if diagonal *BD* is also at an angle of 45 to 50° to *AD*.

Whether the block should be viewed from the left or from the right is a matter of choice which depends largely on the geologic structure. Blocks seen from directly ahead, so that the two sides converge, seldom give satisfactory results; moreover, the side section is lost.

**Conversion of a Map into a Block Diagram.** A small area (about the size of a topographic sheet) can be converted into a block diagram which can be made just as exact and commensurable as the original contour-line map.

First, the map is divided into a network of squares, about 1 inch in size. Then a square block is drawn, regardless of whether the map is square or not, and its front is divided into the same number of divisions as the map. From each division a line is drawn to the vanishing point, which is marked with a pin. If the vanishing point is very distant, *BC* may be divided into the same number of divisions as *AD*, and the points connected. Then a diagonal is drawn, and through each crossing point a horizontal line is drawn. If the map is not an exact square, rows of squares may be added or taken away from the back of the block to conform to the elongation of the map. For spacing additional horizontal lines in the back, a line *MN* perspectively parallel to the diagonal may be used.

The thickness of the block depends on how much of the geological section can be shown. Usually it is advisable to keep the block thin and show less of the unknown geology of great depths; $\frac{1}{2}$ inch is a good average thickness for page-size block diagrams. *FG* meets *DC* at the vanishing point.

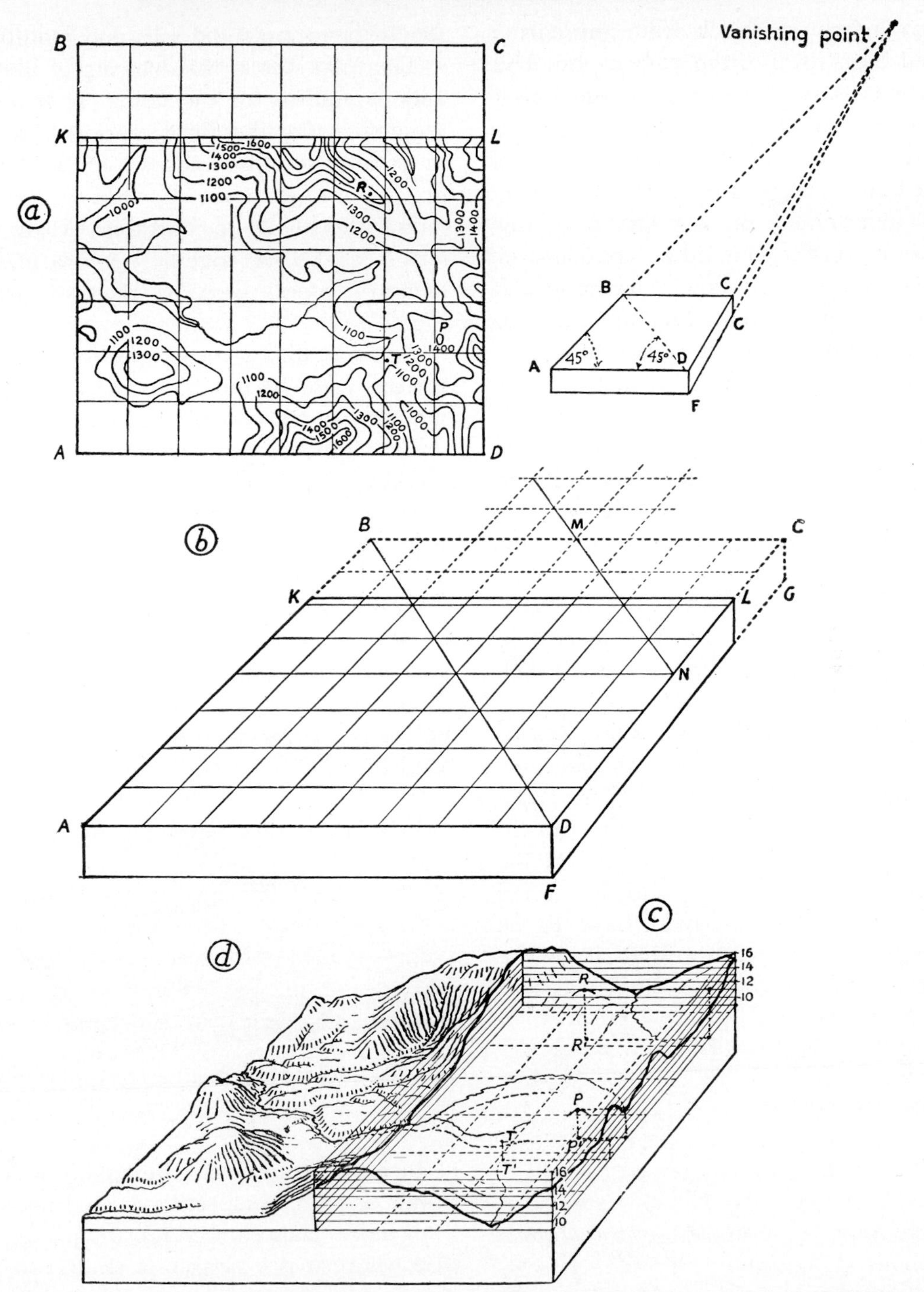


**Fig. 276** Stages in the preparation of block diagrams, drawn in one-point perspective

The surface of the block represents a selected basic level of the topography. This is not necessarily the level of the lowest contour line on the map. Often it is more practical to select the most general level of the larger river valleys. After this base level is determined, the next step is to draw the profiles on the four sides. Vertical scale must be exaggerated—more on large and flat areas, less on small and mountainous regions. With a hard pencil, a "railing" of fine lines is drawn, which is somewhat like a boxing ring. In front and back the railing consists of parallel horizontal lines, each line representing a round number of feet. On the two sides these lines converge to the vanishing point. In front and back the profiles are drawn as usual; on the sides, however, it must be borne in mind that vertical axes of hills and valleys remain verticals, and thus the profile will be considerably distorted.

Next, the outstanding peaks are located and their heights marked on a vertical line, the profile lines on the side being used as a scale. Then the river system is drawn, square by square. The headwaters of the rivers have to be raised, and sometimes the lower portions of rivers have to be depressed. It is important that all rivers, even dry runs, be on the block, because they help to mold the hills and mountains.

The final step is the drawing of the hills and mountains by hachuring. It is well to remember that the direction of the hachure lines indicates the course of the water flowing on the surface and that the lines are foreshortened by perspective. Most land forms can be put together from a few elementary types, such as those shown in Fig. 277.

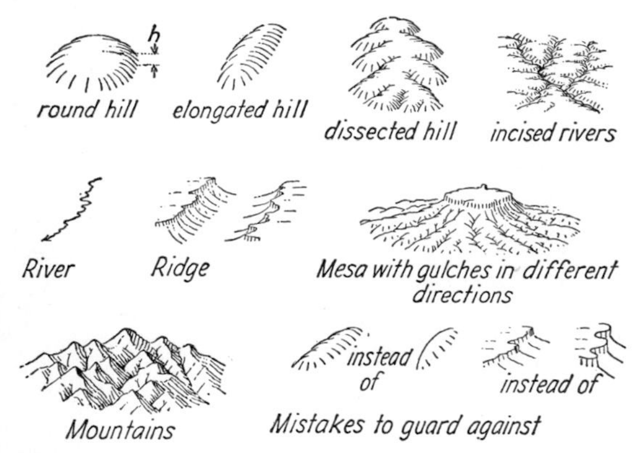


**Fig. 277** The landscape on block diagrams is made up largely from the above basic forms.

Cultural symbols and lettering complete the diagram. As much lettering as possible should go outside the block. Lettering within the block should be "laid down" as it would appear on a photograph of a relief model. If colors can be used, blue rivers, brown slope lines, black culture symbols, and purple plastic shading will make block diagrams very attractive. If it is desirable to show more geological sections than appear on the sides, the block may be sliced and offset, as shown in Fig. 278. Successive stages of erosion are often shown as in Fig. 279.

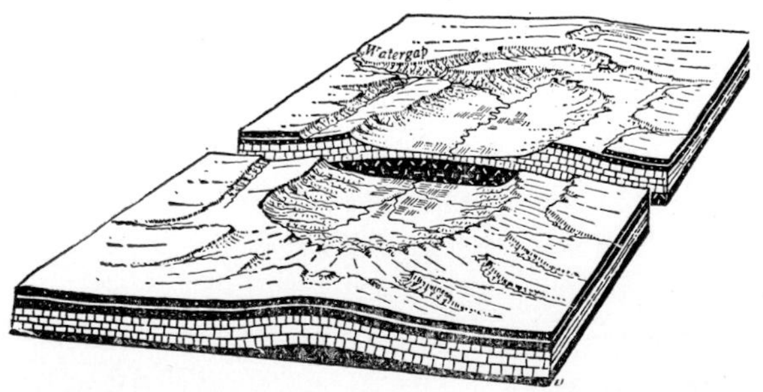


**Fig. 278** Sliced block diagram for showing geologic structure. (*From Preston E. James, "Outline of Geography."*)

**Two-point, or True, Perspective.** Two-point, or true, perspective is used for large and more elaborate block diagrams and also where it is desirable to show two perpendicular geological sections with equal clarity. The simplest method of construction is to select two vanishing points and to choose one of the many possible blocks. The transformation of a map into a block diagram is the same as in one-point perspective. The network of squares is drawn upon the map by successive halvings with the help of the diagonals, as shown in Fig. 280. Two-point blocks look more natural than one-point blocks.

**The Exact Method of Constructing Perspective Blocks.** The following construction produces the exact perspective view of a block as seen from a certain point.

From the eyepoint $E$ we look upon the map $ABCD$ to find how its image would appear if projected upon a vertical plane $PP'$. It is obvious that the size of this projected picture will depend on the distance of the vertical plane $PP'$ from the eyepoint; the nearer the plane, the smaller the picture.

We turn down the vertical plane around $PP'$ axis flush with the paper. The horizon line $V_1V_2$ will appear level with the eye at a chosen elevation $h$ above the bottom of the block. The thickness of the block $FA$ also depends on choice. All parallel horizontal lines meet on the horizon line and the vanishing points for the various sets of parallel lines can be found as shown in Fig. 281. Points $B$, $C$, $D$, and $G$ are found with the help of these vanishing points. The rest of the construction of the block is the same as that described in the one-point perspective.

It often happens that one of the vanishing points will be at a very great distance. To avoid this, the angle of the map with the vertical plane should not be too acute (preferably not under 30°). By another method, if the vanishing point is too far away, the whole construction of the block is made on a small size, half or quarter of the desired scale, and then magnified.

**Dufour Diagrams.** A contour-line map can be transformed into a block diagram with the help of a very simple device—a long rod, one end of which slides along a

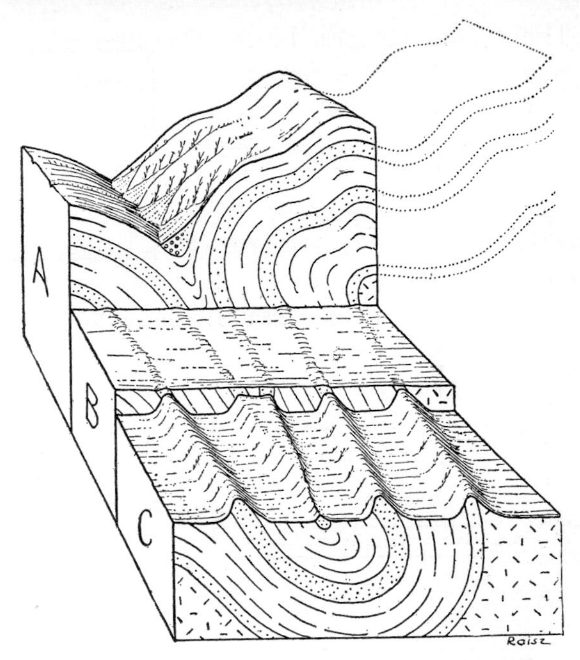


**Fig. 279** Block diagram showing stages in erosion. (*From D. W. Johnson, "Bluebook of the Geological Field Excursion from New York to Gettysburg."*)

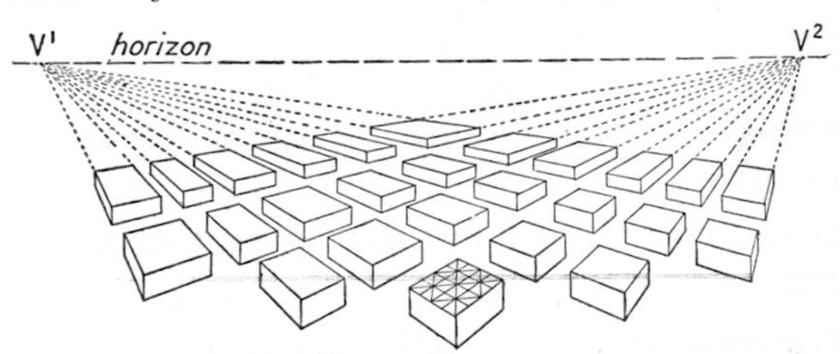


**Fig. 280** Blocks laid out in two-point perspective. Only the blocks in the central part are good for block diagrams. Maps are transferred to the blocks with the help of a diagonal grid, shown in the center block.

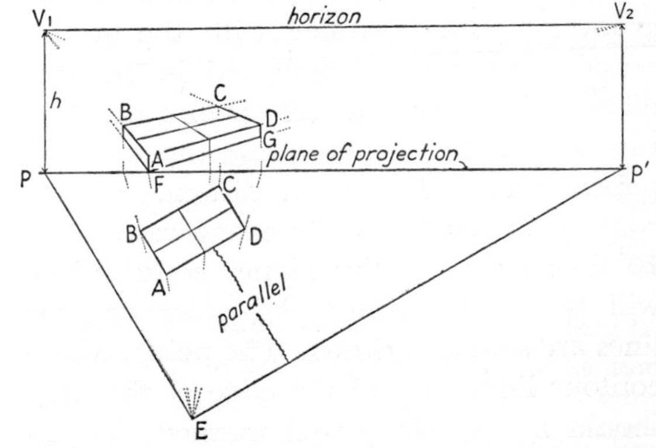


**Fig. 281** The exact method of constructing perspective blocks.

Fig. 286 Sets of zonal profiles are used to illustrate erosion surfaces. (*Courtesy of Prof. R. J. Lougee.*)

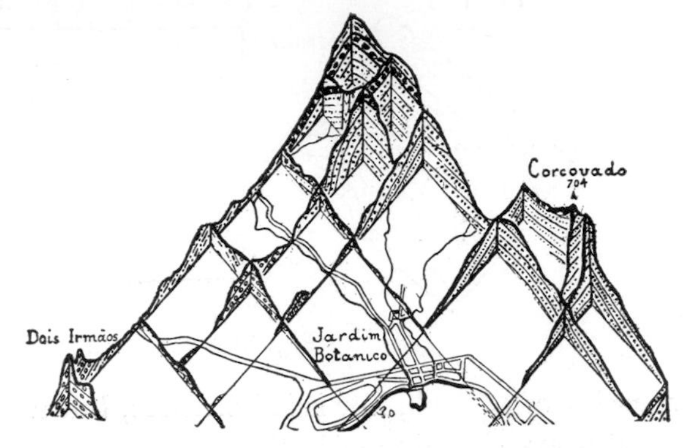


Fig. 287 The compartment diagrams of N. W. Bass derived from interlaced geologic profiles placed over a map.

points along the width of the zone, like the horizontal shadow of a relief model of this zone. This method partly eliminates the effect of river erosion. Professor Douglas Johnson of Columbia University prepared a large set of cardboard profiles of the Middle Appalachian Mountains, with a projected profile for every mile.

**Compartment Diagrams.** This ingenious grouping of profiles in two directions was published by N. W. Bass.[1] A similar effect could be obtained by drawing two perpendicular profile sets on semitransparent vinylite sheets and interlocking them by notching one set halfway from the top and the other from the bottom. A photograph of this setup would present the most complicated geological foundations.

[1] N. W. Bass: *Bull. of the AA Petrol Geol.*, 1934, pp. 1324–1329.

Fig. 288 The mantle maps of Griffith Taylor show well the geologic structure of a region underlain by layered rocks. Similar effect can be achieved by actually cutting out the layers from paper and pasting them over each other. The system is self-explanatory.

# CHAPTER 32: *Maps of the Various Sciences*

If we compare scientific literature of the present with that of only a generation ago, we cannot fail to notice an increasing trend toward the supplementing of books and articles with maps and diagrams.

A map or a diagram will at a glance give a great amount of information in a way that can easily be visualized and remembered and will help to discover the hidden patterns and relationships. Graphic methods also help to make a book or article shorter and more interesting. Much of the factual material can be relegated to maps, diagrams, time charts, etc., and thus the text can be confined to the interpretation of facts. Too often, nevertheless, maps planned or drawn by the average author are ill-conceived and poorly executed. They fail to tell their story simply and effectively. For this reason alone, cartography should be considered an important part of scientific education.

Almost every branch of science uses maps and diagrams. It is natural that the earth sciences should have the most maps, but the social sciences and history also provide interesting problems for cartography. Each branch of science requires special types of maps; they are here discussed along general lines only.

**Astronomical Maps.** Stars and constellations were shown on some of the earliest maps and globes. The oldest globes that have survived, such as the Farnese globe of the second century B.C. and the Arabic globes of the thirteenth century, are celestial. Renaissance artists gave full swing to their imagination in depicting the figures representing the constellations; indeed, the stars themselves were almost lost in the magnificence of the celestial figures.

A modern star map is much more somber. Since the multitude of stars visible by telescope are best shown by photographs, printed star maps are used for small-scale representations only. Such maps will indicate the magnitude (luminosity) of stars. Variables, star clusters, clouds, nebulae, and other types will complete the map. Star maps are important for the surveyor in fixing his latitude and longitude with certain selected stars.

Several projections are used for star maps. Stellar hemispheres are usually shown in some polar projection, with the celestial pole in the center. The polar stereographic projection will show the shapes of constellations more correctly, but the scale will increase toward the periphery of the map. In the latitude of the United States it is necessary to carry the maps beyond the celestial equator, since we see a great distance into the Southern Hemisphere. In atlas maps, where the sky is divided into sections and each section can be developed along its own central meridian, almost any projection can be used, the conic, polyconic, and polyhedric being the most common. The great star atlas, the "Bonn Durchmusterung," which shows the skies in 1855, is in the conic projection. R. A. Proctor in his "Star Atlas," 1870, advocates the use of the azimuthal equidistant projection.

Polar-equatorial coordinates are not the only ones to which stars can be referred. The motion of planets can well be shown on a system where the equator is the ecliptic plane on which the Earth revolves around the Sun.

A photograph of the stars is obviously in gnomonic projection, but, since it shows only a small portion of the sky, the great distortion of this projection is minimized. It is true that on the large reflecting telescopes the photographic film is kept slightly concave by a vacuum pump, but the films are not preserved that way. This is done in order to obtain better focus rather than to avoid peripherial distortion.

Pictures of the moon are in orthographic projection. This can be transformed into any other projection if it is desired to show the peripheral relationships more clearly. An interesting experiment was conducted in Pasadena, Calif., by projecting the moon's photograph upon a globe, thus bringing about the transformation in a simple way.

No map of the sky approaches the effectiveness of a celestial globe, especially if viewed from the inside. Any modern planetarium will bear out this fact.

**Maps of Earth Magnetism.** Charts showing the variation of the compass are probably the earliest scientific maps.[1] These so-called "isogonic charts" show lines connecting places of equal magnetic declination or variation. Charts of earth magnetism are almost always in Mercator projection, because navigators are accustomed to it. This projection, however, is hardly the best for every kind of geomagnetic chart because of its enormous exaggeration of the polar regions. Magnetic phenomena can best be understood from maps on polar projections. A new set of hemispheres on an oblique azimuthal equidistant projection, centered on the north and south magnetic poles and showing isodynamic lines, was prepared in the author's class. For certain purposes similar hemispheres centered on the "geomagnetic poles" at latitude 78.5°N. and longitude 291°, and on the corresponding antipodal point, would serve better. The U.S. Coast and Geodetic Survey, in cooperation with the Carnegie Institution, publishes, in addition to isogonic charts, charts of horizontal and of vertical intensities (magnetic dip) and "isoporic" charts that show how fast the compass changes its variation from year to year.

**Weather Maps.** The first daily weather maps were published in England in 1855. These maps helped to put the science of meteorology on a new basis and made scientific forecasting possible. At present every civilized nation publishes daily weather maps. Weather respects no international boundaries; hence these maps are stimulating cooperation between nations.

The daily weather maps of the U.S. Weather Bureau show the conditions of the atmosphere in an easily comprehensible manner. Although the amount of information conveyed is amazingly rich, the method is simplified to such a degree that their elements can be teletyped by code to the various offices and reproduced there in a short time. These maps show temperature and pressure gradients by isotherms and isobars. Rain is indicated by shading; cold, warm, and stationary fronts are shown by variously barbed lines. Each station can have as many as 20 symbols attached showing temperature, pressure, wind, precipitation, cloudiness, humidity, dew point, changes in the last 2 hours, etc. Special inset maps show the changes in the last 12 hours. A modern weather map with its simple yet expressive symbolism is a great cartographic achievement.

With the growth of air traffic, weather mapping became a highly specialized science. New methods are constantly being developed to show air conditions at various altitudes. Air profiles along the air lines drawn on transparent sheets with delible crayons and transparent air-layer maps with sheets for selected altitudes are two of the new developments. Mapping the rapidly changing air is a new challenge to cartography. Daily weather maps of the entire

[1] BURRUS, CHRISTOPHER, d. 1632. ATHANASIUS KIRCHER, Magnes, Rome, 1643.

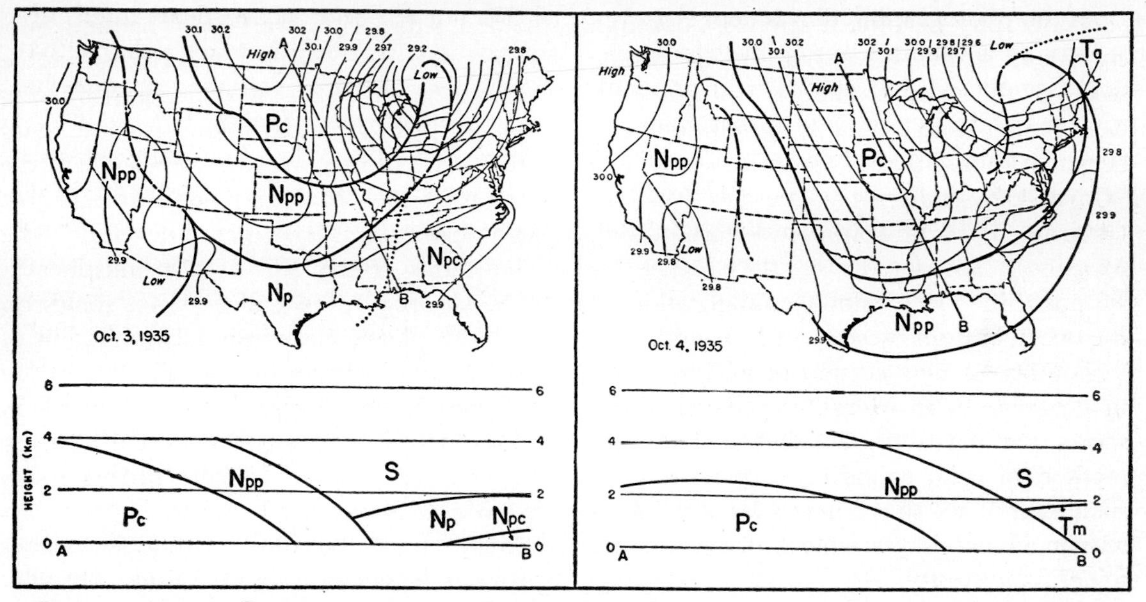


Pp Polar Pacific Air Pc Polar Continental Air S Superior Air Ta Tropical Atlantic Air Tm Tropical Maritime Air
N Transitional Type ———— Cold Front ··········· Warm Front —·—·— Occluded Front

**Fig. 289** Daily weather maps based on air-mass analysis.

Northern Hemisphere help transoceanic travel.

**Climatic Maps.** Climatic maps show the average rainfall, temperature, pressure, wind, cloudiness, length of growing season, evaporation ratio for a certain period of time—5- or 10-year averages being the most common.

An atlas of meteorology and climatology of the world was published in Germany by Berghaus as early as 1838, and later by Bartholomew in 1899. Since that time such an enormous quantity of data has accumulated that a new edition of this atlas would be very helpful. A good atlas of 26 climatic maps of North America, by Charles F. Brooks, A. J. Connor, and others, was published in 1936. At present the best approach to a general atlas of climate is the set of five volumes of "Handbuch der Klimatologie," by Köppen and Geiger; this has many maps on different scales. Climatic maps of the United States are published in several of the volumes of the "Atlas of American Agriculture." These maps use color tints to show variations in rainfall and temperature, length of growing seasons, etc.

During the war, the A.M.S. published detailed climatic maps for each continent and theater of war for each month. Eight classes of temperature on three grades of humidity are expressed by colors and tints. These maps helped in outfitting the soldiers stationed anywhere between the ice of Greenland and the steaming forest of New Guinea. The "Army Air Forces' Preliminary Climatic Atlas of the World" is now in the course of publication.

**Oceanography.** Ocean currents were shown on some of the Renaissance maps, but very little was known of their nature at that time. Scientific oceanography originated with the pioneering work of Matthew F. Maury, U.S. Navy (1806–1873), who compiled his charts from sailors' logbooks. Only when scientific observations and deep-sea expeditions were organized in the second half of the nineteenth century did oceanography become a science. Although enormous strides have been made in the study of the oceans, there is still not sufficient information available to make detailed oceanographic charts of the entire world. The "Carte Gén. Bathymétrique des Océans" (Bureau Hydrographique International, Monaco), sponsored by the Prince of Monaco in 1905, shows configuration of the ocean bottom by contour lines and tints. This atlas—a new edition of which is now in progress—is in Mercator projection and shows the earth on 24 sheets. The new method of echo sounding supplies data of such abundance that a new atlas of the deep seas on a much larger scale is an outstanding scientific necessity.

New interest in the mapping of the ocean bottom was created by the discovery of the submarine canyons on the edge of the continental shelf. The 1:120,000 Coastal Slope maps of the U.S. Coast and Geodetic Survey, by E. C. Veatch, revealed an extremely rugged, almost badland-like appearance of the continental slope. This fact had not been suspected before and raised new problems in the earth's history. At present the detailed mapping of the continental shelf is being carried on with new vigor.

Depth and configuration of the ocean bottom comprise only one phase of oceanography. Many special charts are issued of winds, currents, temperatures, salinity, oozes, and plankton conditions. Variation of these factors with depth offers interesting cartographic problems. The monthly Pilot Charts of the Hydrographic Office contain rich source material for data. A large atlas combining the scattered oceanographic material would be of the greatest advantage to this rapidly growing science.

During the Second World War, new current, temperature, and salinity surveys at various levels and bottom sediment charts helped submarine warfare. The new surveying vessels of the U.S. Hydrographic Office, the U.S. Coast and Geodetic Survey, the Scripps Oceanographic Institute, and other stations increase our knowledge of the oceans at such rate that new cartographic techniques are bound to develop. The "Ice Atlas of the Northern Hemisphere," U.S. Hydrographic Office, 1946, shows on 90 large plates the greatest compilation of sea-ice data hitherto published.

**Seismologic Maps.** Maps are used in seismology for several purposes. For locating earthquakes the seismologist prefers maps in which great-circle routes appear as straight lines, because earthquake waves progress in great-circle directions. Usually, for plotting locations of recorded earthquakes, either a large globe or a gnomonic chart is used. Gnomonic charts, however, distort distances to such extent that they are not convenient for single-station observations. For these, an oblique azimuthal equidistant projection centered on the recording station is the best, since it gives correctly both distances and directions from the station.

For plotting the procession of earthquake waves, the isoseismic lines on an oblique azimuthal projection, centered on the epicenter of the quake would be the best, but it would have to be constructed separately for each earthquake.

Maps showing the seismic region of the earth and the number and intensity of recorded earthquakes are found in many textbooks and atlases. A 1:506,880 map showing the active and dead fault lines of California was published by the Seismological Society of America in 1922.

**Vegetation Maps.** Whereas detailed geological maps are available even for relatively unsurveyed regions, there is a distinct lack of vegetation maps for many important regions of the world. It is true that modern topographical maps, especially of tropical regions, such as the Malay Peninsula, the Dutch East Indies, and Madagascar, show the various vegetation and cultivation types, but for most of Asia, Africa, and South America only highly generalized maps are available. It is hoped that, with the progress of airplane surveying, all new topographic maps will include information on vegetation and cultivation. An atlas of the world's vegetation would be a highly desirable addition to our geographic storehouse.

Cartographically, vegetation maps present many problems. On large-scale maps the vegetation and zoogeography can be shown by colored or black-and-white patterns. In the case of mixed forests, it is well to indicate by means of index letters the composition, age, density, and value of forests.

For certain studies it is important to show what the natural vegetation of the region was before human cultivation changed its pattern. Such a map of the United States is included in the "Atlas of American Agriculture."

Small-scale vegetation maps are published in most European countries and in Japan, India, the Dutch East Indies, Australia, Canada, and Argentina, and one of Brazil is in preparation. There is a difficulty with terminology; the word "bosque," for instance, may mean anything from bush to forest.

An interesting method of finding out the natural vegetation of a country is by place names. For instance, if a place is called Sabana Grande, it may be concluded that the surrounding country was forest; otherwise the savanna would not be so named. On this kind of reasoning Leo Waibel[1] reconstructed the original vegetation of Cuba, finding it more forested than was previously surmised.

The difficulty in making adequate small-scale maps lies in the fact that vegetation types are more transitional and more mixed than either soil or geology. Vegetation maps where these transitions are well represented are rare. A very generalized map of world vegetation is shown in Fig. 290. Transitional colors demand three-color process reproduction, and transitional pattern can be done only by an artist's hands.

Many vegetation maps that show the distribution of a single genus or species are available. These maps are made from the botanical point of view and rarely present any special cartographical problems.

The distribution of animals is even more transitional than that of plants, and regional presentation of faunal data is very difficult. Today only small-scale zoogeographical maps treat animal associations by regions. Maps showing the range of various animals, insects, bird migration, etc., are prepared by the Biological Survey of the U.S. Department of Agriculture.

**Archaeological Maps.** A new aid to archaeological study has been developed from airplane surveying and photographic mapping. A Roman camp in the wheat fields of southern England was clearly visible from the air, although the inhabitants had never suspected its presence. Several Indian mounds and fortresses were spotted from airplanes in Ohio. The Great Wall of Peru was first fully revealed from the air. Old river beds are clearly outlined on airplane photographs, and their location gives important clues to the geography of the past.

The chief aim of an archaeological map is the reconstruction of past conditions, but individual cases vary so that no general advice can be given regarding their preparation. To avoid confusion, the lines representing the geography of the past should

[1] WAIBEL, LEO, Place Names as an Aid in Reconstruction of the Original Vegetation of Cuba, *Geog. Rev.*, 1943, pp. 376–396.

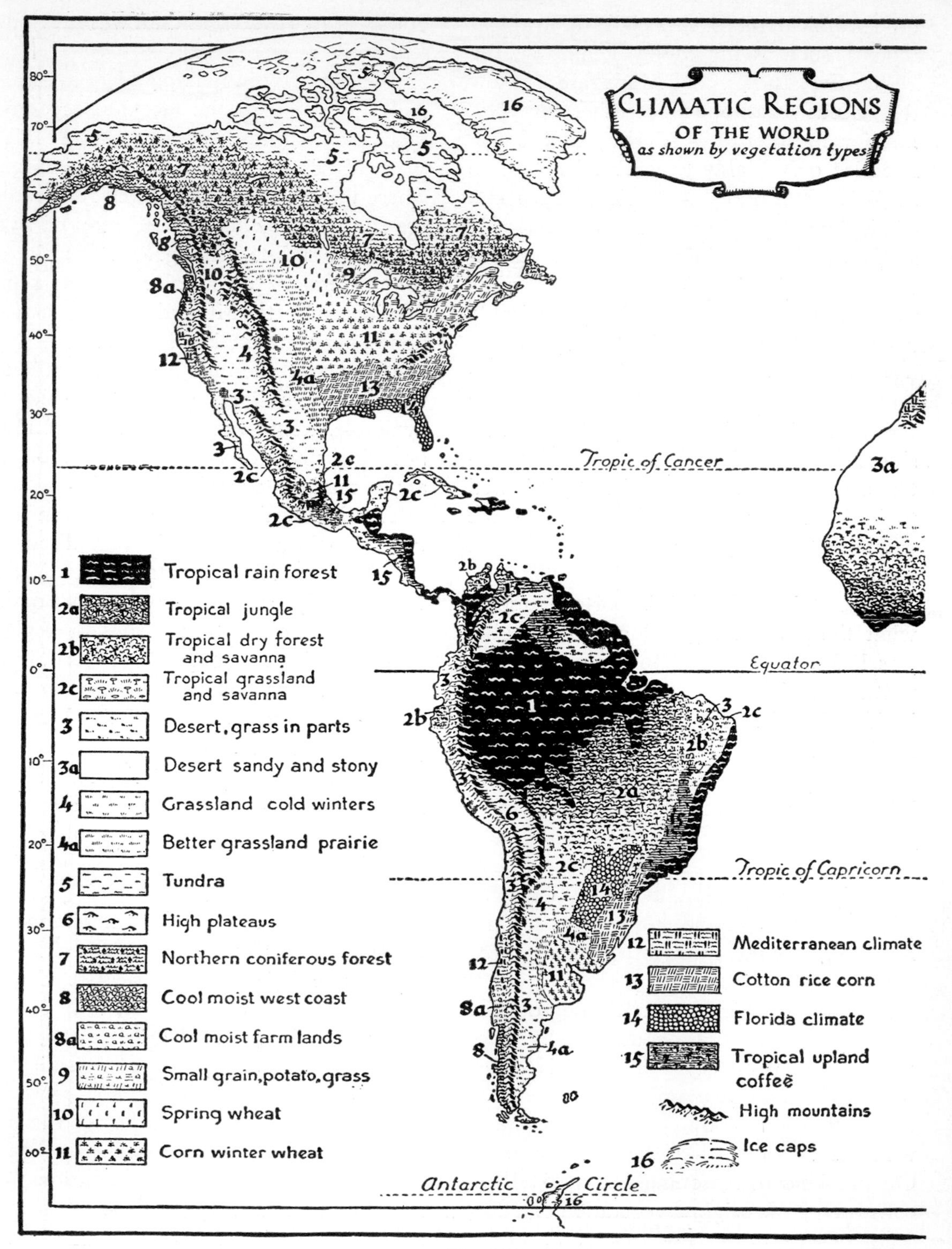


Fig. 290 Small-scale vegetation map, showing symbols

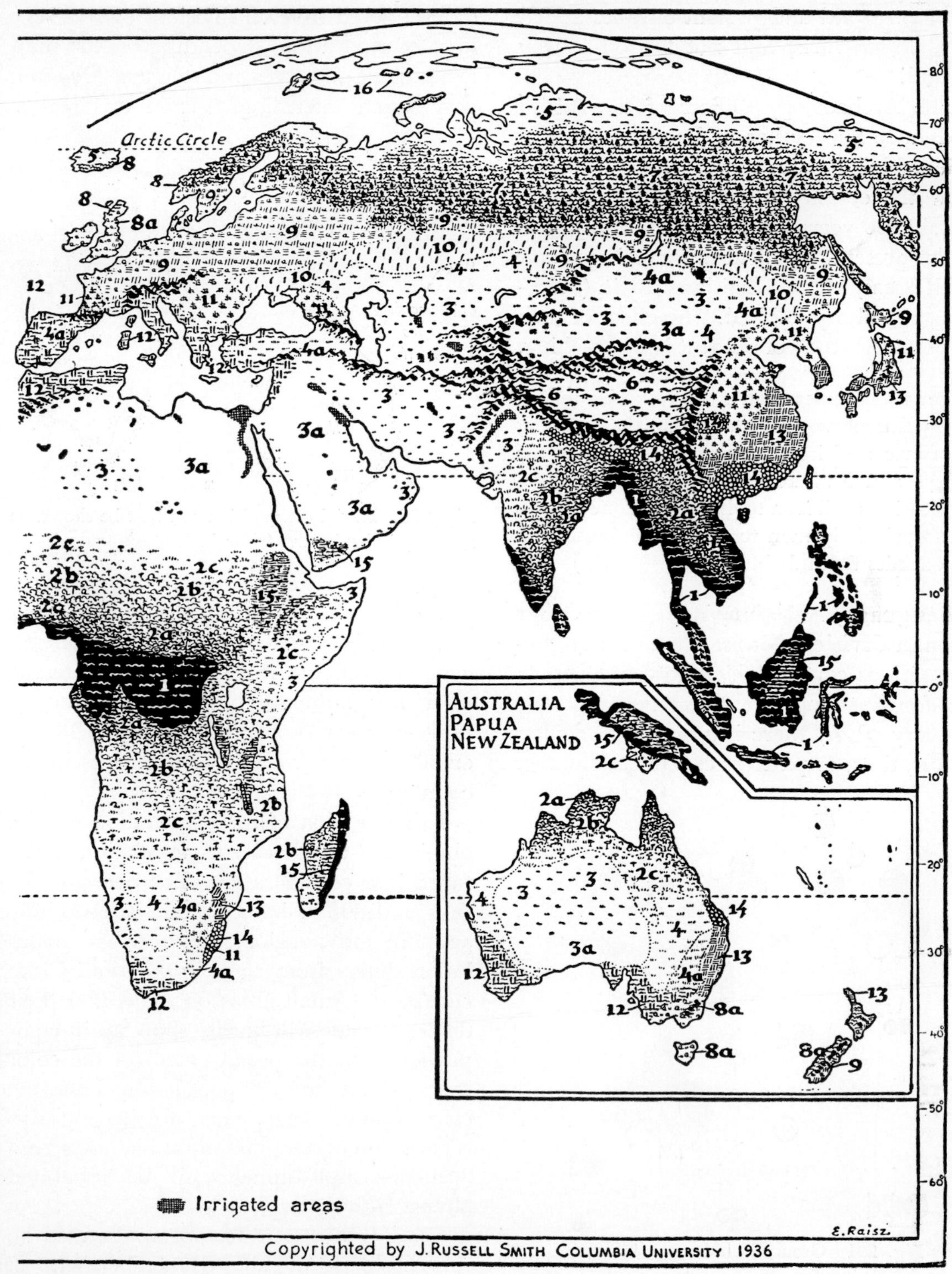


used transitionally. (*Courtesy of J. Russell Smith.*)

be drawn solid and present outlines added with dotted lines, and not the other way around.

The Archaeology Officer of the British Ordnance Survey has under preparation a series of 1:1,000,000 maps by periods; these show the country at intervals of approximately 400 years from the Neolithic period to the present. Detailed maps of important small areas, such as Salisbury Plain (1:25,000), are also published. The effect of such maps on the study of the past is far-reaching.

Our whole conception of the Neolithic way of life in Europe was affected when the mapping of bronze and iron weapons proved that the valleys and lowlands were obstacles to communication until iron tools were in common use that would help men to attack the forests and the enemies that inhabited them. (Jervis.)

**Language, Religion, Race, and Other Human-division Maps.** These maps present serious cartographic problems. If only the *dominant* language or religion is shown at every place, there is but little difficulty. Colors, tints, or patterns can be used, either

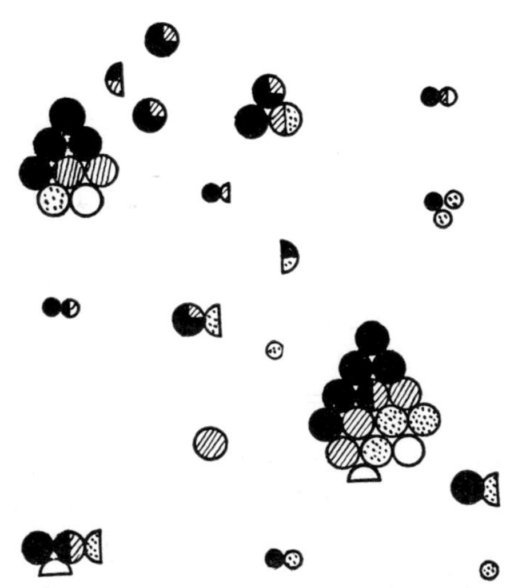

**Fig. 291** Grouped circles provide easy comparison for mixed distribution. (*Modified from Bárczy-Kogutowitz, Language Map of Hungary.*)

differentiated by civil divisions or by exact lines of separation, depending on the data available. Languages and religions are often very much intermingled, and this fact is

**Fig. 292** Racial composition can best be shown on maps by index letters. (*After E. Hooton.*)

frequently expressed by *interdigitation* of colors into narrow strips and thus fading one color into the other. If only one language or religion is shown, its ratio to the total population can well be expressed by isopleth maps, showing for instance, 10, 20, or 30 to 100 per cent of Protestants in the country.

A better idea of the distribution can be obtained if the density of population is also taken into consideration. The necessity for this additional information is especially great in those regions where urban population differs from rural population. Cities occupy but small areas on maps and their different color will hardly show up in comparison with the broad extent of the color representing the rural population. Thus, the city-dwelling Armenians are barely discernible on certain ethnographic maps, and Armenia itself appears to be inhabited almost entirely by Kurds.

Special attention has been directed to this problem by the dismemberment of Hungary in 1919. In parts of Transylvania and eastern Hungary most of the dense city and valley population spoke Hungarian, whereas the uplands were sparsely occupied by Rumanian-speaking pastoral people. Thus, the current dominant language maps showed large areas as Rumanian, and the makers of the Trianon Treaty awarded to Rumania territories in which an actual majority of the people spoke Hungarian.

Count Teleki and other Hungarian cartographers immediately set to work and produced maps to show the true pattern of the distribution of mixed population. One of the solutions was to use the grouped-circle system, whereby every city was represented by a group of circles, the total area of which is proportionate to the population. The circles were colored or ruled differently to show the composition of the population. Rural dwellers were also concentrated into similar circles for each administrative unit.

Races are even more intermingled and indefinite than languages and the preparation of race maps is even more difficult. Some maps show head forms with the gradation of one color, the hair type with another, and blood group with a third, but the results are not quite satisfactory. Perhaps the amount of coincidence could be expressed by a method in which each criterion was mapped separately and tinted on transparent celluloid and the pieces of celluloid superimposed on each other as required. Highly generalized small-scale maps can be made by placing different sized letters on the map, as in Fig. 292.

**Historical Maps.** Many medieval maps were actually historical maps, in that they showed the Roman instead of the medieval world. Almost every Renaissance atlas contained a few maps of the Roman Empire; and the historical atlases of d'Anville, Vaugondy, and many others were just as famous as their modern atlases. At present, historical maps and atlases are published in every language in great quantities.

Historical maps show the geographic pattern of past ages in the same way that modern maps show the present. Contemporaneous old maps, if they could be more easily reproduced and more easily read, would make the best historical maps. Old maps show not only the geographic conceptions of the past but, by their style and composition, reveal the spirit of their age. A medieval map, with its legendary figures and its enormous Holy Land, represents well the medieval man's conception of the world. Since, however, old maps are rarely readable in small-scale reproduction, most history books are supplemented by maps that show the geography of past ages with present-day symbols.

A historical map usually shows the conditions of a single year or of a short period. The development of several decades or centuries is better shown in a series of smaller maps, the composite effect of which is similar to that of a slow-motion picture of the flow of the stream of history. Older-type historical maps rarely showed more than political boundaries, cities, and battlefields. Modern historical atlases usually include not only general maps but also special maps of past economic conditions, population densities, cultural features, and other data that give a more substantial understanding of past ages. The "Atlas of the Historical Geography of the United States," by C. O. Paullin and J. K. Wright (1932), is one of the finest works of this type.

The maps in "An Historical Geography of England before A.D. 1800" (edited by H. C. Darby, Cambridge University Press, 1936) include such items as location names ending in "ing" or "ingham," from which early shore lines can be restored. The 87 maps, cartograms, and diagrams of the book present a vivid picture of the economic life of the past.

Road, commerce, and communication

maps and maps of military operations should always show mountains, for they controlled the movements of humanity in the past to an even greater degree than at present. Mountains on historical maps are often shown successfully by a simplified physiographic method. Movements of mankind or of ideas are often shown by arrows, which give the maps a dynamic character.

**Time Charts.** Historical time relationships are expressed by time charts as space relationships are presented by maps. A historical time chart usually shows a vertical "time line" divided into years. Along this line are recorded the various events of history, often classified into columns according to countries. Such time charts are included in the first chapters of this book, which deal with the history of cartography. It is common in time charts to make the column of any one country wider or narrower according to the importance of that country at certain times, as shown on the "Renaissance" time chart (see Table III).

Dispersion, counterinfluence of ideas, migrations, etc., can well be expressed in historical time charts by arrows and connecting lines, which give the chart a dynamic character. An example of an ingenious time chart of the world's history may be found in H. G. Wells' "Outline of History"; it was drawn by J. F. Horrabin, the noted English cartographer.

Many other sciences, especially in the field of the social sciences, use maps to an increasing degree. They are not further discussed here but, by applying the previously discussed principles, the cartographer will find some solution to most problems.

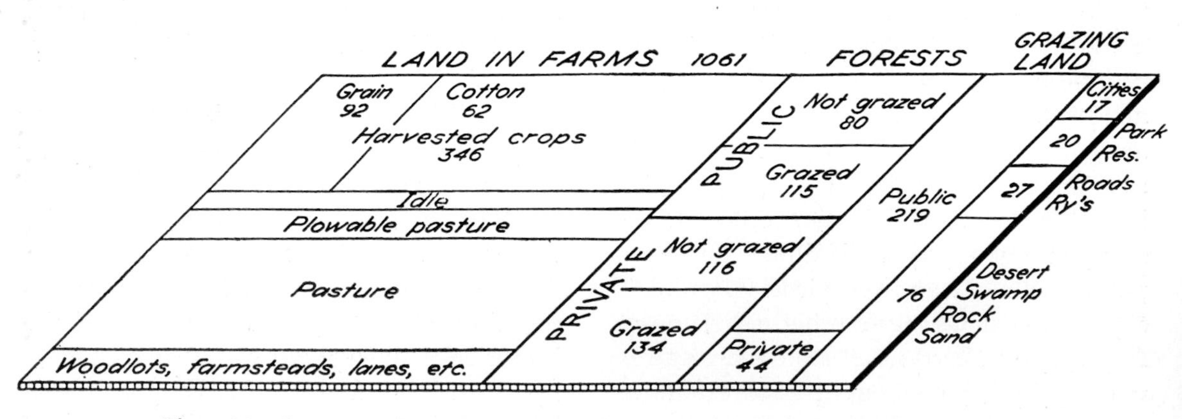


**Fig. 293** Complex subdivisions are best shown graphically in geographical papers.

## Maps of Geography

Among all the sciences, geography is obviously the most dependent on maps. In a certain sense every map is geographic. The original meaning of the term "geography" is "drawing of the earth." The following discussion of maps of the science of geography will necessarily be a summary of the previously discussed methods.

**Maps of Regional Analysis.** The geographic analysis of any region, large or small, is accompanied by a series of maps and diagrams. The sequence and number of maps may vary, and many special maps may be added; only a general arrangement is given here:

1. *Location Map.* A location map shows not only the outlines of the discussed area in relation to larger, generally known regions, but also how the area fits into the main highways of communication and how it is related to river basins and physiographic divisions of a larger area. A detailed location map is an appropriate introduction to a geographic study.

2. *Political or General Map.* In a study of large areas we need a map that shows political boundaries—counties, townships, cities, state parks, national forests, etc. The chief purpose of such a map is to show the geographical names that are discussed in the accompanying text. This map relieves all special maps from the burden of too much lettering and is likely to be the only one indicating parallels and meridians. If roads, railroads, rivers, etc., are added, it becomes a general map or key map of the region, which can be overprinted for the special maps.

3. *Maps Showing Surface Configuration.* In any analysis of a region the first question is the "lay of the land." If the region is small, a contour-line map will give the best information; in mountainous regions a block diagram or Dufour diagram will more easily demonstrate the relief conditions; and for large regions a physiographic map will be of value.

In hilly farming country the analysis of slope conditions is essential. If the region is a maturely dissected plain or plateau, a relative relief map will be required. In more complex regions, an average-slope map will be of greater use. A flatland-ratio map will indicate the land available for the various types of farming. A hypsographoid curve will show the average profile of the land.

The making of a *relief model* is entirely within the scope of the geographic study of a small region. Such a model will clarify many relationships that are not perceptible on maps. Land forms, geology, soil, land utilization, and transportation lines can all be shown on a single relief model.

4. *Geological Maps and Sections.* Soil, ground water, and surface forms are largely dependent on geology. Therefore, the addition of geologic maps and sections will greatly add to the understanding of the region. Geology, however, is too rarely considered in recent geographic studies.

5. *Soil and Erosion Maps.* No geographic paper is complete without a soil map and drawings of the various soil profiles. In small regions, where there is not much variation in soil, this map may be combined with an erosion map. Geology, soil, and relief can well be combined in profile diagrams (see Fig. 262).

6. *Climatic Maps.* Summer and winter rainfall and temperature maps and curves, and maps of growing seasons are almost always presented for the analysis of large regions; for small regions, however, where the variation of climatic elements over the area is negligible, a rainfall and temperature curve is sufficient. Maps and diagrams of winds, sunshine, storms, snow, and other weather elements may also be required for certain crops. The variability of rainfall is an important factor in semiarid regions and is often shown by maps and graphs.

7. *Land-use Maps.* In most studies the land-use map is the most important of the series; hence it deserves special attention. This map will link the environmental maps with those of occupancy. The main types, such as forest, cropland, and pasture land, are usually further differentiated in great detail.

8. *Agricultural Maps.* Dot maps, showing crops and animal products, will be added only if the regions are large and if detailed government-census data are available. The land-use map will give the acreage of various

crops. Large regions require also ratio maps, such as yield per acre and ratio of plowed land to all land. Maps and diagrams expressing the distribution of farm equipment, farm animals, etc., indicate the type of farming.

9. *Maps of Manufacturing and Mining.* Maps showing the location of industrial districts in relation to raw material, power, transportation, labor, housing, and surface configuration are important. Mines, quarries, and sand and clay pits can be shown on this map too. World maps showing the sources of distant raw materials or the distribution of products may add much to the value of the essay.

10. *Maps of Transportation.* Traffic-flow maps are just as important to the geographer as are the diagrams of the circulation system of the human body to the anatomist. It is unfortunate that only in rare instances are sufficient data available to prepare such maps. They are now being issued by the planning boards of the major cities.

11. *Recreation Maps.* Since recreation has become one of the major industries in some parts of the country, maps of the locations of parks, open public places, resorts, beaches, race tracks, and places of scenic and historic interest add much to the geographic picture of a region.

12. *Maps of Social Conditions.* Maps of income groups, health conditions, mortality, races, religions, education, recreation, and amusement are included in increasing numbers in modern geographic papers. Conditions differ to such a degree that each map has to be considered individually. For instance, the ratio of colored population to white may be shown by an isopleth or a choropleth map, the birthplace-residence relationships by a migration map, and increase and decrease of population in a type of line-graph map shown in Fig. 222.

13. *Density-of-population Maps.* Density of population is the resultant of all the previously mentioned factors and, hence, a density-of-population map will be more or less the summary of previous maps, with each of which it can be correlated. An interesting addition to the normal density map is a centrogram of population, especially if it can be compared with centrograms of previous decades.

14. *Airplane Photographs.* The addition of airplane photographs to geographic papers is a growing practice. From these photographs many relationships can clearly be seen, for in a single view they combine the results of several maps. A vertical airplane photograph is effective only if its scale is over 1:20,000. Since airplane photographs have to be reproduced by the half-tone process, they lose some of their effectiveness by printing.

**Rendering.** The rendering of geographical maps depends upon whether or not they are to be published. If the study is intended to be published in book form or in a periodical, the publisher will rarely agree to the inclusion of colored, large-scale maps; instead all maps must be prepared in black and white in a size not to exceed a double page. If the paper is not intended for publication, greater freedom is allowed in the rendering of maps. Colored lines and color tints can be used, and the maps can be of larger size. For easier comparison it is advisable to make all the maps on the same scale on transparent celluloid, so that direct correlation can be made by placing one map over the other. The combination of several maps into one, as, for instance, land forms and transportation, is justified if the design does not appear crowded. Generally, a map should show but one single condition. Lines and lettering which appear on other maps should not be repeated unnecessarily.

# APPENDIX 1: *Preservation and Cataloguing of Maps*

The map collections of American universities are, as a rule, of very miscellaneous origin. They usually contain the following:

1. Old material of local importance that may be of great interest to historians
2. Maps which were used to teach the students of one or two generations ago and which, although obsolete, are not yet old enough to be of historical interest
3. Modern, up-to-date map material

The first task in organization is to separate these three groups. The first two are best preserved in the general university library. The third, in which the geographer is interested, is best preserved in the department of geography. Departmental map collections should be kept strictly modern. As soon as a new map supersedes an old one, the latter should be transferred to the general library.

A map collection consists of loose maps, charts, atlases, wall maps, gazetteers, and books containing important maps, or books and pamphlets attached to maps. These materials can best be preserved in cases, as shown in Fig. 294. The number of cases varies with the size of the collection, but a double case, as shown in Fig. 294, can take care of about 4,000 maps. The cases may be made of wood or steel, the former being much cheaper, and may be protected against dust by glass doors. Sets of drawers are more dustproof but are somewhat more cumbersome to handle, especially if piled high.

**Folders.** The best way to keep loose maps is to collect them in simple, smooth cardboard folders, about 36 by 30 inches in size. Each folder can hold from 30 to 100 maps. A maximum of 10 folders can go into one compartment, but in the beginning it is advisable to use not more than five, so as to allow for future growth. The folders for each compartment are numbered, for example, 221, 222, 223, 224, and 225; and then the next compartment begins with folder No. 231, even when there is not as yet a No. 226 folder. The contents of the folder should be written in large letters as close to the visible edge of the folder as possible.

Each loose map is numbered with the corresponding folder number and a serial number. Thus the twenty-sixth map in folder 997 is numbered "997/26." Topographic maps, or any set of maps having its own numbering system, need only the folder number, since they are arranged in the order of their printed serial

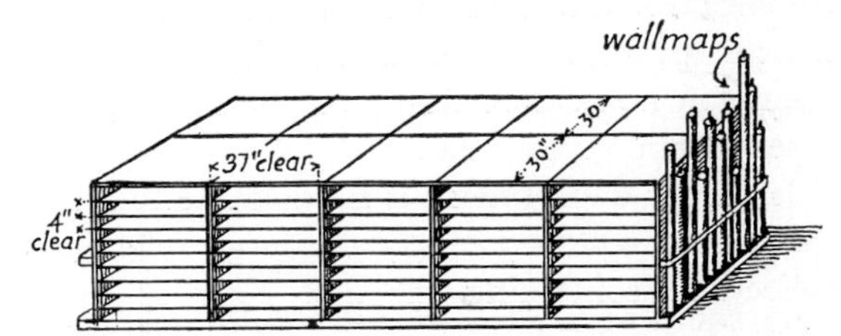


**Fig. 294** These five duplex cases can easily store 30,000 loose maps without using wall space. Top of case can be used for spreading out maps.

numbers. The topographic sheets of the U.S. Geological Survey are usually arranged alphabetically by states. As these are rarely wider than 18 inches, they need narrower cases.

In larger collections it is preferable instead of using running numbers of folders to mark the folders according to the area-breakdown system, which can be obtained directly from the A.M.S. On this, for instance, any map of Saxony would be in folder M4.2.7 (M for Europe, 4 for Germany, 2 for South Germany, 7 for Saxony). If too heavy, it is divided into M4.2.7A, M4.2.7B, etc., folders.

The folders should be arranged regionally by countries and not alphabetically. The best *regional sequence* is obtained by following the order of a standard American geography book or atlas. This is much better than the arrangement by *type* of map. Thus, a rainfall map of Australia will be in the folder "Australia as a Whole" and not in a separate folder for rainfall maps. Within the limits of one country the types can be separated. Thus the geological maps of Canada can be in a separate folder next to the other Canadian maps. A strictly regional order will help to find the maps. Sea charts, however, are exceptions; they may be kept separately, for they do not fit the usual regional order.

Most maps will fit into a 36- by 30-inch folder. Larger maps have to be folded. It is advisable to fold commonly used maps with the printing on the outside, since this will provide for their quicker recognition within the folder.

Atlases are also included in the regional sequence of folders. A world atlas would belong in the section labeled "World as a Whole." An atlas of Yugoslavia would come next to the Yugoslavian folder. An atlas of the French colonies would come under "World," for it contains maps from all over the world. Rolled wall maps can be held vertically on the sides of the cases within a 2-inch slot.

In larger departments it is advisable to have three map collections: (1) the large reference collection, containing the first copy of each map; (2) a duplicate collection, which will hold second copies which can be loaned; and (3) a laboratory collection, which will contain third and more copies to be used in classes. The three collections can be at different places, but they should have the same sequence of numbering.

**Cataloguing.** An average-size map collection needs to be catalogued, chiefly for the convenience of the other departments, so as to inform them of the material available, and also of important maps in books and periodicals. Within the collection itself, it is quicker to find a map by looking through the proper folder than by reading a card catalogue. An acquisition book will also be necessary for reports and financial statements.

A reference card for a map contains its title, author, scale, paper size, series number, colors, insets, year of compilation, place and office of publication, origin, price, folder and individual numbers, and special remarks. The cataloguing of large map collections was worked out by A. B. Williams of the U.S. Army,[1] by S. W. Boggs of the U.S. Department of State, and by Dr. Leonard Wilson of the O.S.S.

The most elaborate method of cataloguing is used in the enormous collections of the A.M.S., the Library of Congress, and the U.S. Department of State. Samples of cards are shown in reduced size in Fig. 295.

**Map Mounting.** Commonly used maps may be mounted on cloth. Mounting, however, distorts the paper and increases its weight. Mounted maps are difficult to trace over the light-table, and the cost of mounting may be more than extra copies of the map. In larger cities there are usually establishments that specialize in this kind of work. If such service is not available, it is not difficult to perform this work individually.

There are two general methods of mounting, wet and dry. The cloth used for mounting is usually muslin, but for valuable maps linen is preferable. In the wet method, the cloth is cut somewhat larger than the map, so as to allow for shrinkage, and is stretched on a mounting board.[2] Paste is then spread over the cloth. The paste can be ordinary flour paste but special mounting pastes, such as Dextrose and Arabol, are preferable. Then the map is placed over the cloth and pressed with a rubber roller from the center outward, so as to squeeze out the superfluous paste. Next, the borders of the map are pressed down to prevent curling during the drying process. When the map is dry, the cloth is trimmed, and the map is mounted on rollers or laid out flat. Pocket maps are usually cut into 4- by 6-inch sections and mounted in sections, with a separation of $\frac{1}{16}$ inch to allow for convenient folding. The disadvantage of wet pasting is that the map expands with moisture and thus becomes out of scale. If the map is made up from sections, they rarely fit each other perfectly.

To avoid expansion, various dry-mounting tissues are on the market, chiefly used for mounting photographs, such as Parafilm, Parawax, and others, and are sold by the various photographic companies. They consist of a film of wax or shellac that is placed between the cloth and the map and pressed with a hot iron. This proc-

[1] Terrell, Lt. Col. J. P., The Williams System, U.S. War Department General Staff, Washington, D.C., 1930.

[2] An ordinary curtain stretcher can easily be transformed into a mounting table.

WASHINGTON, D. C.—SUBURBS—MAPS.

G3850
1944
.U54

U. S. *Geological survey.*

Washington and vicinity; Maryland, Virginia, District of Columbia. Edition of 1944. [Washington, 1944]

col. map. 120 x 106^cm.

Scale 1: 31,680 or 1 inch to ½ mile.
"Polyconic projection."
"Contour interval 10 feet."
"Surveyed in 1913–1915; revised in 1941–1942."
"Routes usually travelled ... 1943" indicated in red.

1. District of Columbia — Maps. 2. Physical geography — District of Columbia—Maps. 3. Washington, D. C.—Suburbs—Maps. I. Title.

Map 45-5

Library of Congress G3850 1944.U54

[2]†

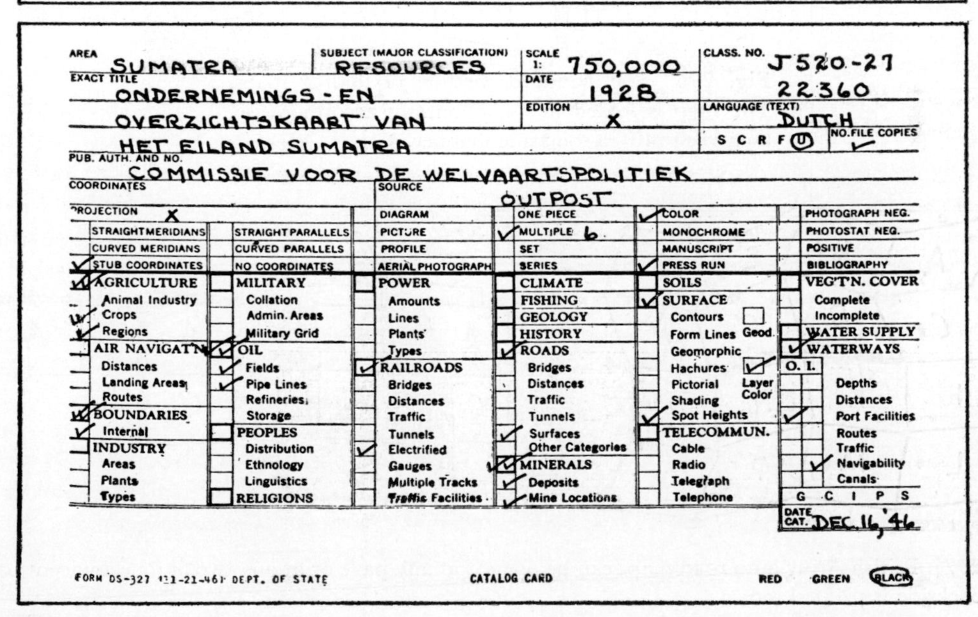
AREA SUMATRA | SUBJECT (MAJOR CLASSIFICATION) RESOURCES | SCALE 1: 750,000 | CLASS. NO. J520-27

EXACT TITLE ONDERNEMINGS-EN OVERZICHTSKAART VAN HET EILAND SUMATRA

DATE 1928 | 22360

EDITION X | LANGUAGE (TEXT) DUTCH

S C R F (U) | NO. FILE COPIES ✓

PUB. AUTH. AND NO. COMMISSIE VOOR DE WELVAARTSPOLITIEK

COORDINATES

SOURCE OUTPOST

| PROJECTION X | | DIAGRAM | ONE PIECE | COLOR | PHOTOGRAPH NEG. |
|---|---|---|---|---|---|
| STRAIGHT MERIDIANS | STRAIGHT PARALLELS | PICTURE | MULTIPLE 6 | MONOCHROME | PHOTOSTAT NEG. |
| CURVED MERIDIANS | CURVED PARALLELS | PROFILE | SET | MANUSCRIPT | POSITIVE |
| STUB COORDINATES | NO COORDINATES | AERIAL PHOTOGRAPH | SERIES | PRESS RUN | BIBLIOGRAPHY |
| AGRICULTURE | MILITARY | POWER | CLIMATE | SOILS | VEG'TN. COVER |
| Animal Industry | Collation | Amounts | FISHING | SURFACE | Complete |
| Crops | Admin. Areas | Lines | GEOLOGY | Contours | Incomplete |
| Regions | Military Grid | Plants | HISTORY | Form Lines Geod. | WATER SUPPLY |
| AIR NAVIGAT'N | OIL | Types | ROADS | Geomorphic | WATERWAYS |
| Distances | Fields | RAILROADS | Bridges | Hachures | O. I. |
| Landing Areas | Pipe Lines | Bridges | Distances | Pictorial Layer Color | Depths |
| Routes | Refineries | Distances | Traffic | Shading | Distances |
| BOUNDARIES | Storage | Traffic | Tunnels | Spot Heights | Port Facilities |
| Internal | PEOPLES | Tunnels | Surfaces | TELECOMMUN. | Routes |
| INDUSTRY | Distribution | Electrified | Other Categories | Cable | Traffic |
| Areas | Ethnology | Gauges | MINERALS | Radio | Navigability |
| Plants | Linguistics | Multiple Tracks | Deposits | Telegraph | Canals |
| Types | RELIGIONS | Traffic Facilities | Mine Locations | Telephone | G C I P S |

DATE CAT. DEC. 16, '46

FORM DS-327 DEPT. OF STATE CATALOG CARD RED GREEN BLACK

**Fig. 295** The map catalogue cards of the Library of Congress (above) and the Department of State (below) give a great deal of information on the map using different methods.

ess requires clever handling in order to avoid creases. Dry mounting is especially recommended for mounting on cardboard. If the map is used in the field, a second coating of the same wax sheet may be applied on the surface.[1]

**Folding of Maps.** Maps are folded in various ways; there is no well-established convention for uniform folding. This is unfortunate, for faulty refolding often causes their premature destruction. As a general rule, maps should be folded accordionwise—first horizontally and then vertically—to the desired size. By this method the map can be opened at any place with the least amount of manipulation. Ingenious methods of folding are used in automobile road maps in Europe. These maps,

[1] Mackin, T. H., A Method of Mounting Maps, *Science*, Vol. 84, pp. 233–234, 1936.

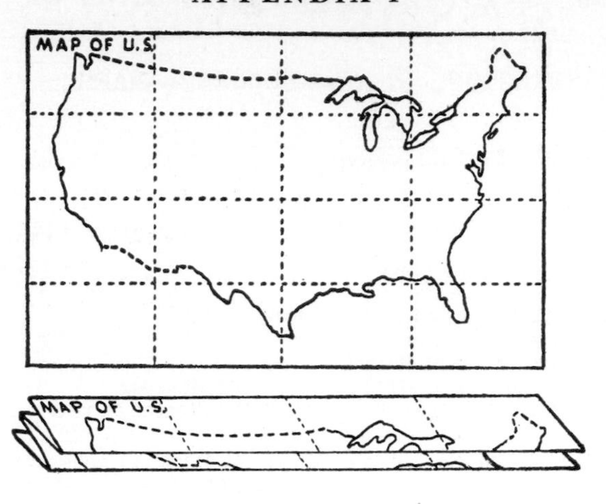

**Fig. 296** The standard method of folding maps. The map is folded first horizontally accordionwise, then vertically in the same manner.

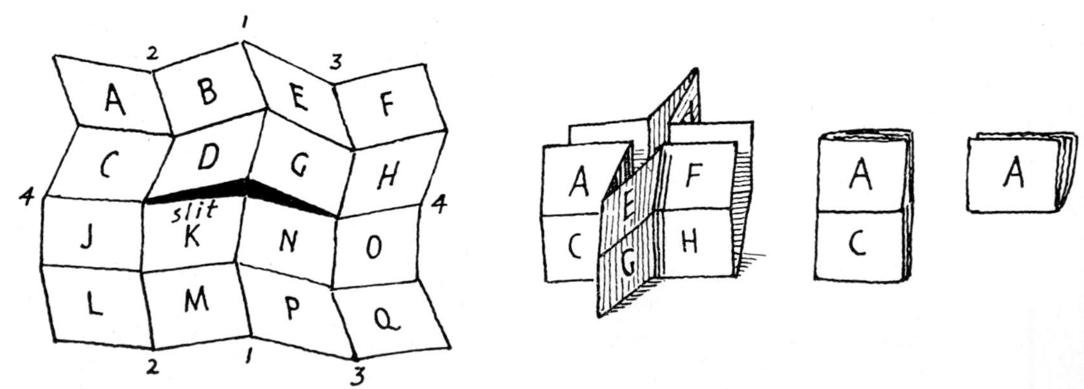


**Fig. 297** British Army auto road maps can be opened at any page or at any two or four adjacent pages. The backside is printed too.

covering a square yard or more, printed on both sides, are folded to pocket size in such a way that they can be opened on any desired place.

**Copyright.** Maps are published with the notice "Copyright by . . . . . 19 . ." Promptly after publication, two copies of the map, an application on Form F, and $4 should be sent to the Copyright Office of the Library of Congress. This gives protection against exact copying of your map, but how much somebody else's general design may be followed has often had to be decided in court. One may copy governmental maps freely, but a reference to the source is a matter of courtesy.

# APPENDIX 2: *Exercises*

Cartography is primarily a practical discipline, and its methods are best learned in the drafting room. The exercises that follow are suggested for one year's work. The instructor will find, however, that there will seldom be enough time available for every student to finish the entire set. He will also find that many, especially graduate students, will have map problems of their own that they wish to prepare during laboratory hours. This should be encouraged because new problems bring new stimulus to cartography. Even if the entire set of exercises cannot be finished by each student, it is better to distribute them all among the students and discuss them collectively rather than to omit any.

It is good practice to exhibit all drawings after their receipt, with the instructor's remarks added. Generally, the instructor will find that his students are eager to hand in well-finished drawings. For the purpose of learning, it is better to finish many exercises of one-afternoon maps; but for the purpose of satisfaction of accomplishment, and in order to obtain an impressive exhibit, it is better to make a few large ones. In general, the former course is recommended for beginners, but second-year students will often find more interest in a single, large, well-executed map.

## Exercises for Book I

In the beginning of a course in cartography, while the lecture hours deal with the history of maps, the laboratory hours can best be utilized for exercises in lettering and in learning the use of drawing instruments.

**Exercise 1.** *Practice in Muscular Coordination.* Draw the routine of Fig. 298 on a piece of notebook paper with a fountain pen. Use full-arm motion and try to "follow through." Begin the motion in the air, bring your pen down on the paper, and when you lift it off at the end of the line, continue the motion in the air. The 5-minute routine may be repeated before each exercise in lettering. It is interesting to repeat these lines with eyes closed. A man with good muscular control will do almost as well as with eyes open.

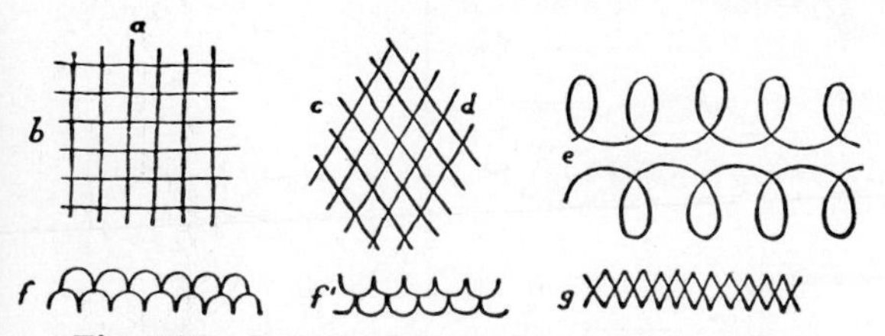


**Fig. 298** Exercise for muscular coordination.

**Exercise 2.** *Lettering*

*a.* Read carefully the Rules of Lettering.

*b.* Take a sheet of ruled notebook paper, and with a fountain pen draw vertical block (gothic) capitals. Draw the same letter five times and number in the following order, following strictly the Rules of Lettering. Be careful that the letters are vertical and that their standard width is maintained.

I H L F E T<br>
V W M N Z A K X Y<br>
O Q C G J S D P B R<br>
1 2 3 4 5 6 7 8 9 0

*c.* Draw in the same order the vertical gothic lower-case letters. Use for models the letters in Fig. 119.

*d.* Draw the inclined gothic capitals in the order of the alphabet. Try to space the letters evenly.

*e.* Draw an alphabet of the inclined gothic lower-case letters.

*f.* Draw a row of numerals in inclined gothic.

*g.* Draw your own name in vertical and inclined gothic.

**Exercise 3.** *Map Lettering and Coloring*

*a.* Read Chap. 13 carefully.

*b.* Copy an outline map of the United States, and thereon lay out very lightly in pencil the names of the following;

Ten large cities
Ten large rivers
Each of the Great Lakes, Great Salt Lake, Lake Champlain, Atlantic Ocean, Pacific Ocean, Gulf of Mexico, United States, Canada, Mexico, Appalachian Mountains, Rocky Mountains, and Sierra Nevada. The names of mountains should strictly follow the trend of the mountain.

*c.* Draw fine guidelines with a very sharp pencil. All horizontal lettering should be parallel with the parallels. Extended lettering, as of countries and oceans, should be evenly spaced from one end of the area to the other.

*d.* Ink in the lettering—the larger the lettering, the heavier the pen required. Erase pencil lines.

*e.* Color the United States yellow, Canada pink, Mexico green, and water surfaces light blue. (Read the method of coloring on page 151.)

*f.* Paint out imperfections with reproduction white. This can be done only after the map has been colored: otherwise it might wash off.

**Exercise 4.** *Use of Drawing Instruments.* Read Chap. 15 on Drawing Instruments and then prepare a page in the manner of Fig. 299, using your own set of tools.

**Exercise 5.** *Scale Reduction and Enlargement*

*a.* Draw a graphic scale for a map 1:100,000.

*b.* Draw a line $5\frac{3}{8}$ inches long, and divide it into 10 parts according to Fig. 34.

*c.* Enlarge to double size a small part of a simple map by the square method.

*d.* Reduce the same map to one-half its size, using a pantograph.

*e.* Do the same with a camera lucida or any other optical instrument.

*f.* Calibrate a line $\frac{3}{8}$ inch long by dividing it

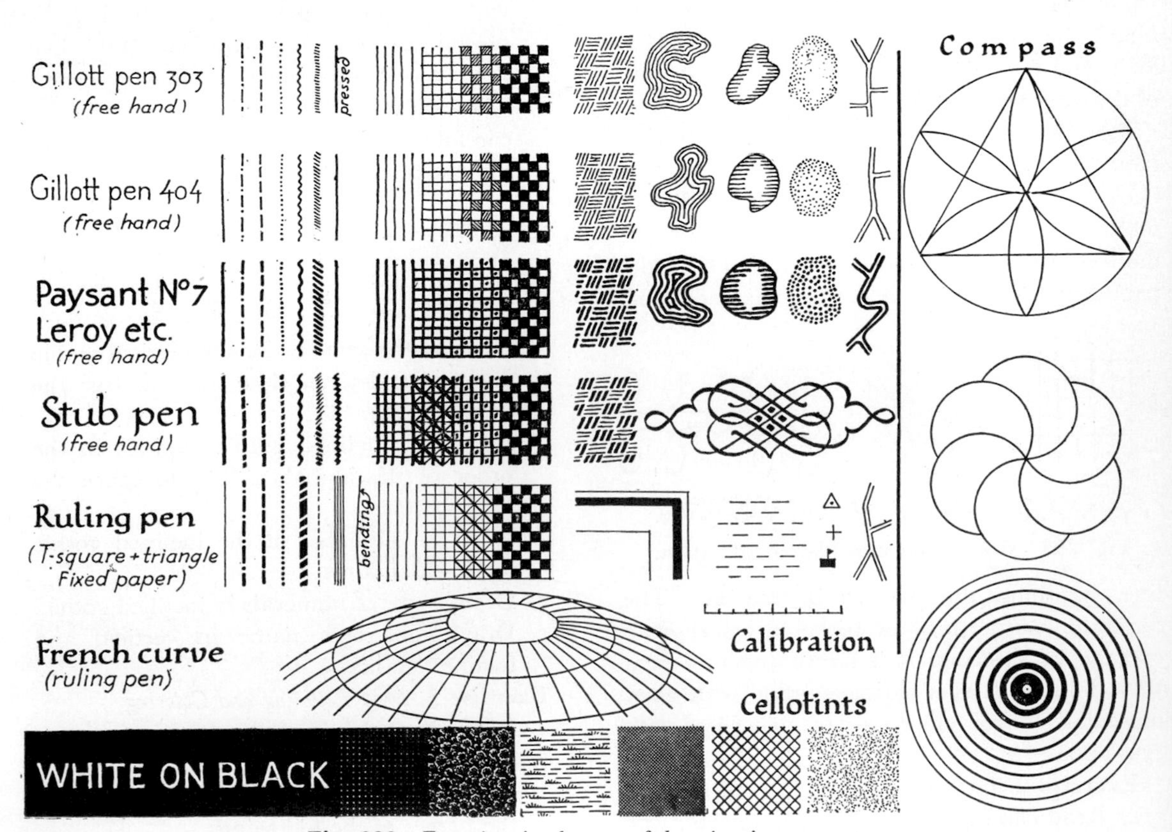


**Fig. 299** Exercises in the use of drawing instruments.

freehand into five parts. Try it at least five times.

The ability to calibrate exactly is an important attribute of a cartographer. The instructor should make a careful examination with a magnifier. This is a good "ability" test.

**Exercise 6.** *Projections.* Draw the parallels 40°, 50°, and 60°, and the meridians 10°, 0°, 10°, corresponding to a globe of 72-inch circumference, in the following projections.

*a.* Equirectangular, with 50° lat. as standard parallel

*b.* Mercator

*c.* Sinusoidal

*d.* Mollweide

*e.* Simple conic projection; standard parallel N 50°

*f.* Polyconic projection

*g.* Bonne projection; standard parallel N 50°

Draw in pencil only, but hand in calculation sheets.

**Exercise 7.** *Azimuthal Projections.* Draw one of the following maps in the specified projections, with parallels and meridians at every 10°. Ink in the map, parallels, and meridians with hairlines, the equator with a heavier line, and the Arctic Circle and the tropics with dashed hairlines. Color land yellow and oceans blue, but paint only a narrow strip of blue along the shores.

*a.* Draw an outline map of the world as projected from the center of the globe upon a tangent cube. Open up the cube, and lay it down flat to form a cross consisting of two polar and four equatorial projections.

*b.* Draw a map of the land hemisphere in oblique stereographic projection, centered on 47°N and 1°W. Make the diameter of the hemisphere 12 inches.

*c.* Draw a hemisphere on oblique orthographic projection centered on N 60° lat. and W 90° long.; make the diameter of the hemisphere 12 inches.

*d.* Draw the Western Hemisphere in globular projection. Diameter of the hemisphere should be 12 inches.

*e.* Draw a north polar projection in the Lambert azimuthal equal-area network as far as 55°S.

*f.* Make a map of the world in the Aitof projection. Make the length of the equator 14.4 inches.

*g.* Construct a star or butterfly projection of your own.

*h.* Draw an orthoapsidal world map of your own design.

**Exercise 8.** *Symbols.* Transform a small airplane photograph into a map on the same scale. Copy first in pencil all lakes, rivers, houses, roads, outlines of fields, etc. Use for each feature an appropriate symbol. Name the main features (with imaginary names if real names are not known). Draw title, scale, and key of symbols. Ink in the drawing with colored inks: hydrography, blue; railroads, borders of fields, lettering, frame, etc., black; roads and houses, red; forest, bush, etc., green; hayfields and grassland, yellow; plowed fields, brown; yards, gardens, and city blocks, pink. These colors are suggestions only; use patterns and colors according to your own judgment.

**Exercise 9.** *Hachuring and Plastic Shading.* From a topographic sheet select 4 square inches of hilly territory.

*a.* Draw hachure lines on the map according to the Lehman system, first in pencil and then in India ink.

*b.* Select another, more rugged, piece on the map, and try to make an even shading with a soft, circular motion of the crayon. Smudge it even with fingers or smudger. Imagine the light as coming from the WNW. This will result in a map in plastic shading with oblique illumination.

**Exercise 10.** *Contour-line Problems.* Assignments for these exercises should be selected from topographic sheets covering, preferably, regions known to the students.

*a.* Draw a profile along a straight line indicated on a topographic sheet. Indicate horizontal and vertical scale and vertical exaggeration.

*b.* Lay out an automobile road to cover a distance extending from a chosen point to a lookout point on a peak. (Slope of road, 500 feet per mile.) Draw two alternative routes.

c. Draw a cut-and-fill profile along a proposed railroad line. At what height would you lay out the railroad if the maximum slope were 60 feet per mile?
d. Draw the visibility from a peak within 5 miles in a selected general direction.
e. Draw the landscape visible from a point in a certain selected direction.

**Exercise 11.** *Imaginary Map.* Draw a map of an imaginary region on a scale of 1:62,500. It should show a harbor city of about 2,000 people in a well-dissected mountain region with peaks that are over 1,500 feet. Contour interval should be 100 feet. Show complete river system, lakes, salt marshes, plateaus, cliffs, sandbanks, harbor facilities, lighthouses, roads, railroads, etc. Use conventional symbols and colors.

**Exercise 12.** *Physiographic Map, Map Composition, Lettering, and Make-up.*

NOTE. This map is the final and most important map in connection with Book I.

Draw a landform map of a state or of any large area in a scale ranging from 1:1,000,000 to 1:5,000,000, according to the size of the area chosen. Outlines can be traced from available maps. Relief can be drawn freehand from an available physiographic map, but the student is expected not to copy it line by line. Indicate major cities, rivers, lakes, mountain peaks, etc. On the side of the map add insets of interesting places. Make a well-balanced composition of the main map, insets, title cartouche, and border. Parallels and meridians are indicated on the borders only. The sequence of preparation is as follows:

a. Lay out roughly in pencil the composition of the map on tracing paper.
b. Transfer the composition to drawing paper, and, with pencil, draw every detail of the map. Use very light lines.
c. Clean the map with eraser powder.
d. Ink in lettering and borders with black ink.
e. Ink in rivers, lakes, and shore lines with blue.
f. Ink in relief with brown.
g. Erase all traces of pencil lines.
h. Color lakes and sea with flat blue wash.
i. Paint out imperfections with white.
j. Trim map, mount it on cardboard, and cover it with cellophane.

## Exercises for Book II[1]

**Exercise 13.** *Compass Traverse.* Select a relatively open piece of ground about 1,000 feet long without heavy iron fences, rails, or pipes. Each student should bring a sighting compass and traverse notebook. A 100-foot tape and an aneroid barometer is brought for the whole class. An Abney level and a pedometer are also useful.

Each student (singly) carries through a closed traverse according to Chap. 17. Plenty of side readings should be taken. Each student should take somewhat different routes if possible. Each student should count his steps along the 100-foot tape.

On returning to the laboratory, the scale should be figured out so that the map is 100 feet per inch. Add or subtract to each azimuth reading the magnetic declination, and layout the traverse on drawing paper.

Cut a large enough piece of paper, and select point *A* so that the map does not run off the paper. Draw a vertical line through *A* with the T-square, and with a protractor lay out the azimuth and on it the distance to point *B*, etc., until the traverse is closed.

Distribute your error of closure, draw in side readings, render scale, title, and border, and finish in pencil only.

**Exercise 14.** *Plane Tabling.* Select an open piece of ground that is relatively level. Divide the students into groups of three; each group should bring a plane table with tripod, a rod, a telescopic alidade, a pin, a ruler divided into tenths of inches, a slide rule for the Beaman arc, a pair of binoculars, and a number of pegs or a hatchet with which to cut them in the field.

[1] In winter, start with Exercise 16.

Special care should be taken in selecting the scale and the location of the first point so that the map does not run off the paper.

The plane tabling should be carried out according to Chap. 17. Emphasis should be not only on obtaining the stations but also on drawing the map.

As the schedule for exercises for Book II is heavy, the inking in of the plane-table map is not required at this stage.

**Exercise 15.** Lay out a U.S. Progressive Military Grid on an old 1:62,500 topographic sheet. (As the older sheets have no grid marks, this layout is often required from cartographers.) The *U.S. Coast and Geodetic Survey Special Publication* 59 gives the coordinates of the four corners of every topographic sheet, and the limiting lines are easily obtained by measuring down and left from each corner the distance to the next 5,000-yard grid line. Interior grid lines are laid out parallel at scale distance. Draw them with pencil only.

**Exercise 16.** Express graphically the following data by subdivision of a rectangular graph. Total and parts should be properly labeled.

| *U.S. Imports from Cuba*, 1945 | *Millions of Dollars* |
|---|---|
| Brown sugar | $183.6 |
| White sugar | 27.2 |
| Molasses | 50.5 |
| Alcohol | 11.5 |
| Rum | 12.1 |
| Other liquors | 1.9 |
| Leaf tobacco | 31.0 |
| Manufactured tobacco | 15.7 |
| Manganese | 11.3 |
| Chromium | 4.3 |
| Copper | 1.2 |
| Nickel | 1.2 |
| Diamond | 6.0 |
| Foods | 14.3 |
| Animal products | 2.8 |
| Forest products | 2.9 |
| Miscellaneous | 8.2 |
| Total | $385.7 |

**Exercise 17.** Express the following data graphically. Emphasis is on the choice and the proper building of a continuous diagram.

Educational Attainment of the Population Twenty-five Years Old and Over, 1940

| *School Years Completed* | *Number of Persons in Millions* |
|---|---|
| No school years completed | 2.8 |
| Grade school: | |
| 1 to 4 years | 7.3 |
| 5 and 6 years | 8.5 |
| 7 and 8 years | 25.9 |
| High school: | |
| 1 and 3 years | 11.2 |
| 4 years | 10.6 |
| College: | |
| 1 to 3 years | 4.1 |
| 4 years and more | 3.4 |
| Total | 73.8 |

**Exercise 18.** Make an isometric choropleth map of the population of the New England states. Details of coast line can be omitted.

| *State* | *Population* | *Area, thousand square miles* |
|---|---|---|
| Connecticut | 1.7 million | 5.0 |
| Massachusetts | 4.3 million | 8.3 |
| Rhode Island | 0.7 million | 1.2 |
| New Hampshire | 0.5 million | 9.3 |
| Vermont | 0.4 million | 9.6 |
| Maine | 0.9 million | 33.2 |

**Exercise 19.** Draw a statistical map showing the distribution of colleges and universities in your state according to student population. Subdivide symbols for men and women, and mark type of school. Select your own system.

**Exercise 20.** *Economic Map.* Each student should select a state or a small foreign country or colony and prepare an economic map of it, showing land-use types, such as forest, pasture land, cultivated land, desert, etc., in colors and main transportation lines and cities. No representation of relief is required and rivers are shown only if they are used for navigation or as a source of water or power. Cities are shown by block-pile graphs.

Surround the maps with diagrams and cartograms including bar graphs, line graphs, pie graphs, small rainfall map, small dot map showing an important product, small traffic-flow map, and anything else for which there is available data. ("Foreign Agriculture" is a good source of information.) Colors can be used freely. The map should be visualized as a double page in an economic school atlas. (This map can be worked out in conjunction with the geography department.)

**Exercise 21.** *Topographic Model.* Prepare a topographic model of a selected small region, preferably one known to the students. Enlarge the topographic sheet twice. Figure vertical exaggeration of about two times, and secure cardboards of corresponding thickness. Paste carbon paper on the reverse of the map and

*a.* Copy each contour on a separate cardboard, indicating the position of the next higher contour.
*b.* Cut out every contour line with a jig saw.
*c.* Build up a positive model by pasting and nailing the cardboards upon each other.
*d.* Smooth the cardboards with plastiline, being careful that no thick accumulation of plastiline covers the valleys. Model the rivers, roads, cliffs, etc., with modeling tools.
*e.* Prepare a frame around the cardboard model, and make a negative cast. Place the negative into the frame, and shellac and oil it.
*f.* Prepare a positive cast.
*g.* Paint its surface with water colors, add lettering, and paint the geologic sections on the sides of the model.

Some students should be encouraged to prepare rough large-scale terrain models from any kind of material available without cutting contours.

**Exercise 22.** *Dufour Diagram.* Select an area 10 to 20 square miles on a topographic sheet, and enlarge it twice by photostating.

*a.* Prepare a Dufour pantograph, if one is not available. The rod should preferably be $\frac{1}{2}$ by 1 inch thick and about 6 feet long. The groove is made of two pieces of board nailed parallel to each other. (Instead of a groove, the edge of the table can be used, and the rod can be held close by a long rubber band.)
*b.* Draw the successive contour lines, as discussed in Chap. 31.
*c.* Draw profiles on all four sides by connecting the ends of the contour lines. Draw the sides of the block.
*d.* Add hachure lines, cultural symbols, and lettering; draw geological sections on the sides.
*e.* Ink in the map in the same color scheme as before, but use orange for the contour lines. Add plastic shading in purple.

**Exercise 23.** *Land-slope Analysis.* On a topographic sheet assign an area of about 9 square miles to each student. A planimeter will greatly speed up the work of measuring areas. If none is available, transparent paper divided in $\frac{1}{10}$-inch squares will do.

*a.* Draw a *hypsographic curve* of the region.
*b.* Draw a *hypsographoid.*
*c.* By the Wentworth method, give an *index number* for each square mile.
*d.* Draw a general *land-slope curve.*
*e.* Draw a *flatland-ratio curve,* considering as flatland all land below 200 feet per mile of slope.
*f.* Divide your area into 5-minute squares, and make a *relative relief* map on a small scale. (This work may be divided among the students. If there are not enough topographic sheets available, any other state may be selected.)

**Exercise 24.** *Land-utilization Survey*

*a.* Obtain a cadastral or assessor's map of an area on the outskirts of your town, where various types of land utilization are intermingled. Make a copy of the map, which may have to be enlarged or reduced for convenient handling. If none is available, an enlarged airplane photograph will serve.
*b.* Work out a code index system suitable for the units of your area.
*c.* Survey in the field the assigned territory, and give an index figure to each unit of land, calling a unit any piece of land that has approximately the same slope, soil, erosion, and utilization. Slope may vary to such an extent that the units may be too

small. In this case slightly variable slopes may be included in the same unit and marked in several places. Indicate the direction of slope with arrows.

*d.* With proper symbols mark on the map fences, ledges, sand pits, swamps, and all other important features not shown on the original maps.

*e.* Copy the field map on drawing paper in pencil.

*f.* Ink in with black all property boundaries, houses, roads, railroads, and lettering.

*g.* Indicate all land-use types by colors and patterns.

*h.* Indicate with red index figures the slope, soil, and erosion types.

*i.* After the map is painted, indicate water features with blue.

*j.* Finish the map with a key, title, scale, border, and annotations.

**Exercise 25.** *Land-type Map.* Take an area, preferably the same county that was mapped in the economic map, and make a land-type map of it. Show relief by trachographic or landform symbols, vegetation by colors or patterns, cities by red block piles, transportation by the usual symbols, cultivation by brown-bordered yellow and green checkerboards, etc. This is the final map of this set of exercises and embodies all previous experience in composition, lettering, painting, etc. This map is prepared for reproduction by the four-color process.

# APPENDIX 3: *Tables*

**Table A · 1** Squares, Square Roots, Cubes, and Cubic Roots of Nos. 1 to 100

| *No.* | *Square* | *Cube* | *Square root* | *Cube root* | *No.* | *Square* | *Cube* | *Square root* | *Cube root* | *No.* | *Square* | *Cube* | *Square root* | *Cube root* |
|---|---|---|---|---|---|---|---|---|---|---|---|---|---|---|
| 1 | 1.000 | 1.000 | 1.000 | 1.000 | 35 | 1,225 | 42,875 | 5.916 | 3.271 | 68 | 4,624 | 314,432 | 8.246 | 4.081 |
| 2 | 4 | 8 | 1.414 | 1.259 | 36 | 1,296 | 46,656 | 6.000 | 3.301 | 69 | 4,761 | 328,509 | 8.306 | 4.101 |
| 3 | 9 | 27 | 1.732 | 1.442 | 37 | 1,369 | 50,653 | 6.082 | 3.332 | 70 | 4,900 | 343,000 | 8.366 | 4.121 |
| 4 | 16 | 64 | 2.000 | 1.587 | 38 | 1,444 | 54,872 | 6.164 | 3.362 | 71 | 5,041 | 357,911 | 8.426 | 4.140 |
| 5 | 25 | 125 | 2.236 | 1.710 | 39 | 1,521 | 59,319 | 6.245 | 3.391 | 72 | 5,184 | 373,248 | 8.485 | 4.160 |
| 6 | 36 | 216 | 2.449 | 1.817 | 40 | 1,600 | 64,000 | 6.324 | 3.420 | 73 | 5,329 | 389,017 | 8.544 | 4.179 |
| 7 | 49 | 343 | 2.645 | 1.913 | 41 | 1,681 | 68,921 | 6.403 | 3.448 | 74 | 5,476 | 405,224 | 8.602 | 4.198 |
| 8 | 64 | 512 | 2.828 | 2.000 | 42 | 1,764 | 74,088 | 6.480 | 3.476 | 75 | 5,625 | 421,875 | 8.660 | 4.217 |
| 9 | 81 | 729 | 3.000 | 2.080 | 43 | 1,849 | 79,507 | 6.557 | 3.503 | 76 | 5,776 | 438,976 | 8.717 | 4.235 |
| 10 | 100 | 1,000 | 3.162 | 2.154 | 44 | 1,936 | 85,184 | 6.633 | 3.530 | 77 | 5,929 | 456,533 | 8.775 | 4.254 |
| 11 | 121 | 1,331 | 3.316 | 2.224 | 45 | 2,025 | 91,125 | 6.708 | 3.556 | 78 | 6,084 | 474,552 | 8.831 | 4.272 |
| 12 | 144 | 1,728 | 3.464 | 2.289 | 46 | 2,116 | 97,336 | 6.782 | 3.583 | 79 | 6,241 | 493,039 | 8.888 | 4.290 |
| 13 | 169 | 2,197 | 3.605 | 2.351 | 47 | 2,209 | 103,823 | 6.855 | 3.608 | 80 | 6,400 | 512,000 | 8.944 | 4.308 |
| 14 | 196 | 2,744 | 3.741 | 2.410 | 48 | 2,304 | 110,592 | 6.928 | 3.634 | 81 | 6,561 | 531,441 | 9.000 | 4.326 |
| 15 | 225 | 3,375 | 3.873 | 2.466 | 49 | 2,401 | 117,649 | 7.000 | 3.659 | 82 | 6,724 | 551,368 | 9.055 | 4.344 |
| 16 | 256 | 4,096 | 4.000 | 2.519 | 50 | 2,500 | 125,000 | 7.071 | 3.684 | 83 | 6,889 | 571,787 | 9.110 | 4.362 |
| 17 | 289 | 4,913 | 4.123 | 2.571 | 51 | 2,601 | 132,651 | 7.141 | 3.708 | 84 | 7,056 | 592,704 | 9.165 | 4.379 |
| 18 | 324 | 5,832 | 4.242 | 2.620 | 52 | 2,704 | 140,608 | 7.211 | 3.732 | 85 | 7,225 | 614,125 | 9.219 | 4.396 |
| 19 | 361 | 6,859 | 4.358 | 2.668 | 53 | 2,809 | 148,877 | 7.280 | 3.756 | 86 | 7,396 | 636,056 | 9.273 | 4.414 |
| 20 | 400 | 8,000 | 4.472 | 2.714 | 54 | 2,916 | 157,464 | 7.348 | 3.779 | 87 | 7,569 | 658,503 | 9.327 | 4.431 |
| 21 | 441 | 9,261 | 4.582 | 2.758 | 55 | 3,025 | 166,375 | 7.416 | 3.803 | 88 | 7,744 | 681,472 | 9.380 | 4.448 |
| 22 | 484 | 10,648 | 4.690 | 2.802 | 56 | 3,136 | 175,616 | 7.483 | 3.825 | 89 | 7,921 | 704,969 | 9.434 | 4.464 |
| 23 | 529 | 12,167 | 4.795 | 2.843 | 57 | 3,249 | 185,193 | 7.549 | 3.848 | 90 | 8,100 | 729,000 | 9.486 | 4.481 |
| 24 | 576 | 13,824 | 4.899 | 2.884 | 58 | 3,364 | 195,112 | 7.615 | 3.870 | 91 | 8,281 | 753,571 | 9.539 | 4.497 |
| 25 | 624 | 15,625 | 5.000 | 2.924 | 59 | 3,481 | 205,379 | 7.681 | 3.893 | 92 | 8,464 | 778,688 | 9.591 | 4.514 |
| 26 | 676 | 17,576 | 5.099 | 2.962 | 60 | 3,600 | 216,000 | 7.746 | 3.914 | 93 | 8,649 | 804,357 | 9.643 | 4.530 |
| 27 | 729 | 19,683 | 5.196 | 3.000 | 61 | 3,721 | 226,981 | 7.810 | 3.936 | 94 | 8,836 | 830,584 | 9.695 | 4.546 |
| 28 | 784 | 21,952 | 5.291 | 3.036 | 62 | 3,844 | 238,328 | 7.874 | 3.957 | 95 | 9,025 | 857,375 | 9.746 | 4.562 |
| 29 | 841 | 24,389 | 5.385 | 3.072 | 63 | 3,969 | 250,047 | 7.937 | 3.979 | 96 | 9,216 | 884,736 | 9.798 | 4.578 |
| 30 | 900 | 27,000 | 5.477 | 3.107 | 64 | 4,096 | 262,144 | 8.000 | 4.000 | 97 | 9,409 | 912,673 | 9.848 | 4.594 |
| 31 | 961 | 29,791 | 5.567 | 3.141 | 65 | 4,225 | 274,625 | 8.062 | 4.020 | 98 | 9,604 | 941,192 | 9.899 | 4.610 |
| 32 | 1,024 | 32,768 | 5.656 | 3.174 | 66 | 4,356 | 287,496 | 8.124 | 4.041 | 99 | 9,801 | 970,299 | 9.949 | 4.626 |
| 33 | 1,089 | 35,937 | 5.744 | 3.207 | 67 | 4,489 | 300,763 | 8.185 | 4.061 | 100 | 10,000 | 1,000,000 | 10.000 | 4.641 |
| 34 | 1,156 | 39,304 | 5.831 | 3.239 | | | | | | | | | | |

This table and the next will be particularly useful in drawing two- and three-dimensional graphs.

**Table A · 2** Common Fractions Reduced to Decimals

| *8ths* | *16ths* | *32ds* | *64ths* | *8ths* | *16ths* | *32ds* | *64ths* | *8ths* | *16ths* | *32ds* | *64ths* |
|---|---|---|---|---|---|---|---|---|---|---|---|
| | | | 0.015625 | | | | 0.359375 | | 11 | 22 | 0.6875 |
| | | 1 | 0.03125 | 3 | 6 | 12 | 0.375 | | | | 0.703125 |
| | | | 0.046875 | | | | | | | 23 | 0.71875 |
| | 1 | 2 | 0.0625 | | | | 0.390625 | | | | 0.734375 |
| | | | 0.078125 | | | 13 | 0.40625 | 6 | 12 | 24 | 0.75 |
| | | 3 | 0.09375 | | | | 0.421875 | | | | |
| | | | 0.109375 | | 7 | 14 | 0.4375 | | | | 0.765625 |
| 1 | 2 | 4 | 0.125 | | | | 0.453125 | | | 25 | 0.78125 |
| | | | | | | 15 | 0.46875 | | | | 0.796875 |
| | | | 0.140625 | | | | 0.484375 | | 13 | 26 | 0.8125 |
| | | 5 | 0.15625 | 4 | 8 | 16 | 0.5 | | | | 0.828125 |
| | | | 0.171875 | | | | | | | 27 | 0.84375 |
| | 3 | 6 | 0.1875 | | | | 0.515625 | | | | 0.859385 |
| | | | 0.203125 | | | 17 | 0.53125 | 7 | 14 | 28 | 0.875 |
| | | 7 | 0.21875 | | | | 0.546875 | | | | |
| | | | 0.234375 | | 9 | 18 | 0.5625 | | | | 0.890625 |
| 2 | 4 | 8 | 0.25 | | | | 0.578125 | | | 29 | 0.90625 |
| | | | | | | 19 | 0.59375 | | | | 0.921875 |
| | | | 0.265625 | | | | 0.609375 | | 15 | 30 | 0.9375 |
| | | 9 | 0.28125 | 5 | 10 | 20 | 0.625 | | | | 0.953125 |
| | | | 0.296875 | | | | | | | 31 | 0.96875 |
| | 5 | 10 | 0.3125 | | | | 0.640625 | | | | 0.984375 |
| | | | 0.328125 | | | 21 | 0.65625 | 8 | 16 | 32 | 1. |
| | | 11 | 0.34375 | | | | 0.671875 | | | | |

**Table A · 3** Units of Length

| *Inches* | *Millimeters* | *Feet* | *Meters (m)* | *Miles* | *Kilometers* |
|---|---|---|---|---|---|
| 1 = | 25.4001 | 1 = | 0.304801 | 1 = | 1.609347 |
| 2 = | 50.8001 | 2 = | 0.609601 | 2 = | 3.218694 |
| 3 = | 76.2002 | 3 = | 0.914402 | 3 = | 4.828042 |
| 4 = | 101.6002 | 4 = | 1.219202 | 4 = | 6.437389 |
| 5 = | 127.0003 | 5 = | 1.524003 | 5 = | 8.046736 |
| 6 = | 152.4003 | 6 = | 1.828804 | 6 = | 9.656083 |
| 7 = | 177.8004 | 7 = | 2.133604 | 7 = | 11.265431 |
| 8 = | 203.2204 | 8 = | 2.438405 | 8 = | 12.874778 |
| 9 = | 228.6005 | 9 = | 2.743205 | 9 = | 14.484125 |
| 0.03937 | = 1 | 3.28083 | = 1 | 0.621370 | = 1 |
| 0.07874 | = 2 | 6.56167 | = 2 | 1.242740 | = 2 |
| 0.11811 | = 3 | 9.84250 | = 3 | 1.864110 | = 3 |
| 0.15748 | = 4 | 13.12333 | = 4 | 2.485480 | = 4 |
| 0.19685 | = 5 | 16.40417 | = 5 | 3.106850 | = 5 |
| 0.23622 | = 6 | 19.68500 | = 6 | 3.728220 | = 6 |
| 0.27559 | = 7 | 22.96583 | = 7 | 4.349590 | = 7 |
| 0.31496 | = 9 | 26.24667 | = 8 | 4.970960 | = 8 |
| 0.35433 | = 9 | 29.52750 | = 9 | 5.592330 | = 9 |

| *Square inches* | *Square centimeters* | *Square feet* | *Square meters* | *Acres* | *Hectares* | *Square miles* | *Square kilometers* |
|---|---|---|---|---|---|---|---|
| 1 = | 6.452 | 1 = | 0.09290 | 1 = | 0.4047 | 1 = | 2.5900 |
| 2 = | 12.903 | 2 = | 0.18581 | 2 = | 0.8094 | 2 = | 5.1800 |
| 3 = | 19.355 | 3 = | 0.27871 | 3 = | 1.2141 | 3 = | 7.7700 |
| 4 = | 25.807 | 4 = | 0.37161 | 4 = | 1.6187 | 4 = | 10.3600 |
| 5 = | 32.258 | 5 = | 0.46452 | 5 = | 2.0234 | 5 = | 12.9500 |
| 6 = | 38.710 | 6 = | 0.55742 | 6 = | 2.4281 | 6 = | 15.5400 |
| 7 = | 45.161 | 7 = | 0.65032 | 7 = | 2.8328 | 7 = | 18.1300 |
| 8 = | 51.613 | 8 = | 0.74323 | 8 = | 3.2375 | 8 = | 20.7200 |
| 9 = | 58.065 | 9 = | 0.83613 | 9 = | 3.6422 | 9 = | 23.3100 |
| 0.15500 | = 1 | 10.764 | = 1 | 2.471 | = 1 | 0.3861 | = 1 |
| 0.31000 | = 2 | 21.528 | = 2 | 4.942 | = 2 | 0.7722 | = 2 |
| 0.46500 | = 3 | 32.292 | = 3 | 7.413 | = 3 | 1.1583 | = 3 |
| 0.62000 | = 4 | 43.055 | = 4 | 9.884 | = 4 | 1.5444 | = 4 |
| 0.77500 | = 5 | 53.819 | = 5 | 12.355 | = 5 | 1.9305 | = 5 |
| 0.93000 | = 6 | 64.583 | = 6 | 14.826 | = 6 | 2.3166 | = 6 |
| 1.08500 | = 7 | 75.347 | = 7 | 17.297 | = 7 | 2.7027 | = 7 |
| 1.24000 | = 8 | 86.111 | = 8 | 19.768 | = 8 | 3.0888 | = 8 |
| 1.39500 | = 9 | 96.875 | = 9 | 22.239 | = 9 | 3.4749 | = 9 |

For instance, a peak 2,856 meters high will be

6,561.67
2,624.67
164.04
19.68
9,370.06 feet high

(*Courtesy of the World Almanac.*)

**Table A · 4** Natural Sines, Cosines, Tangents, and Cotangents

| ° | sine | d | tang | d | cotang | d | cosine | d | ° |
|---|---|---|---|---|---|---|---|---|---|
| ↓ | | + | | + | | − | | − | |
| 0 | 0.0000 | 175 | 0.0000 | 175 | ∞ | | 1.0000 | 2 | 90 |
| 1 | 0.0175 | 174 | 0.0175 | 174 | 57.290 | | 0.9998 | 4 | 89 |
| 2 | 0.0349 | 174 | 0.0349 | 175 | 28.636 | | 0.9994 | 8 | 88 |
| 3 | 0.0523 | 175 | 0.0524 | 175 | 19.081 | | 0.9986 | 10 | 87 |
| 4 | 0.0698 | 174 | 0.0699 | 176 | 14.301 | | 0.9976 | 14 | 86 |
| 5 | 0.0872 | 173 | 0.0875 | 176 | 11.430 | | 0.9962 | 17 | 85 |
| 6 | 0.1045 | 174 | 0.1051 | 177 | 9.514 | | 0.9945 | 20 | 84 |
| 7 | 0.1219 | 173 | 0.1228 | 177 | 8.144 | | 0.9925 | 22 | 83 |
| 8 | 0.1392 | 172 | 0.1405 | 179 | 7.115 | | 0.9903 | 26 | 82 |
| 9 | 0.1564 | 172 | 0.1584 | 179 | 6.314 | | 0.9877 | 29 | 81 |
| 10 | 0.1736 | 172 | 0.1763 | 181 | 5.671 | 526 | 0.9848 | 32 | 80 |
| 11 | 0.1908 | 171 | 0.1944 | 182 | 5.145 | 440 | 0.9816 | 35 | 79 |
| 12 | 0.2079 | 171 | 0.2126 | 183 | 4.705 | 374 | 0.9781 | 37 | 78 |
| 13 | 0.2250 | 169 | 0.2309 | 184 | 4.331 | 320 | 0.9744 | 41 | 77 |
| 14 | 0.2419 | 169 | 0.2493 | 186 | 4.011 | 279 | 0.9703 | 44 | 76 |
| 15 | 0.2588 | 168 | 0.2679 | 188 | 3.732 | 245 | 0.9659 | 46 | 75 |
| 16 | 0.2756 | 168 | 0.2867 | 190 | 3.487 | 216 | 0.9613 | 50 | 74 |
| 17 | 0.2924 | 166 | 0.3057 | 192 | 3.271 | 193 | 0.9563 | 52 | 73 |
| 18 | 0.3090 | 166 | 0.3249 | 194 | 3.078 | 174 | 0.9511 | 56 | 72 |
| 19 | 0.3256 | 164 | 0.3443 | 197 | 2.904 | 157 | 0.9455 | 58 | 71 |
| 20 | 0.3420 | 164 | 0.3640 | 199 | 2.747 | 142 | 0.9397 | 61 | 70 |
| 21 | 0.3584 | 162 | 0.3839 | 201 | 2.605 | 130 | 0.9336 | 64 | 69 |
| 22 | 0.3746 | 161 | 0.4040 | 205 | 2.475 | 119 | 0.9272 | 67 | 68 |
| 23 | 0.3907 | 160 | 0.4245 | 207 | 2.356 | 110 | 0.9205 | 70 | 67 |
| 24 | 0.4067 | 159 | 0.4452 | 211 | 2.246 | 101 | 0.9135 | 72 | 66 |
| 25 | 0.4226 | 158 | 0.4663 | 214 | 2.145 | 95 | 0.9063 | 75 | 65 |
| 26 | 0.4384 | 156 | 0.4877 | 218 | 2.050 | 87 | 0.8988 | 78 | 64 |
| 27 | 0.4540 | 155 | 0.5095 | 222 | 1.963 | 82 | 0.8910 | 81 | 63 |
| 28 | 0.4695 | 153 | 0.5317 | 226 | 1.881 | 77 | 0.8829 | 83 | 62 |
| 29 | 0.4848 | 152 | 0.5543 | 231 | 1.804 | 72 | 0.8746 | 86 | 61 |
| 30 | 0.5000 | 150 | 0.5774 | 235 | 1.732 | 68 | 0.8660 | 88 | 60 |
| 31 | 0.5150 | 149 | 0.6009 | 240 | 1.664 | 64 | 0.8572 | 92 | 59 |
| 32 | 0.5299 | 147 | 0.6249 | 245 | 1.600 | 60 | 0.8480 | 93 | 58 |
| 33 | 0.5446 | 146 | 0.6494 | 251 | 1.540 | 57 | 0.8387 | 97 | 57 |
| 34 | 0.5592 | 144 | 0.6745 | 257 | 1.483 | 55 | 0.8290 | 98 | 56 |
| 35 | 0.5736 | 142 | 0.7002 | 263 | 1.428 | 52 | 0.8192 | 102 | 55 |
| 36 | 0.5878 | 140 | 0.7265 | 271 | 1.376 | 49 | 0.8090 | 104 | 54 |
| 37 | 0.6018 | 139 | 0.7536 | 277 | 1.327 | 47 | 0.7986 | 106 | 53 |
| 38 | 0.6157 | 136 | 0.7813 | 285 | 1.280 | 45 | 0.7880 | 109 | 52 |
| 39 | 0.6293 | 135 | 0.8098 | 293 | 1.235 | 43 | 0.7771 | 111 | 51 |
| 40 | 0.6428 | 133 | 0.8391 | 302 | 1.192 | 42 | 0.7660 | 113 | 50 |
| 41 | 0.6561 | 130 | 0.8693 | 311 | 1.150 | 39 | 0.7547 | 116 | 49 |
| 42 | 0.6691 | 129 | 0.9004 | 321 | 1.111 | 39 | 0.7431 | 117 | 48 |
| 43 | 0.6820 | 127 | 0.9325 | 332 | 1.072 | 36 | 0.7314 | 121 | 47 |
| 44 | 0.6947 | 124 | 0.9657 | 343 | 1.036 | 36 | 0.7193 | 122 | 46 |
| 45 | 0.7071 | | 1.0000 | | 1.000 | | 0.7071 | | 45 |
| | | − | | − | | + | | + | ↑ |
| ° | Cosine | d | cotang | d | tang | d | sine | d | ° |

This table can be used in finding the true lengths of degrees of longitude and for construction of map projections in general. The functions at the bottom refer to the degrees on the right, thus sin $\alpha$ = cos $(90° - \alpha)$ making sine 60° = cos 30° = 0.8660 and in the same way tan 60° = cot 30° = 1.732. If fractions of degrees are wanted, a proportionate amount of $d$ can be used. For very exact large-scale maps, however, a book of logarithms is necessary.

**Table A · 5** Conversion of Degrees to Mils*
(Conversion factor—1 degree = 17.77778 mils; 1 minute = 0.29630 mils)

| Degrees | Mils | Degrees | Mils | Degrees | Mils | Minutes | Mils | Minutes | Mils |
|---|---|---|---|---|---|---|---|---|---|
| 1 | 17.8 | 31 | 551.1 | 61 | 1,084.4 | 1 | 0.3 | 31 | 9.2 |
| 2 | 35.6 | 32 | 568.9 | 62 | 1,102.2 | 2 | 0.6 | 32 | 9.5 |
| 3 | 53.3 | 33 | 586.7 | 63 | 1,120.0 | 3 | 0.9 | 33 | 9.8 |
| 4 | 71.1 | 34 | 604.4 | 64 | 1,137.8 | 4 | 1.2 | 34 | 10.1 |
| 5 | 88.9 | 35 | 622.2 | 65 | 1,155.6 | 5 | 1.5 | 35 | 10.4 |
| 6 | 106.7 | 36 | 640.0 | 66 | 1,173.3 | 6 | 1.8 | 36 | 10.7 |
| 7 | 124.4 | 37 | 657.8 | 67 | 1,191.1 | 7 | 2.1 | 37 | 11.0 |
| 8 | 142.2 | 38 | 675.6 | 68 | 1,208.9 | 8 | 2.4 | 38 | 11.3 |
| 9 | 160.0 | 39 | 693.3 | 69 | 1,226.7 | 9 | 2.7 | 39 | 11.6 |
| 10 | 177.8 | 40 | 711.1 | 70 | 1,244.5 | 10 | 3.0 | 40 | 11.9 |
| 11 | 195.6 | 41 | 728.9 | 71 | 1,262.2 | 11 | 3.3 | 41 | 12.1 |
| 12 | 213.3 | 42 | 746.7 | 72 | 1,280.0 | 12 | 3.6 | 42 | 12.4 |
| 13 | 231.1 | 43 | 764.4 | 73 | 1,297.8 | 13 | 3.9 | 43 | 12.7 |
| 14 | 248.9 | 44 | 782.2 | 74 | 1,315.6 | 14 | 4.1 | 44 | 13.0 |
| 15 | 266.7 | 45 | 800.0 | 75 | 1,333.3 | 15 | 4.4 | 45 | 13.3 |
| 16 | 284.4 | 46 | 817.8 | 76 | 1,351.1 | 16 | 4.7 | 46 | 13.6 |
| 17 | 302.2 | 47 | 835.6 | 77 | 1,368.9 | 17 | 5.0 | 47 | 13.9 |
| 18 | 320.0 | 48 | 853.3 | 78 | 1,386.7 | 18 | 5.3 | 48 | 14.2 |
| 19 | 337.8 | 49 | 871.1 | 79 | 1,404.5 | 19 | 5.6 | 49 | 14.5 |
| 20 | 355.6 | 50 | 888.9 | 80 | 1,422.2 | 20 | 5.9 | 50 | 14.8 |
| 21 | 373.3 | 51 | 906.7 | 81 | 1,440.0 | 21 | 6.2 | 51 | 15.1 |
| 22 | 391.1 | 52 | 924.4 | 82 | 1,457.8 | 22 | 6.5 | 52 | 15.4 |
| 23 | 408.9 | 53 | 942.2 | 83 | 1,475.6 | 23 | 6.8 | 53 | 15.7 |
| 24 | 426.7 | 54 | 960.0 | 84 | 1,493.3 | 24 | 7.1 | 54 | 16.0 |
| 25 | 444.5 | 55 | 977.8 | 85 | 1,511.1 | 25 | 7.4 | 55 | 16.3 |
| 26 | 462.2 | 56 | 995.6 | 86 | 1,528.9 | 26 | 7.7 | 56 | 16.6 |
| 27 | 480.0 | 57 | 1,013.3 | 87 | 1,546.7 | 27 | 8.0 | 57 | 16.9 |
| 28 | 497.8 | 58 | 1,031.1 | 88 | 1,564.5 | 28 | 8.3 | 58 | 17.2 |
| 29 | 515.6 | 59 | 1,048.9 | 89 | 1,582.2 | 29 | 8.6 | 59 | 17.5 |
| 30 | 533.3 | 60 | 1,066.7 | 90 | 1,600.0 | 30 | 8.9 | 60 | 17.8 |

*Examples:*

1. Convert 64°29′ to mils.

64° = 1,137. 8 mils
29′ = 8. 6
64°29′ = 1,146. 4 mils

2. Convert 87.95° to mils.

87° = 1,546. 7 mils
.90° = 16. 0
.05° = 0.889 = 0. 9
87.95° = 1,563. 6 mils

* From U.S. War Department, *Tech. Man.* 5-236.

**Table A · 6** Methods of Expressing Gradients*
(The different methods of expressing gradients have their values given for the usual range and to the customary degree of accuracy of their use)

| *Angle* | *Feet per 100 feet horizontal or per cent* | *Feet to the mile horizontal* | *1 vertical on or in—* |
|---|---|---|---|
| *Degrees* | | | *horizontal* |
| $\frac{1}{4}$ | 0.44 | 23.0 | 229 |
| $\frac{1}{2}$ | 0.87 | 46.1 | 115 |
| $\frac{3}{4}$ | 1.31 | 69.1 | 76 |
| 1 | 1.74 | 92.2 | 57 |
| $1\frac{1}{4}$ | 2.18 | 115.1 | 46 |
| $1\frac{1}{2}$ | 2.62 | 138.3 | 38 |
| $1\frac{3}{4}$ | 3.06 | 161.2 | 33 |
| 2 | 3.49 | 184.4 | 29 |
| $2\frac{1}{2}$ | 4.37 | 230.5 | 23 |
| 3 | 5.24 | 276.7 | 19 |
| $3\frac{1}{2}$ | 6.12 | 322.9 | 16 |
| 4 | 6.99 | 369.2 | 14 |
| $4\frac{1}{2}$ | 7.37 | 415.5 | 13 |
| 5 | 8.75 | 461.9 | 11.4 |
| 6 | 10.51 | 555 | 9.5 |
| 7 | 12.28 | ..... | 8.1 |
| 8 | 14.05 | ..... | 7.1 |
| 9 | 15.84 | ..... | 6.3 |
| 10 | 17.63 | ..... | 5.7 |
| 15 | ..... | ..... | 3.7 |
| 20 | ..... | ..... | 2.7 |
| 25 | ..... | ..... | 2.1 |
| 30 | ..... | ..... | 1.7 |

* From U.S. War Department, *Tech. Man.* 5-236.

**Table A · 7** Map Scales in English Measure and Metric Units*

| *Scale, 1 to—* | *Miles per inch* | *Kilo-meters per inch* | *Feet per inch* | *Inches per mile* | *Inches per kilo-meter* |
|---|---|---|---|---|---|
| 500,000 | 7.891 | 12.700 | 41,666 | 0.1267 | 0.07874 |
| 250,000 | 3.945 | 6.350 | 20,833 | 0.2534 | 0.15748 |
| 125,000 | 1.972 | 3.175 | 10,416 | 0.5068 | 0.31496 |
| 100,000 | 1.578 | 2.540 | 8,333 | 0.6336 | 0.39370 |
| 63,360 | 1.000 | 1.609 | 5,280 | 1.000 | 0.6213 |
| 62,500 | 0.986 | 1.587 | 5,208 | 1.0137 | 0.6299 |
| 40,000 | 0.6313 | 1.016 | 3,333 | 1.584 | 0.9842 |
| 31,680 | 0.500 | 0.804 | 2,640 | 2.000 | 1.2427 |
| 25,000 | 0.3945 | 0.635 | 2,083 | 2.534 | 1.5748 |
| 20,000 | 0.3156 | 0.508 | 1,666 | 3.168 | 1.9685 |
| 10,000 | 0.15782 | 0.254 | 833.3 | 6.336 | 3.937 |
| 2,500 | 0.0394 | 0.0635 | 208.3 | 25.34 | 15.748 |
| 1,200 | 0.0189 | 0 0305 | 100 | 52.8 | 32.808 |

* From U.S. War Department, *Tech. Man.* 5-236.

**Table A · 8** Values of Various Prime Meridians Reckoned from Greenwich

| *Cities* | *Longitude from Greenwich* | *Map of* |
|---|---|---|
| Batavia | 106° 48′ 38″ E | Java |
| Padang | 100° 22′ E | Sumatra |
| Sofia | 23° 19′ 39″ E | Bulgaria |
| København | 12° 34′ 40.35″ E | Denmark |
| Helsingfors | 24° 57′ 16.5″ E | Finland |
| Paris | 2° 20′ E | France |
| | 2° 20′ 14″ | Yugoslavia |
| | 2° 20′ 13″ | Poland |
| Ferro | 17° 40′ W | Spain |
| Athens | 23° 42′ 58.5″ E | Greece |
| Roma (Monte Mario) | 12° 27′ 07.06″ E | Italy |
| Oslo | 10° 43′ 22.5″ E | Norway |
| Lisboã (Castle) | 9° 7′ 54.86″ W | Portugal |
| Bucuresti | 26° 06 E | Rumania |
| Pulkovo | 30° 19′ 38.49″ E | Russia |
| Leningrad | 30° 17′ 15″ E | Russia |
| Madrid | 3° 41′ 14.55″ W | Spain |

# APPENDIX 4: *Bibliography of Easily Available References*[1]

GENERAL CARTOGRAPHY

ALEXANDER, W., and W. J. D. ALLAN: "The Observer's Handbook on Maps, Charts and Projections," George Allen & Unwin, Ltd., London, 1941.

Key to a Better Understanding of Maps, American Map and Geographic Research Service, Washington, D.C., 1945.

BAUER, HUBERT A.: "Globes, Maps, and Skyways," Air Age Education Series, The Macmillan Company, New York, 1943.

BIRDSEYE, C. H.: Topographic Instructions of the *U.S. Geol. Survey Bull.* 788, Washington, D.C., 1928.

BEAMAN, W. M.: Topographic Mapping, U.S. Department of the Interior, *U.S. Geol. Survey Bull.* 788-E, Washington, D.C., 1928.

CAMERON, J. W.: "Maps and Map-work," George G. Harrap & Co., Ltd., London, 1932.

DEBENHAM, F.: "Exercises in Cartography," Blackie & Son, Ltd., Glasgow, 1937.

Consolidated Vultee Aircraft Corporation, "Maps . . . and How to Understand Them," 2d rev. ed., New York, 1943.

d'AGAPAYEFF, A., and E. C. R. HADFIELD: "Maps," Oxford University Press, New York, 1943.

DEBENHAM, F.: "Map Making," M. S. Mill Co., New York, 1936. 239 pp.

DEETZ, C. H.: "Cartography," *U.S. Coast and Geodetic Survey Spec. Pub.* 205, Washington, D.C., 1936.

ECKERT-GREIFENDORFF, M.: "Kartenkunde," Walter De Gruyter & Company, Berlin, 1936.

ECKERT, M.: "Die Kartenwissenschaft," 2 vols., Walter De Gruyter & Company, Berlin, 1921 and 1925.

ECKERT, MAX: "Geographische Praktikum," H. Wagner and E. Debes, Leipzig, 1931.

Encyclopedia Americana: Cartography, Cartogram, Chart, Diagram, Map, 1946.

FINCH, J. K.: "Topographic Maps and Sketch Mapping," John Wiley & Sons, Inc., New York, 1920.

GREENHOOD, DAVID: "Down to Earth," Holiday House, Inc., New York, 1944. 262 pp.

GROLL, M., and O. GRAF: "Kartenkunde," 2 vols., Walter De Gruyter & Company, Berlin, 1931.

HAWLEY, J. H.: Hydrographic Manual, *U.S. Coast and Geodetic Survey Spec. Pub.* 143, Washington, D.C.

HINKS, A. R.: "Maps and Survey," 3d ed., Cambridge University Press, London, 1933.

LLOYD, MALCOLM: "A Practical Treatise on Mapping and Lettering," The Blakiston Company, Philadelphia, 1930.

National Resources Committee, "Suggested Symbols for Plans, Maps, and Charts," Washington, D.C., 1937.

Permanent Committee on Geographical Names, *Lists of Names*, Royal Geog. Soc., London.

RIDGWAY, J. L.: The Preparation of Illustrations for Reports of the United States Geological Survey, *U.S. Geol. Survey Bull.*, Washington, D.C., 1920.

———: "Scientific Illustration," Stanford University Press, Stanford University, Palo Alto, Calif., 1938.

ROBERTS, L. B.: "Topographic Mapping," The Society of American Military Engineers, Washington, D.C., 1924.

SAUNDERS, H. R., and H. C. IVES: "Map Drafting and Lettering," Benson Book Co.

SLOANE, R. C., and J. M. MONTZ: "Elements of Topographic Drawing," McGraw-Hill Book Company, Inc., New York, 1943. 251 pp.

Union Géographique Internationale, *Comptes Rend.* of different International Geographic Congresses contain rich material on cartography.

U.S. Department of Agriculture, Forest Service, "Forest Service Map Standards," Govern-

[1] Short articles on special items are recorded as footnotes only and are not repeated here.

ment Printing Office, Washington, D.C., 1936.

U.S. Navy Department, Bureau of Aeronautics, "Air Navigation, Part I, Introduction to Earth," U.S. Navy Flight Preparation Training Series, McGraw-Hill Book Company, Inc., New York, 1943.

U.S. War Department, Topographic Drafting, *Tech. Man.* 230, Government Printing Office, Washington, D.C., 1940.

U.S. War Department, Topography and Surveying Map Reproduction in the Field, *Tech. Man.* 5-245, Government Printing Office, Washington, D.C., 1942.

WINTERBOTHAM, H. S. L.: "A Key to Maps," Blackie & Son, Ltd., Glasgow, Scotland, 1936.

HISTORY OF MAPS

CONOVER, M.: "The General Land Office, Its History, Activities, and Organization," Johns Hopkins Press, Baltimore,1923.

COTTLER, J., and H. JAFFE: "Map Makers," Little, Brown & Company, Boston, 1938.

CURNOW, I. J.: "The World Mapped," Sifton Pread and Company, Ltd., London, 1930.

DICKINSON, R. E., and O. J. R. HOWARTH: "The Making of Geography," Oxford University Press, New York, 1933.

EMMONS, G.: Technique of Drawing Isobars on Weather Maps (on back of Chart No. 3500), U.S. Navy Department, Hydrographic Office, Washington, D.C.

FITE, E. D., and A. FREEMAN: "A Book of Old Maps," Harvard University Press, Cambridge, Mass., 1926.

FORDHAM, H. G.: "Maps, Their History, Characteristics and Uses," Cambridge University Press, London, 1927.

———: "Some Notable Surveyors and Mapmakers of the Sixteenth, Seventeenth, and Eighteenth Centuries and Their Work," Cambridge University Press, London, 1929.

HEIDEL, W. A.: "The Frame of the Ancient Greek Maps," American Geographical Society, New York, 1937.

HUMPHREYS, A. L.: "Old Decorative Maps and Charts," Minton, Balch & Co., New York, 1926.

KARPINSKI, L. C.: "Bibliography of the Printed Maps of Michigan," Michigan Historical Commission, Lansing, Mich., 1931.

LYNAM, E.: "British Maps and Map Makers," William Collins Sons & Co., Ltd., New York, 1944. 48 pp.

MACFADDEN, CLIFFORD H.: "A Bibliography of Pacific Area Maps," American Council, Institute of Pacific Relations, San Francisco, New York, Honolulu, 1941.

MCNEILL, JOHN M.: Historical Maps and Charts, *Sci. Monthly*, May, 1940, pp. 435–446.

MILLER, KONRAD: "Mappae-mundi, Die Ältesten Weltkarten," 6 vols., J. Roth, Stuttgart, 1898.

NORDENSKIÖLD, A. E.: "Facsimile Atlas to the Early History of Cartography," Stockholm, 1889.

———: "Periplus: An Essay on the Early History of Charts and Sailing Directions," P. A. Norstedt, Stockholm, 1897.

PAULLIN, C. O., and J. K. WRIGHT: "Atlas of the Historical Geography of the United States," Carnegie Institution, Washington, D.C., and American Geographical Society, 1932.

PHILLIPS, P. L.: "A List of Geographical Atlases in the Library of Congress with Bibliographical Notes," 4 vols., Government Printing Office, Washington, D.C., 1909–1920.

STEVENSON, E. L.: "Portolan Charts," Hispanic Society of America, New York, 1911.

———: "Terrestrial and Celestial Globes," 2 vols., The Hispanic Society of America, New York, 1921.

WAGNER, H. R.: "The Cartography of the Northwest Coast of America to the Year 1800," 2 vols., University of California Press, Berkeley, Calif., 1937.

WIEDER, F. C.: "Monumenta Cartographica—Reproduction of Unique and Rare Maps, Plans and Views in the Actual Size of the Originals," 5 vols., M. Nijhoff, The Hague, 1925–1933.

WINSOR, JUSTIN: "Narrative and Critical History of America," 8 vols., Houghton Mifflin Company, Boston, 1884–1889.

MAP PROJECTIONS

ADAMS, O. S.: "Plane-coordinate Systems," *U.S. Coast and Geodetic Survey*, No. 562, U.S. Department of Commerce, 1936.

Birdseye, C. H.: Formulas and Tables for the Construction of Polyconic Projections, *U.S. Geol. Survey Bull.* 809, 1929.

Bowie, W., and O. S. Adams: Grid System for Progressive Maps in the United States, *U.S. Coast and Geodetic Survey Spec. Pub.* 59, No. 112, U.S. Department of Commerce, 1919.

Deetz, Charles H.: The Lambert Conformal Projection, *U.S. Coast and Geodetic Survey Spec. Pub.* 47, Washington, D.C. 1918.

——— and O. S. Adams: Elements of Map Projection . . . , *U.S. Coast and Geodetic Survey Spec. Pub.* 68, 4th ed., Washington, D.C., 1934.

Driencourt et Laborde: "Traité des projections des cartes géographiques," Paris, 1932.

Fisher, Irving, and O. M. Miller: "World Maps and Globes," Essential Books, New York, 1944.

Flexner, W. W., and G. L. Walker: "Military and Naval Maps and Grids," The Dryden Press, Inc., New York, 1942.

Hinckley, A.: "Map Projections by Practical Construction," George Philip & Son, Ltd., The London Geographical Inst., London, 1942.

Hinks, A. R.: "Map Projections," 2d ed., Cambridge University Press, London, 1921.

Hoffmeister, H. A.: "Construction of Map Projections," McKnight & McKnight, Bloomington, Ill., 1946.

Mainwaring, J.: "An Introduction to the Study of Map Projections," Macmillan & Co., Ltd., London, 1942.

Scheffers, G.: "Wie findet und zeichnet man Gradnetze von Land- und Sternkarten?" B. G. Teubner, Leipzig, 1934.

Steer, J. A.: "An Introduction to the Study of Map Projections," University of London Press, Ltd., Bickley, Kent, England, 1927.

U.S. Coast and Geodetic Survey, Tables for Polyconic Projection of Maps, *Spec. Pub.* 5, Washington, D.C., 1930.

## MAP READING

Eardley, A. J.: "Aerial Photographs: Their Use and Interpretation," Harper & Brothers, New York, 1942.

Esson, Capt. C. C., and G. S. Philip: "Map Reading Made Easy," George Philip & Son, Ltd., The London Geographical Inst., London, 1941.

Field, R. M., and H. T. Stetson: "Map Reading and Avigation," D. Van Nostrand Company, Inc., New York, 1942.

Heavey, Col. W. F.: "Map and Aerial Photo Reading Simplified," Military Service Publishing Co., Harrisburg, Pa., 1942.

Holmes, J. M.: "Practical Map Reading," Angus and Robertson, Ltd., Sydney, Australia, 1942.

Lobeck, A. K., and W. J. Tellington: "Military Maps and Air Photographs," McGraw-Hill Book Company, Inc., New York, 1944.

McLean, Norman F., and C. Olson Everett: "Manual for Instruction in Military Maps and Aerial Photographs," Harper & Brothers, New York, 1942.

Peattie, Roderick: "How to Read Military Maps," George W. Stewart, Publisher, Inc., New York, 1942.

Putnam, W. C.: "Map Interpretation with Military Applications," McGraw-Hill Book Company, Inc., New York, 1943.

U.S. War Department, Advanced Map and Aerial Photograph Reading, *Field Man.* 21–26, Washington, D.C.

U.S. War Department, Elementary Map and Aerial Photograph Reading, *Field Man.* 21–25, Washington, D.C.

## SURVEYING

Bagley, Lt. Col. J. W.: "Aerophotography and Aerosurveying," McGraw-Hill Book Company, Inc., New York, 1941.

Lyon, T. C.: Practical Air Navigation and the Use of the Aeronautical Charts of the United States Coast and Geodetic Survey, *Spec. Pub.* 197, Government Printing Office, Washington, D.C., 1939.

McCurdy, P. G.: "Manual of Aerial Photogrammetry," U.S. Navy Department, Hydrographic Office, Washington, D.C., 1940.

Sharp, H. O.: "Geodetic Control Surveys," John Wiley & Sons, Inc., New York, 1943.

Smith, H. T. U.: "Aerial Photographs and Their Application," D. Appleton-Century Company, Inc., New York, 1943.

U.S. Department of Commerce, Horizontal

Control Data, *U.S. Coast and Geodetic Survey Spec. Pub.* 227, Washington, D.C., 1941.

The United States Coast and Geodetic Survey—Its Work, *Spec. Pub.* 216, Government Printing Office, Washington, D.C., 1941.

U.S. Department of the Interior, "Manual of Instruction for Public Land Surveys," Washington, D.C., 1930.

U.S. War Department, Surveying, *Tech. Man.* 5-235, Government Printing Office, Washington, D.C., 1940.

U.S. War Department, Surveying Tables, *Tech. Man.* 5-236, Washington, D.C.

SPECIAL CARTOGRAPHY

BAKER, O. E.: "A Graphic Summary of American Agriculture Based Largely on the Census," U.S. Department of Agriculture, Washington, D.C., 1931.

BRINTON, W. C.: "Graphic Presentation," Brinton Associates, New York, 1939. 512 pp.

DAVIS, W. M.: "Die erklärende Beschreibung der Landformen," B. G. Teubner, Leipzig, 1912.

FIORINI, M.: "Erd- und Himmelsgloben, ihre Geschichte und Konstruction," Bearbeitet von Siegmund Günther, Leipzig, 1895.

FLEXNER, W. W., and G. L. WALKER: "Military and Naval Maps and Grids," The Dryden Press, Inc., New York, 1942.

LOBECK, A. K.: "Block Diagrams," John Wiley & Sons, Inc., New York, 1924.

National Association of Assessing Officers, "Construction and Use of Tax Maps," Chicago, 1937.

OLSON, E. C., and A. WHITMARSH: "Foreign Maps," Harper & Brothers, New York, 1944.

RIGGLEMAN, J. R.: "Graphic Methods for Presenting Business Statistics," 2d ed., McGraw-Hill Book Company, Inc., New York, 1936.

The Committee of the Surveying and Mapping Division on City Surveys, American Society of Civil Engineers, Technical Procedure for City Surveys, *Manuals of Engineering Practice* No. 10, 1934.

THIELE, W.: "Official Map Publications," American Library Association, Chicago, 1938.

U.S. War Department, Field Service Pocketbook-sketching, *Field Man.* 21–35, Washington, D.C.

# Index

D

F



G

H



I

M

Q



R

S